The book that tells you HOW TO GO METRIC

— more than 600 charts, tables, and illustrations

— how to convert from inches to millimetres and back, also all other conversions

— how the SI system works

— how to read metric precision measuring tools

— how to design and make drawings in metrics

— how to convert machines to metric

— how to use metrics in all fields including woodworking, graphic arts, electronics, metalworking, home economics, etc.

— metric standards—also explains difference between ISO standards and SI system

— a history of the metric system

— bibliography of books, audio-visuals, and metric periodicals

— hundreds of sources for metric products

And so much more . . . a metric "seminar" at your fingertips

**SI METRIC HANDBOOK,
A BASIC REFERENCE FOR
HOME, OFFICE, INDUSTRY AND EDUCATION**

JOHN L. FEIRER, Founder of Center for Metric Education and Head of Industrial Education, Western Michigan University, Kalamazoo, Michigan

Charles Scribner's Sons, New York
Chas. A. Bennett Co., Peoria, Illinois

SI METRIC HANDBOOK

John L. Feirer
The Metric Company

CHARLES SCRIBNER'S SONS, NEW YORK
CHAS. A. BENNETT CO., PEORIA, ILLINOIS

Distributed to the trade by:
  Charles Scribner's Sons, 597 Fifth Avenue, New York, New York, 10017
Distributed to schools by:
  Chas. A. Bennett Co., 809 West Detweiller Drive, Peoria, Illinois, 61614

PREFACE

This **Metric Handbook** is designed to serve as a reference for all individuals interested in metric conversion in basic occupational (career) areas. This handbook can also serve effectively as a metric textbook for education, business and industry.

This handbook has been divided into two volumes consisting of eight major sections as follows:

Volume A—SI Measuring System and ISO Standards
Section 1. The SI measuring system.
Section 2. Precision measuring tools.
Section 3. National and international standards with explanation of the difference between ISO standards and SI metric.

Volume B—Applied Metrics
Section 4. Metric design and drafting.
Section 5. Metrics in the metalworking industry.
Section 6. Metrics in other important industrial areas such as woodworking, building construction, graphic arts, electricity-electronics and automechanics. Each of these areas will be affected somewhat differently by metric conversion.
Section 7. Metrics in office practice, business, marketing and distribution.
Section 8. Metrics in foods, clothing, agriculture, health and home living.

Several important matters should be kept in mind when using this handbook. For one thing, there is a great deal of difference between the SI metric measuring system, which is *only* a measuring system, and international standards (ISO). Individuals in science and mathematics will need to be concerned only with the SI metric measuring system. However, in most industrial and vocational areas, the use of national and international standards will be one of the critical matters in metric conversion. Today there are only about 150 to 200 international standards based on metric measurement. In the 10 or 15 years ahead it has been estimated that the world will need at least 11 000 standards if true international interchange of goods and services is to be possible. Since only a few of the metric standards are now available, it has been necessary to suggest what these standards might be, based on national metric standards being developed in other English-speaking countries now "going metric".
These primarily include England, South Africa, Australia, Canada, and New Zealand. If the publishers were to wait until all national and international standards in metric were available in all areas, it would be impossible to produce a handbook of this type for at least 10 or 15 years. As standards are established, these will be included in future editions of this handbook.

Another problem is the matter of spelling. At the present time, for example, all English-speaking countries going metric prefer met*re* and lit*re*. It is also acceptable to use the spelling ending *er*. Therefore, you will find both spellings used in this handbook. There is no complete agreement among industries now going metric as to which spelling to use.

In a handbook as comprehensive as this one there is no guarantee against some mathematical errors. The publisher has checked all illustrations and content for accuracy. Any reader who finds an error should feel free to inform the publisher. This service would be greatly appreciated.

The Publishers

ACKNOWLEDGEMENTS

American National Metric Council
American National Standards Institute
Bridgeport Machines Corporation
Brown & Sharpe Manufacturing Company
Bruning, Division of Addressograph, Multigraph
Canadian Standards Association
Central Instrument Company
Cessna Corporation
Clausing Corporation
The Doall Corporation
ELM Systems, Inc.
Eastman Kodak Corporation
Echo, Inc.
Eli Lilly and Company
Foley Manufacturing Company
Ford Motor Company
Gamet Products Limited
General Motors Corporation
Heidennain Corporation
Industrial Fasteners Institute
International Business Machines Corporation
International Harvester Company
The L. S. Starret Company
LeBlond Machine Company
MTI Corporation
Metra-Tech Corporation
Miller Clock Company
National Aeronautics and Space Administration
National Bureau of Standards
The Pillsbury Company
Regal Beloit Corporation
Sears & Roebuck Company
Staveley Machine Tools, Inc.
Stanley Tools
U. S. Department of Agriculture
U. S. Department of Commerce
United Greenfield, Division of TRW, Inc.
Vichers Limited Engineering Group
Western Electric
Zelenda Machine and Tools Corporation

CONTENTS

UNIT 1
HISTORY OF MEASUREMENT

Noah was an accomplished woodworker, for the ark he built endured the heaviest rainstorms and worst floods ever recorded in history, staying on the water more than 120 days! According to specifications dictated to Noah, his ark was 300 cubits long, 50 cubits wide, and 30 cubits high. Even today, this would be considered a fairly good-sized vessel. Since a cubit is roughly 18 inches long, that meant that the ark measured about 450 feet from stem to stern. Fig. 1-1.

Size was not the only thing that made the job outstanding for that time. Noah managed to build his Ark according to instructions without the aid of a "yard-stick", which had not yet been invented.

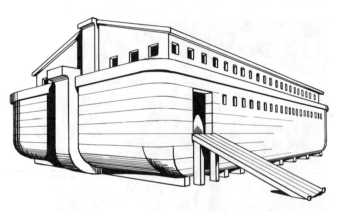

Fig. 1-1
In the metric system, Noah's ark would have measured 137 metres long, 23 metres wide and 14 metres high.

In those days the lack of a yardstick was not a serious drawback because the ancients had a rather crude method of measuring things. Though far from accurate, this method was good enough for most practical purposes. As long as only one craftsman did the measuring, and completed one job at a time rather than try to make a number of articles piecemeal to be assembled later, it didn't make much difference how accurate the measuring sticks were or even how long they were.

Even today it doesn't make much difference how long is a mile, yard or inch or how heavy is a pound or ounce. What is really important is that everyone means the same thing when referring to each unit of measurement. Measurements must be *standard* to mean the same thing to everyone.

The cubit of Noah's time was the length of a man's forearm or the distance from the tip of the elbow to the end of his middle finger. Fig. 1-2. In some respects this was handy, because it was readily available, convenient, and couldn't be mislaid. However, it was not a positive fixed dimension . . it was not *standard*.

While the cubit is no longer used as a unit of measurement, there are many customary standards that originated in about the same way. Our foot-rule started out as the length of a man's foot. So, in the early days of history, the foot varied in length, sometimes as much as 3 or 4 inches. Once the ancients started using arms and feet for measuring distance, it

was only natural that they also thought of using fingers, hands and legs. Fig. 1-3. They also may have discovered that some surprising ratios existed in body measurements. What is now called an inch originally was the width of a man's thumb. It also was the length of the forefinger from the tip to the first joint. Twelve times that distance made a foot. Three times the length of the foot was the distance from the tip of a man's nose to the end of his outstretched arm. This distance very closely approximates what is called the *yard*. Two yards equalled a fathom which, thousands of years ago, was the distance across a man's outstretched arms. Half a yard was the 18-inch cubit, and half a cubit was called a span, which was the distance across

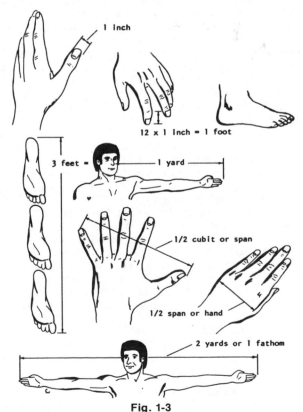

Fig. 1-2
The cubit was the first unit of measure recorded by history.

1 inch

12 x 1 inch = 1 foot

3 feet = 1 yard

1/2 cubit or span

1/2 span or hand

2 yards or 1 fathom

Fig. 1-3
The parts of the body were convenient measuring units.

the hand from the tip of the thumb to the tip of the little finger when the fingers were spread out as far as possible. A hand was half a span.

For thousands of years, this was the way people measured comparatively short distances. Each succeeding civilization added its bit to mankind's knowledge, building an accumulation of measuring standards and techniques. Some contributed weight measures. Others showed us how to measure time. Still others gave us methods for surveying big areas of land and establishing boundaries.

When man first gained the concept of distance and how to measure it, he also began to wonder about weight. He knew fairly early that size had nothing to do with weight. From experience, he knew that he had to work just as hard to carry a stone as he did to carry a bundle of straw, but oftentimes it was difficult to tell which was the heavier. Then someone invented the balance. With this he could tell which object was heavier.

It was several thousand years before the Babylonians made an important improvement. Instead of merely comparing the weights of two objects, they compared the weight of each object with a set of stones kept just for that purpose. In the ruins of their cities, archaeologists have found some of these stones finely shaped and polished. It is believed that these were the world's first weight standards.

Apparently, the Babylonians used different stones for weighing different commodities. And even in modern English history, somewhat the same basis has been used for weight measurements. For the horseman, the "stone" weight was 14 pounds. In weighing wool the stone was 16 pounds. For the butcher and fishmonger, the stone was 8 pounds. The only legal stone weight in the Imperial system was 14 pounds.

Other civilizations made further contributions. Both the Egyptians and the Greeks used a wheat seed as the smallest unit of weight, a standard that was exceptionally uniform and accurate for the times. The grain is still in limited use as a standard of weight. However, we no longer actually put wheat seeds in the pan of the balance scale. Rather, we arbitrarily have assigned a weight to what we call the grain . . . and it is a weight that is practically the same as that of an average grain of wheat.

The Arabs, too, established a small weight standard for gold, silver and precious stones which very often were a part of trade or barter deals. In weighing such small valuable quantities, they used as a weight standard a small bean called a *karob*. This was the origin of the word *carat* which jewelers still use to express the weight of gems and precious metals.

In trading between tribes and nations, many of these methods for measuring weights and distances gradually became intermixed, particularly by the Romans who spread this knowledge throughout the known world at that time, also adding some standards of their own. As the Roman soldiers marched, they kept track of the distance they traveled by counting paces. A pace was the distance covered from the time one foot touched the ground until that same foot touched the ground again, or the length of a double step.

A Double Standard for the World

When the Roman Empire finally passed into history about six hundred years after the time of Christ,

Europe drifted into the Dark Ages; six or seven hundred years, mankind generally made little progress.

Sometime after the Magna Charta was signed in the Thirteenth Century, King Edward I of England took a tremendous step forward. He ordered a permanent measuring stick made of iron to serve as a master standard yardstick for the entire kingdom. Fig. 1-4. This master yardstick was called the "iron ulna", after the bone of the forearm, and it was standardized as the length of a yard, surprisingly close to the length of our present-day yard. King Edward realized that constancy and permanence were the key to any standard. He also decreed that the foot measure should be one-third the length of the yard, and the inch one thirty-sixth. King Edward II, in 1324, reverted back to the seed idea of the ancients and passed a statute that "three barleycorns, round and dry," make an inch. Fig. 1-5. However, seeds as well as fingers and feet were no match for a world that soon was to emerge from the ignorance and crudities of the Dark Ages.

Fig. 1-4
King Edward I established the first standard measuring stick.

In 1672, Sir Isaac Newton presented the world with some new ideas on the nature of light and color. He had noticed that when two very flat pieces of glass were pressed together, he could see circular bands of rainbow-like colors. These were called Newton's Rings. Actually, Newton had within his grasp an almost incredibly precise method of measurement . . . but he didn't recognize it as such at the time. Later, other scientists were to build on Newton's groundwork and establish a new branch of science called *interferometry*. Today, this method of using a ray of light as a measuring stick enables man to measure distances within millionths of an inch or a millimetre.

Meanwhile, as the scientists were experimenting in their laboratories, practical tradesmen were making themselves permanent standards. In 1793, during Napoleon's time, the French government adopted an

Fig. 1-5
King Edward II used the more commonly available barleycorns to indicate an inch. Which king's unit of measurement was a better standard?

entirely new system of standards called the *metric system,* based on what they called the metre. The *metre* was supposed to be one ten-millionth part of the distance from the North Pole to the Equator when measured on a straight line running along the surface of the earth through Paris. Fig. 1-6. With the metre

Fig. 1-6
The metre was first defined as one ten-millionth of the distance from the earth's equator to the North Pole on a line running through Paris.

thus determined as the basis of the metric system, other linear units of the system were set up in decimal ratios with the metre. With this system, all units are in multiples of ten: ten decimetres in a metre, a hundred centimetres in a metre, and a thousand millimetres in a metre. In the other direction, there are ten metres in a dekametre, a hundred metres in a hectometre, and a thousand metres in a kilometre. Compared to the yardstick, the metre is just a little longer: 39.37 inches long.

The metric system also has volume, liquid capacity, and weight measures. The *litre* is the basic measure of liquid capacity. It corresponds roughly to a quart. For weight, the basic unit in the metric system was at first the gram; now it is the kilogram. The gram was a very small unit, for it takes a thousand grams—or what is known as a kilogram—to equal about 2.2 pounds.

The French government thought it had a scientific, foolproof system of weights and measures that would be easy to use and would be welcomed by everyone. However, people were accustomed to thinking in terms of yards, inches, pounds and quarts.

At first the new metre as a measure of length proved confusing. Most Frenchmen thought in the old familiar terms, doing some mental arithmetic to convert one quantity into another and, after nineteen years, Napoleon finally was forced to renounce the metric system. However, in 1837, France again went back to the metre, this time to stay, hoping to make it universal throughout the world. Today almost all of the countries of the world use a modernized metric system called the SI metric system.

While France was evolving the metric system, England also was setting up a more scientifically accurate determination of the yard. Where the French relied on the assumed constancy of the earth's size as a basis for the permanency of their standards, the British turned to the measured beat of the pendulum.

Galileo already had learned the secrets of a pendulum. He found that the length of time it took for a pendulum to complete a swing depended upon the length of the pendulum itself. The longer the pendulum, the slower it swung. He also found that a pendulum a little over 39 inches long would swing through its arc in exactly one second. Since a pendulum always behaves exactly the same way under the same conditions, here was another unchanging distance upon which to base a standard measurement.

In 1824, the English Parliament legalized a new standard yard which had been made in 1760. It was a brass bar containing a gold button near each end. A dot was engraved in each of these two buttons. These two dots were spaced exactly 1 yard apart. Fig. 1-7. The same act that legalized this bar as the standard for England also made the provision that, in the event it was lost or destroyed, it should be replaced using the pendulum method to determine its length.

A few years later, copies of both the English yard and the French metre standards were brought to the United States. The English system of measuring was almost universally adopted in the United States.

Measuring Systems in the United States
Since colonialists brought with them the measuring practices and methods of their homeland, confusing and contradictory measuring systems came to America. For example, the Imperial gallon used in

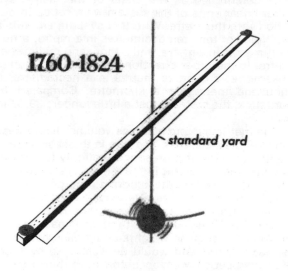

1760-1824

standard yard

Fig. 1-7
This is the standard yard based on the swinging of a pendulum.

England did not come to America. The U.S. gallon is a smaller one, and was called the Queen Anne wine gallon by the British. Fig. 1-8. Today this difference in size between the Imperial gallon and the U.S. gallon causes confusion when converting to the metric system.

WINE GALLON 1707

Fig. 1-8
This wine gallon is the predecessor of our current U.S. gallon.

The law of 1792, under the new Constitution of the United States, provided for fractional coinage and for the decimal system. The adoption of the decimal system for coins shows that the American leaders recognized the advantages of the simple decimal system.

In 1795, France tried to convince the United States to use the metric system but ran into opposition. Congress did nothing.

In 1821 John Quincy Adams wrote an eloquent and comprehensive report for Congress based on a four-year investigation. His report dealt with the metric question and the modernization of our measurement system. In part it read as follows:

"Weights and Measures may be ranked among the necessaries of life to every individual of human society. They enter into the economical arrangements and daily concerns of every family. They are necessary to every occupation of human industry; to the distribution and security of every species of property; to every transaction of trade and commerce; to the labors of the husbandman; to the ingenuity of the artificer; to the studies of the philosopher; to the researches of the antiquarian; to the navigation of the mariner, and the marches of the soldier; to all the exchanges of peace, and all the operations of war. The knowledge of them, as in established use, is among the first elements of education, and is often learned by those who learn nothing else, not even to read and write. This knowledge is riveted in the memory by the habitual application of it to the employments of men throughout life."

This was the first U.S. metric study. Although three decades earlier, Thomas Jefferson also had written a report for the Congress on the need for modernization of weights and measures, the metric system was no more than a conception in his time, and his report was considered only an alternative not to be entertained seriously by the newly founded United States of America. Inventive genius that he was, he proposed his own measurement system.

In spite of repeated requests in Congress, there was no legal length standard in the States until 1832.

More or less authentic copies of the British copies of the yard were used as length prototypes. In 1832, the Treasury Department decided to admit as a legal Yard the distance between the lines 27 and 63 of a certain bronze bar, 82 inches in length, bought in 1813 in England for the Federal Survey Department.

When the British yard bar, which was destroyed in 1834, was replaced in 1855, a new bronze copy No. 11 was sent to the States which became the legal *American Yard Standard*.

Even though progress was slow, there was an improvement in establishment of the metric standards which all the world recognized. Like the United Kingdom, the Americans found it necessary to define their customary measures in terms of international metric standard. Our units of length, mass and volume are all stated in terms of the metric standards.

In 1863, the United States was represented at two important international congresses convened to consider matters of weights and measures. The International statistical Congress in Berlin declared that uniformity in weights and measures was of the highest importance, particularly for international commerce. Recommendations made by the Postal Congress held at Paris resulted in the adoption of the metric system for international postal service.

Congress passed a Bill in 1866 which permitted use of the metric system of measurement in the United States. The value for the metre was given as: 1 metre = 39.37 inches or 1 yard = 0.914 401 829 metre. The metric prototype chosen was a metal bar known as the *Committee Meter* because it had been guaranteed to conform to the Metre des Archives by the French Committee in 1799.

In 1873, metric weights were extended to silver coins. The weight of the half dollar is 12.5 grams; the quarter is 6.25 grams; the nickel is 5 grams and the dime is 2.5 grams. In 1875 the United States entered into a treaty with 17 other countries establishing the International Bureau of Weights and Measures.

In 1890, the United States received two of the international prototype metres and two of the kilogram artifacts. One of each of these standards was adopted as the National Prototype Metre and Kilogram and as the primary standards for the United States. As such they became the fundamental standards for determining the yard and the pound. The prototype metres and kilograms are preserved at the National Bureau of Standards.

In 1896, and again in 1901, bills were introduced recommending the adoption of the metric system for all weights and measures in the United States . . . but for one reason or another the bills failed to pass. In the ensuing years many bills have been introduced which recommended establishing the metric system as the legal standard of the United States . . . however, very little action has been taken.

In 1968, Congress asked for a three-year, sweeping investigation of the metric question because it sensed that the world trend toward metric called for a new assessment. The investigation involved public hearings, supplemented by surveys on international trade, business and industry, education, national security—almost every activity in our society—and in 1971, the final report titled *A Metric America—A Decision Whose Time Has Come* was released. It consisted of the comprehensive report plus twelve sub-study reports covering all aspects of the study.

Finally in 1975 Congress passed the Metric Conversion Act. The major provisions of the bill provide for:

—Adaptation of SI as predominant system of measurement units
—No specific timetable
—Voluntary participation
—**A Metric Board**
—Costs of Conversion
  —treat as other costs of doing business
  —no tax credits or subsidies
  —hardship cases to be reviewed by Board

IMPORTANT DATES IN U.S. METRIC HISTORY

1791- "Jefferson Report." Thomas Jefferson described England's weights and measures standards to Congress "on the supposition that the present measures and weights are to be retained," and also outlined a decimal system of weights and measures of Jefferson's conception.

1821- "Adams Report." John Quincy Adams recommended to Congress that they act to bring about uniformity in weights and measures, and described France's young Metric System as a praiseworthy attempt at uniformity.

1866- "Law of 1866." Congress made use of the Metric System legally permissible throughout the United States.

1875- "Treaty of the Meter." On May 20, the United States entered into a treaty with 17 powers establishing the International Bureau of Weights and Measures, and providing for its administration.

1890- The United States officially received Metre No. 27 and Kilogram No. 20.

1893- "The Mendenhall Order." The Secretary of the Treasury announced that the international metre and kilogram would be regarded as fundamental standards by the Office of Standard Weights and Measures (which became the National Bureau of Standards in 1901).

1902- A bill brought before the Congress to make the Metric System mandatory within the Federal Government was defeated.

1957- In September, a committee of the Organization of American States proposed that the Metric System be adopted throughout the Western Hemisphere.

1959- Australia, Canada, New Zealand, South Africa, the United Kingdom, and the United States adopted common standards for the inch-pound system in metric terms. One inch was made equivalent to 2.54 centimetres and 1 pound was made equivalent to 0.453 592 37 kilograms. (The Coast and Geodetic Survey, which had used a slightly different conversion factor previously, retained their established relationship of 1 inch equaling 2.540 005 centimetres because of the extensive revisions which would be necessary to their charts and measurement records. The resulting foot based on this retained conversion is known as the U.S. Survey foot).

1965- On May 24, the British Board of Trade announced that the government consider it desirable to adopt metric units in the United Kingdom, with a target date for conversion of 10 years.

1968- An Act providing for a 3-year program to determine the impact of increasing use of the metric system on the United States was passed by Congress and signed into law by the President.

1969- New Zealand began an eight-year conversion to metric units.

1970- Australia announced plans for a 10-year change over to SI metric measurement.

1970- Canada announced its commitment to metric conversion.

1971- The comprehensive report on the U.S. Metric study titled *A Metric America: A Decision Whose Time Has Come* is released.

1972- The Senate by voice vote passed the Pell Bill dealing with metric conversion. However, the House did not act on the legislation.

1973- The American National Standards Institute established the American National Metric Council with offices in Washington, D.C.

1974- Congress passed the first official legislation concerning conversion to the metric system as part of Public Law 93-380, to extend and amend the Elementary and Secondary Education Act of 1965. Under Section 403 of this Act entitled, "Education for the Use of the Metric System of Measurement", it states "the metric system of measurement will have increased use in the United States, and as such, the metric system will become the dominant system of weights and measures in the United States."

1975- Congress passed the Metric Conversion Act.

1976- The U.S. Metric Board appointed.

UNIT 2
BASIC SI METRIC

Weights and measures were among the earliest tools invented by man. Primitive societies needed simple measures for many jobs, such as building shelters to a certain size and shape, making clothing or buying and selling food or raw materials.

Man first used parts of his body and his natural surroundings for measuring. Early Babylonian and Egyptian records and the Bible indicate that length was first measured with the forearm, hand, or finger and that time was measured by the periods of the sun, moon, and other heavenly bodies. When it was necessary to compare the capacities of containers such as gourds or clay or metal vessels, they were filled with plant seeds which were then counted to measure the volumes. When means for weighing were invented, seeds and stones served as standards. For instance, the "carat", still used as a unit for gems, was derived from the carob seed.

Weights and measures became more complex as society developed. The invention of numbering systems and the science of mathematics made it possible to create whole systems of weights and measures suited to trade and commerce, land division, taxation, or scientific research. For these, it was necessary not only to weigh and measure more complex things, but it was also necessary to do it accurately time after time and in different places. However, exchange of goods and communication of ideas was limited between countries. Therefore, different systems for the same purpose developed and became established in different parts of the world and even in different parts of a single continent.

The Customary or English System

The measurement system commonly used in the United States today is nearly the same as that brought by the colonists from England. These measures had their origins in such cultures as Babylonian, Egyptian, Roman, Anglo-Saxon, and Norman French. The ancient "digit," "palm," "span," and "cubit" units somehow became the "inch," "foot," and "yard."

Roman contributions include the use of the number 12 as a base (our foot is divided into 12 inches) and words from which we derive many of our present weights and measures names. For example, the 12 divisions of the Roman "pes," or foot, were called *unciae.* Our words "inch" and "ounce" both come from that Latin word.

The "yard" as a measure of length can be traced back to the early Saxon kings. They wore a sash or girdle that could be removed and used as a convenient measuring device. Thus the word "yard" comes from the Saxon word "gird" meaning the circumference of a person's waist.

Weights and measures developed in fascinating ways. King Henry I, for example, decreed that the yard should be the distance from the tip of his nose to the end of his thumb. The length of a furlong (or furrowlong) was established by early Tudor rulers as 220 yards, and Queen Elizabeth I declared in the 16th century that the traditional Roman mile of 5,000 feet would be replaced by one of 5,280 feet, making the mile exactly 8 furlongs.

Thus, through royal edicts, England by the 18th century had achieved a greater degree of stan- dardization than the continental countries. The English units were well suited to commerce and trade because they had been developed and refined to meet commercial needs. Through colonization and dominance of world commerce during the 17th, 18th, and 19th centuries, the English system of weights and measures was accepted in many parts of the world, including the American colonies.

When the American Colonies separated from England, they retained the weights and measures of England. It is probable that these were at that time the best standardized and widely used weights and measures in the world.

However, standards still differed too greatly for commerce among the 12 colonies. The need for greater uniformity led to clauses in the Articles of Confederation (ratified in 1781) and the Constitution of the United States (ratified in 1790) giving power to Congress to fix uniform standards for weights and measures. Today, standards supplied to all the States by the National Bureau of Standards assure uniformity throughout the country.

England's standards for weights and measures have remained essentially unchanged until recently. However, in 1965, the United Kingdom made a commitment to SI metric.

The Metric System

The need for a single worldwide coordinated measurement system was recognized over 300 years ago. In 1670, Gabriel Mouton, Vicar of St. Paul in Lyons, proposed a comprehensive decimal measurement system based on the length of one minute of arc of a great circle of the earth. In 1671 Jean Picard, a French astronomer, proposed the length of a pendulum beating seconds as the unit of length. (Such a pendulum would have been easy to reproduce, thus facilitating the widespread distribution of uniform standards.) Other proposals were made, but over a century elapsed before any action was taken.

In the early 1700's no uniformity of weights and measures existed on the European continent. Weights and measures differed not only from country to country, but even from town to town and from one trade to another. This lack of uniformity led the National Assembly of France on May 8, 1790, to enact a decree, sanctioned by Louis XVI. This called upon the French Academy of Sciences together with the Royal Society of London to "deduce an invariable standard for all of the measures and all weights." This decision was made in the midst of the French Revolution. However, the English did not participate in the French undertaking, so the French proceeded with their endeavor alone. The result is what is known as the metric system.

The Commission appointed by the Academy created a system that was both simple and scientific. The unit of length was to be a portion of the earth's circumference. Measures for capacity (volume) and mass (weight) were to be derived from the unit of length, thus relating the basic units of the system to each other and to nature. Furthermore, the larger and smaller versions of each unit were to be created by multiplying or dividing the basic units by 10 and its multiples. This feature provided a great convenience to users of the system, by eliminating the need for such calculations as dividing by 16 (to convert ounces to pounds) or by 12 (to convert inches to feet). Similar calculations in the metric system could be performed simply by shifting the decimal point. Thus the metric system is a "base-10" or "decimal" system.

The Commission assigned the name *metre* to the unit of length. This name was derived from the Greek word *metron,* meaning "a measure." The physical standard representing the metre was to be constructed so that it would equal one ten-millionth of the distance from the north pole to the equator along the meridian of the earth running near Dunkirk in France and Barcelona in Spain. An attempt was made to measure this meridian from northern France to southern France, from which the true distance from the pole to the equator could be calculated. The best techniques then available were used. Although the operations were carried out during a politically disturbed time, the results were in error only by about 2,000 metres, a remarkable achievement in those days.

Meanwhile the National Assembly preempted the geodetic survey, upon which the metre was to be based, and established a provisional metre bar.

The metric unit of mass, called the "gram," was defined as the mass of one cubic centimetre (a cube that is 1/100 of a metre on each side) of water at its temperature of maximum density. Since this was too small a quantity to be measured with the desired precision the determination was made on one cubic decimetre of water, and metal weights of equivalent mass were constructed for standards. Although it was later found to be in error by 28 parts in a million, the metal weights were still retained as standards.

The cubic decimetre (a cube 1/10 of a metre on each side) was chosen as the unit of fluid capacity. This measure was given the name "litre."

In this manner, while decimal relationships were preserved between the units of length, fluid capacity, and weight the relationships were not kept to the simplest possible form. Although there was some discussion at the time of decimalizing the calendar and the time of day, the system did not include any unit for time.

The metric system was not accepted with enthusiasm at first, but was soon adopted by other nations after France made it compulsory in 1840. The metric system is well suited to scientific and engineering work and the rapid spread of the system coincided with an age of rapid technological development. In 1866, the United States Congress made it "lawful throughout the United States of America to employ the weights and measures of the metric system in all contracts, dealings or court proceedings."

Both the British system of weights and measures and the metric system had been developed primarily for use in trade and commerce rather than for science and engineering.

Technological achievement depends to a considerable extent upon the ability to make physical measurements. America and Britain proceeded to adapt their system of measurements to the requirements of the new technology of the 19th century, in spite of the fact that the newly developed metric system would have been better. The industries of both the United States and Great Britain soon became dependent on their own system.

The new metric system found much favor with scientists of the 19th century because: it was intended to be an international system of measurement, the units of measurement were independently reproducable, and its decimal nature was simple. These scientists proceeded to derive new units for the various physical quantities with which they had to deal. They based the new units of elementary laws on physics and related them to the units of mass and length of the metric system. The system found increasing acceptance in various European countries which found any other system unacceptable.

By the late 1860's, even better metric standards were needed to keep pace with scientific advances. In 1875, an international treaty, the "Treaty of the Metre," set up well-defined metric standards for length and mass, and established permanent machinery to recommend and adopt further refinements in the metric system. This treaty, known as the Metric Convention, was signed by 17 countries, including the United States.

As a result of the Treaty, metric standards were constructed and distributed to each nation that ratified the Convention. Since 1893, the internationally agreed-to metric standards have served as the fundamental weights and measures standards of the United States.

By 1900 a total of 35 nations—including the major nations of continental Europe and most of South America—had officially accepted the metric system. Between 1965 and 1972 the United Kingdom, Australia, Canada, New Zealand, and several other English-speaking countries adopted the SI metric system. The United States and a few small countries were the last to accept the SI metric system. Now, almost the entire world is using the metric system or is committed to such use.

The International Bureau of Weights and Measures located at Sevres, France, serves as a permanent secretariat for the Metric Convention, coordinating the exchange of information about the use and refinement of the metric system. The diplomatic organization made up of adherents of the Convention, called the General Conference of Weights and Measures, meets periodically to ratify improvements in the system and the standards. It is their job to develop more precise and easily reproducible ways of defining the measuring units.

In 1960, the General Conference adopted an extensive revision and simplification of the system. The name *Le Système International d'Unités* (International System of Units), with the international abbreviation SI, was adopted for this modernized metric system. Further improvements in and additions to SI were made by the General Conference in 1964, 1968, 1971, and 1975.

UNIT 3
TECHNICAL SI METRICS

Since 1875 all international matters concerning the metric system have been the responsibility of the General Conference of Weights and Measures (CGPM). This Conference was constituted following the Metric Convention signed in Paris in that year. The CGPM meets in Paris, and under its direction are the International Committee of Weights and Measures (CIPM) and various Consultative Committees as well as the International Bureau of Weights and Measures (BIPM).

The laboratories of the International **Bureau** of Weights and Measures at Sevres, France, are the repositories of the standard prototype kilogram and the former standard prototype metre. The kilogram is still defined in terms of the international prototype at Sevres, but the metre is now defined in terms of a specific number of wavelengths of a particular radiation of light.

At its tenth meeting in 1954, the General Conference of Weights and Measures (CGPM) adopted a coherent system of units based on the four MKSA units, together with the kelvin as the unit of temperature and the candela as the unit of luminous intensity. At the eleventh CGPM meeting in 1960 the formal title 'Systeme International d'Unites' was taken. The abbreviation is 'SI' in all languages. At the 14th CGPM in 1971 the mole (mol) was adopted as the unit for amount of substance; this is the seventh base unit. Two additional special names and symbols were adopted as follows: pascal (Pa) for newton per square metre, and siemens (S) for reciprocal ohm.

The 15th General Conference of Weights and Measures added two new units, namely the becquerel (Bq) and gray (Gy) as well as two additional prefixes, namely peta (P) and exa (E).

For the individual who must know all aspects of the SI metric system and its correct uses, three publications are essential:
1. The NBS publication 330—*The International System of Units* which details the formal content of the system.
2. *ISO 1000 SI units and recommendations for the use of their multiples and of certain other units* which is the official document on the use of the SI metric system. This is available from the American National Standards Institute, 1430 Broadway, New York, NY 10018. It is important to make a distinction between the *formal content* of the SI metric system, included in the first bulletin and the advice concerning the *use* of the system of units, outlined in the second bulletin. The formal content of the SI metric system is developed by the *General Conference of Weights and Measures* (CGPM) while the recommendations for its use are developed by the *ISO* (*International Organization for Standardization*). ISO 1000 is periodically updated and revised as small changes in the use of the SI system develop. The ISO also is responsible for developing international standards based on metric units. It is very important that the reader make a clear distinction between these two, since SI is concerned only with a system of weights and measures, while ISO deals with the use of the system in all kinds of activities.

3. National metric practice guide. Each country that is going metric has developed one or more of these practice guides that deal with how, when and where to use SI metric units as well as applications in various technical areas. It is critically important that there should be national uniformity in the adopted system and in its application of practices. In the U.S. the best known practice guides keyed to ISO 1000 include:

E380-76 ASTM *Standard for Metric Practice.* Philadelphia, PA; ASTM 1916 Race St. 19103

ASME *Orientation and Guide for Use of Metric Units*, American Society of Mechanical Engineers, 345 E. 47th Street, New York, NY 10017.

National Standard of Canada: Metric Practice Guide. Approved by Standards Council of Canada. Reference CSA Z234.1-1973. Rexdale, Ont.: Canadian Standards Association.

IEEE Std 268-1975 *Standard for Metric Practice.* New York, NY: The Institute of Electrical and Electronic Engineers 345 East 47th Street.

Elements

There are three classes of units in SI;
1. The first comprises the quantities of length, mass, time, electric current, temperature, amount of substance, and luminous intensity. The seven units defining these quantities are called *base* units. Fig. 3-1.
2. Two additional *supplementary* units make up the second class, and are used to measure plane and solid angles. Fig. 3-2.
3. A third class known as *derived* units represents compound units formed by the algebraic combination of base units, supplementary units, or other derived units. Most commonly used units in this class have been assigned special names and symbols. Fig. 3-3. The remaining derived units are identified by the names and symbols of the given algebraic expression. Fig. 3-4.

To accommodate an increase or decrease in magnitude of a given unit without the need for large numerical values, SI provides a series of prefixes (in name and symbol) based on the powers of ten. Fig. 3-5. When attached to a unit, a prefix creates a new unit which is a decimal multiple of submultiple of the original unit.

Properties of SI Metric

SI is coherent. The set of primary SI units is *coherent*. This means that all derived units are formed by multiplying and dividing other units without introducing any numerical conversion factors (other than "one").

Examples:
```
1 watt (W) = 1 joule/1 second
1 joule (J) = 1 newton x 1 metre
1 newton (N) = 1 kilogram x 1 metre per second
                 squared
1 hertz (Hz) = 1/1 second
1 coulomb (C) = 1 ampere x 1 second
```

A great advantage of SI is its coherency. If all the given data in a technical problem is stated in primary units, it is then unnecessary to make any special numerical conversions. This simplification reduces calculations in all fields of measurement to a minimum.

In earlier metric systems, energy has been stated in such units as the erg, the calorie, the kilowatt hour and others, all of which are different and none of which are coherent with SI base units. The SI unit of energy is the joule, and only the joule (with suitable prefixes). The coherence of the joule is seen as follows:

1 joule = 1 newton metre
= 1 watt second
= 1 coulomb volt
= 1 kilogram x 1 metre per second squared

Some non-coherent units will continue in use. The kilowatt hour will remain in the measurement of electrical consumption. People will worry over diets in terms of Calories (kilocalories) rather than joules. However, many non-coherent units will eventually be phased out.

SI is consistent. In SI, each physical quantity has one and only one primary unit associated with it. This means that:

All lengths should be stated in terms of the metre
All speeds should be stated in terms of the metre per second
All forces should be stated in newtons
All densities should be stated in kilograms per cubic metre, etc.

Only these units should be used. Strict adherence to this principle means the adoption of a completely *consistent* system. A consistent system is one in which there is a minimum number of units for all measurement purposes and only one for each measurable quantity.

In actual practice this is too idealistic. In specialized fields such as astronomy or physics, the parsec (30 857 terametres) and the angstrom (0.1 nanometre) will continue in use for the measurement of distance or length. Also in daily life the measurement of time will not be restricted to seconds nor that of angles to radians. While pure SI may be consistent, there will in practice be a number of examples where inconsistencies arise.

SI is coordinated. This property of SI refers to the fact that the same set of prefixes may be applied to all primary units in order to form multiples and submultiples. This is especially important when dealing with ranges of measurement from the very large to the very small. The set of prefixes is coordinated with our number system since all the prefixes are powers of 10, making the entire system suitable for decimal arithmetic.

In practice, some non-coordinated units, such as the minute, hour and day are used.

Units Permitted with SI

In addition to the base, supplementary and derived units that make up the SI metric system, there are several units used in daily life, business and industry that are acceptable even though not SI. The most common of these is "degree Celsius" which is the temperature scale used for everyday activities even though the "kelvin" is officially used in science and engineering. A commonly non-preferred prefix used primarily for body measurement and clothing is the centimetre. The following are examples of metric units (not pure SI) that will be commonly used in daily life:

degree Celsius	—commonly used instead of kelvin
litre	**—equivalent to cubic decimetre**
millilitre	—equivalent to cubic centimetre
hectare	—equivalent to square hectometre
metric ton	—equivalent to megagram

Some metric units (not SI) are used in certain specialized fields. For example, the fluid power industry and many companies continue to use the bar instead of the pascal. The following are metric units related to SI units by a power of ten:

bar	equals 100 000 Pa
millibar	equals 100 Pa
angstrom	equals 10^{-10} m

Some non-metric units originated centuries before any thought was given to the metric system. These are so universal that they will continue to be used with SI. The following are a few examples:
minute, hour and day—units of time
degrees, minutes and seconds of arc—units for measuring angles

Fig. 3-1
Base SI units.

Base SI Units

metre
(m)

The metre is the length equal to 1 650 763.73 wavelengths in vacuum of the radiation corresponding to the transition between the levels $2p_{10}$ and $5d_5$ of the krypton-86 atom. (11th CGPM, 1960)

kilogram
(kg)

The kilogram is the unit of mass; it is equal to the mass of the international prototype of the kilogram. (1st and 3rd CGPM, 1889 and 1901)

second
(s)

The second is the duration of 9 192 631 770 periods of the radiation corresponding to the transition between the two hyperfine levels of the ground state of the caesium-133 atom. (13th CGPM, 1967)

ampere
(A)

The ampere is that constant current which, if maintained in two straight parallel conductors of infinite length, of negligible circular cross-section, and placed 1 metre apart in vacuum, would produce between these conductors a force equal to 2×10^{-7} newton per metre of length. (CIPM, 1946, approved by 9th CGPM, 1948)

kelvin
(K)

The kelvin, unit of thermodynamic temperature, is the fraction 1/273.16 of the thermodynamic temperature of the triple point of water. (13th CGPM, 1967)

candela
(cd)

The candela is the luminous intensity, in the perpendicular direction, of a surface of 1/600 000 square metre of a black body at the temperature of freezing platinum under a pressure of 101 325 newtons per square metre. (13th CGPM, 1967)

mole
(mol)

The mole is the amount of substance of a system which contains as many elementary entities as there are atoms in 0.012 kilogram of carbon 12.
(Note: when the mole is used, elementary entities must be specified and may be atoms, molecules, ions, electrons, other particles, or specified groups of such particles.) (14th CGPM, 1971)

Fig. 3-2
Supplementary SI units.

Supplementary SI Units

radian
(rad)

The radian is the plane angle between two radii of a circle which cut off on the circumference an arc equal in length to the radius.

steradian
(sr)

The steradian is the solid angle which, having its vertex in the center of a sphere, cuts off an area of the surface of the sphere equal to that of a square having sides of length equal to the radius of the sphere.

Fig. 3-3
Derived SI units with special names.

Derived SI Units with Special Names

hertz (Hz)	The hertz is the number of repetitions of a regular occurrence in 1 second.
newton (N)	The newton is that force which, applied to a mass of 1 kilogram, gives it an acceleration of 1 metre per second squared.
pascal (Pa)	The pascal is the pressure produced by a force of 1 newton applied, uniformly distributed, over an area of 1 square metre.
joule (J)	The joule is the work done when the point of application of a force of 1 newton is displaced through a distance of 1 metre in the direction of the force.
watt (W)	The watt is the power which in 1 second gives rise to energy of 1 joule.
coulomb (C)	The coulomb is the quantity of electricity carried in 1 second by a current of 1 ampere.
volt (V)	The volt is the difference of electric potential between two points of a conducting wire carrying a constant current of 1 ampere, when the power dissipated between these points is equal to 1 watt.
ohm (Ω)	The ohm is the electrical resistance between two points of a conductor when a constant potential difference of 1 volt, applied to these points, produces in the conductor a current of 1 ampere, the conductor not being the seat of any electromotive force.
farad (F)	The farad is the capacitance of a capacitor between the plates of which there appears a difference of electric potential of 1 volt when it is charged by a quantity of electricity of 1 coulomb.
weber (Wb)	The weber is the magnetic flux which, linking a circuit of 1 turn, would produce in it an electromotive force of 1 volt if it were reduced to zero at a uniform rate in 1 second.
henry (H)	The henry is the inductance of a closed circuit in which an electromotive force of 1 volt is produced when the electric current in the circuit varies uniformly at the rate of 1 ampere per second.
tesla (T)	The tesla is equal to 1 weber per square metre of circuit area.
lumen (lm)	The lumen is the luminous flux emitted within unit solid angle of 1 steradian by a point source having a uniform intensity of 1 candela.
lux (lx)	The lux is equal to an illuminance of 1 lumen per square metre.
siemens (S)	The siemens is the electric conductance of a conductor having an electric resistance of one ohm.
gray (Gy)	The gray is the unit of absorbed dose of radiation equal to one joule absorbed by one kilogram.
becquerel (Bq)	The becquerel is the unit of radioactivity equal to one disintegration per second.

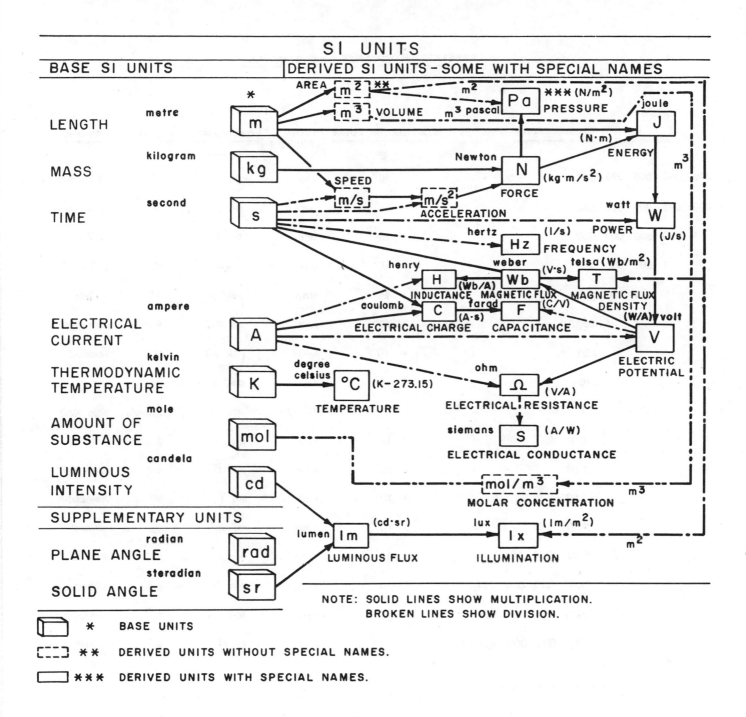

Fig. 3-4
Chart showing the relationship of SI units.

Decimal Form	Exponent or Power	Prefix	Pronunciation	Symbol	Meaning
1 000 000 000 000 000 000	$= 10^{18}$	exa	ex′a	E	quintillion
1 000 000 000 000 000	$= 10^{15}$	peta	pet′a	P	quadrillion
1 000 000 000 000	$= 10^{12}$	tera	tĕr′ ā	T	trillion
1 000 000 000	$= 10^{9}$	giga	jĭ′ gā	G	billion
1 000 000	$= 10^{6}$	mega	mĕg′ ā	M	million
1 000	$= 10^{3}$	kilo	kĭl′ ō	k	thousand
100	$= 10^{2}$	hecto	hĕk′ tō	h	hundred
10	$= 10^{1}$	deka	dĕk′ ā	da	ten
1					base unit
0.1	$= 10^{-1}$	deci	dĕs′ ĭ	d	tenth
0.01	$= 10^{-2}$	centi	sĕn′ tĭ	c	hundredth
0.001	$= 10^{-3}$	milli	mĭl′ ĭ	m	thousandth
0.000 001	$= 10^{-6}$	micro	mī′ krō	ᴀ	millionth
0.000 000 001	$= 10^{-9}$	nano	nă n′ ō	n	billionth
0.000 000 000 001	$= 10^{-12}$	pico	péc ō	p	trillionth
0.000 000 000 000 001	$= 10^{-15}$	femto	fĕm′ tō	f	quadrillionth
0.000 000 000 000 000 001	$= 10^{-18}$	atto	ăt′ tō	a	quintrillionth

░░░ most commonly used

Fig. 3-5
A table of multiples and submultiples showing prefixes, exponents and symbols.

The following lists summarized non-SI units that can
be used with the SI metric system:

UNIVERSALLY USED WITH SI			
Unit and symbol	**Value and application**		
minute (min)	1 min	= 60 s	units of
hour (h)	1 h	= 60 min	time
day (d)	1 d	= 24 h	
degree of arc (°)	180°	= π rad	plane
minute of arc (')	60'	= 1°	angle
second of arc ('')	60''	= 1'	
litre (l) or (ℓ)	1 (l) or (ℓ)	= 1 dm³	volume
millilitre (ml)	1 ml	= 1 cm³	
metric ton or tonne (t)	1 t	= 1000 kg	weight (mass)
kilometre per hour (km/h)	1 km/h	= 0.28 m/s	speed

PERMITTED IN SPECIALIZED AREAS			
Unit and symbol	**Value and application**		
electronvolt (eV)	1 eV	= 1.6×10^{-19} J	energy
unit of atomic mass (u)	1 u	= 1.7×10^{-27} kg	mass
astronomical unit (AU)	1 AU	= 150 Gm	length
parsec (pc)	1 pc	= 30 857 Tm	length

PERMITTED FOR THE PRESENT TIME			
Unit and symbol	**Value and application**		
nautical mile	1 nautical mile	= 1852 m	length
knot	1 kn	= 0.51 m/s	speed
angstrom (Å)	1 Å	= 0.1 nm	length
hectare (ha)	1 ha	= 10 000 m²	area
bar (bar)	1 bar	= 100 kPa	pressure
standard atmosphere (atm)	1 atm	= 101.3 kPa	pressure
kilowatt hour (kW·h)	1 kW·h	= 3.6 MJ	energy

Notes:

1. There is no internationally recognized symbol for astronomical unit. The abbreviation is AU in English and UA in French.
2. The symbol for knot is often shown as kn but this is not internationally recognized.
3. Nautical mile is sometimes unofficially abbreviated as n mile.
4. The hectare (ha) will be used in measuring land areas.
5. The kilometre per hour (km/h) will be used in land transportation.
6. The kilowatt hour (kW·h) will be used for measuring consumption of electrical energy.
7. The bar should be replaced by the pascal as soon as possible.

Physical Quantities and Their Use

The following chart shows examples of SI units used in various areas of education, science and technology. Also shown are some of the non-SI units in common use. While the common multiples and submultiples are shown, these are not the only ones used. The selection of multiples and submultiples may be different in various areas of education, science and technology.

Examples of SI derived units
expressed in terms of base units

Quantity	SI unit	Unit Symbol
area	square metre	m^2
volume	cubic metre	m^3
speed, velocity	metre per second	m/s
acceleration	metre per second squared	m/s^2
wave number	1 per metre	m^{-1}
density, mass density	kilogram per cubic metre	kg/m^3
current density	ampere per square metre	A/m^2
magnetic field strength	ampere per metre	A/m
concentration (of amount of substance)	mole per cubic metre	mol/m^3
Activity (radioactive)	1 per second	s^{-1}
specific volume	cubic metre per kilogram	m^3/kg
luminance	candela per square metre	cd/m^2

Examples of SI derived units expressed by means of special names

Quantity	Name	SI units		Expression in terms of SI base units
		Name	Symbol	
dynamic viscosity	pascal second	Pa·s		$m^{-1} \cdot kg \cdot s^{-1}$
moment of force	metre newton	N·m		$m^2 \cdot kg \cdot s^{-2}$
surface tension	newton per metre	N/m		$kg \cdot s^{-2}$
heat flux density, irradiance	watt per square metre	W/m^2		$kg \cdot s^{-3}$
heat capacity, entropy	joule per kelvin	J/K		$m^2 \cdot kg \cdot s^{-2} \cdot K^{-1}$
specific heat capacity, specific entropy	joule per kilogram kelvin	J/(kg·K)		$m^2 \cdot s^{-2} \cdot K^{-1}$
specific energy	joule per kilogram	J/kg		$m^2 \cdot s^{-2}$
thermal conductivity	watt per metre kelvin	W/(m·K)		$m \cdot kg \cdot s^{-3} \cdot K^{-1}$
energy density	joule per cubic metre	J/m^3		$m^{-1} \cdot kg \cdot s^{-2}$
electric field strength	volt per metre	V/m		$m \cdot kg \cdot s^{-3} \cdot A^{-1}$
electric charge density	coulomb per cubic metre	C/m^3		$m^{-3} \cdot s \ A$
electric flux density	coulomb per square metre	C/m^2		$m^{-2} \cdot s \cdot A$
permittivity	farad per metre	F/m		$m^{-3} \cdot kg^{-1} \cdot s^4 \cdot A^2$
permeability	henry per metre	H/m		$m \cdot kg \cdot s^{-2} \cdot A^{-2}$
molar energy	joule per mole	J/mol		$m^2 \cdot kg \cdot s^{-2} \ mol^{-1}$
molar entropy, molar heat capacity	joule per mole kelvin	J/(mol·K)		$m^2 \cdot kg \cdot s^{-2} \ K^{-1} \cdot mol^{-1}$

SI derived units with special names

Quantity	SI unit			
	Name	Symbol	Expression in terms of other units	Expression in terms of SI base units
frequency	hertz	Hz		s^{-1}
force	newton	N		$m \cdot kg \cdot s^{-2}$
pressure, stress	pascal	Pa	N/m^2	$m^{-1} \cdot kg \cdot s^{-2}$
energy, work, quantity of heat	joule	J	$N \cdot m$	$m^2 \cdot kg \cdot s^{-2}$
power, radiant flux	watt	W	J/s	$m^2 \cdot kg \cdot s^{-3}$
quantity of electricity, electric charge	coulomb	C	$A \cdot s$	$s \cdot A$
electric potential, potential difference, electromotive force	volt	V	W/A	$m^2 \cdot kg \cdot s^{-3} \cdot A^{-1}$
capacitance	farad	F	C/V	$m^{-2} \cdot kg^{-1} \cdot s^4 \cdot A^2$
electric resistance	ohm	Ω	V/A	$m^2 \cdot kg \cdot s^{-3} \cdot A^{-2}$
conductance	siemens	S	A/V	$m^{-2} \cdot kg^{-1} \cdot s^3 \cdot A^2$
magnetic flux	weber	Wb	$V \cdot s$	$m^2 \cdot kg \cdot s^{-2} \cdot A^{-1}$
magnetic flux density	tesla	T	Wb/m^2	$kg \cdot s^{-2} \cdot A^{-1}$
inductance	henry	H	Wb/A	$m^2 \cdot kg \cdot s^{-2} \cdot A^{-2}$
luminous flux	lumen	lm		$cd \cdot sr$ (a)
illuminance	lux	lx		$m^{-2} \cdot cd \cdot sr$ (a)

(a) In this expression the steradian (sr) is treated as a base unit.

Examples of conversion factors from non-SI units to SI

Physical Quantity	Name of Unit	Symbol for Unit	Definition of Unit
length	inch	in	2.54×10^{-2} m
mass	pound (avoirdupois)	lb	0.453 592 37 kg
force	kilogram-force	kgf	9.806 65 N
pressure	atmosphere*	atm	$101\ 325\ N \cdot m^{-2}$
pressure	torr	Torr	$(101\ 325/760)$ $N \cdot m^{-2}$
pressure	conventional millimetre of mercury	mmHg	$13.5951 \times 980.665 \times 10^{-2}\ N \cdot m^{-2}$
energy	British Thermal Unit	BTU	1055.06 J
energy	kilowatt-hour	kWh	3.6×10^{6} J
energy	thermochemical calorie	cal_{th}	4.184 J
energy	I.T. calorie	cal_{it}	4.1868 J
activity (radioactive nuclides)	curie*	Ci	$3.7 \times 10^{10}\ s^{-1}$
exposure (x or γ rays)	röntgen*	R	$2.58 \times 10^{-4}\ C \cdot kg^{-1}$

*The CIPM has sanctioned the use of these units for a limited period of time.

PHYSICAL QUANTITY	THE PRIMARY SI UNIT AND ITS SYMBOL	COMMON MULTIPLES	SOME PERMITTED NON-SI UNITS	NOTES
Part 1: Space and Time				
Plane angle	radian (rad)	mrad μrad	degree of arc (°) minute (') second ('')	Use of the decimal degree is to be encouraged: e.g. 54.75° is preferred to 54° 45'.
Solid angle	steradian (sr)			
Length	metre (m)	km cm mm μm nm	nautical mile = 1852 m used in navigation	The angstrom is to be replaced by 0.1 nm. The decimetre (dm) may be used in education.
Area	square metre (m²)	km² cm² mm²	hectare (ha) = 10 000 m² used for measurement of land areas	
Volume	cubic metre (m³)	cm³ mm³	1 kilolitre (kl) = 1 m³ 1 litre (ℓ) = 1 dm³ 1 millilitre (ml) = 1 cm³	The obsolete abbreviation "cc" is sometimes used in place of cm³ or ml.
Time	second (s)	ms μs ns ps	day (d) hour (h) minute (min)	The week, month and year will continue in common use.
Velocity, Speed	metre per second (m/s)	cm/s	kilometre per hour (km/h)	The nautical mile per hour or knot (1852 m/3600 s) is used in navigation.
Acceleration	metre per second squared (m/s²)	cm/s²		Standard acceleration due to gravity = 9.806 65 m/s².
Angular velocity	radian per second (rad/s)			
Angular acceleration	radian per second squared (rad/s²)			
Frequency	hertz (Hz)	THz GHz MHz kHz		
Rotational frequency	reciprocal second (s⁻¹)	Hz	min⁻¹	Rotational frequency is often stated in revolutions per minute (rpm).
Part 2: Mechanics				
Mass	kilogram (kg)	Mg g mg	1 metric ton or tonne (t) = 1000 kg	In everyday activities, weight and mass are the same.
Density	kilogram per cubic metre (kg/m³)	Mg/m³ kg/dm³ g/cm³	t/m³ kg/ℓ g/ml	Density of water is approximately 1000 kg/m³ or 1 g/cm³.
Momentum	kilogram metre per second (kg·m/s)			
Force	newton (N)	MN kN mN		The kilogram force (= 1 kilopond) is not permitted with SI.

PHYSICAL QUANTITY	THE PRIMARY SI UNIT AND ITS SYMBOL	COMMON MULTIPLES	SOME PERMITTED NON-SI UNITS	NOTES
Part 2: Mechanics (continued)				
Moment of force	newton metre (N·m)	MN·m kN·m		
Pressure, Stress	pascal (Pa)	GPa MPa kPa	Note: 1 N/mm² = 1 MPa	1 bar = 100 kPa 1 mbar = 0.1kPa
Viscosity (dynamic)	pascal second (Pa·s)	mPa·s		The centipoise (= 1 mPa·s) is not permitted with SI.
Viscosity (kinematic)	square metre per second (m²/s)	mm²/s		The centistokes (= 1 mm²/s) is not permitted with SI.
Surface tension	newton per metre (N/m)	mN/m		
Energy, Work	joule (J)	MJ kJ mJ	electronvolt (eV) is used in particle physics	The international calorie (= 4.1868 J) is not used with SI.
Power	watt (W)	MW kW mW μW		
Part 3: Heat				
Thermodynamic temperature	kelvin (K)		In general, degree Celsius (°C) may be used instead of kelvin (K)	Freezing point of water= 273.15K Boiling point of water= 373.15K
Common temperature	degree Celsius (°C)			Freezing point of water = 273.15 K Boiling point of water = 373.15 K
Temperature interval	kelvin (K)			
Linear expansion coefficient	reciprocal kelvin (K^{-1})			
Heat, Quantity of	joule (J)	MJ kJ		The international calorie (= 4.1868 J) is not permitted with SI.
Heat flow rate	watt (W)	kW		
Heat capacity	joule per kelvin (J/K)	kJ/W		°C may be used instead of K
Specific heat capacity	joule per kilogram kelvin (J/(kg·K)	kJ/(kg·K)		°C may be used instead of K
Specific latent heat	joule per kilogram (J/kg)	MJ/kg kJ/kg		Calorie per gram is not permitted with SI.

PHYSICAL QUANTITY	THE PRIMARY SI UNIT AND ITS SYMBOL	COMMON MULTIPLES	SOME PERMITTED NON-SI UNITS	NOTES
Part 4: **Electricity and Magnetism**				
Electric current	ampere (A)	kA mA μA		
Electric charge	coulomb (C)	kC μC		$1 \text{ A·h} = 3.6 \text{ kC}$
Electric potential difference	volt (V)	MV kV mV		
Capacitance	farad (F)	μF nF pF		
Electric field strength	volt per metre (V/m)	kV/m = V/mm V/cm mV/m		
Magnetic field strength	ampere per metre (A/m)	kA/m = A/mm		The oersted (corresponding to $1000/4\pi$ A/m) is not used in SI.
Magnetic flux density	tesla (T)	mT μT		The gauss (corresponding to 10^{-4} T) is not used in SI.
Magnetic flux	weber (Wb)	mWb		The maxwell (corresponding to 10^{-8} Wb) is not used in SI.
Inductance	henry (H)	mH μH		
Resistance	ohm (Ω)	MΩ kΩ mΩ $\mu\Omega$		
Conductance	siemens (S)	kS mS μS		The siemens replaces the unit "mho".
Part 5: **Light**				
Wavelength	metre (m)	nm pm		The angstrom is to be replaced by 0.1 nm: e.g. 6000 Å = 600 nm.
Radiant intensity	watt per steradian (W/sr)			
Luminous intensity	candela (cd)			
Luminous flux	lumen (lm)			
Quantity of light	lumen second (lm·s)			$1 \text{ lm·h} = 3600 \text{ lm·s}$
Luminance	candela per square metre (cd/m²)			
Illuminance	lux (lx)			Also called illumination
Light exposure	lux second (lx·s)			

PHYSICAL QUANTITY	THE PRIMARY SI UNIT AND ITS SYMBOL	COMMON MULTIPLES	SOME PERMITTED NON-SI UNITS	NOTES
Part 6: Acoustics				
Period or periodic time	second (s)	ms μs		
Frequency	hertz (Hz)	MHz kHz		
Wavelength	metre (m)	mm		
Density	kilogram per cubic metre (kg/m^3)			
Sound velocity	metre per second (m/s)			
Sound energy flux, power	watt (W)	kW mW μW		
Sound intensity	watt per square metre (W/m^2)	mW/m^2 $\mu W/m^2$		
Sound power level				The decibel (dB)
Part 7: Physical chemistry				
Amount of substance	mole (mol)	kmol mmol		
Molar mass	kilogram per mole (kg/mol)	g/mol		
Molar volume	cubic metre per mole (m^3/mol)	dm^3/mol cm^3/mol	ℓ/mol	
Radio-activity	becquerel (Bq)		$1\ s^{-1}$ or (disintegration)/s	A special name for reciprocal second
Absorbed dose	gray (Gy)			$1\ Gy = 1\ J/kg$

UNIT 4
LENGTH

word—metre (or meter)

symbol—m

definition—The metre (common Americanized spelling meter) is defined as 1 650 763.73 wavelengths in vacuum of orange-red line of the spectrum of krypton-86. Fig. 4-1a, b, c.

SI base unit	Recommended SI multiples and submultiples	Other SI* multiples and submultiples
metre (m)	kilometre (km) 1 km = 1000 m	
		centimetre (cm) 1 cm = 1/100 m = 0.01 m
	millimetre (mm) 1 mm = 1/1000 m = 0.001 m	
	micrometre (µm) 1 µm = 1/1 000 000 m = 0.000 001 m	

*The *nautical mile* and *knot,* while not SI units, will continue to be used for navigation.

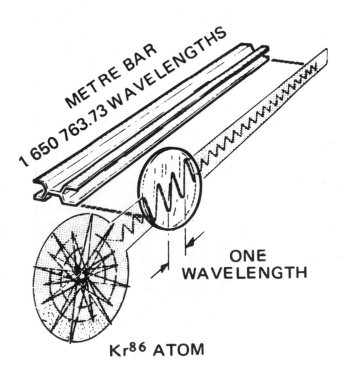

METRE BAR 1 650 763.73 WAVELENGTHS

ONE WAVELENGTH

Kr⁸⁶ ATOM

Fig. 4-1a
An interferometer is used to measure length by means of lightwaves.

The *metre,* with its recommended multiples and submultiples, the *kilometre* and *millimetre,* are the units that are used almost exclusively in manufacturing, construction, and other technical fields. The micrometre is used for very precise measurements such as the surface finish on metals. Fig. 4-2. The *centimetre* is used in the textile and clothing industries. Body measurements are also given in centimetres. Many everyday length units used in the home are in centimetres. The metre is a little longer than a yard (about 3.37" longer). Fig. 4-3. Like other metric units, the metre is relatively easy to use. It is divided into units of ten, Fig. 4-4 as follows:

1 metre = 10 decimetres or 100 centimetres or 1000 millimetres

1 decimetre = 10 centimetres

1 centimetre = 10 millimetres

In the opposite direction:

1 deckametre = 10 metres

1 hectometre = 10 dekametre

1 kilometre = 10 hectometres or 100 dekametres or 1000 metres

The metric system is decimal, like our money system, and therefore a direct relationship can be made with it. Fig. 4-5. For effective use of the metre and its multiples and submultiples as the unit of length, it is important to begin to "think metric." The sizes of familiar objects will provide you with the correct mental image.

Use of Length Units.

The following possible uses of linear units will give some idea of what may be expected as the United States goes metric.

The *millimetre* (mm) will be used to express dimensions of thumb tacks, paper clips, stamps, money, films, lenses, matches, buttons, ball bearings, drills, nails, hinges, screws, nuts, and bolts; sizes of wrenches, chisels and screwdrivers; thickness of glass, plywood, and sheet metal; allowances for seams; widths of ribbons and cello-tape; sizes of paper, thickness and widths of lumber; sizes of shoes; and amount of rainfall. Fig. 4-6. The millimetre is the *only* dimension used on all technical and engineering drawings.

The *centimetre* (cm) will be used to indicate body sizes, such as our heights; bust, waist and hip measurements; arm length, hand span and neck sizes; width of textiles and wallpaper; dimensions in dress patterns and knitting instructions; lengths of scissors, pencils, chalk, zippers, shoelaces, ties and belts; lengths and widths of sheets, pillowcases, bedspreads, towels, tablecloths and diapers; and dimensions of most furniture and appliances. Fig. 4-7.

The *metre* (m) will be used when indicating the dimensions of plot plans, swimming pools, athletic courts and ball fields; track and field events and horse racing; lengths of cloth, rope, extension cords, garden hoses and lumber; heights of buildings, trees, mountains, and flight paths of aircraft; the width of a highway and the turning radius of a car; the length of a whale and the height of a giraffee; the depth of a mine shaft or of waters in navigations; and the length of a driveway when shovelling snow. Fig. 4-8.

The *kilometre* (km) will be essential on maps, in travel, on road signs, in long distance running and driving events, in measuring lengths of rivers, national boundaries, and distances to planets. Odometers will be designed to show kilometres, and speed limits will be expressed in kilometres per hour. Fig. 4-9.

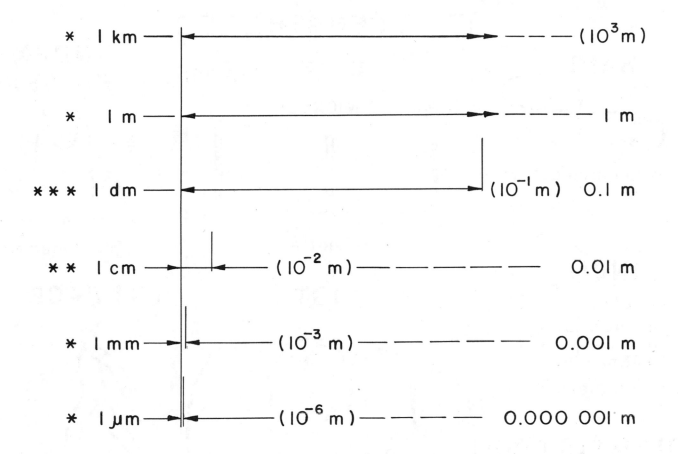

*   1 km $(10^3 m)$

*   1 m   1 m

* * *   1 dm $(10^{-1}m)$ 0.1 m

* *   1 cm $(10^{-2} m)$ 0.01 m

*   1 mm $(10^{-3} m)$ 0.001 m

*   1 μm $(10^{-6} m)$ 0.000 001 m

*   PREFERRED UNITS FOR INDUSTRY AND BUSINESS.

* *   DESIRABLE UNIT FOR CONSUMER USE.

* * *   RARELY USED EXCEPT FOR TEACHING AND SPECIAL USE,
FOR EXAMPLE — 1 cubic decimetre equals 1 litre.

Fig. 4-1b
The metre with its multiples and submultiples.

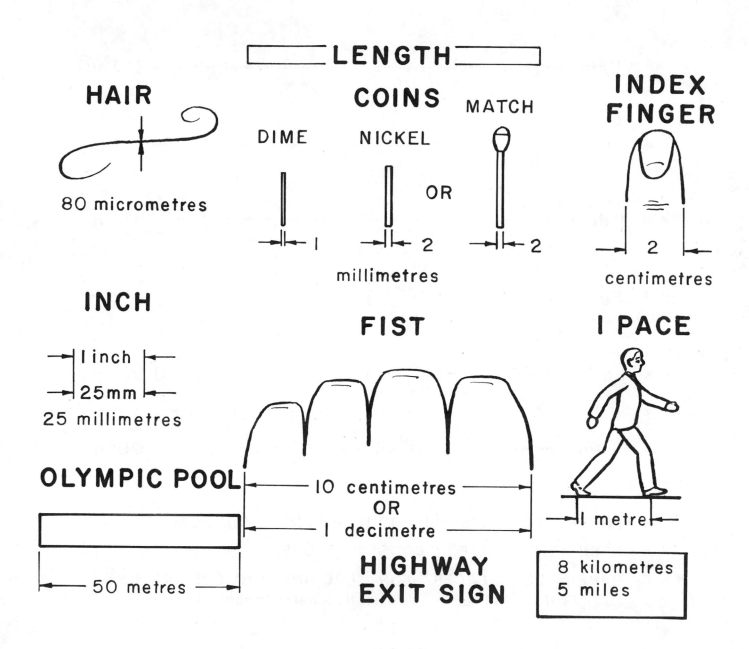

Fig. 4-1c
Common examples of length units.

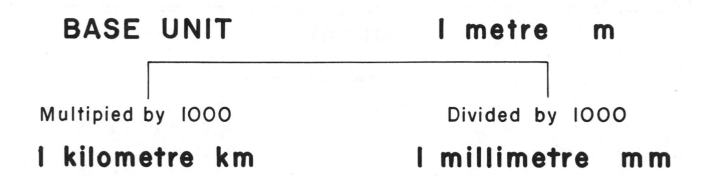

BASE UNIT   I metre   m

Multipied by 1000   Divided by 1000

I kilometre km   I millimetre mm

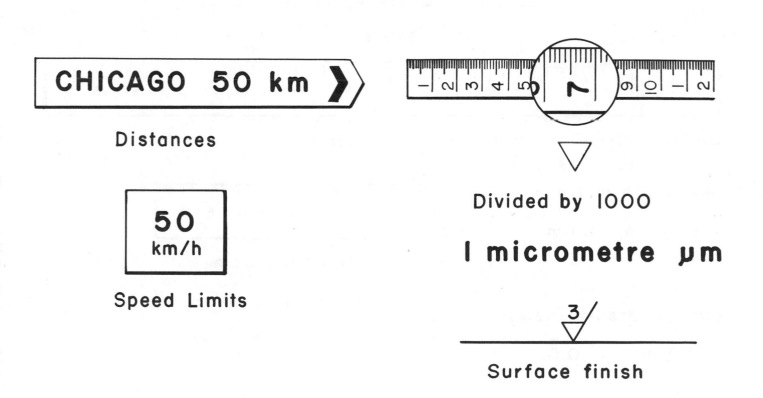

Distances

50 km/h

Speed Limits

Divided by 1000

I micrometre μm

Surface finish

Fig. 4-2
The base unit is the metre.

YARD

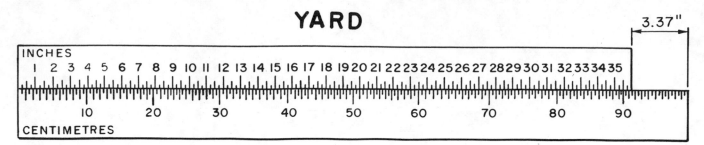

Fig. 4-3
The metre is a little longer than the yard.

METRE

LENGTH

metre m

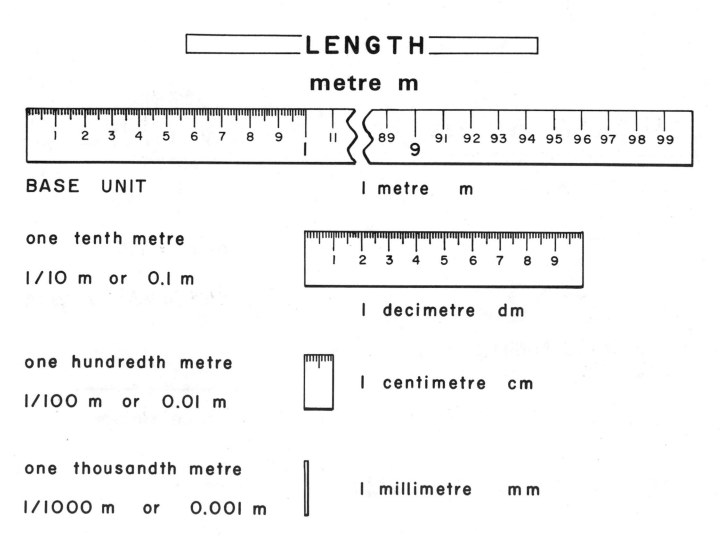

BASE UNIT

1 metre   m

one tenth metre

1/10 m or 0.1 m

1 decimetre dm

one hundredth metre

1/100 m or 0.01 m

1 centimetre   cm

one thousandth metre

1/1000 m   or   0.001 m

1 millimetre   mm

Fig. 4-4a
Note how the metre is divided into units of ten.

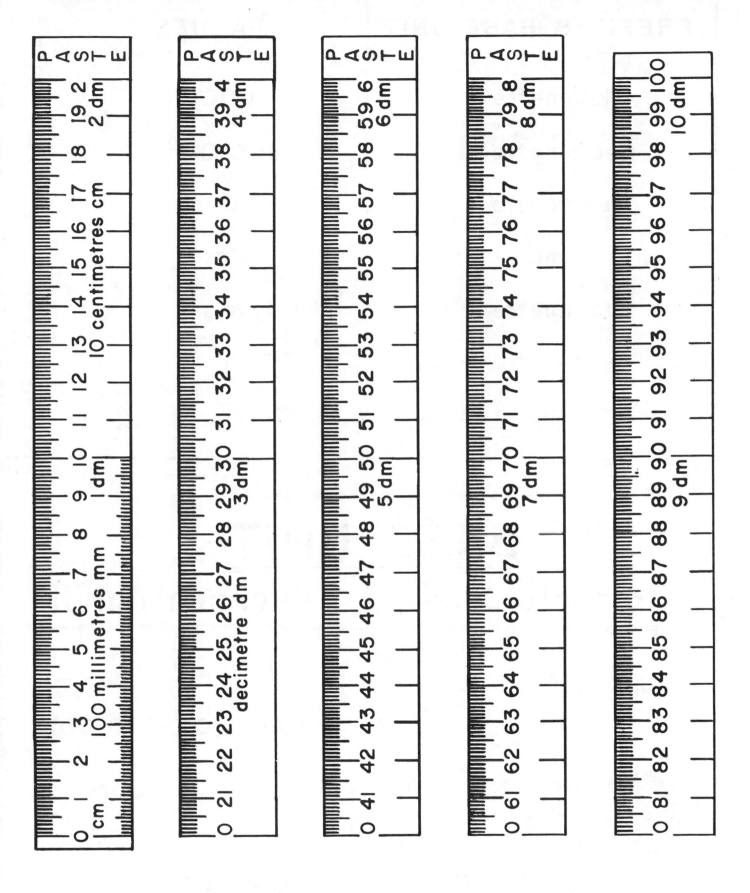

Fig. 4-4b
This full size drawing can be used to make a metre stick.

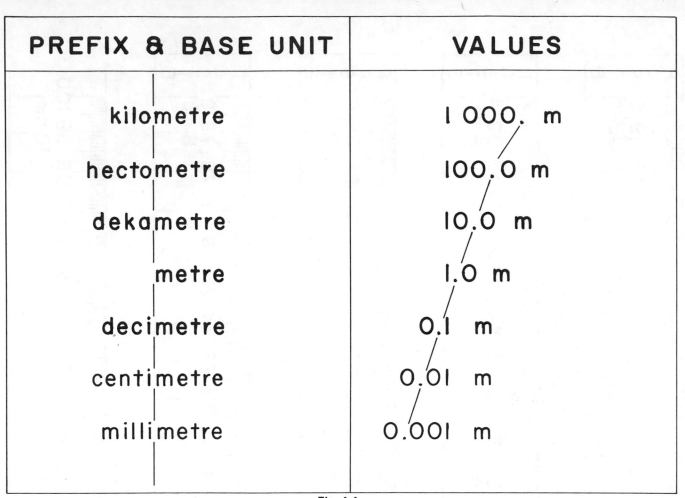

PREFIX & BASE UNIT	VALUES
kilometre	1 000. m
hectometre	100.0 m
dekametre	10.0 m
metre	1.0 m
decimetre	0.1 m
centimetre	0.01 m
millimetre	0.001 m

Fig. 4-4c
Note how the values can be changed by moving the decimal point.

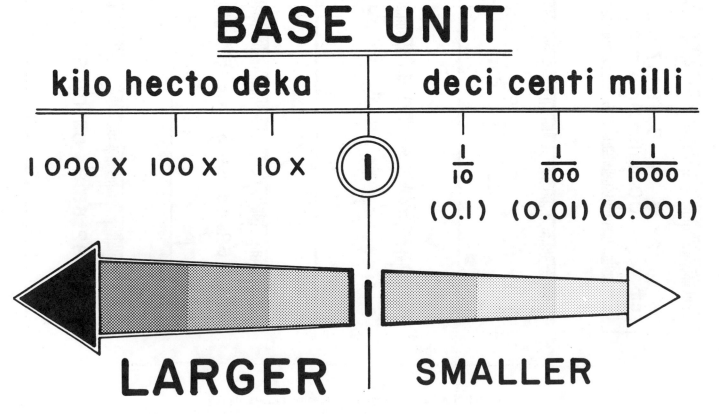

BASE UNIT

kilo hecto deka   **deci centi milli**

1000 X   100 X   10 X   (1) $\frac{1}{10}$ $\frac{1}{100}$ $\frac{1}{1000}$

(0.1)   (0.01)   (0.001)

LARGER   **SMALLER**

Fig. 4-4d
Note how prefixes are used to make larger and smaller units.

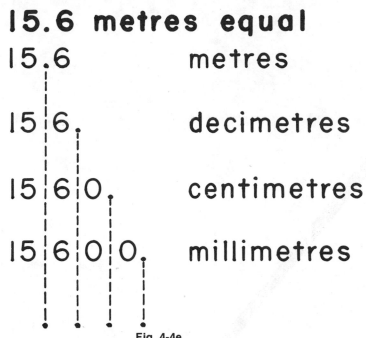

15.6 metres equal

15.6   metres

156.   decimetres

1560.   centimetres

15600.   millimetres

Fig. 4-4e
To change larger units to smaller units move the decimal point to the right.

YOUR MONEY AND METRIC LENGTH

YOUR MONEY	METRIC LENGTH	SYMBOL	NUMBER OF METRES
$1,000.00	kilometre	km	1 000.
$100.00	hectometre	hm	100.
$10.00	dekametre	dam	10.
$1.00	metre	m	1.
DIME ◯	decimetre	dm	0.1
CENT ◯	centimetre	cm	0.01
MILL ◯	millimetre	mm	0.001

Fig. 4-5
An easy way to remember the multiples and submultiples in metric is to compare them to your money.

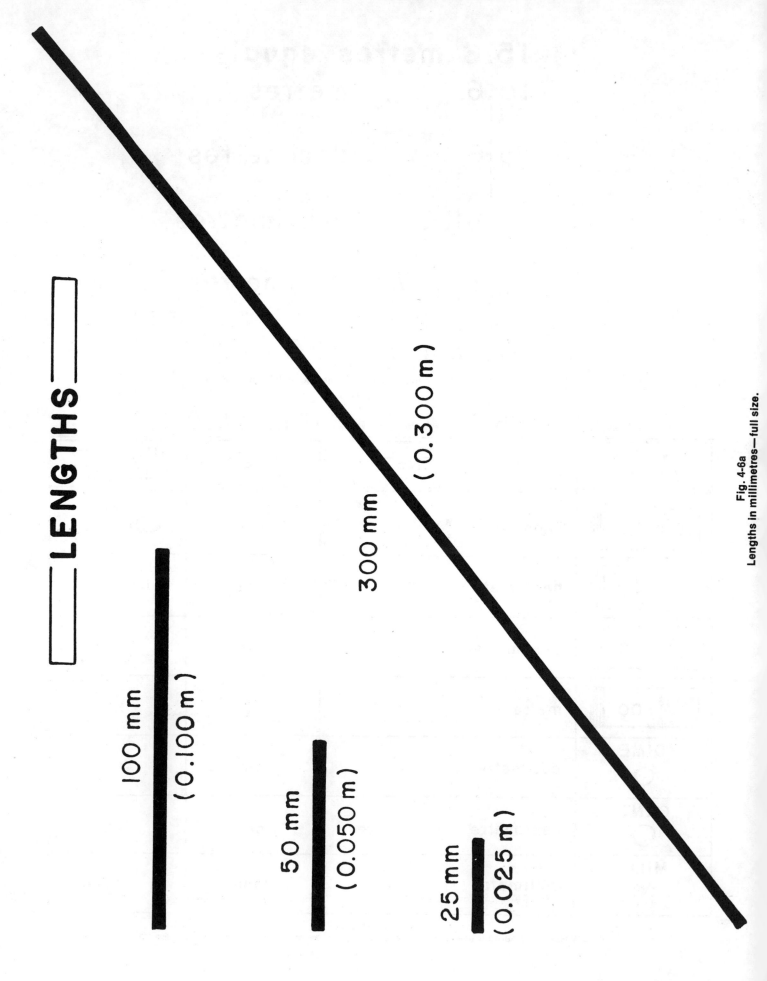

LENGTHS

100 mm
(0.100 m)

50 mm
(0.050 m)

25 mm
(0.025 m)

300 mm
(0.300 m)

Fig. 4-6a
Lengths in millimetres—full size.

4-9

MEASURING
in millimetres (mm)

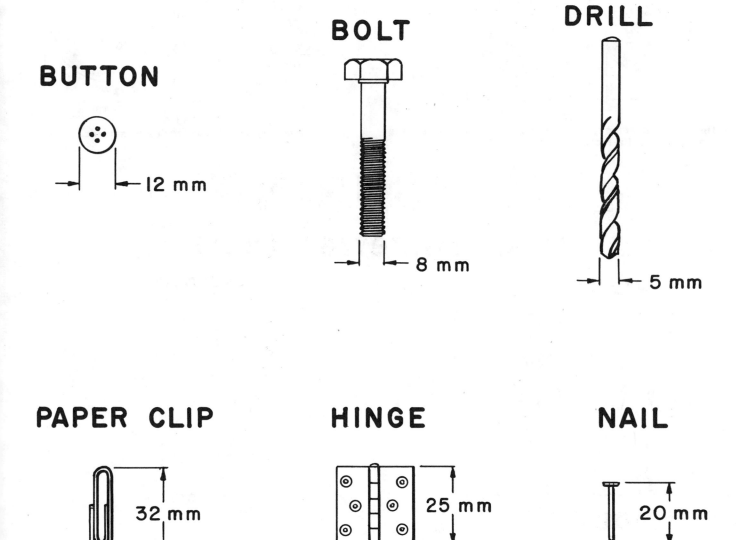

BUTTON

12 mm

BOLT

8 mm

DRILL

5 mm

PAPER CLIP

32 mm

HINGE

25 mm

NAIL

20 mm

Fig. 4-6b
Become familiar with these common items and be able to estimate their size in millimetres.

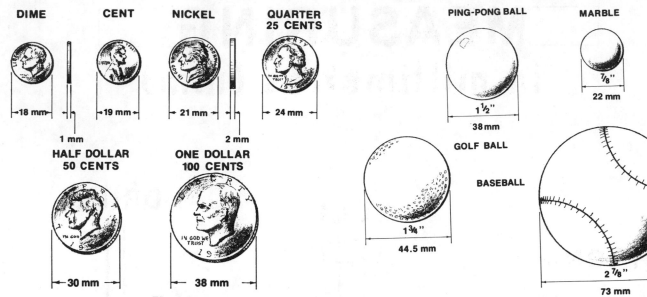

Fig. 4-6c
The size of your money is a good reference, since the dime is 1 mm thick and the nickel is 2 mm thick.

Fig. 4-6d
Common sports balls and their size in metric.

MEASURING
in centimetres (cm)

PEOPLE

BODY MEASUREMENTS

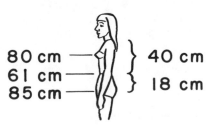

FABRIC

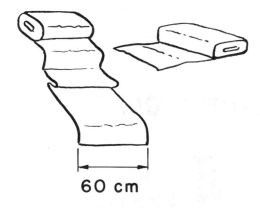

TOWEL

Fig. 4-7a
Common uses for the centimetre.

HEIGHT (LENGTH)

AVERAGE HEIGHT OF MEN: 175 centimetres.
AVERAGE HEIGHT OF WOMEN: 160 centimetres.

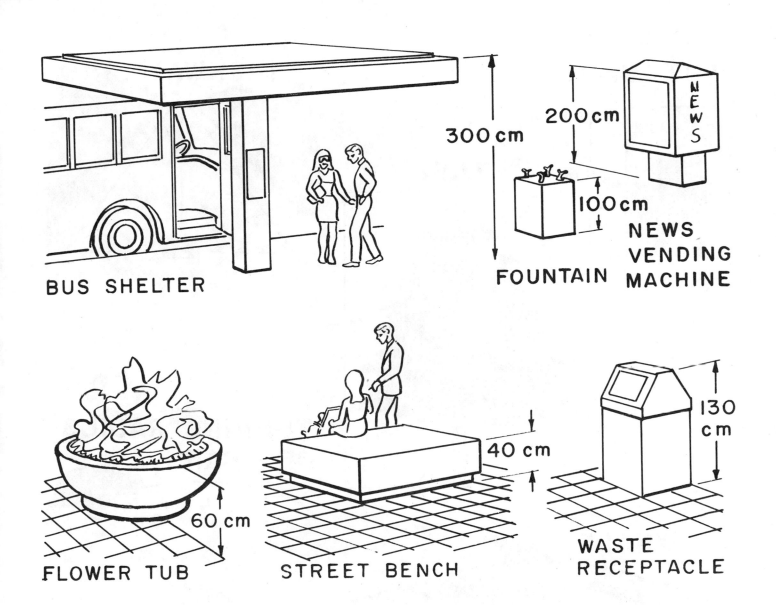

BUS SHELTER

300 cm

200 cm

100 cm

FOUNTAIN

NEWS VENDING MACHINE

60 cm

FLOWER TUB

40 cm

STREET BENCH

130 cm

WASTE RECEPTACLE

Fig. 4-7b
Common items you may see everyday in a large city.

MEASURING
in metres (m)

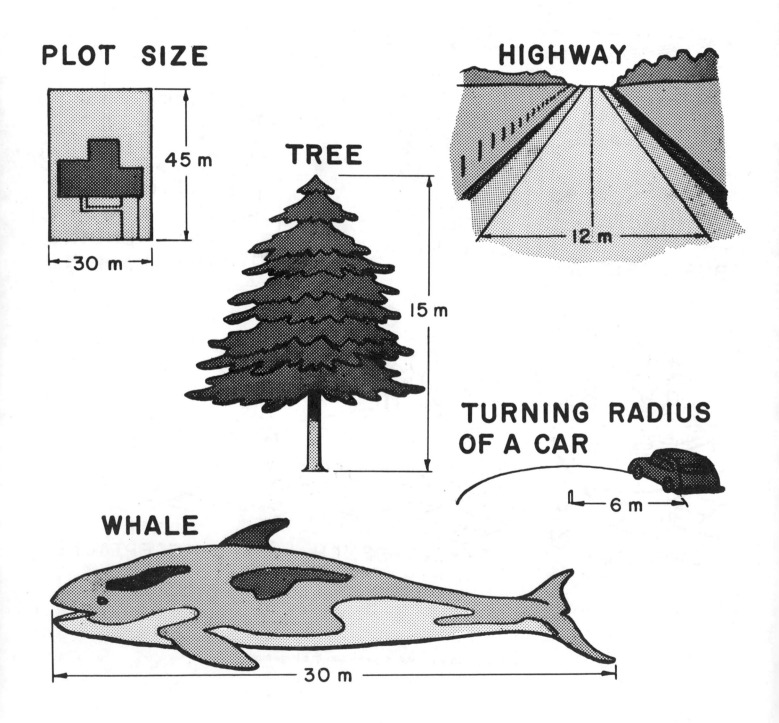

PLOT SIZE

45 m

30 m

TREE

15 m

HIGHWAY

12 m

TURNING RADIUS OF A CAR

6 m

WHALE

30 m

Fig. 4-8
Common uses for the metre.

DISTANCES

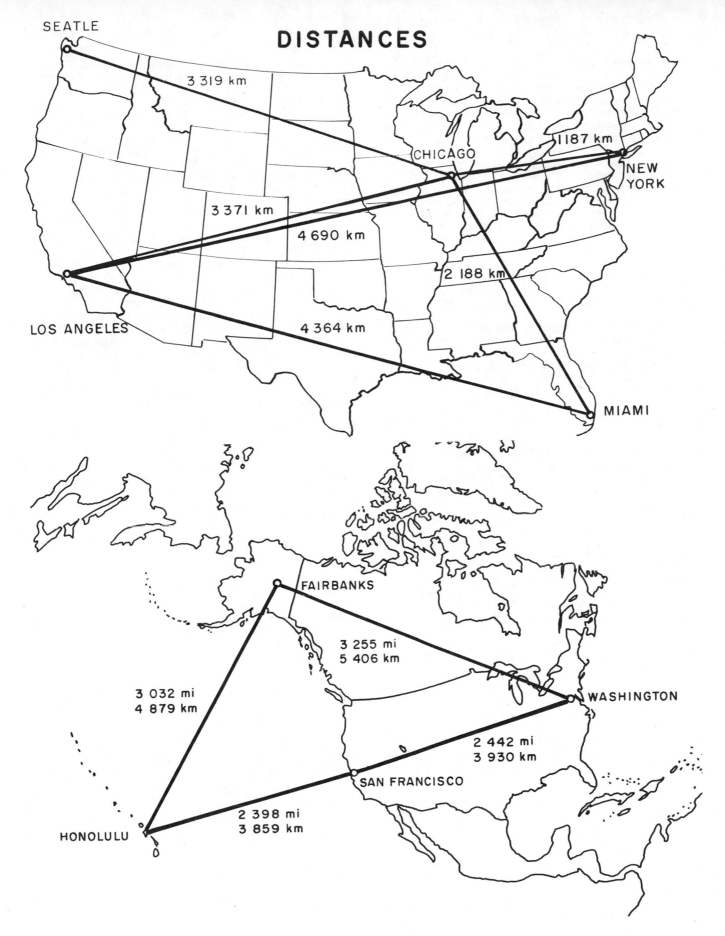

Fig. 4-9
Major reference points and their distances in kilometres.

4-14

The *decimetre* (dm) is not in common use but is a convenient size for students first using the metric system. The decimetre cube is related to the litre in studies on volume. The *dekametre* is rarely found in real life. The *hectometre* will generally be expressed in terms of 100 m as in the 100 metre dash. A knowledge of this unit is useful in visualizing an area of one *hectare* which equals a *square hectometre.*

The international nautical mile, used primarily for navigation, is equal to 1852 metres or 6076.12 feet. The international nautical mile is equal to the average length of a minute of latitude and corresponds to a latitude of 45°. The *knot* (nautical mile per hour) is equal to 1852/3600 or 0.5144 metres per second. These units will be used for both sea and air navigation.

Conversion

A few common reference points will be useful.

1. A metre is about 10 percent longer than a yard and a yard is about 10 percent shorter than a metre. Fig. 4-9.

2. The centimetre is much smaller (less than half) of an inch. There are about 2.5 centimetres in an inch. To change centimetres to inches multiply by 4 and divide by 10. For example, 5 centimetres equals 5 x 4/10 or about 2 inches. To change inches to centimetres divide by 4 and multiply by 10. For example, 3 inches equals 3/4 x 10 or approximately 7.5 centimetres.

3. A mile is much longer than a kilometre. There are about 1.6 kilometres in a mile. Fig. 4-11. To change kilometres to miles divide by 2 and add 20 percent. For example, 10 kilometres equals 10/2 or 5 plus (20 percent) or about 6 miles. To change miles to kilometres double the miles and subtract 20 percent. For example, 15 miles x 2 = 30 - 6 (20 percent) = 24 km.

The following are the approximate conversions:

1 ft. equals about 300 mm or 30 cm (305 mm)
1 yd. equals about 91 cm or 910 mm (914 mm)
1 in. equals about 2.5 cm or 25 mm
1 mi. equals 1609 m or about 1.6 km
1 km equals 0.625 mi or about 0.6 mi

For more accurate conversions from customary to metric length and vice versa various tables and charts can be used, Figs. 4-12, 4-13, 4-14, 4-15.

Calculating in Linear Measure

Customary lengths are often given in more than one unit. For example, the length of a room may be listed as 7'3". To convert this to metric it is necessary to first change the customary measurements all to the same unit. For example, in this case all in inches. 7'3" = 7 x 12 + 3 or 87". This number (87) can be multiplied by 25.4 and the result is 2209.8 mm or rounded to 2210 mm. This measurement could also be listed as 221 cm or 2.21 m. In the metric system all lengths are normally given in a single unit. For example, 2.56 m or 256 cm or 2560 mm.

Technical

The definition of the metre has been refined through three stages of history:

1. The *metre* was originally defined as one ten millionth of the distance from the North Pole to the equator on a meridian line running through Paris. Fig. 4-16. In order to check their measurement, two astronomers measured with great accuracy the distance from Dunkirk in France to Montsuich in Spain. Although this operation was carried out in politically disturbed times, the result was in error by only 2288.3 metres, a remarkable achievement in those days. At the time of that definition, the metre was intended to be one forty-millionth of the earth's circumference. On the basis of our present knowledge we know that this definition of the metre is 0.2 mm (0.02%) too short.

2. To improve the accuracy of the definition of the metre, a second standard was developed. The French National Assembly preempted the geodetic survey upon which the metre was based and appointed a committee to produce a more accurate standard. This committee produced in 1799 several platinum-iridium metre bars to use as the master standard. In 1870, France invited the nations to a conference to discuss the advisability of constructing new metric standards to supplant those of the Archives. Nations represented at this conference included France, Austria, Columbia, Ecuador, Great Britain, Greece, Italy, Norway, Peru, Portugal, Russia, Spain, Switzerland, Turkey and the United States. Work at the conference was seriously handicapped by turmoil of the Franco-Prussian War then in progress so that little was accomplished.

Another conference in 1872 was more successful. It resulted in a decision to reconstruct the basic metric standards to conform in length and weight with those of the Archives. A permanent committee was organized to carry out this decision. By 1875, its work was sufficiently complete for another general convention to be called.

At a convention in 1875 held in Paris, a treaty was negotiated whereby a permanent International Bureau of Weights and Measures was established.

A place for the Bureau's headquarters was provided by France at Sevres, a suburb of Paris in the Parc de St. Cloud.

By 1889, 31 metre bars were constructed and approved by the Bureau's governing committee. The bar which agreed most closely with their respective counterparts at the Archives was selected as the new International Standard. The remainder were distributed to the nations represented in the Bureau. The United States received metres No. 21 and 27 together with kilograms No. 4 and 20. Fig. 4-17.

The metre bar composed of 90% platinum and 10% iridium was made in what is termed the Tresca section, for maximum physical rigidity. This, the *international prototype metre,* is kept in a massive concrete vault, guarded by heavy iron doors three flights of steps below the ground floor of a white stone building in the Parc de St. Cloud. This was the master in terms of which the world's measurements were defined until 1960.

3. The third stage, developed in 1960, defines the metre as the length equal to 1 650 763.73 wave lengths in a vacuum of the radiation corresponding to the transition between the levels $2p^{10}$ and $5d^5$ of the krypton-86 atom. The reason the metre is defined in terms of the wavelength of light is so that it can be reproduced in any good scientific laboratory. The metre and the yard are defined in terms of one another. The best definition of the yard is that it is 0.9144 of a metre. The standard for the metre is obtained by using krypton-86 lamps operated under well defined conditions in accordance with international recommendations which reproduce the specific wavelength to an accuracy of one part in a hundred million.

Twelve secondary wavelength standards selected from the spectra of krypton-86, mercury 198 and cadmium 114 have been evaluated in terms of the primary krypton-86 standard and internationally accepted for use in length determinations by interferometry.

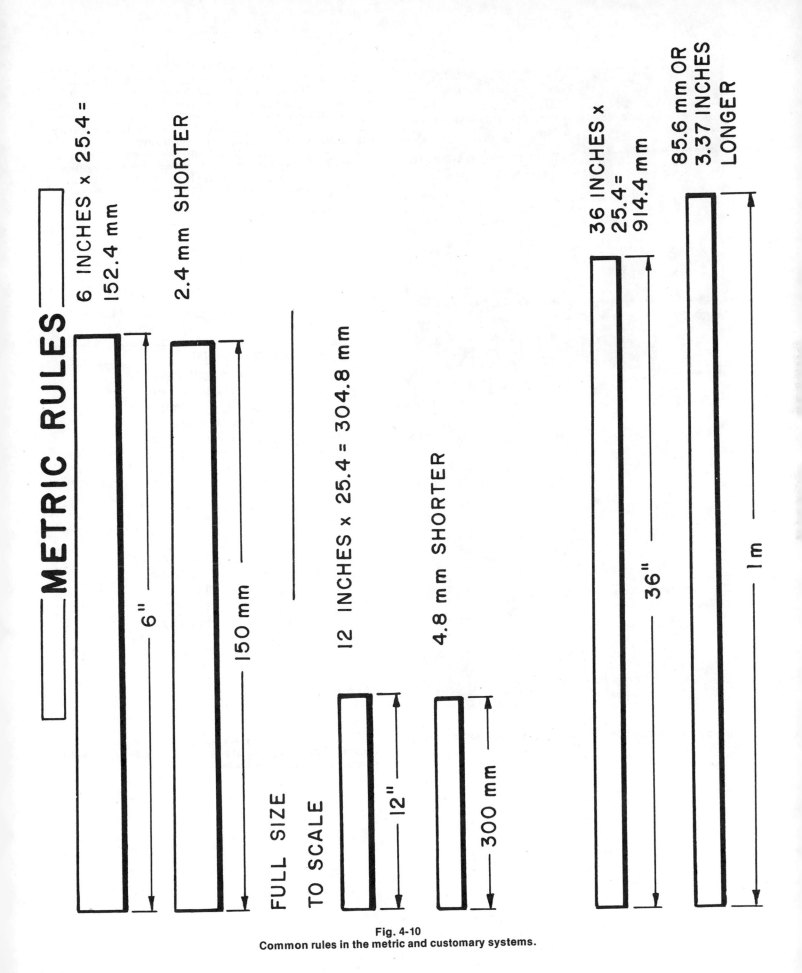

Fig. 4-10
Common rules in the metric and customary systems.

Fig. 4-11
This sign illustrates the comparison between kilometres and miles.

Another promising source of standard wavelengths is the gas laser which emits highly coherent light. In particular the red radiation from the helium-neon laser has been stabilized by a servo control system. In terms of the primary krypton-86 standard the wavelength is 632.9914 m, and provides a very useful secondary standard for measuring long distances.

Longer distances (up to 3 km) are measured with an instrument employing light which is polarization-modulated at about 500 MHz. It has a sensitivity of + 0.1 mm and an accuracy of + 3 mm in 1 km.

LENGTH

Customary to Metric		
1 inch =	25.4	millimetres*
1 inch =	2.54	centimetres*
1 foot =	30.48	centimetres
1 foot =	0.3048	metre
1 yard =	91.44	centimetres
1 yard =	0.9144	metre
1 mile =	1.609	kilometres

Metric to Customary		
1 millimetre =	0.039 37	inch
1 centimetre =	0.3937	inch
1 metre =	39.37	inches
1 metre =	3.2808	feet
1 metre =	1.0936	yards
1 kilometre =	0.621 37	mile

*Accurate

Fig. 4-12a,b,c,d,e
Common tables you can use to convert customary to metric measurement and vice versa.

To Convert from centimetres	
To	Multiply by
inches	39.370 08
feet	3.280 840
yards	1.093 613
miles	0.000 621 37
millimetres	1 000
centimetres	100
kilometres	0.001

To Convert from inches	
To	Multiply by
feet	0.083 333 33
yards	0.027 777 78
centimetres	2.54
metres	0.025 4

To Convert from yards	
To	Multiply by
inches	36
feet	3
miles	0.000 568 18
centimetres	91.44
metres	0.914 4

To Convert from metres	
To	Multiply by
inches	0.398 700 8
feet	0.032 808 40
yards	0.010 936 13
metres	0.01

To Convert from feet	
To	Multiply by
inches	12
yards	0.333 333 3
miles	0.000 189 39
centimetres	30.48
metres	0.304 8
kilometres	0.000 304 8

To Convert from miles	
To	Multiply by
inches	63 360
feet	5 280
yards	1 760
centimetres	160 934.4
metres	1 609.344
kilometres	1.609 344

		kilometres	metres	centimetres	millimetres	miles	yards	feet	inches
1	kilometre	1.0	1 000.0	100 000.0	1 000 000.0	0.621	1 093.613	3 280.839	39 370.079
1	metre	0.001	1.0	100.0	1 000.0	---	1.094	3.281	39.370
1	centimetre	0.000 01	0.01	1.0	100.0	---	0.010 94	0.032 81	0.393 7
1	millimetre	---	0.001	10.0	1.0	---	0.001	0.003	0.039
1	mile	1.609	1 609.344	91.44	1 609 344.0	1.0	1 760.0	5 280.0	63 360.0
1	yard	---	0.914	---	914.4	---	1.0	3.0	36.0
1	foot	---	0.305	30.48	304.8	---	0.333	1.0	12.0
1	inch	---	0.025 4	0.254	25.4	---	0.028	0.083	1.0

Customary Units	Metric Units
1 parsec	= 30.84×10^{15} m
1 light year	= 9 464 Tm
1 league	= 4.828 km
1 nautical mile	= 1.852 km
1 mile	= 1.609 km
1 chain	= 20.12 m
1 rod	= 5.029 m
1 fathom	= 1.83 m
1 yard (yd)	= 0.914 m
1 foot (ft)	= 0.3048 m
1 hand	= 101.6 mm
1 inch (in)	= 25.4 mm
1 point (printer's)	= 0.353 mm
1 micron	= 1 μm
1 angstrom (Å)	= 0.1 nm

Useful approximations:

1 km	= 5/8 mile
10 cm	= 4 in
1 mm	= 40 thousandths
10 ft	= 3 m
2.5 cm	= 1 in
25 mm	= 1 in
30 cm	= 1 ft

Fig. 4-13
These conversion scales will help you get the feel for the difference between customary and metric measurement. For example, note how easy it is to see that 50 mm is less than 2 in, that 200 metres is somewhat more than 200 yards, and that 50 miles is approximately 80 kilometres.

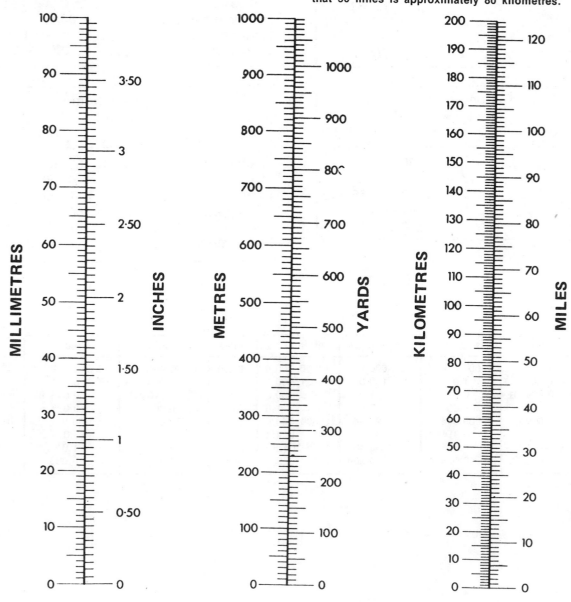

LENGTH

1 inch - in = 25.4 millimetres - mm
1 millimetre - mm = 0.03937 inch - in

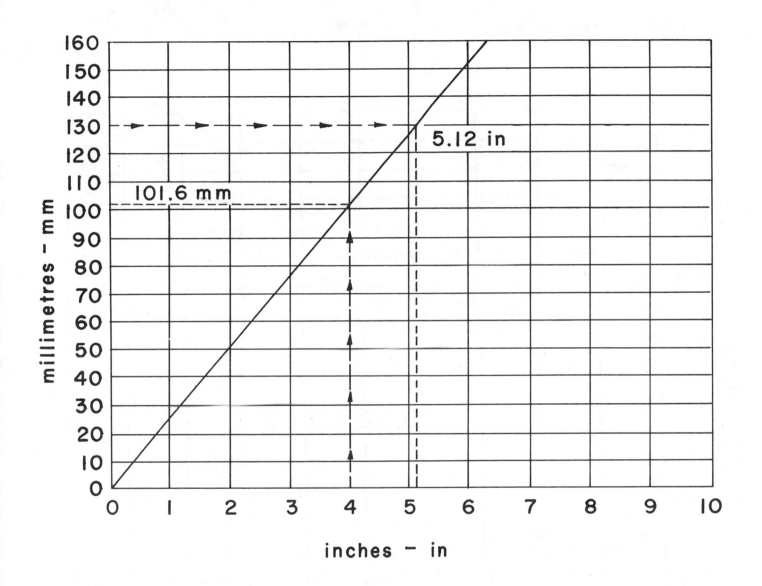

Fig. 4-14a
Graphs to compare customary and metric units.

LENGTH

l inch - in = 2.54 centimetres - cm
l centimetre - cm = 0.3937 inch - in

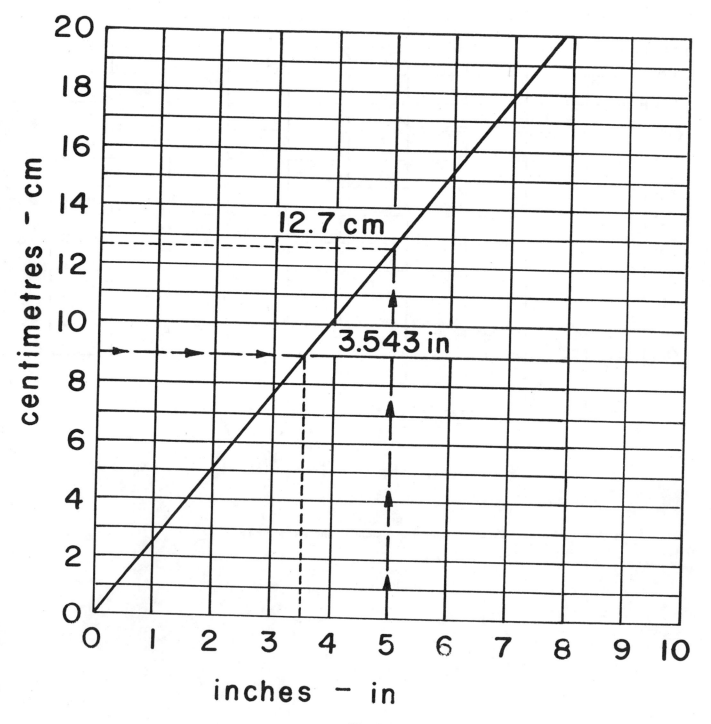

Fig. 4-14b

4-21

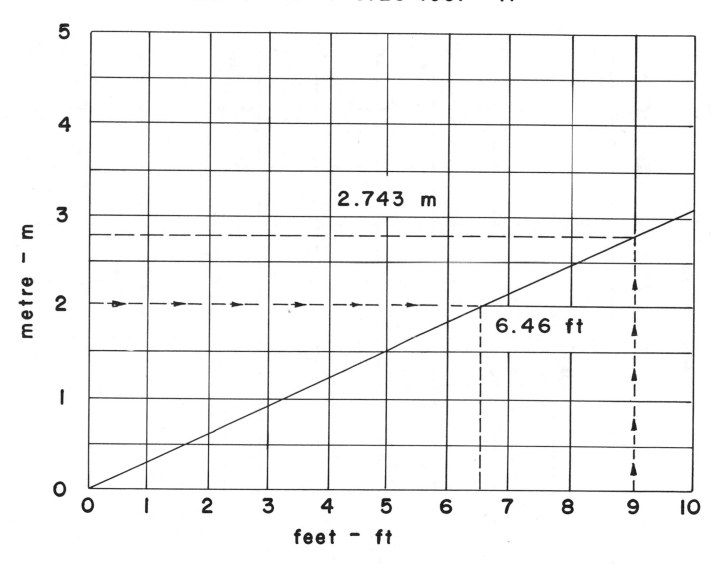

LENGTH

l foot - ft = 0.3048 metre - m
l metre - m = 3.28 feet - ft

Fig. 4-14c

LENGTH

I yard - yd = 0.914 4 metre - m

I metre - m = 1.093 6 yards - yd

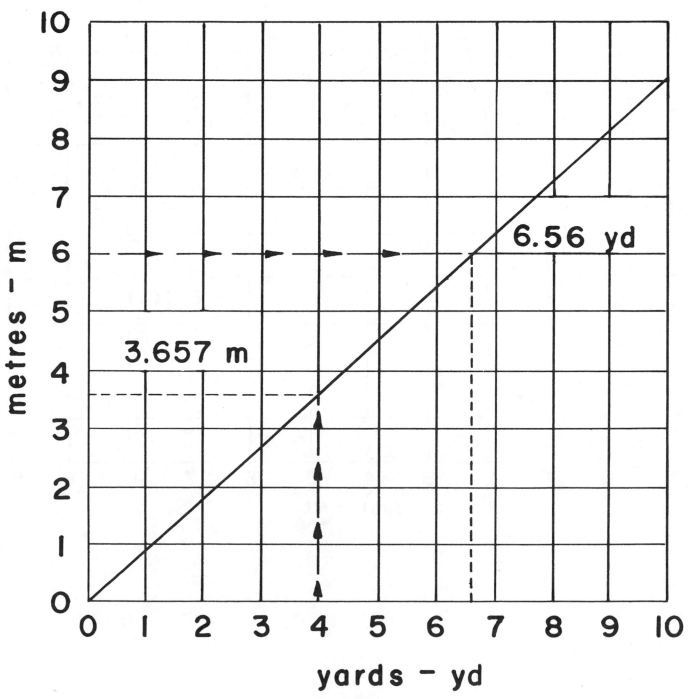

Fig. 4-14d

LENGTH

I mile – mi = 1.609 kilometres – km
I kilometre – km = 0.6215 miles – mi

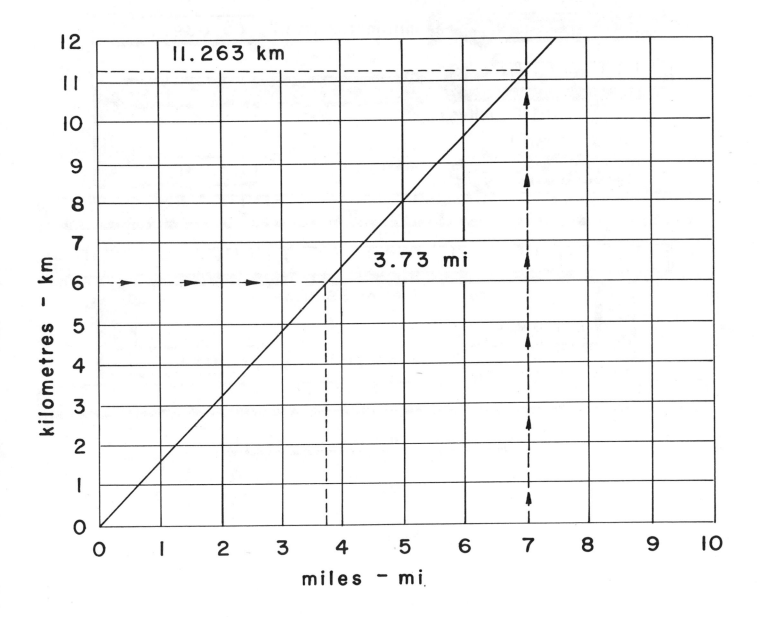

Fig. 4-14e

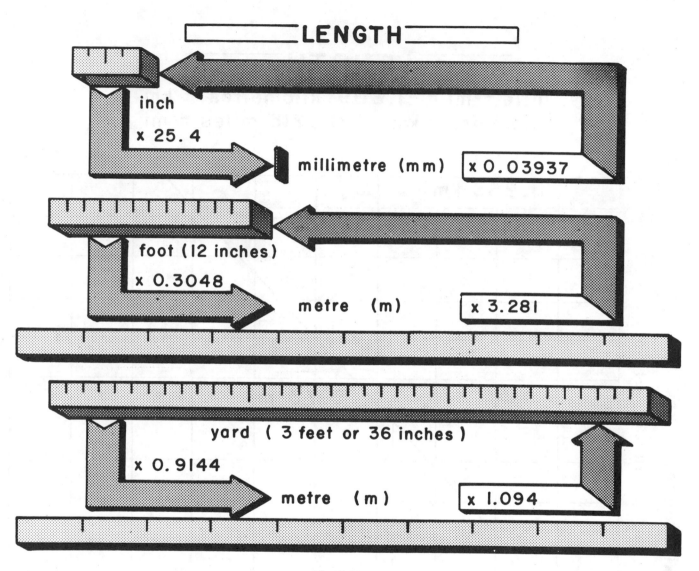

Fig. 4-15a
Visual charts to convert from customary to metric and vice versa.

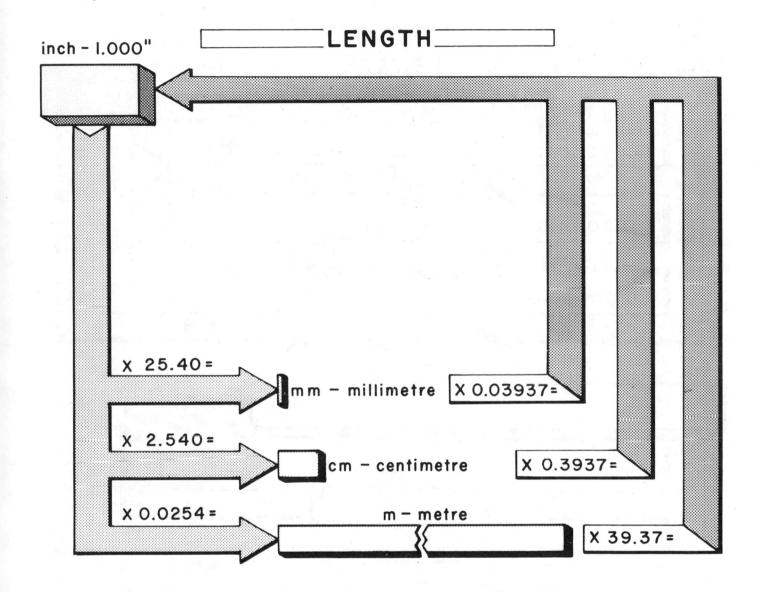

LENGTH

inch – 1.000"

X 25.40 =   mm – millimetre   X 0.03937=

X 2.540 =   cm – centimetre   X 0.3937 =

X 0.0254 =   m – metre   X 39.37 =

Fig. 4-15b

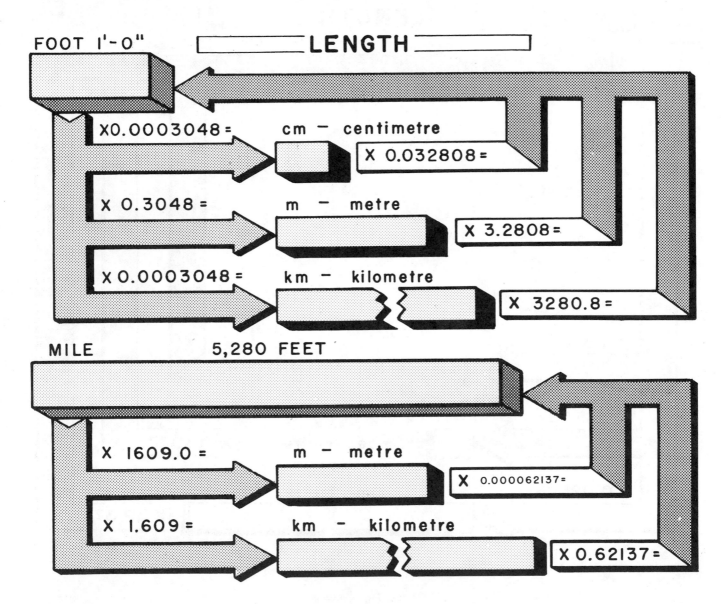

Fig. 4-15c

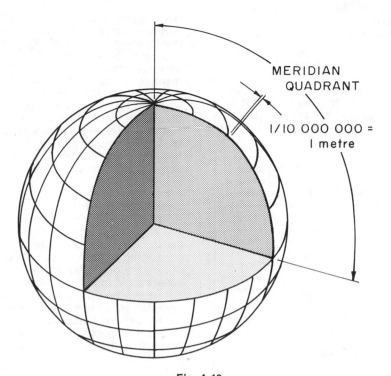

MERIDIAN QUADRANT

1/10 000 000 = 1 metre

Fig. 4-16
The first definition of the metre was in terms of the earth's circumference.

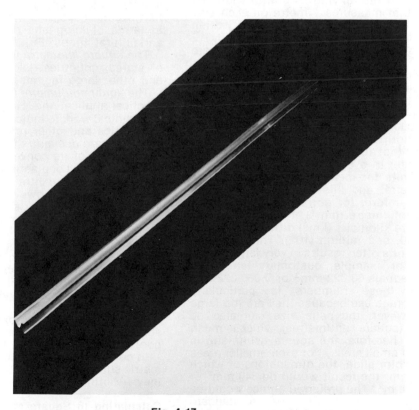

Fig. 4-17
Photograph of the metre bar kept at the National Bureau of Standards. The metre bar was the national standard for length measurements for 70 years. In 1960, it was replaced by a new and more accurate standard based on a wavelength of light. However, the bar is still a most valued measuring tool.

UNIT 5
AREA

word—square metre (or square meter)
symbol—m
definition—The SI unit of area is the square metre, an area that measures on metre by one metre. It is a derived unit without a special name, based on the unit of length. Fig. 5-1.

SI base unit	SI multiples and submultiples	Multiples of SI units with special names
square metre (m²)	square kilometre (km²) 1 km² = 1 000 000 m²	hectare (ha) 1 ha = 10 000 m² = 1 hm²
	square centimetre (cm²) 1 cm² = 0.000 1 m² = 1/10 000 m²	
	square millimetre (mm²) 1 mm² = 0.000 001 m² = 1/1 000 000 m²	

Basic

Area is obtained by multiplying length (or width) by length. A square that measures 1 metre on each side has an enclosed area of 1 square metre which is written 1 m². Fig. 5-2. If an area measures 9 metres by 12 metres, then the enclosed area is 12 x 9, or 108 square metres, or 108 m². Fig. 5-3. A square that measures 1 metre by 1 metre can also be expressed in millimetres as follows: since 1 metre equals 1000 millimetres (mm), then 1 metre times 1 metre also equals 1000 millimetres times 1000 millimetres, or 1 million square millimetres, or 1 000 000 mm². Note that because you must multiply length x length, there are 1 million square millimetres (not 1000 square millimetres as you might first estimate) in a square metre.

The preferred units for measurement of length are the millimetre, metre, and kilometre. They differ in steps of 1000. Therefore, for corresponding units of area, the square millimetre (mm²), the square metre (m²), and the square kilometre (km²) differ in the steps of 1000 times 1000, or 1 million (10⁶). Therefore, the use of only these units often results in very large or very small numbers. For example, customary letter size paper (8-1/2 x 11) equals 60 322 mm² or 0.060 322 m². Neither one of these numbers is particularly satisfactory for average use because they are too large or too small. However, the page size can also be written as 603 cm² (square centimetres), which is much more convenient. Therefore, the square centimetre is commonly used for small areas. For even smaller areas such as a 35 mm color slide, the dimensions of which are 35 mm by 24 mm, the result would be 840 mm² or 8.4 cm² or 0.000 84 m². The preferred choice would be either 8.4 cm² or 840 mm². Fig. 5-4. A standard postage stamp measures 22 mm x 25 mm, and the area is 550 mm². The square millimetre is convenient unit for very small areas, the square centimetre for small areas, the square metre for larger areas such as carpeting or room sizes, and the square kilometre for very

large areas. Fig. 5-5. The square kilometre equals 1 million squares metres, or 1 000 000 m². Here again, the difference between the square metre and square kilometre is very great so there is need for a unit between these two sizes. The *hectare* is a unit that measures 100 metres on each side and equals ten thousand square metres, or 10 000 m². Anyone familiar with the 100 metre dash in track and field will find this helpful in visualizing the hectare. A square with sides 100 m in length encloses an area of one hectare, that is, 10 000 square metres. The hectare is not an SI unit, but has been accepted in most countries as a convenient size for such purposes.

Uses of Area Units

Examples of some uses of area units are as follows: The *square centimetre* (cm²) can be used for the area of cards, footprints, tiles, birds' wings, leaves, photographs, newspaper advertisements; the surfaces of small blocks, boxes, tin cans, and balls; the space covered by many geometric and irregular shapes cut out of cardboard, cloth and paper; areas on scale maps in order to calculate actual land areas.

The *square metre* (m²) is useful in stating areas of floors, carpets, walls, paint coverage, wallpaper, drapery material, plastic sheeting, driveways, lawns, patios; space requirements in homes, offices, trailers, elevators, classrooms, cages in zoos, flower beds, greenhouses, and swimming pools. Many goods such as carpets will be priced by the square metre. Lawn fertilizers will be spread in accordance with numbers of square metres. Fig. 5-6.

The *hectare* (ha) will indicate areas of farms, parks, municipalities, and many medium-sized properties. Fertilizers, seeds, and insecticides will be distributed in terms of kilograms or litres per hectare in most agricultural zones. Fig. 5-7.

The *square kilometre* (km²) will help describe areas of states, countries, lakes, oceans, deserts, forests, and other large regions. Fig. 5-8.

The *square millimetre* (mm²) is a very small area for practical applications. However, the unit may be used in technical work to indicate sizes of miniature parts for electronics and other precision equipment.

The *square decimetre* (dm²) will be a good teaching aid because of its convenient size. Fig. 5-9. Squares cut of cardboard or plastics can also be made to form a cubic decimetre or litre in the study of volume. The square decimetre, however, probably will not be used in daily life unless it is used as a unit in building construction for such items as wall or floor tile.

Conversion

A few common reference points will be useful.
1. The square inch is about 6-1/2 times as large as the square centimetre. Fig. 5-10.
2. The square metre is about 20 percent larger than the square yard.
3. The hectare is approximately 2-1/2 acres, and is about equivalent in size to 10 olympic swimming pools. There are about 2 football fields in a hectare.

In converting from customary square measure to the metric square measure, the following tables and charts may be utilized. Figs. 5-11, 5-12, 5-13, 5-14.

Calculating in Square Measure

The average size commercial door to a building measures 1 metre wide and 2 metres high. The area, therefore, would be 2 m x 1 m = 2 m². For areas smaller in size, the square centimetre (cm²) and the square millimetre (mm²) can be used. A typical business calling card is 5 cm x 9 cm. The area would, therefore, be 5 cm x 9 cm = 45 square centimetres, or 45 cm². In technical work, the area of small items is given in square millimetres (mm²). For example, a small door magnet that is 14 mm wide and 22 mm long has an area of 14 mm x 22 mm = 308 mm². For very large areas the square kilometre can be used. A parking lot that measures 1 kilometre plus 300 metres on one side and 1 kilometre plus 600 metres along the other has an area of 1.3 km x 1.6 km, or 2.08 km². For measuring large areas there is need for a unit between the square metre (1 m²) and the square kilometre (1 km²), or 1000 metres x 1000 metres, or 1 million square

metres. In other words, if there were no unit between 1 m² and 1 km², all areas smaller than 1 km² would have to be expressed in square metres; therefore, the figure could be 5 or 6 digits. For example, an area of 258 metres x 625 metres equals 161 250 square metres. For this reason the *hectare* was selected for land measurements even though it is not strictly an SI unit. It was a very convenient measurement between the m² and the km². The hectare (ha) pronounced "hect-are" has an area of 100 m x 100 m which equals 10 000 square metres. For example, a piece of farm land that measures 175 metres by 360 metres equals 63 000 square metres or 6.3 hectares.

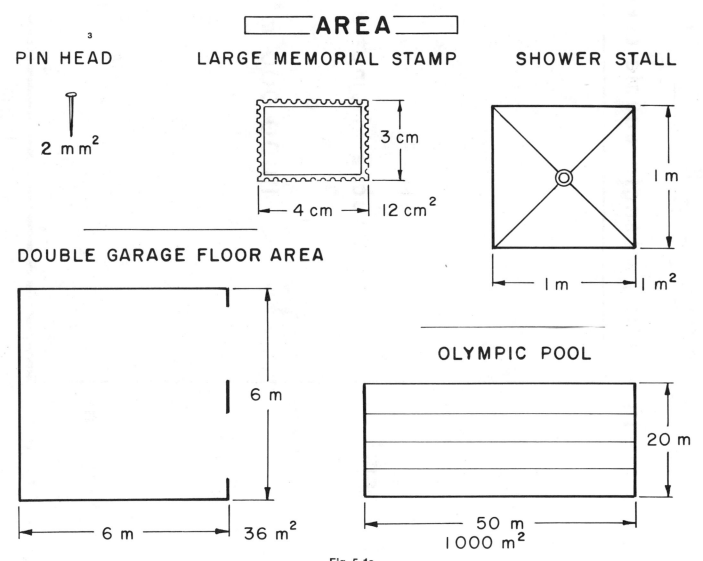

Fig. 5-1a
A comparison of the common area measurements in metric.

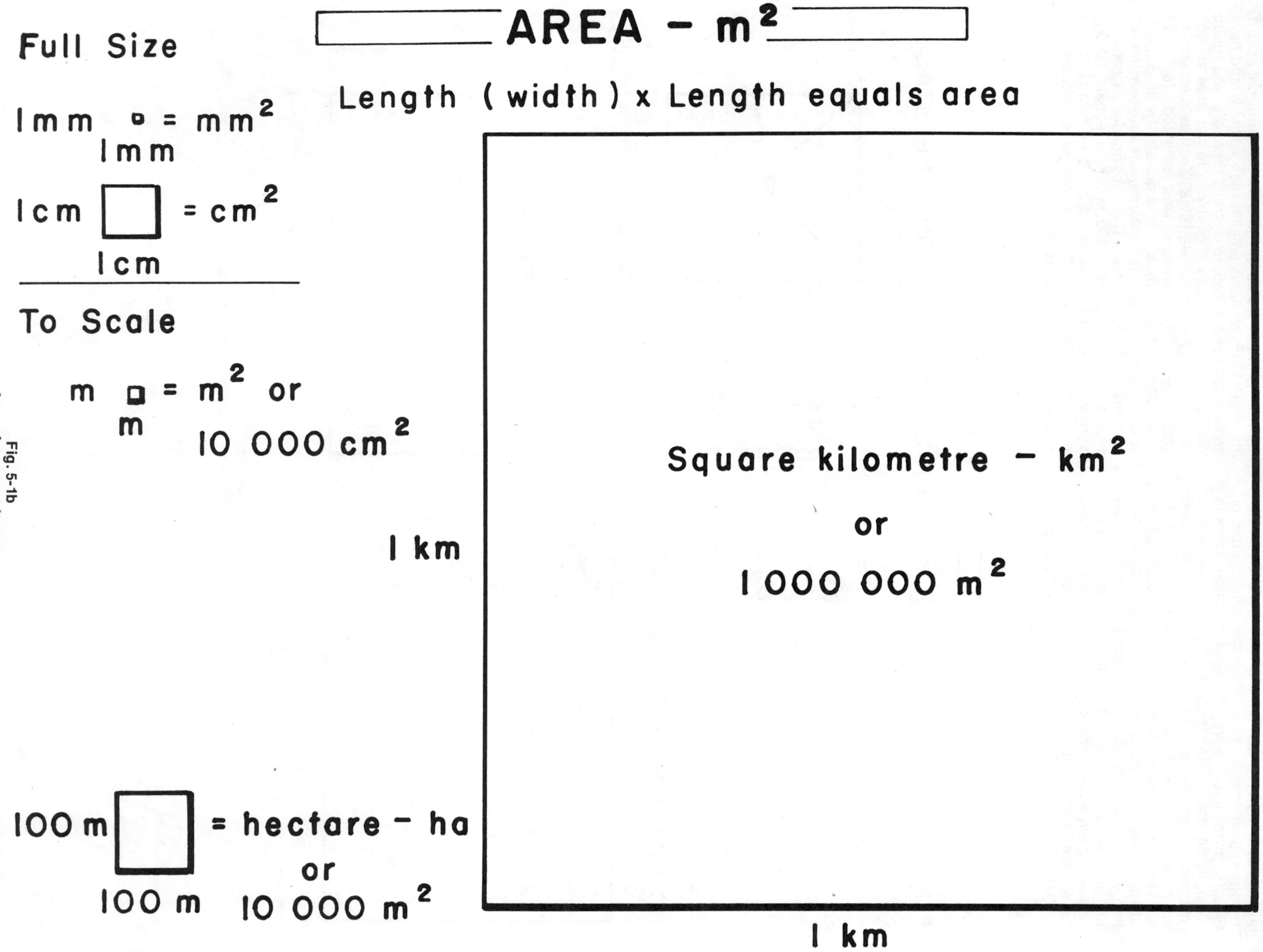

AREA – m²

Full Size

Length (width) x Length equals area

1mm □ = mm²
1mm

1cm □ = cm²
1cm

To Scale

m □ = m² or
m 10 000 cm²

Square kilometre – km²

or

1 000 000 m²

1 km

1 km

100 m □ = hectare – ha
or
100 m 10 000 m²

Fig. 5-1b
Area of common items.

Fig. 5-2
This projection screen is 1 square metre in size. You can get some idea of its comparative size by observing the sheet of 8-1/2" x 11" paper placed over the screen.

Fig. 5-3
Figuring areas in square metres. If the material costs $5 per square metre, what will be the total cost?

SMALL AREA MEASURES

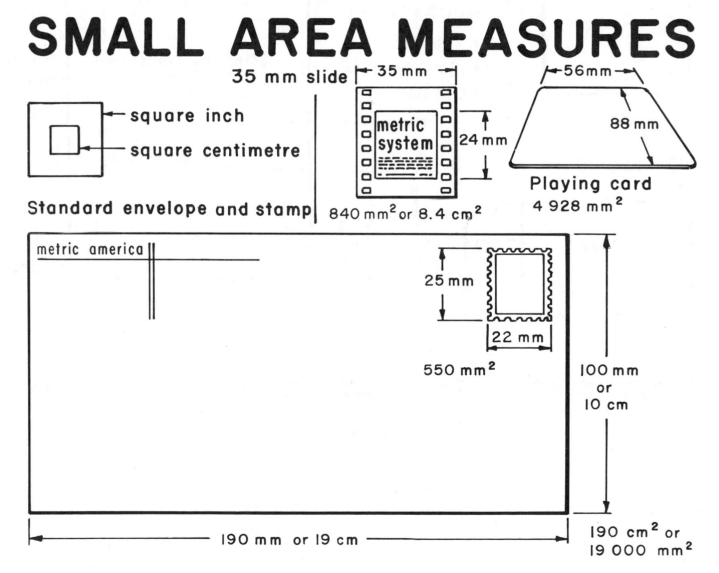

← square inch

← square centimetre

Standard envelope and stamp

35 mm slide |← 35 mm →|

metric system

24 mm

840 mm² or 8.4 cm²

|← 56mm →|

88 mm

Playing card
4 928 mm²

metric america

25 mm

22 mm

550 mm²

100 mm
or
10 cm

|← 190 mm or 19 cm →|

190 cm² or
19 000 mm²

Fig. 5-4
Small areas are given either in square millimetres or square centimetres.

AREA

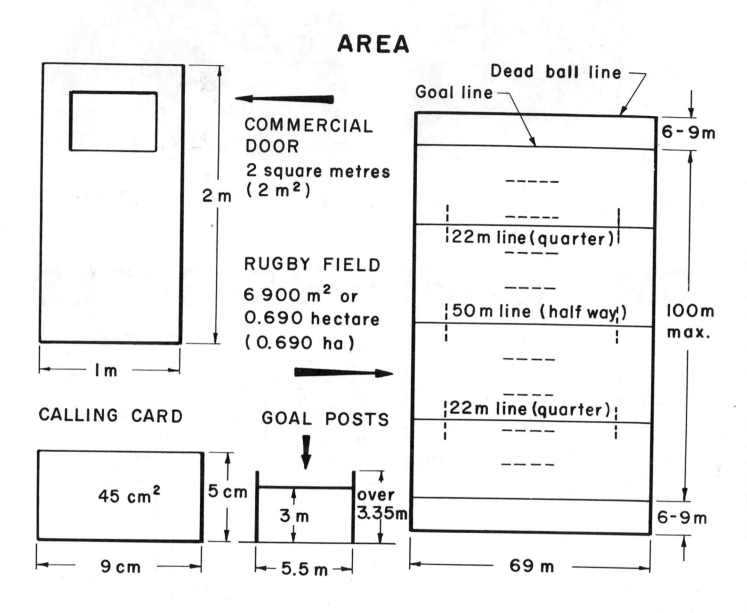

Fig. 5-5
Three commonly used area measures are shown here. For a calling card, the square centimetre is used, for the door, the square metre, and for the rugby field, the area is shown in square metres and hectares.

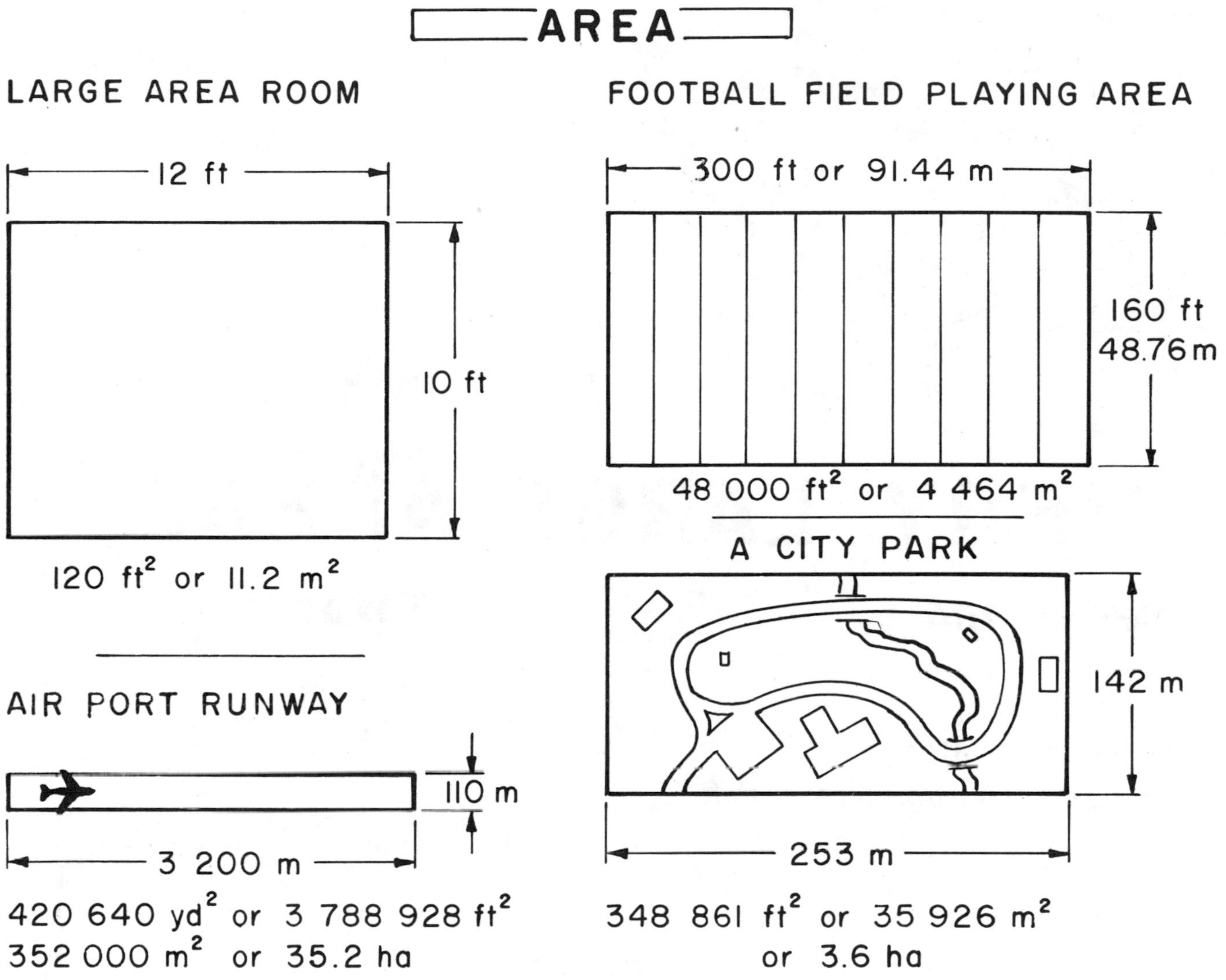

AREA

LARGE AREA ROOM

— 12 ft —

10 ft

120 ft² or 11.2 m²

AIR PORT RUNWAY

110 m

3 200 m

420 640 yd² or 3 788 928 ft²
352 000 m² or 35.2 ha

FOOTBALL FIELD PLAYING AREA

— 300 ft or 91.44 m —

160 ft
48.76 m

48 000 ft² or 4 464 m²

A CITY PARK

142 m

253 m

348 861 ft² or 35 926 m²
or 3.6 ha

Fig. 5-6
Larger areas are shown in square metres.

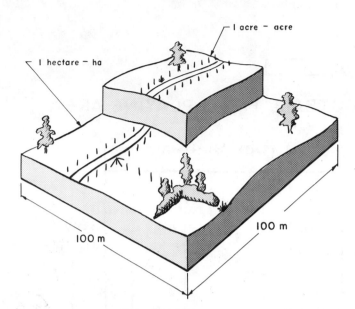

Fig. 5-7
Farms and other plots of land are shown in hectares.

VERY LARGE AREAS

Rhode Island

1 049 square miles
2 717 square kilometres – km²

I square mile

I square kilometre

Texas

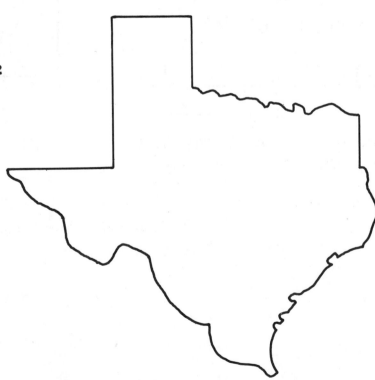

262 134 square miles
678 927 square kilometres – km²

Fig. 5-8
Very large areas, such as the sizes of states, are shown in square kilometres.

A SQUARE metre – m^2

50 of these square decimetres – dm^2

50 of these square decimetres – dm^2

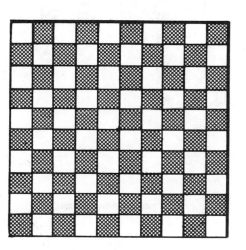

Fig. 5-9

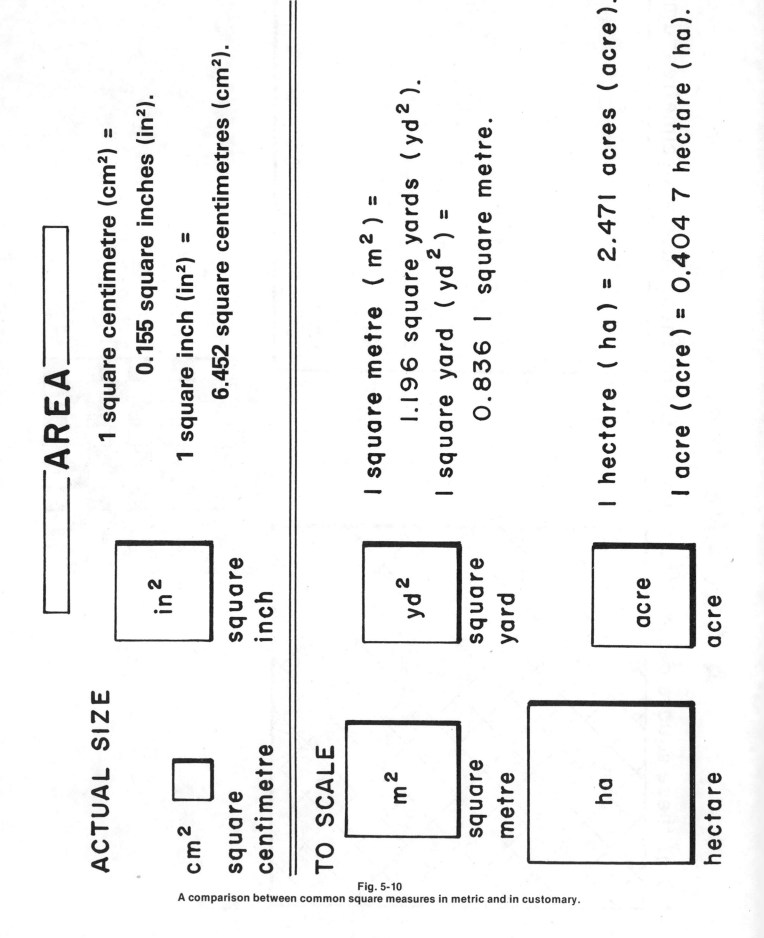

AREA

ACTUAL SIZE

1 square centimetre (cm²) = 0.155 square inches (in²).

1 square inch (in²) = 6.452 square centimetres (cm²).

in²
square inch

cm²
square centimetre

TO SCALE

1 square metre (m²) = 1.196 square yards (yd²).

1 square yard (yd²) = 0.836 1 square metre.

1 hectare (ha) = 2.471 acres (acre).

1 acre (acre) = 0.404 7 hectare (ha).

yd²
square yard

m²
square metre

acre
acre

ha
hectare

Fig. 5-10
A comparison between common square measures in metric and in customary.

Area

	hectare	square metre	square millimetre	square mile	acre	square yard	square foot	square inch
1 hectare	1.0	1 000.0	---	0.004*	2.471	---	---	---
1 square metre	---	1.0	---	---	---	1.196	10.764	1 550.003
1 square mile	258.999	---	---	1.0	640.0	---	---	---
1 acre	0.405	4 046.856	---	---	1.0	4 840.0	---	---
1 square yard	---	0.836	---	---	---	1.0	9.0	1 296.0
1 square foot	---	0.093*	92 903.04	---	---	0.111	1.0	144.0
1 square inch	---	---	645.16	---	---	---	0.007*	1.0

*Round off. Use with caution

Fig. 5-11a,b
Use these tables to convert customary to metric square measure and vice versa.

Units of Area

To Convert from square centimetres	
To	Multiply by
square inches 0.155 000 3	
square feet 0.0001 076 39	
square yards 0.000 119 599	
square metres 0.000 1	

To Convert from hectares	
To	Multiply by
square feet 107 639.1	
square yards 11 959.90	
acres 2.471 054	
square miles 0.003 861 02	
square metres 10 000	

To Convert from square feet	
To	Multiply by
square inches 144	
square yards 0.111 111 1	
acres 0.000 022 957	
square centimetres 929.030 4	
square metres 0.092 903 04	

To Convert from square inches	
To	Multiply by
square feet 0.006 944 44	
square yards 0.000 771 605	
square centimetres 6.451 6	
square metres 0.000 645 16	

To Convert from square metres	
To	Multiply by
square inches 1 550.003	
square feet 10.763 91	
square yards 1.195 990	
acres 0.000 247 105	
square centimetres 10 000	
hectares 0.000 1	

To Convert from square yards	
To	Multiply by
square inches 1 296	
square feet 9	
acres 0.000 206 611 6	
square miles 0.000 000 322 830 6	
square centimetres 8 361.273 6	
square metres 0.836 127 36	
hectares 0.000 083 612 736	

To Convert from square miles	
To	Multiply by
square feet 27 878 400	
square yards 3 097 600	
acres 640	
square metres 2 589 988.110 336	
hectares 258.998 811 033 6	

To Convert from acres	
To	Multiply by
square feet 43 560	
square yards 4 840	
square miles 0.001 562 5	
square metres 4 046.856 422 4	
hectares 0.404 685 642 24	

AREA

I square inch $- in^2 = 6.45$ square centimetres $- cm^2$
I square centimetre $- cm^2 = 0.155$ square inches $- in^2$

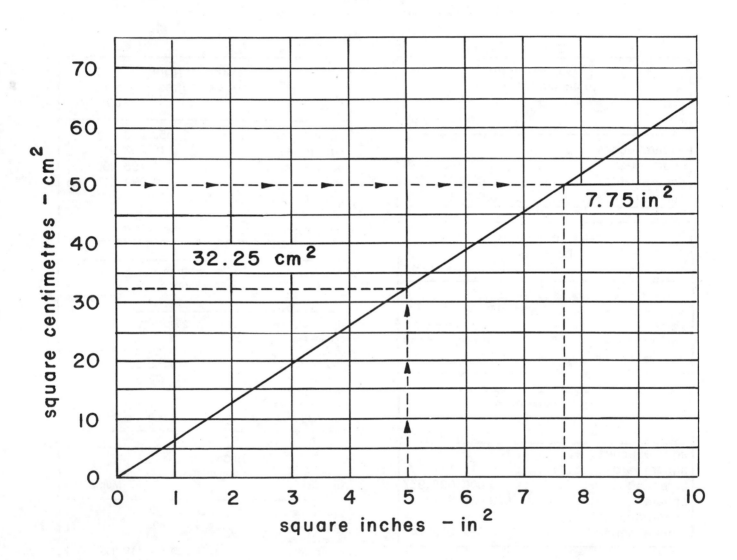

Fig. 5-13a
Graphs showing comparative sizes in customary measurement and metric measurement.

AREA

1 square foot – ft^2 = 0.093 square metre – m^2
1 square metre – m^2 = 10.763 square feet – ft^2

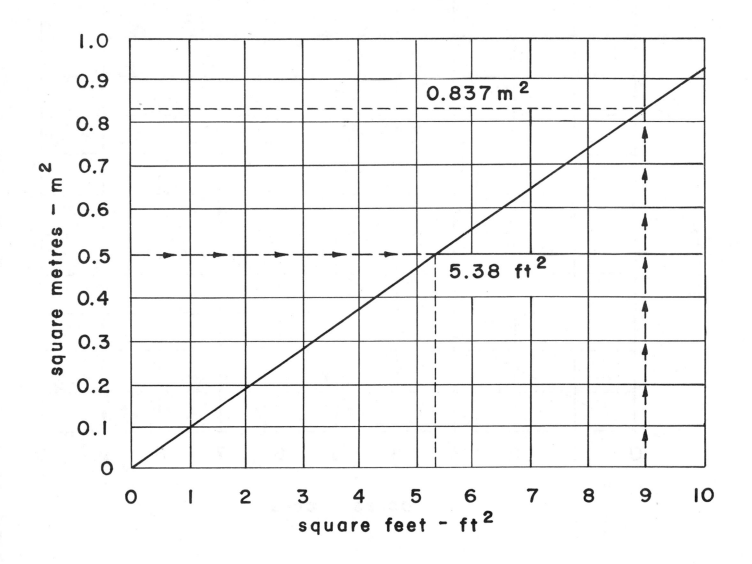

Fig. 5-13b

AREA

1 acre - acre = 0.405 hectares - ha
1 hectare - ha = 2.471 acres - acre

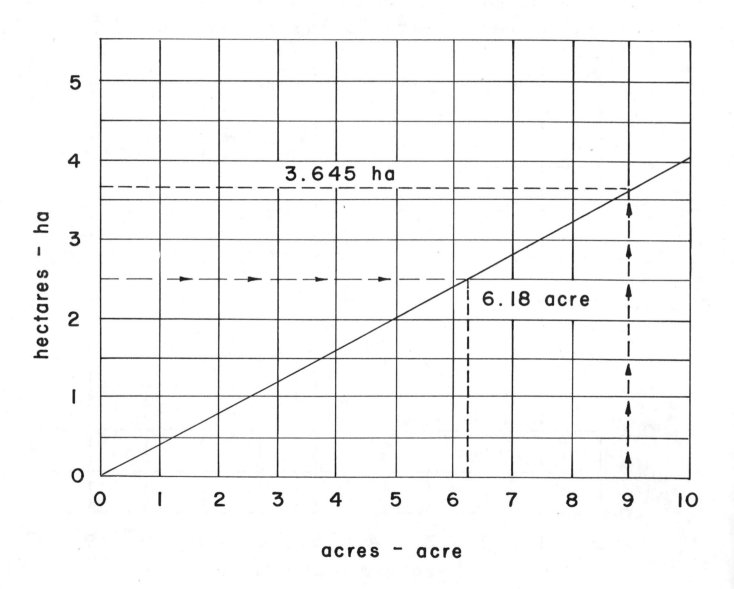

Fig. 5-13c

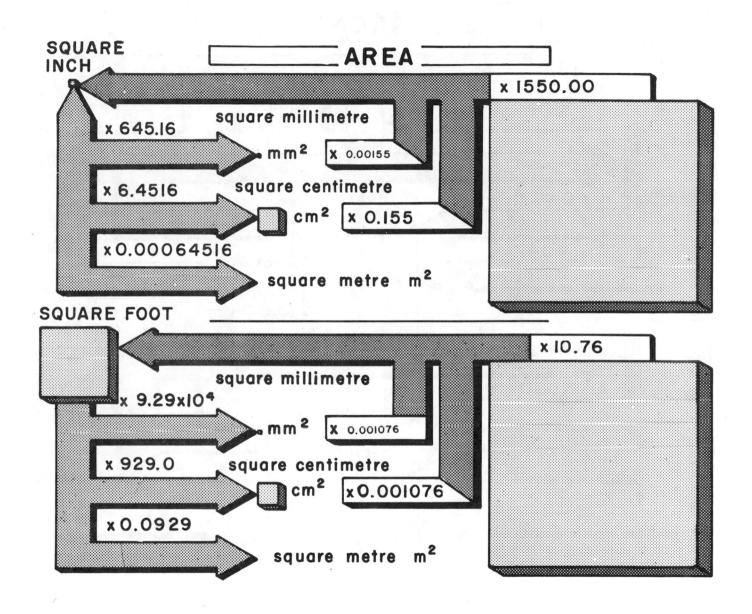

Fig. 5-14a
Visual charts used to convert customary to metric and vice versa.

AREA

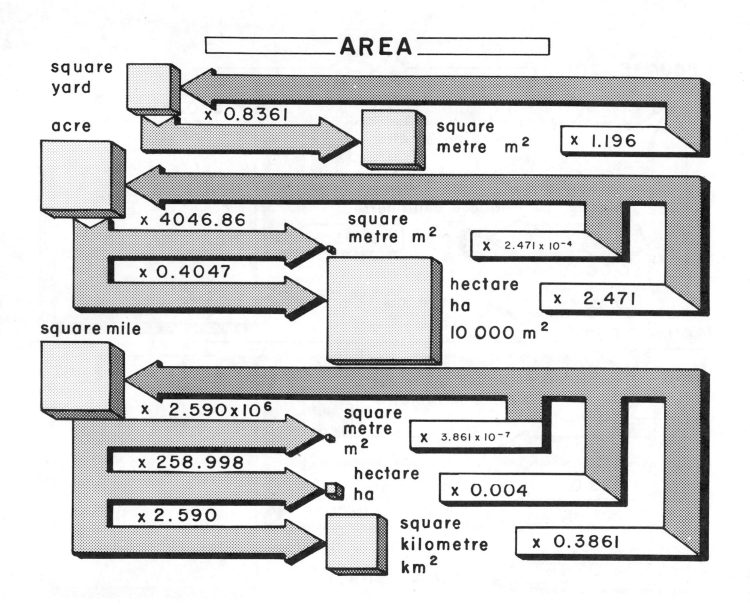

Fig. 5-14b

UNIT 6
VOLUME AND CAPACITY
(Fluid Volume)

word—cubic metre (or cubic meter)
symbol—m^3
word—litre (or liter)
symbol—l or ℓ * or L**
definition—The SI unit of volume is the cubic metre (m^3). It is a derived unit without a special name, based on the unit of length. The litre (0.001 cubic metre or 1 cubic decimetre), although not an SI unit, is commonly used to measure fluid volume. Fig. 6-1.

**The International Committee for Weights and Measures (CIPM) has recommended to the General Conference of Weights and Measures (CGPM) that the symbol L be used for the litre. Final approval may not come before 1980. However, the National Bureau of Standards (NBS) has adopted this symbol (L) for all its publications.

SI base unit	SI multiples and submultiples	Non-SI units with special names
cubic metre (m^3)		kilolitre (kl) 1 kl = 1000 litres = 1 m^3
	cubic decimetre (dm^3) 1 dm^3 = 0.001 m^3 = 1/1000 m	litre (l) or (ℓ)* 1 litre = 1000 cm^3 (= 1 dm^3)
	cubic centimetre (cm^3) 1cm^3 = 0.000 001 m^3 = 1/1 000 000 m^3	millilitre (ml) 1 ml = 0.001 litre = 1 cm^3
	cubic millimetre (mm^3) 1mm^3 = 0.000 000 001m^3 = 1/1 000 000 000 m^3	

*The italic or script (ℓ) is used in Canada, England, Australia, New Zealand and other English speaking countries going metric

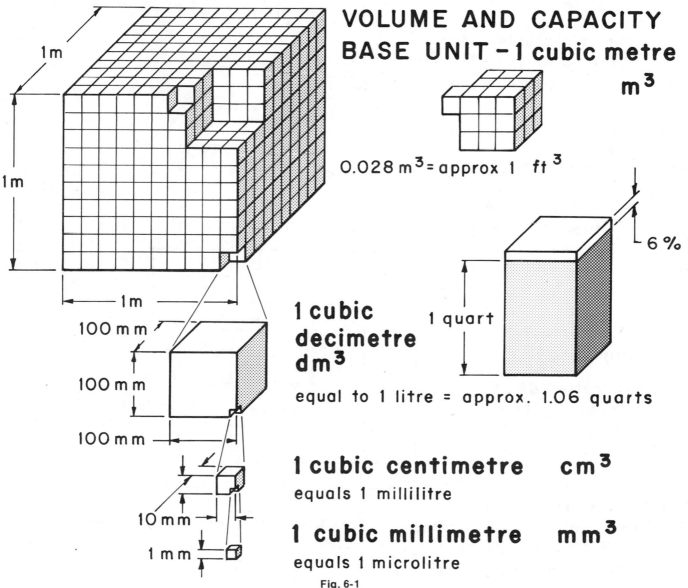

VOLUME AND CAPACITY
BASE UNIT – 1 cubic metre
m^3

0.028 m^3 = approx 1 ft^3

6 %

1 quart

1 cubic decimetre dm^3

equal to 1 litre = approx. 1.06 quarts

1 cubic centimetre cm^3
equals 1 millilitre

1 cubic millimetre mm^3
equals 1 microlitre

Fig. 6-1
The cubic metre is the base unit for volume and liquid capacity.

Volume and Capacity

Volume units which are designated by "cubic" or "cubed" such as cm³ are often referred to as dry units. Those which contain the word "litre" are classified as fluid or liquid capacity. This distinction is not a matter of extreme importance but rather of custom and communication. You could refer to a cubic centimetre of water or a millilitre of water equally well. It is permissible to speak of a litre of strawberries or a cubic metre of air, interchanging dry and fluid units, and yet the volume of a brick would not be stated in millilitres. In spite of this rather indefinite usage, there is a tendency to refer to volumes of liquids in millilitres in preference to cubic centimetres.

The volume of an object is obtained by multiplying *length* x *width* x *height*, or volume is the amount of space occupied in three dimensions. For example, a cube that measures 1 metre on each side has a volume of 1 cubic metre and is written as 1 m³. Note that the volume was obtained by multiplying 1 metre x 1 metre x 1 metre. The cubic metre is a large volume—too large for most uses except for technical calculation and for finding the cubic volume of large containers such as a large trailer truck or the volume of a room. The steps between units of volume derived from the preferred units of millimetre, metre and kilometre are very large, because three distances (length, width and height) must be multiplied. For example, a cubic metre (1 m³) also equals 1 billion cubic millimetres (1 000 000 000 mm³). This is obtained by multiplying 1000 mm x 1000 mm x 1000 mm. A cubic kilometre (1 km³) equals one billion cubic metres (1 000 000 000 m³). Because of this large difference, the common submultiples used for volume are the *cubic decimetre* and the *cubic centimetre.* The cubic decimetre (dm³) is equal to 1/1000 cubic metre (0.001 m³). Fig. 6-2. This is obtained by multiplying 1/10 m x 1/10 m x 1/10 m (0.1 m x 0.1 m x 0.1 m = 0.001 m³). The cubic decimetre, when used for liquid capacity or fluid volume, is called the *litre.*

In writing or typing the symbol for the litre, a vertical "l" or a script or italic "ℓ" should be used to avoid confusion with the number 1 (one). However, for multiples and sub-multiples, this isn't necessary because there is no chance for confusion.

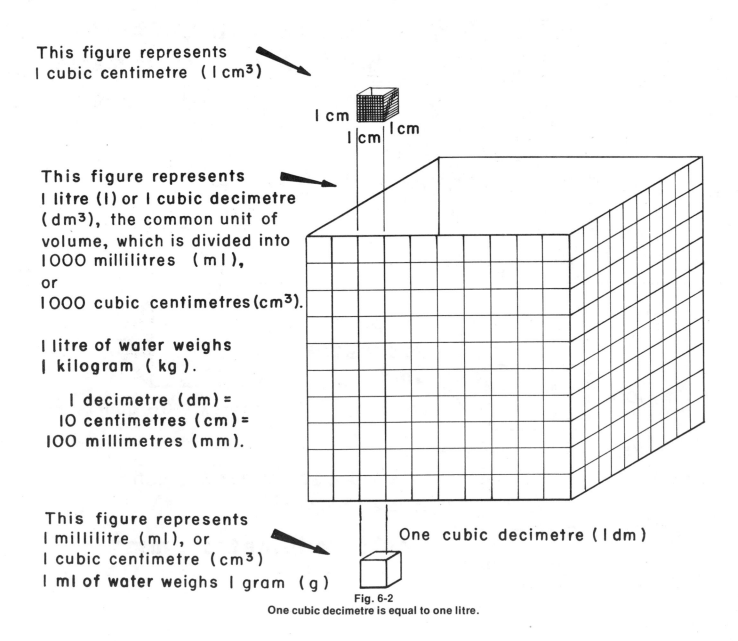

This figure represents
I cubic centimetre (I cm³)

I cm
I cm   I cm

This figure represents
I litre (I) or I cubic decimetre (dm³), the common unit of volume, which is divided into I000 millilitres (ml),
or
I000 cubic centimetres (cm³).

I litre of water weighs I kilogram (kg).

I decimetre (dm) = I0 centimetres (cm) = I00 millimetres (mm).

This figure represents
I millilitre (ml), or
I cubic centimetre (cm³)
I ml of water weighs I gram (g)

One cubic decimetre (I dm)

Fig. 6-2
One cubic decimetre is equal to one litre.

The litre was defined in 1964 as being precisely equal to 1 cubic decimetre (1000 cubic centimetres). This replaced the older definition of the litre as the volume of 1 kilogram of water at 4 degrees Celsius (centigrade). The earlier definition of the litre was slightly larger and equalled 1.000 028 cubic decimetres. In other words, the new definition made a difference of 0.000 28 litres in the size of the litre. For practical purposes, however, the relationship between volume, liquid capacity and weight still remains, since 1 cubic decimetre equals 1 litre and weighs almost exactly 1 kilogram when filled with water. The cubic centimetre (cm³) equals one millionth (1/1 000 000) of a cubic metre or one thousandth (1/1000) of a cubic decimetre. One cubic centimetre (cm³) also equals 1 millilitre when used for fluid capacity.

While the litre with its multiples and submultiples is not an SI unit, it is widely used because:

1. It is an historic part of the older metric system and has been in common use for many years.

2. The litre is easier to use than the cubic decimetre. For example, it is easier to say that you want to buy a litre of milk tan to say that you want to buy 1 cubic decimetre of milk.

3. The prefixes mega-, kilo- and milli-, etc., can be used with the litre to form larger and smaller units. For example, 1 litre (ℓ) = 1 cubic decimetre (dm³).

1 kilolitre (kl) = 1000 litres (ℓ) = 1 cubic metre (m³)
1 litre = 1000 millilitres (ml) = 1 cubic decimetre (dm³)
1 millilitre (ml) = 1/1000 (0.001) litre = 1 cubic centimetre (cm³)

The correct symbol for cubic centimetre is cm (equal to 1 millilitre). In the older metric system it was a practice to refer to this as cc or cc., which is incorrect. In the SI metric system cc would stand for centi- centi-, which has no meaning, since double prefixes are never used.

Uses of Volume and Capacity Measure

Some of the common metric measurements include:

The *cubic centimetre* (cm³) can be used to express the volume of small rectangular boxes, blocks, cylinders, spheres, cones and other solids whose volumes can be determined by mathematical formulae. Fig. 6-3.

The *cubic metre* (m³) will be used to state the volume of a building, the hold in a ship, the amount of concrete in a dam, the earth moved in an excavation, and the gravel, sand or loam delivered by a truck. Fig. 6-4.

The *millilitre* (ml) will be used when stating volumes of milk, drinks, oils, paraffin, fluid medicines, shampoos, toothpaste, lotions, solvents, paints and similar fluids in containers holding less than one litre. The millilitre will appear on measuring spoons and in recipe books. Medicinal doses will often be administered by 5 ml teaspoonful. Fig. 6-5.

The *litre* (l) will be used to express a measure of gasoline, oil, antifreeze, paint, solvents, milk and various drinks, and household liquids having volumes of one litre or more. The capacity of car radiators, gas tanks, refrigerators and wheelbarrows will be given in litres. Fig. 6-6.

The *kilolitre* (kl) will help describe large fluid volumes such as water consumption shown on hydrometres or the capacity of a swimming pool, reservoir, gasoline truck or oil tank. Fig. 6-7.

Conversion

A few common reference points for volume will be useful:

1. A *cubic centimetre* (cm³) is about 6 percent as large as a *cubic inch*. In other words a cubic inch (in³) is about 16 times larger than a cubic centimetre. Fig. 6-8.

2. A *cubic metre* (m³) is about 35 times larger than a *cubic foot* (ft³).

3. A *cubic metre* (m³) is about 30 percent larger than a *cubic yard* (yd³)

In converting from customary (volume and liquid capacity) measure to metric measure, the following tables and charts may be utilized. Figs. 6-9 to 6-14.

Conversion from traditional liquid capacity measurements to metric liquid volume has an additional problem. This is because the customary unit of liquid capacity used in the United States is not the same as the Imperial unit used in Great Britain, Canada, Australia, South Africa, New Zealand, and other countries formerly a part of the British Empire. The Imperial gallon is about 20 percent larger than the U.S. gallon. The U.S. gallon is based on what the British called the Queen Anne wine gallon. Therefore, before making conversion to the metric system, make sure to specify whether the liquid capacity is a customary (U.S.) measure or an Imperial measure. Fig. 6-15. Unless otherwise specified, the conversion charts and tables show U.S. liquid capacity units. A few common reference points will be useful:

1. The litre (1.057 quarts) is about 6 percent larger than the U.S. quart.

2. The litre is about 88 percent as large as an Imperial quart. In other words the litre is larger than the U.S. quart and smaller than the Imperial quart. The Imperial *pint* is a much more common measure than the quart and is equal to 0.568 litres. Fig. 6-16.

In the metric system there is a definite relationship between volume (as defined by length), liquid capacity and weight. The cubic container that measures 1 decimetre on each side is equal to and will hold 1 litre of liquid and, if filled with water, will weigh almost exactly 1 kilogram.

Calculation of Volume and Liquid Capacity

A standard 4-drawer filing cabinet is about 0.333 of a cubic metre, while the legal size cabinet is about 0.4 of a cubic metre. The average size shower stall is about 1 square metre at the base and about 2.5 metres tall, so that the volume is about 2.5 cubic metres (1 x 1 x 2.5 = 2.5 m³). An average size refrigerator has about 0.4 cubic metre capacity. The average gas tank for a standard U.S. sedan (22 gallons) holds about 83 litres of gas. A standard bottle of wine holds 750 millilitres. The half size wine bottle is 375 millilitres (often listed as 3/8 litre). To find the volume of a container that measures 35 cm x 45 cm x 1.45 m, first change all numbers to the same unit; in this illustration change 1.45 m to 145 cm. Then multiply the three figures to obtain a total of 228 375 cm (35 cm x 45 cm x 145 cm = 228 375 cm³). Since there are 1 *million cubic centimetres* in 1 *cubic metre* it would be preferred to list the result as 0.228 375 m³. This could be rounded off to 0.228 m³.

VOLUME

cubic centimetres (cm³)

CUBE OR SOLID RECTANGULAR FORM

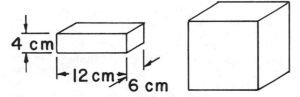

Volume = length x width x height
$V = 12 \times 6 \times 4 = 288$ cm³

CYLINDER

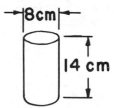

Volume = area of base x altitude
Area of base = square of diameter
    x 0.7854

$V = (8 \times 8 \times 0.7854) \times 14$
$V = 50.3 \times 14 = 704$ cm³

PYRAMID

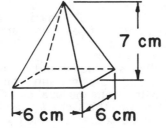

Volume = area of base x
    1/3 altitude

$V = 6 \times 6 \times 7/3$
$V = 36 \times 2.33 = 84$ cm³

CONE

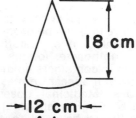

Volume = area of base x
    1/3 altitude

$V = (12 \times 12 \times 0.7854) \times 18/3$
$V = 113.1 \times 6 = 678.6$ cm³

Fig. 6-3
Small amounts of volume should be given in cubic centimetres.

Fig. 6-4
A grain storage facility should be given in cubic centimetres.

FLUID VOLUME
LIQUID CAPACITY

millilitres

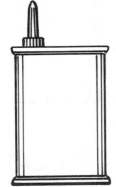

HOUSEHOLD OIL

100 millilitres =
3.38 liquid ounces

MEDICINE

150 millilitres =
5 liquid ounces

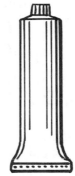

TOOTH PASTE

200 millilitres family size=
6.76 liquid ounces

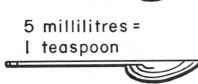

5 millilitres =
1 teaspoon

15 millilitres =
1 tablespoon

MEASURING
SPOONS

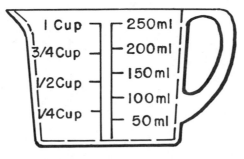

1 Cup	—	250ml
3/4 Cup	—	200ml
1/2 Cup	—	150ml
1/4 Cup	—	100ml
	—	50 ml

MEASURING
CUP

SODA

SOFT DRINK

500 millilitres =
1.06 pints

Fig. 6-5
All small liquid and semi-liquid containers would
have the capacity shown in millilitres.

FLUID VOLUME
LIQUID CAPACITY

litres

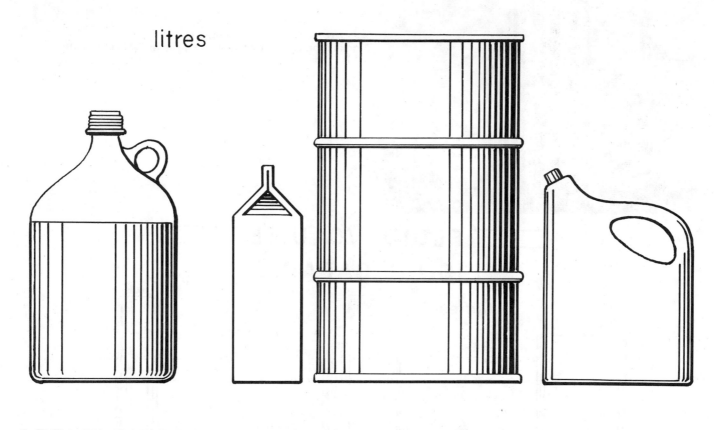

APPLE CIDER

4 litres =
1.06 gallons

MILK

1 litre =
1.06 quarts

OIL BARREL

160 litres =
42 gallons

CLEANER

2 litres =
2.12 quarts

Fig. 6-6
The litre will be the common unit of liquid volume for many items.

Fig. 6-7
The liquid capacity of this huge rubber storage tank would be given as 378.5 kilolitres (100 000 gallons).

CUBIC VOLUME

FULL SIZE

cubic centimetre - cm³

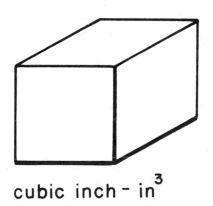

cubic inch - in³

TO SCALE

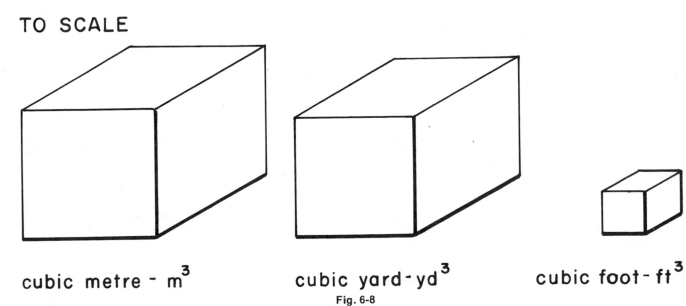

cubic metre - m³

cubic yard - yd³

cubic foot - ft³

Fig. 6-8
Relative sizes of cubic volume in metric and customary units.

INTERNATIONAL VOLUME

1 cubic inch
1 cubic foot = 1728 cubic inches
1 cubic yard = 27 cubic feet

CUSTOMARY LIQUID MEASURE

1 minim
1 fluid dram = 60 minims
1 fluid ounce = 8 fluid drams
1 gill = 4 fluid ounces
1 liquid pint = 4 gills
1 liquid quart = 2 liquid pints
1 gallon = 4 liquid quarts
1 petroleum barrel = 42 gallons

CUSTOMARY DRY MEASURE

1 dry pint
1 dry quart = 2 dry pints
1 peck = 8 dry quarts
1 bushel = 4 pecks
1 board foot = 144 cubic inches

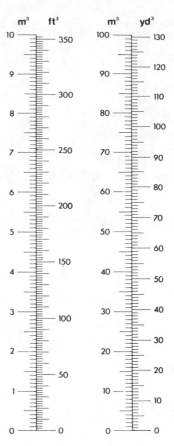

Fig. 6-9
Common volume measures used in the customary system.

Fig. 6-10
Comparison scale of customary and metric volume units.

Volume And Capacity (US)

	cubic metres	cubic decimetres; or litres	cubic centimetres or millilitres	cubic yards	cubic feet	gallons	quarts	fluid ounces (Liquid)
1 cubic metre	1.0	1 000.0	1 000 000.0	1.308	35.315	264.172	---	33.814
1 litre	0.001	1.0	1 000.0	---	0.035	0.264	1.056	0.033
1 millilitre	---	0.001	1.0	---	---	---	0.001*	---
1 cubic yard	0.765	764.555	---	1.0	27.0	201.974	---	957.506
1 cubic foot	0.028	28.317	28 316.847	0.037*	1.0	7.480	29.922	128.0
1 gallon (US)	0.003 785	3.785	37 854.117	0.005	0.134*	1.0	4.0	32.0
1 quart (US)	---	0.946	946.352	---	0.033*	4.0	1.0	1.0
1 fluid ounce (US) (Liquid)	---	0.029 6	29.573	---	0.001*	0.008*	0.031	

Volume and Capacity (Imperial)

	cubic metres	cubic decimetres or litres	cubic centimetres or millilitres	cubic yards	cubic feet	gallons [Imperial]	pints	gills	fluid ounces
1 cubic metre	1.	1 000.	1 000 000.	1.308	35.315	219.969	1 759.75	—	—
1 litre	0.001	1.	1 000.	—	0.035	0.220	1.760	7.039	35.195
1 millilitre	—	0.001	1.	—	—	—	—	0.007	0.035
1 cubic yard	0.765	764.555	—	1.	27.	168.178	1 345.428	—	—
1 cubic foot	0.028	28.317	28 316.847	0.037*	1.	6.229	49.831	199.323	—
1 gallon (Imperial)	0.005	4.546	4 546.09	0.006*	0.161	1.	8.	32.	160.
1 pint	—	0.568	568.261	—	0.020*	0.125	1.	4.	20.
1 gill	—	0.142	142.065	—	0.005*	0.031	0.25	1.	5.
1 fluid Ounce	—	—	28.413	—	0.001*	0.006*	0.05	0.2	1.

Fig. 6-11
Volume and capacity comparisons for the U.S. customary and Imperial systems.

Units of Capacity, or Volume, Liquid (Fluid) Measure

To Convert from millilitres

To	Multiply by
minims	16.230 73
liquid ounces	0.033 814 02
gills	0.008 453 5
liquid pints	0.002 113 4
liquid quarts	0.001 056 7
gallons	0.000 264 17
cubic inches	0.061 023 74
litres	0.001

To Convert from cubic metres

To	Multiply by
gallons	264.172 05
cubic inches	61 023.74
cubic feet	35.314 67
litres	1 000
cubic yards	1.307 950 6

To Convert from liquid (fluid) pints

To	Multiply by
liquid ounces	16
gills	4
liquid quarts	0.5
gallons	0.125
cubic inches	28.875
cubic feet	0.016 710 07
millilitres	473.176 473
litres	0.473 176 473

To Convert from litres

To	Multiply by
liquid ounces	33.814 02
gills	8.453 506
liquid pints	2.113 376
liquid quarts	1.056 688
gallons	0.264 172 05
cubic inches	61.023 74
cubic feet	0.035 314 67
millilitres	1 000
cubic metres	0.001
cubic yards	0.001 307 95

To Convert from gills

To	Multiply
liquid ounces	4
liquid pints	0.25
liquid quarts	0.125
gallons	0.031 25
cubic inches	7.218 75
cubic feet	0.004 177 517
millilitres	118.294 118 25
litres	0.118 294 118 25

To Convert from liquid (fluid) ounces

To	Multiply by
gills	0.25
liquid pints	0.062 5
liquid quarts	0.031 25
gallons	0.007 812 5
cubic inches	1.804 687 5
cubic feet	0.001 044 38
millilitres	29.573 53
litres	0.029 573 53

Fig. 6-12a
Use these tables to convert volume or liquid capacity.

To Convert from cubic feet	
To	Multiply by
liquid ounces	957.506 5
gills	239.376 6
liquid pints	59.844 16
liquid quarts	29.922 08
gallons	7.480 519
cubic inches	1 728
litres	28.316 846 592
cubic metres	0.028 316 846 592
cubic yards	0.037 037 04

To Convert from liquid (fluid) quarts	
To	Multiply by
liquid ounces	32
liquid pints	2
gallons	0.25
cubic inches	57.75
cubic feet	0.033 420 14
millilitres	946.352 946
litres	0.946 352 946

To Convert from cubic inches	
To	Multiply by
liquid ounces	0.554 112 6
gills	0.138 528 1
liquid pints	0.034 632 03
liquid quarts	0.017 316 02
gallons	0.004 329 0
cubic feet	0.000 578 7
millilitres	16.387 064
litres	0.016 387 064
cubic metres	0.000 016 387 064
cubic yards	0.000 021 43

To Convert from gallons	
To	Multiply by
liquid ounces	128
liquid pints	8
liquid quarts	4
cubic inches	231
cubic feet	0.133 680 6
millilitres	3 785.411 784
litres	3.785 411 784
cubic metres	0.003 785 411 784
cubic yards	0.004 951 13

Fig. 6-12b

To Convert from litres	
To	Multiply by
dry pints	1.816 166
dry quarts	0.908 082 98
pecks	0.113 510 4
bushels	0.028 377 59

To Convert from cubic feet	
To	Multiply by
dry pints	51.428 09
dry quarts	25.714 05
pecks	3.214 256
bushels	0.803 563 95

To Convert from cubic metres	
To	Multiply by
pecks	113.510 4
bushels	28.377 59

To Convert from pecks	
To	Multiply by
dry pints	16
dry quarts	8
bushels	0.25
cubic inches	537.605
cubic feet	0.311 114
litres	8.809 767 5
cubic metres	0.008 809 77
cubic yards	0.011 522 74

To Convert from dry pints	
To	Multiply by
dry quarts	0.5
pecks	0.062 5
bushels	0.015 625
cubic inches	33.600 312 5
cubic feet	0.019 444 63
litres	0.550 610 47

To Convert from cubic inches	
To	Multiply by
dry pints	0.029 761 6
dry quarts	0.014 880 8
pecks	0.001 860 10
bushels	0.000 465 025

To Convert from dry quarts	
To	Multiply by
dry pints	2
pecks	0.125
bushels	0.031 25
cubic inches	67.200 625
cubic feet	0.038 889 25
litres	1.101 221

To Convert from cubic yards	
To	Multiply by
pecks	86.784 91
bushels	21.696 227

To Convert from bushels	
To	Multiply by
dry pints	64
dry quarts	32
pecks	4
cubic inches	2 150.42
cubic feet	1.244 456
litres	35.239 07
cubic metres	0.035 239 07
cubic yards	0.046 090 96

Fig. 6-12c

VOLUME

I cubic foot - ft^3 = 0.028 316 cubic metre - m^3

I cubic metre - m^3 = 35.314 67 cubic feet - ft^3

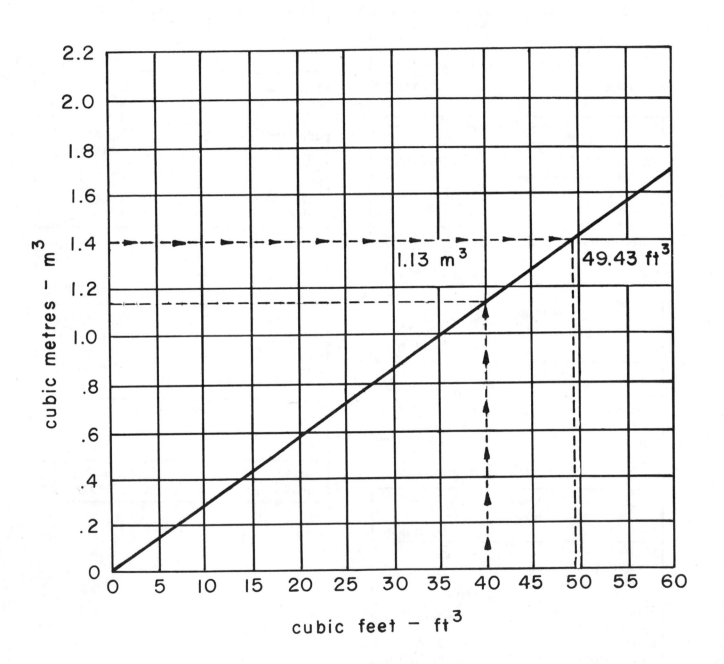

Fig. 6-13a

These graphs give you a visual comparison between customary and metric units.

VOLUME

I cubic yard − yd^3 = 0.764 cubic metres − m^3

I cubic metre − m^3 = 1.307 950 cubic yards − yd^3

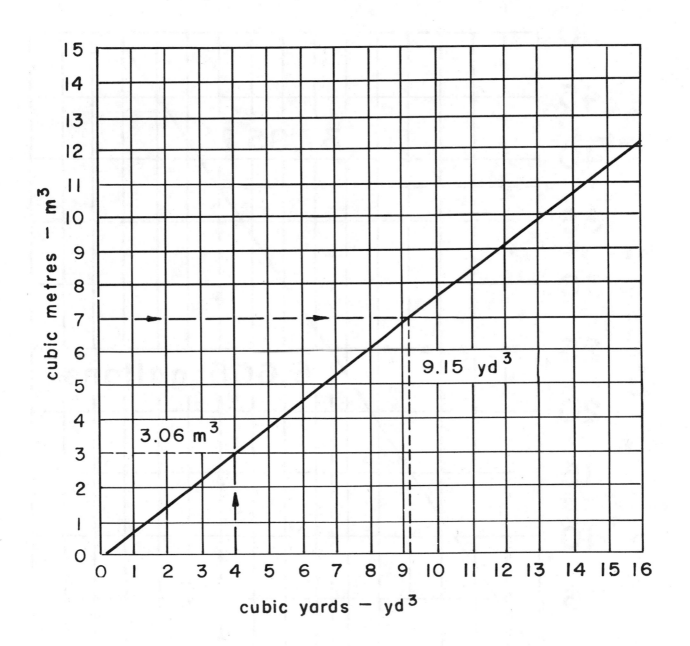

Fig. 6-13b

LIQUID CAPACITY

1 U S gallon = 3.785 litres - ℓ

1 litre - ℓ = 0.2642 U S gallons - gal

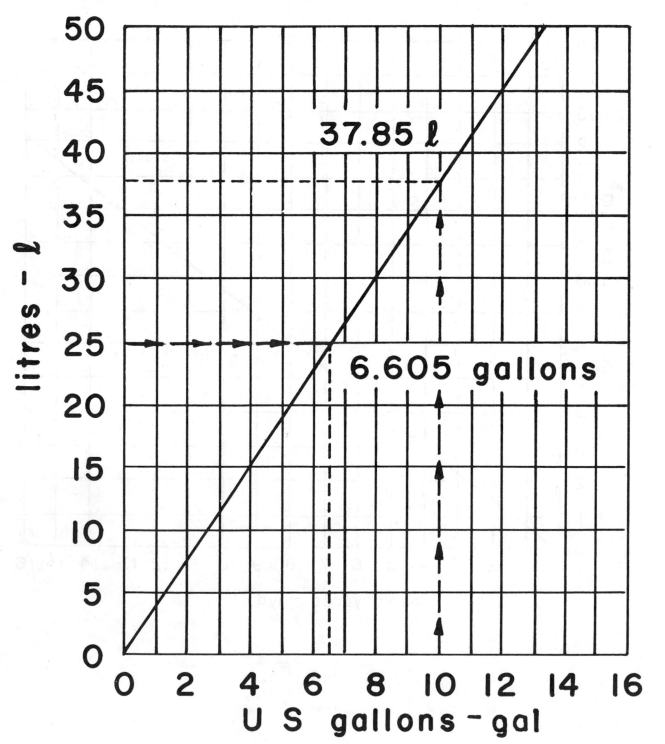

Fig. 6-13c

CUBIC INCH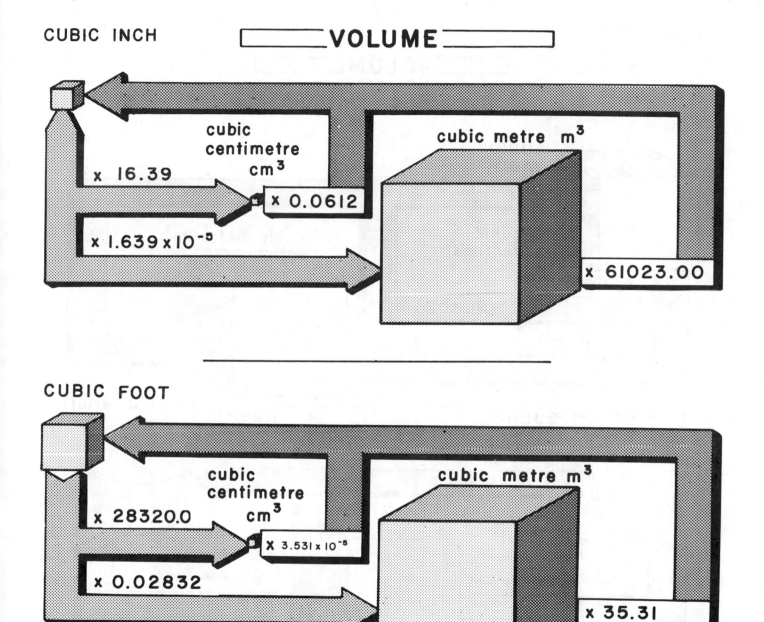

VOLUME

cubic
centimetre
cm^3

cubic metre m^3

x 16.39

x 0.0612

x 1.639 x 10^{-5}

x 61023.00

CUBIC FOOT

cubic
centimetre
cm^3

cubic metre m^3

x 28320.0

X 3.531 x 10^{-5}

x 0.02832

x 35.31

Fig. 6-14a
Use these visual charts to make conversions from customary to metric and vice versa.

VOLUME

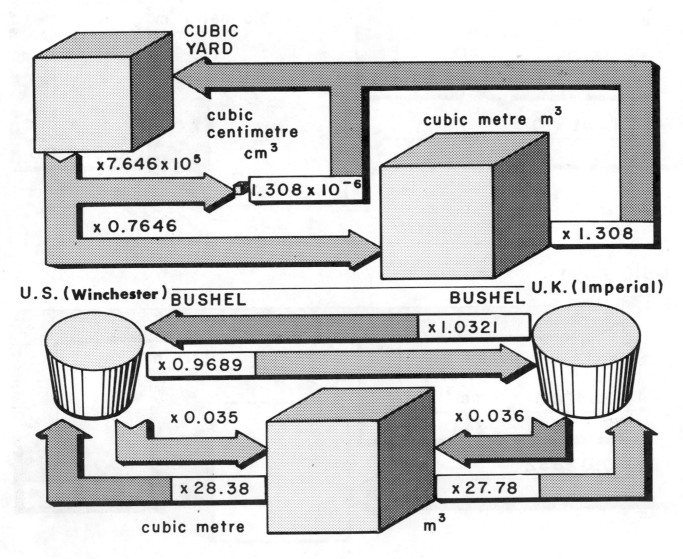

Fig. 6-14b

LIQUID CAPACITY

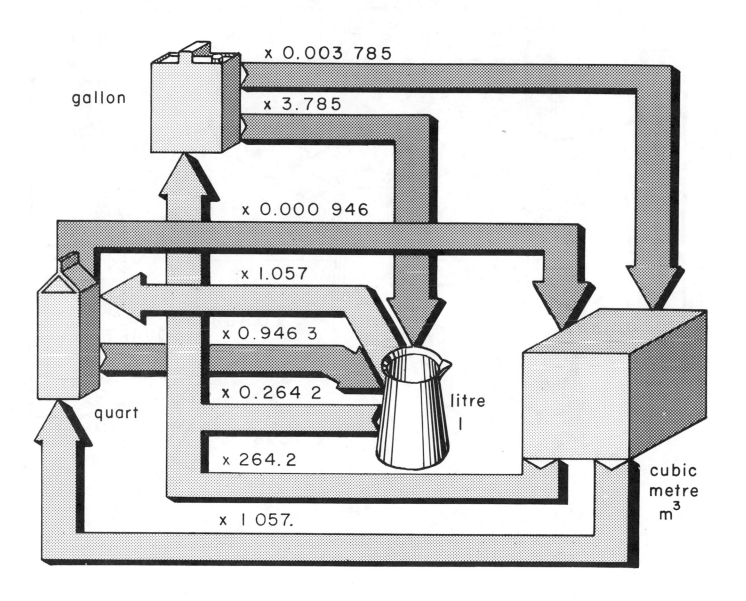

gallon

x 0.003 785

x 3.785

x 0.000 946

x 1.057

x 0.946 3

x 0.264 2

quart

x 264.2

litre
l

cubic
metre
m³

x 1 057.

Fig. 6-14c

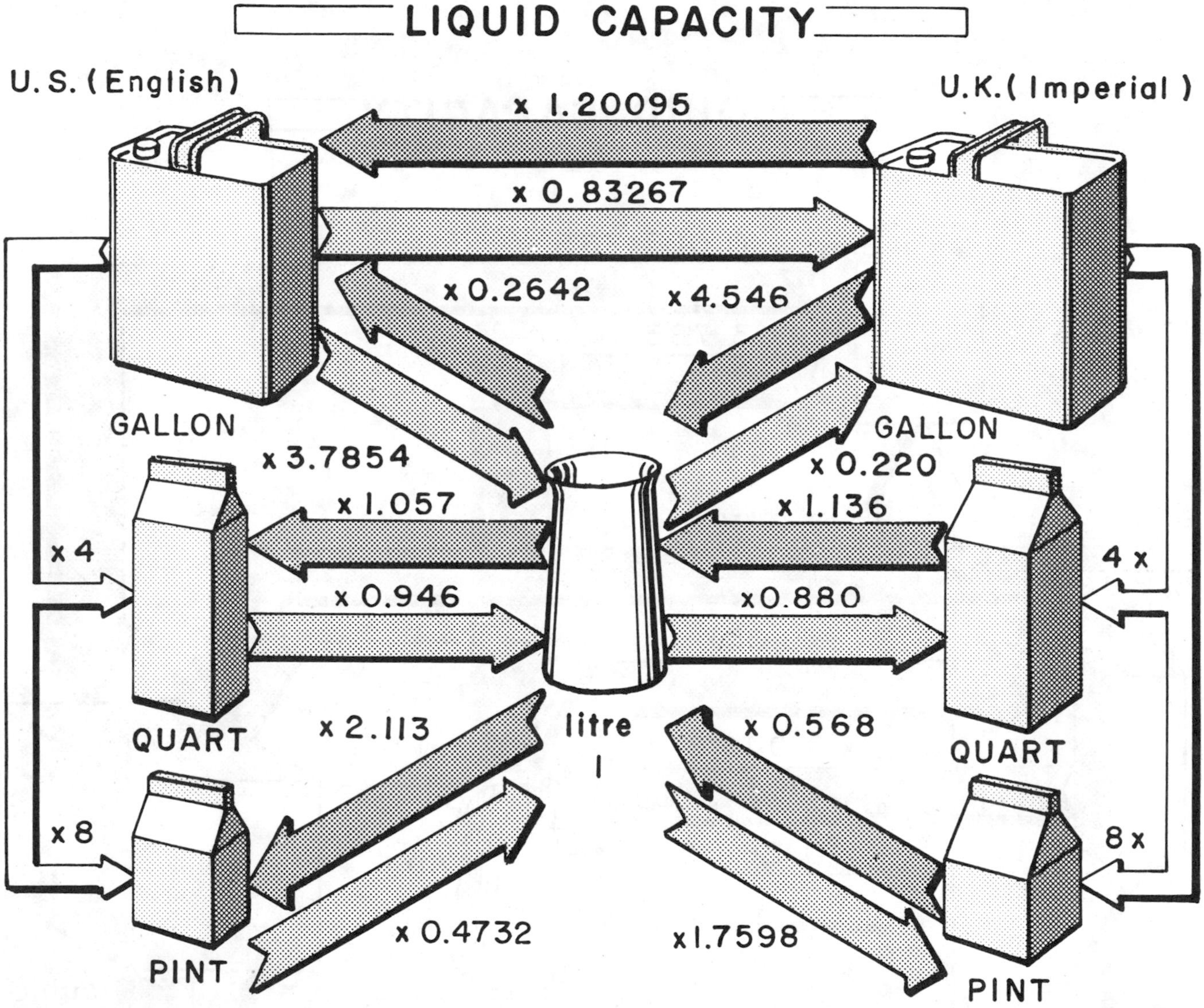

LIQUID CAPACITY

U.S. (English)

U.K. (Imperial)

x 1.20095

x 0.83267

x 0.2642   x 4.546

GALLON

x 3.7854

x 1.057

GALLON

x 0.220

x 1.136

x 4

QUART

x 0.946   x 0.880

litre
l

4 x

QUART

x 2.113   x 0.568

x 8

PINT

x 0.4732   x 1.7598

8 x

PINT

Fig. 6-14d

COMPARISON OF LIQUID CAPACITY

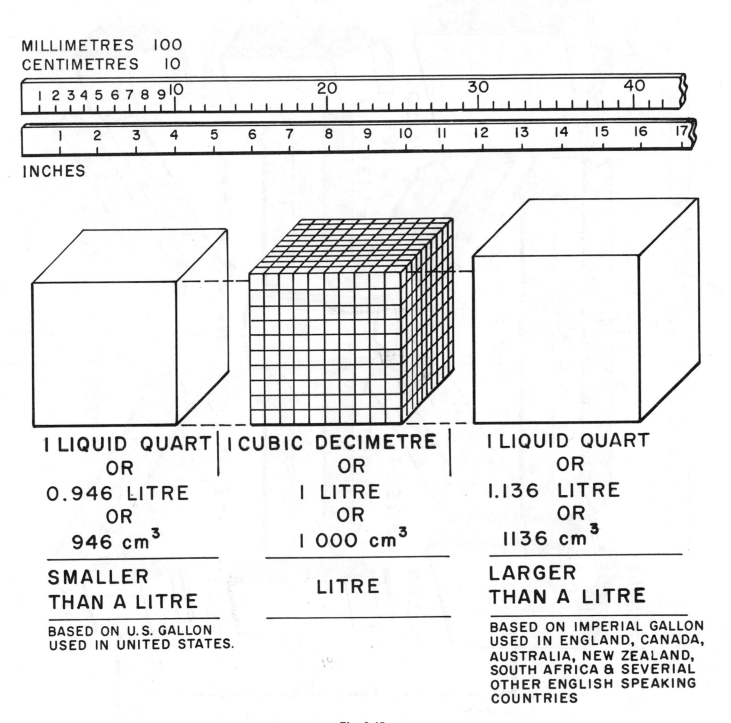

MILLIMETRES 100
CENTIMETRES 10

1 2 3 4 5 6 7 8 9 10   20   30   40

1 2 3 4 5 6 7 8 9 10 11 12 13 14 15 16 17

INCHES

I LIQUID QUART	I CUBIC DECIMETRE	I LIQUID QUART
OR	OR	OR
0.946 LITRE	I LITRE	1.136 LITRE
OR	OR	OR
946 cm^3	I 000 cm^3	1136 cm^3
SMALLER THAN A LITRE	LITRE	LARGER THAN A LITRE
BASED ON U.S. GALLON USED IN UNITED STATES.		BASED ON IMPERIAL GALLON USED IN ENGLAND, CANADA, AUSTRALIA, NEW ZEALAND, SOUTH AFRICA & SEVERIAL OTHER ENGLISH SPEAKING COUNTRIES

Fig. 6-15
Note the difference in the size of the liquid quart based on the U.S. gallon and on the Imperial gallon.

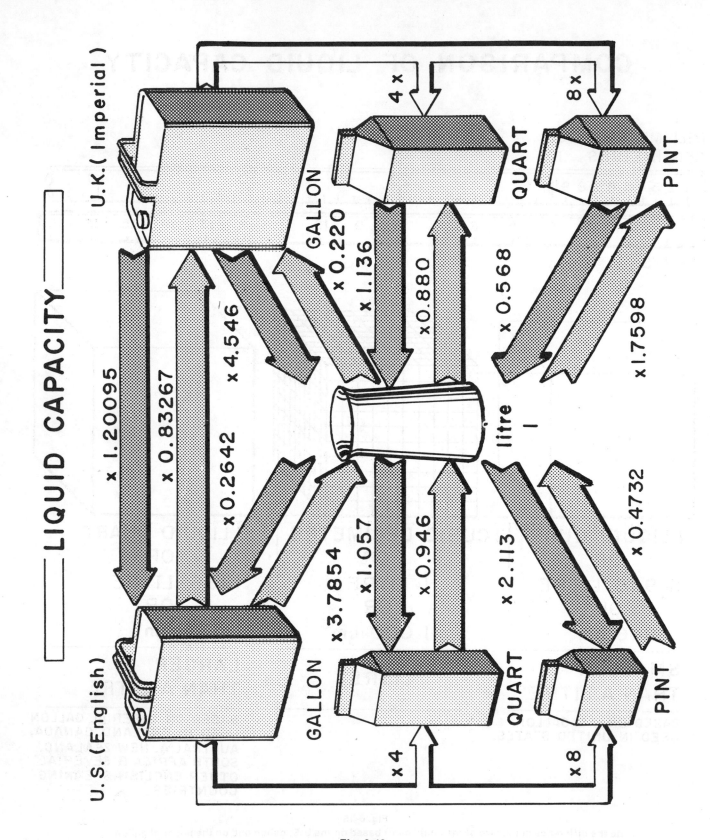

Fig. 6-16a

Use these conversion factors to change metric to either U.S. customary or Imperial units and vice versa.

SMALL LIQUID CAPACITY

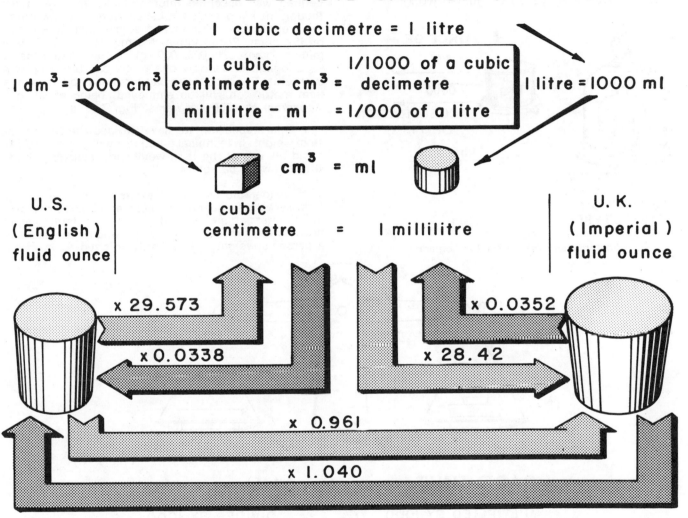

1 cubic decimetre = 1 litre

1 dm³ = 1000 cm³

| 1 cubic centimetre – cm³ = | 1/1000 of a cubic decimetre |
| 1 millilitre – ml | = 1/000 of a litre |

1 litre = 1000 ml

cm³ = ml

U.S.
(English)
fluid ounce

1 cubic centimetre = 1 millilitre

U.K.
(Imperial)
fluid ounce

x 29.573

x 0.0352

x 0.0338

x 28.42

x 0.961

x 1.040

Fig. 6-16b

UNIT 7
MASS AND WEIGHT

word: kilogram

symbol: kg

definition: The kilogram is the unit of mass. It is equal to the mass of the international prototype of the kilogram. This prototype is a cylinder of platinum-iridium alloy kept by the International Bureau of Weights and Measures at Paris. Fig. 7-1 and 7-2. A duplicate in the custody of our National Bureau of Standards serves as the mass standard for the United States. This is the only base unit still defined by an artifact (an object produced by human work).

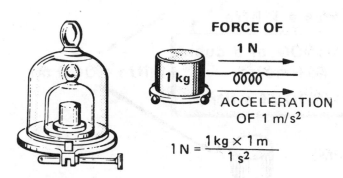

INTERNATIONAL PROTOTYPE

Fig. 7-1
International prototype for the kilogram.

FORCE OF

1 N

1 kg

ACCELERATION OF 1 m/s²

$$1\,N = \frac{1\,kg \times 1\,m}{1\,s^2}$$

In contrast to all other base units the kilogram is the only SI base unit that uses a prefix. This unfortunate situation is due to the fact that the kilogram was named about 200 years ago. During the 18th century, the kilogram was defined as the mass of 1 cubic decimetre volume of water at a temperature of 4 degrees Celsius. However, a more accurate standard was needed. In 1889, metal kilogram standards (40 in all) were made. One was selected as the international standard and kept in the Archives near Paris. Duplicates were made available to other nations, so the standards became international. The United States obtained No. 4 and No. 20 of these standards. The kilogram as now defined was accepted internationally in 1889. Even though the *kilogram* is the base unit and not the *gram*, the prefixes for multiples and submultiples are based on the gram. For example, the megagram which is a million grams (1 000 000 g) is not listed as a kilokilogram since only one prefix can be used with each unit. For most everyday business activities, the term metric ton will be employed, being equal to 1 *megagram* or 1000 *kilograms*. Fig. 7-3.

In this discussion we have avoided the use of the term weight. In technical practice it will be advisable to avoid the use of the term weight for reasons given in the following paragraph.

"Considerable confusion exists in the use of the term weight as a quantity to mean either force or mass. In commercial and everyday use, the term weight nearly always means mass; thus, when one speaks of a person's weight, the quantity referred to is mass.

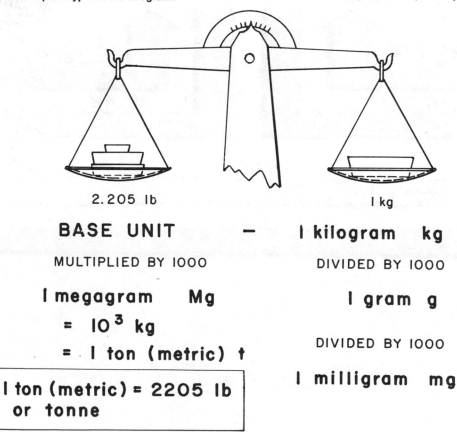

2.205 lb

BASE UNIT — 1 kilogram kg

MULTIPLIED BY 1000

1 megagram   Mg

= 10³ kg

= 1 ton (metric) t

1 ton (metric) = 2205 lb or tonne

1 kg

DIVIDED BY 1000

1 gram g

DIVIDED BY 1000

1 milligram   mg

Fig. 7-2
The base unit is the kilogram, and the preferred multiple is the megagram, more commonly known as metric ton, and the preferred submultiple the gram.

MASS — WEIGHT

gram:

A large thumbtack has a mass (weight) of about I gram.

kilogram:

This book has a mass (weight) of about I kilogram.

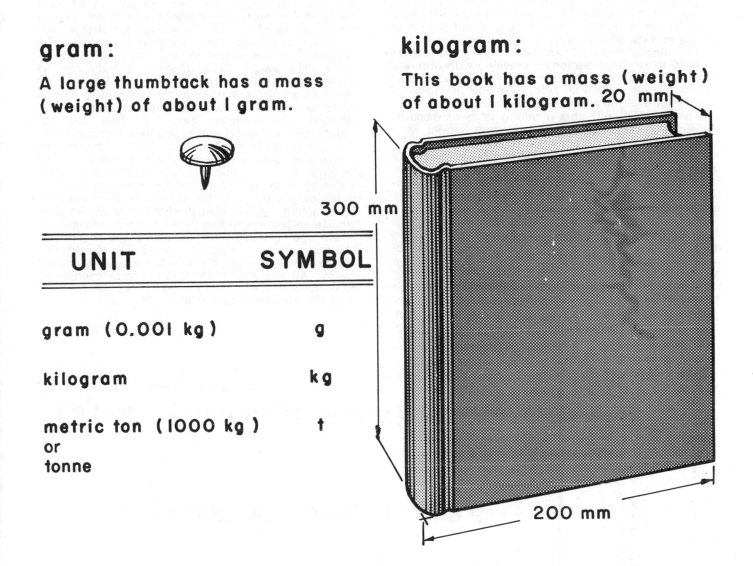

UNIT	SYMBOL
gram (0.001 kg)	g
kilogram	kg
metric ton (1000 kg) or tonne	t

Fig. 7-3
Mass or weight with the basic units and their symbols.

This non-technical use of the term weight in everyday life will probably persist. In science and technology, the term weight of a body has usually meant the force that if applied to the body would give it an acceleration of free fall. The adjective "local" in the phrase "local acceleration of free fall" has usually meant a location on the surface of the earth; in this context the "local acceleration of free fall" has the symbol g (sometimes referred to as "acceleration of gravity") with observed values of g differing by over 0.5 percent at various points on the earth's surface. The use of "force of gravity" (mg = mass times acceleration of gravity) in lieu of "weight" with this meaning is recommended. Because of the dual use of the term weight as a quantity, this term should be avoided in technical practice except under circumstances in which its meaning is completely clear. When the term is used, it is important to know whether mass or force is intended, and to use SI units properly by using kilograms for mass or newtons for force."

Implementation of the recommended procedure will mean that the term weight will not be used in engineering standards and in other technical publications. Instead the term "force of gravity," a much more descriptive term, will be used. On the other hand as the wording of the above paragraph states, the nontechnical use of the term weight in everyday life as being synonymous with mass will probably persist. Accordingly in communications with the general public and also in many areas of school education, including vocational education, the term weight will be used prolifically as being synonymous with mass. That is the way in which the term weight is used in this unit.

Because weight was in the past often used as a force, a brief explanation of that usage will be of interest. The weight as a force of a body can be visualized as being the force of reaction that the body exerts on all forces that are in contact with it. This is the force that can be measured with a spring balance, calibrated in newtons. Fig. 7-4. This type of visualization will better enable you to see why it is that an astronaut when he is in space "falling" toward the earth or during his long voyage in skylab was said to be "weightless"; i.e., that his weight was zero. This obviously does not mean that his mass was zero. It means only that except for gravitation there were no forces acting on him against which to react. He thus felt "weightless" even though he was not "massless."

This type of visualization will also better enable you to see why it is that a person's or object's weight was said to increase when the elevator was accelerating upward. All this meant was that the force exerted by the elevator in the person or object was greater than when the elevator was stationary.

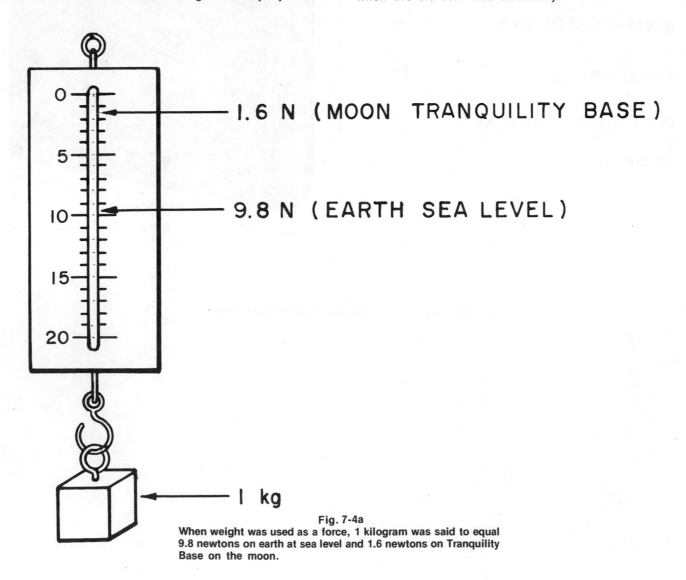

1.6 N (MOON TRANQUILITY BASE)

9.8 N (EARTH SEA LEVEL)

1 kg

Fig. 7-4a
When weight was used as a force, 1 kilogram was said to equal 9.8 newtons on earth at sea level and 1.6 newtons on Tranquility Base on the moon.

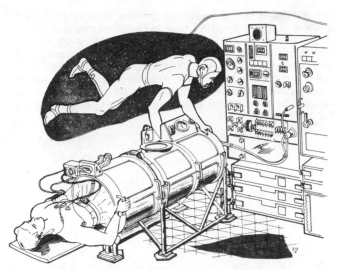

Fig. 7-4b

The astronauts operating on the Skylab became "weightless" in the outmoded use of weight as a force because there were no forces other than gravity against which to react.

Uses of Weight (Mass) Units

As the United States goes metric, units of mass (weight) as follows will be used:

The *gram* (g) will be used for most small amounts of products. Among these will be butter, cheese, packaged meat slices, jams, jellies, spices, canned fruits, nuts, candies, nails, putty and paste fillers. Knitting wool will be shown in grams. Fig. 7-5.

The *kilogram* (kg) will be used in buying meat, vegetables, fruits, sugar, flour, fertilizer, lawn seed, cement. Baggage limits when traveling by air will be stated in kilograms. The kilogram will also be used to express a person's weight. Fig. 7-6.

The *metric ton* (t) will be used to express the annual yield in grain crops, in specifying the weight of very large loads such as truck load of bricks, or almost any type of cargo which may be shipped or transported from one place to another. Fig. 7-7.

The *milligram* (mg) is a very small unit of mass and, therefore, is not too common in daily life except in pharmaceutical quantities where the contents of drugs are shown in milligrams.

Conversion

A few common reference points will be useful:

1. A gram is a very small unit, about 3-1/2 percent as large as an ounce. An ounce is about 28 times as large as a gram. Fig. 7-8.

2. A kilogram is approximately twice a *pound* (2.2 pounds or 2 pounds 4 ounces). A *pound* is about 10 percent less than one half a *kilogram*.

3. A metric ton is about 10 percent more than the short ton commonly used in the customary system, and is only slightly less than the long ton.

In converting from customary to metric weight measurement, tables, charts and graphs can be used. Fig. 7-9, 7-10, 7-11 and 7-12.

Determining Mass (Weight)

There are two general methods of determining mass (weight), namely the platform balance (balance scale) and the spring scale. Fig. 7-13. The first and the most accurate is the *platform balance* or *balance scale*. The object of which the mass (weight) is already known is placed on one side of the balance and the object of

unknown mass (weight) is placed on the other until the balance is equal. The force of gravity on each of the objects is proportioned to the mass (weight) of the object. If the forces are equal, then the masses are equal. While force of gravity is used to compare the masses (weights), it is not necessary to know the value of the force of gravity to determine the mass. The same method for determining mass could be used on the moon, and it will give the same results even though the force of gravity on the object on the moon is only 1/6 of the corresponding force on earth. Fig. 7-14a,b. The balance scale is an instrument, therefore, that is used to determine mass (weight) by using the force of gravity. In everyday use people are primarily interested in mass, and they usually call it *weight*. For example, the average housewife is interested in the quantity of the matter being purchased, and not the force with which the earth attracts it. She would want to buy a kilogram (mass) of butter, whether she were living on earth, in a space station, or on the moon, even though on the moon, the force of gravity in the butter would be approximately one sixth that on the earth. The physicians for the astronauts are interested in the body mass of their patients, not in what a spring balance would give as their weight. When an astronaut becomes "weightless" in space, in the outmoded context of weight being a force, his doctor is not worried, but when his mass suddenly goes down a few kilograms it may seriously affect the state of his health.

The second method of determining mass (weight) is with the spring scale. While the spring scale measures the earth's force of gravity on the object, it can be used on earth for measuring mass. The spring scale is calibrated or adjusted for a specific location and it is then quite accurate in measuring mass (weight). Of course, if a sensitive spring scale calibrated for use at sea level is taken to a mountain location, it must be readjusted to weigh (determine mass of) the object accurately.

Calculation

For most products weight is listed in either grams or kilograms. Very heavy products (such as coal or iron ore) are listed in metric tons. For example, if the product weighs 12 ounces in the customary system, it is listed as 340 grams (12 x 28.35) in the metric system. A product marked 4 pounds would be listed as 1.8 kilograms (4 x 0.453 6). A short ton of coal in the customary system would be 0.906 metric ton. If a product is listed in pounds and ounces and must be converted to metric, both the customary units must be changed to either grams or kilograms and then added to give a single metric unit. For example, to convert 6 pounds 10 ounces to metric measurement, change both units to *kilograms*

$$6 \text{ lb} \times 0.4536 = 2.2720$$
$$10 \text{ oz} \times 0.02835 = \underline{0.2835}$$
$$2.5555 \text{ kilograms}$$

This might be rounded off to 2.6 kilograms.

If a product is listed as 1 pound 2 ounces, then the change could be to grams

1 lb x 453.592 = 453.592
2 oz x   28.35 =   56.70
                  510.292 grams

This *could* be rounded off to
510 grams

Relationships in the Metric System

In the metric system there is a very definite relationship between length, area, volume, liquid capacity and weight (mass). In the metric system 1 cubic decimetre equals 1 litre in fluid volume and 1 litre of water will weigh about 1 kilogram. **Fig. 7-15**. Also a one cubic centimetre container has a fluid capacity of 1 millilitre and will weight about 1 gram when filled with water. In contrast, in the customary system, it would take a container with a volume of 61 cubic inches to equal 1.06 quarts and this would weigh approximately 2.2 pounds of water.

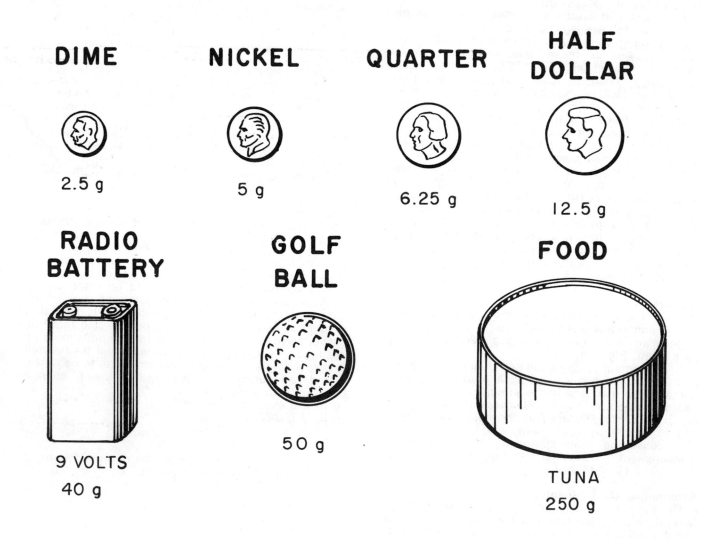

WEIGHT (MASS) IN GRAMS

DIME

2.5 g

NICKEL

5 g

QUARTER

6.25 g

HALF DOLLAR

12.5 g

RADIO BATTERY

9 VOLTS

40 g

GOLF BALL

50 g

FOOD

TUNA

250 g

Fig. 7-5
The gram is used for many common weight measures.

WEIGHT (MASS) IN KILOGRAMS

T-BONE STEAK

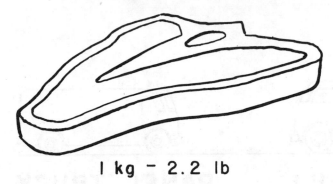

1 kg - 2.2 lb

FULL SUIT CASE

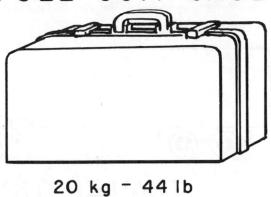

20 kg - 44 lb

BAG OF FERTILIZER

50 kg - 110 lb

COMPACT CAR

1 100 kg - 2 424 lb

Fig. 7-6
The kilogram will be used for weight measures that in the customary system would be in pounds.

WEIGHT (MASS)
IN METRIC TONS

TRAILER TRUCK - 8 t   **PANEL TRUCK
2 t**

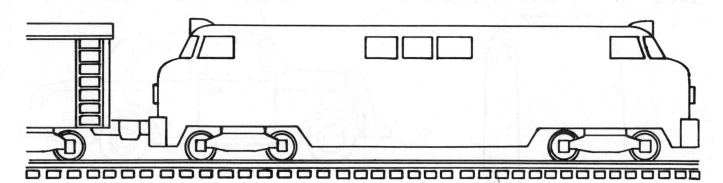

**TRAIN - 2000 t
LOCOMOTIVE - 140 t**

Fig. 7-7
Very large weight measures will be given in metric tons.

WEIGHT (MASS)

METRIC	CUSTOMARY	METRIC RELATIONSHIP TO CUSTOMARY

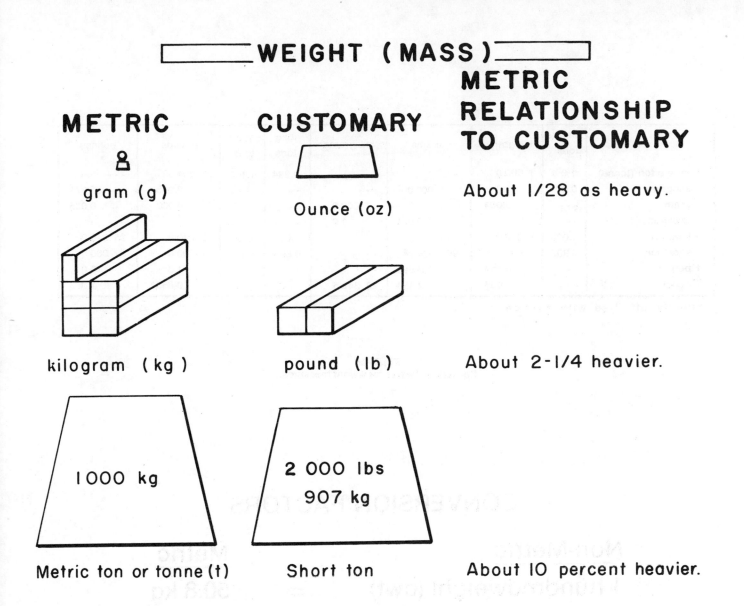

METRIC

gram (g)

kilogram (kg)

1000 kg

Metric ton or tonne (t)

CUSTOMARY

Ounce (oz)

pound (lb)

2 000 lbs
907 kg

Short ton

METRIC RELATIONSHIP TO CUSTOMARY

About 1/28 as heavy.

About 2-1/4 heavier.

About 10 percent heavier.

Fig. 7-8

A comparison in size of the weight units in metric and customary. Note that the gram is very much smaller than the ounce. The kilogram is somewhat more than 2 pounds. The metric ton is about 10 percent larger than the short ton.

	metric tons	kilograms	grams	milligrams	long tons	short tons	pounds	ounces
1 metric ton (tonne)	1.0	1 000.0	- - -	- - -	0.984	1.102	2 204.62	- - -
1 kilogram	0.001	1.0	1 000.0	- - -	- - -	- - -	2.205	35.274
1 gram	- - -	0.001	1.0	1 000.0	- - -	- - -	0.002	0.035
1 milligram	- - -	- - -	0.001	1.0	- - -	- - -	- - -	- - -
1 long ton	1.016	1 016.05	- - -	- - -	1.0	1.12	2 240.0	35 840.0
1 short ton	0.907	907.185	907 184.74	- - -	0.893	1.0	2 000.0	32 000.0
1 pound	- - -	0.454	453.592	- - -	- - -	- - -	1.0	16.0
1 ounce	- - -	0.028*	28.350	28 349.5	- - -	- - -	0.063*	1.0

*Round off. Use with caution

Fig. 7-9a
Conversion factors for weight measures.

CONVERSION FACTORS

Non-Metric		Metric
1 hundredweight (cwt)	=	50.8 kg
1 slug	=	14.59 kg
1 quarter	=	12.7 kg
1 stone	=	6.35 kg
1 pennyweight (dwt)	=	1.555 g
1 carat	=	0.206 g
1 metric carat	=	0.2 g
1 grain (gr)	=	64.8 mg
1 dram	=	1.77 g

Fig. 7-9b
Some unusual non-metric weight units.

Units of Mass or Weight

To Convert from grams	
To	Multiply by
ounces	0.035 273 96
pounds	0.002 204 62
milligrams 1 000	
kilograms	0.001

To Convert from kilograms	
To	Multiply by
ounces	35.273 96
pounds	2.204 623
grams	1 000
short tons	0.001 102 31
long tons	0.000 984 2
metric tons (tonne)	0.001

To Convert from metric tons (tonne)	
To	Multiply by
pounds 2 204.623	
short tons	1.102 311 3
long tons	0.964 206 5
kilograms 1 000	

To Convert from ounces	
To	Multiply by
pounds	0.062 5
grams	23.349 523 125
kilograms	0.028 349 523 125

To Convert from pounds	
To	Multiply by
ounces 16	
kilograms	0.453 592 37
short tons	0.000 5
long tons	0.000 446 428 6
metric tons (tonne)	0.000 453 592 37

To Convert from long tons	
To	Multiply by
ounces 35 840	
pounds 2 240	
short tons	1.12
kilograms 1 016.046 908 8	
metric tons (tonne) . .	1.016 046 908 8

To Convert from short tons	
To	Multiply by
pounds 2 000	
long tons	0.892 857 1
kilograms	907.184 74
metric tons (tonne)	0.907 184 74

Fig. 7-9c
Tables for converting from one unit to the other.

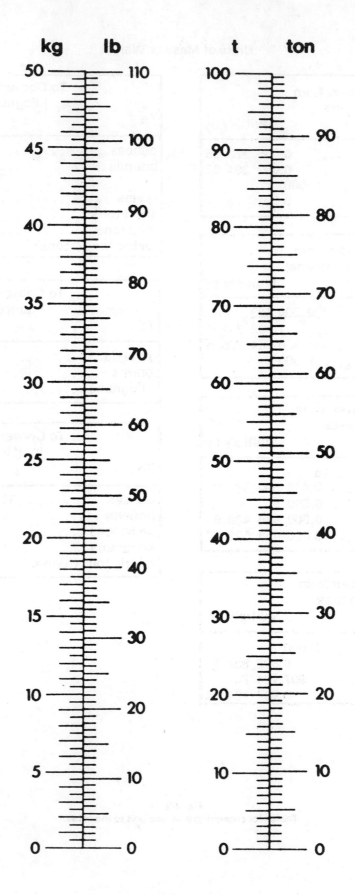

Fig. 7-10
Conversion scale.

MASS OR WEIGHT

1 ounce - oz = 28.35 grams - g

1 gram - g = 0.035 273 ounce - oz

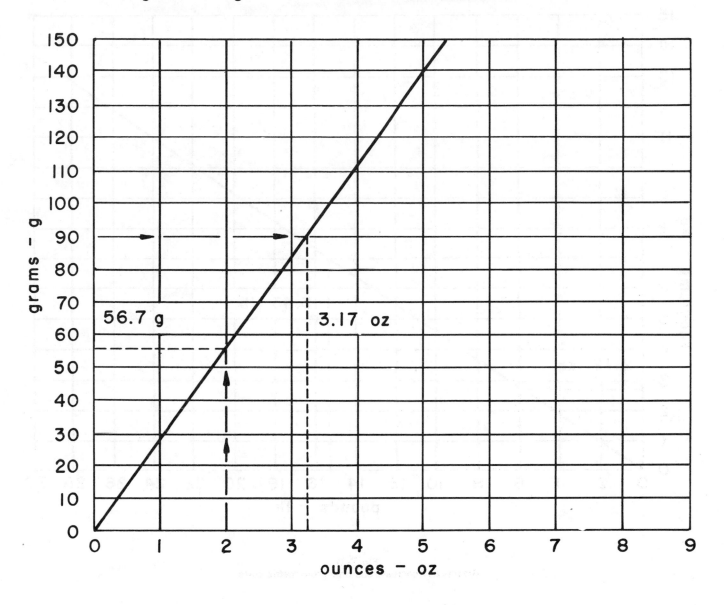

MASS OR WEIGHT

1 pound – lb = 0.453 597 kilograms – kg

1 kilogram – kg = 2.2046 pounds – lb

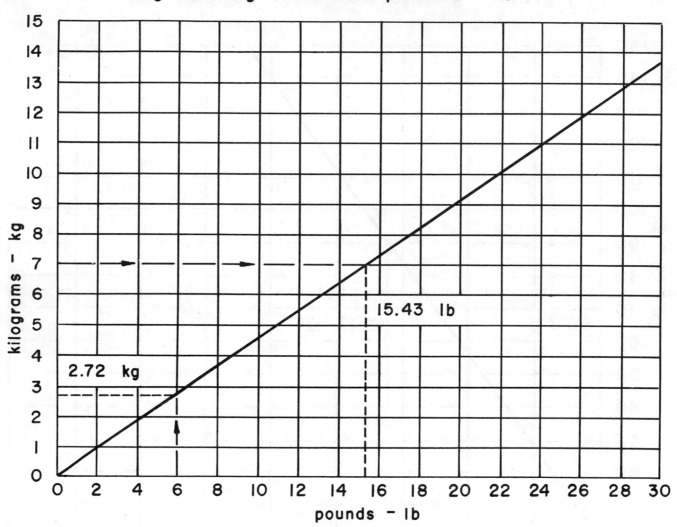

Fig. 7-11
Graphs that compare customary and metric units.

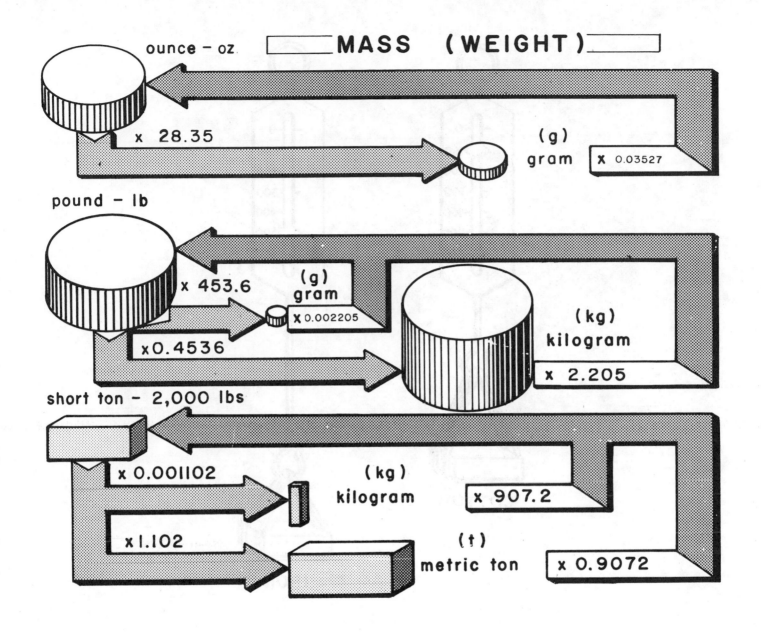

MASS (WEIGHT)

ounce - oz

x 28.35

(g) gram

x 0.03527

pound - lb

x 453.6

(g) gram

x 0.002205

x 0.4536

(kg) kilogram

x 2.205

short ton - 2,000 lbs

x 0.001102

(kg) kilogram

x 907.2

x 1.102

(t) metric ton

x 0.9072

Fig. 7-12
Use this visual chart for making common conversions.

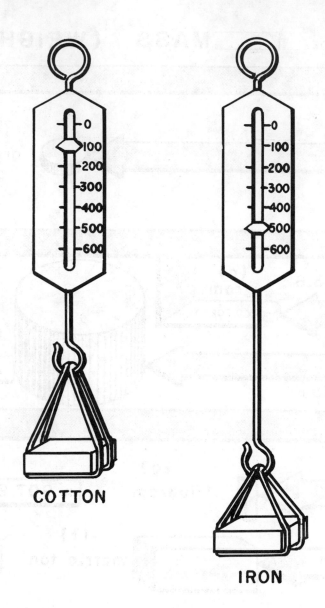

Fig. 7-13
Weighing by means of the spring scale depends on both mass and force of gravity. The greater the mass and the greater the force of gravity the greater the indicated weight.

A spring scale can be calibrated with known mass pieces (weights) to measure mass (weight) correctly in mass units for any specific location.

If it is moved to another location which is different in elevation and/or latitude, it must be recalibrated.

ON EARTH

SPRING SCALE

PLATFORM BALANCE

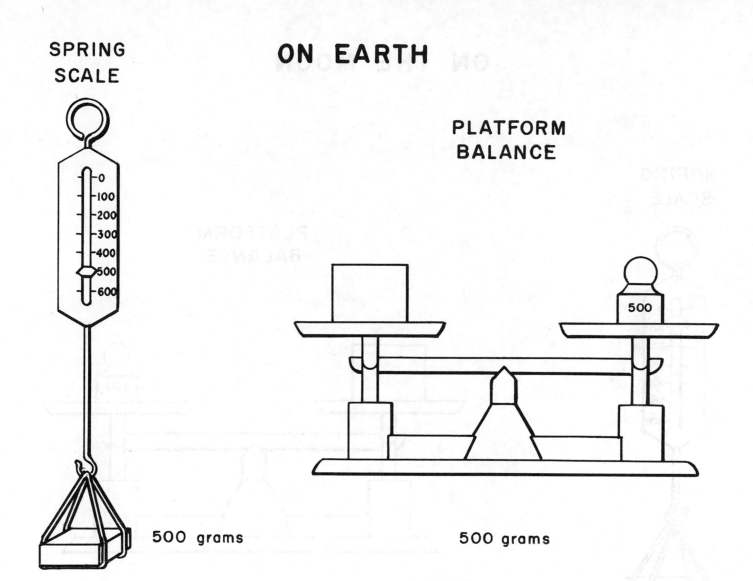

500 grams

500 grams

Fig. 7-14a
Note that on earth an object placed on the platform balance
and a spring scale will weigh about the same.

ON THE MOON

SPRING SCALE

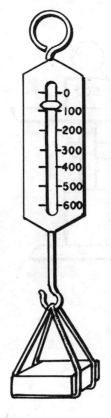

83 grams

PLATFORM BALANCE

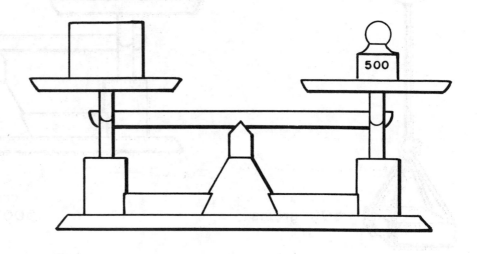

500 grams

Fig. 7-14b
On the moon the object on the platform balance will weigh
the same as on earth, while the same object on the spring
scale will seem to weigh much less because the spring scale
was calibrated on the earth.

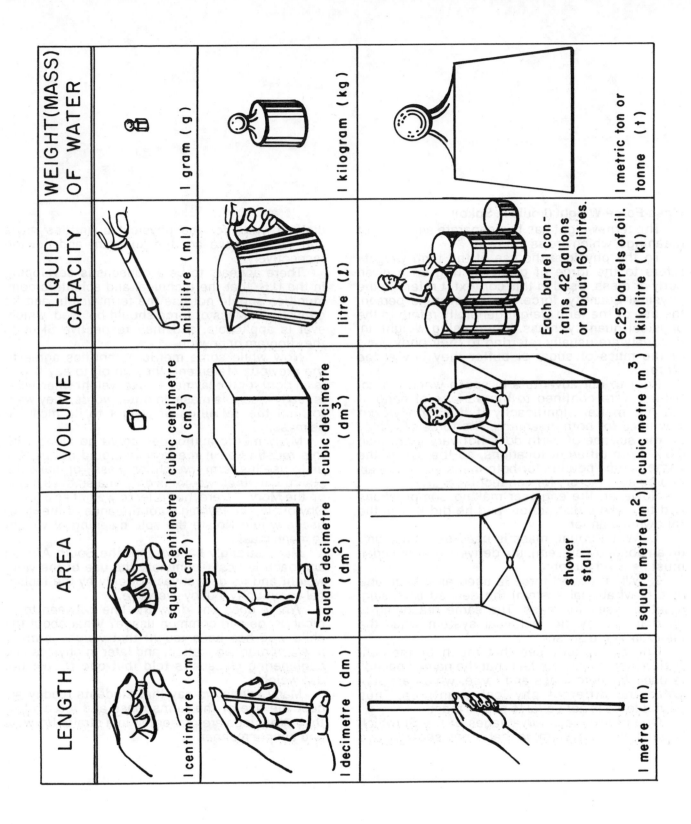

Fig. 7-15
The metric system incorporates simple relationships between
length, area, volume, liquid capacity and mass (weight).

Mass-Force-Weight (Louis F. Sokol)

The term weight has two separate and distinct meanings, which are as follows:

To the physicist the use of the term weight refers to the force of gravity acting on a given body or mass. Used in this context it refers to the physical quantity, force. To the average person, the use of the term weight generally refers to the physical quantity, mass. When using weight, individuals are usually referring to their body mass or the mass of sugar or butter they buy at the store.

Prior to our adventure in space when our activities were confined to the surface of earth, it did not matter significantly if the term weight was used for both meanings. The force of gravity on the surface of earth does not vary more than 0.5% from different locations, so the use of the same name "pound" for both mass and force appeared satisfactory for non-technical uses.

However, the engineer making computations had to make a distinction, and he did this in the following manner:

1. When pound mass is used as a base unit (in an absolute system), the derived unit, poundal, must be used for force.

2. When pound force is used as a base unit in a gravitational system) the derived unit, slug, must be used for mass. The same reasoning is used in the metric technical system when the kilogram force is used.

One can readily see that much of the confusion stems from the fact that the name "pound" is used for both mass and force, which are separate and different physical quantities. Thus pound force is not equal to pound mass.

One of the major advantages of the SI (which is an absolute system) is that it has separate and distinct units for the physical quantities mass and force. These are the kilogram and newton respectively.

There appears to be a consensus developing in the U.S. that the technical and scientific communities should not use the term weight and its derivatives. Mass or force should be used, whichever is applicable, and their respective SI units the kilogram or newton.

Now while some metric authorities agree to the previous statement, they go on to say that it is all right for the layman to use weight when what is really meant is mass. In other words, they want to limit the definition of weight to its meaning as mass.

Many metric authorities could go along with this redefinition if the layman would not continue to use the term "weightlessness" or make the statement "their weight is only one-sixth as much on the Moon." Here they refer to weight as a force. Obviously, the layman's continuance of the latter usage would violate the sole meaning of weight to mean mass.

Many strongly believe that the South African approach is best—eliminate the use of the word weight and its derivatives not only by the technical community, but by everyone.

Where does one draw the line between technical usage and common usage? What about the child who has been taught that weight is mass in elementary education, and later in physics and engineering classes is told that one should not use weight.

Many educators say that students readily accept the use of the terms mass and force when their meanings are presented in a straightforward and simple manner.

UNIT 8
Temperature

Everyday Use	Scientific
word—degree Celsius	kelvin
symbol—°C	K
definition—	

The SI unit of temperature is the kelvin (symbol K) which replaces the old degree absolute. Note that the SI unit is only kelvin (K) and not degree kelvin (°K). This scale is used for scientific work. The *kelvin* is defined as the fraction 1/273.16 of the thermodynamic temperature of the triple point of water. Fig. 8-1. The triple point is the point at which the solid, liquid and vapor states of water are in equilibrium. The triple point of water is 273.16 K or 0.01 °C or 32.02 °F. The triple point cell, an evacuated glass cylinder filled with pure water, is used to define a known fixed temperature. When the cell is cooled until a mantle of ice forms around the re-entrant well, the temperature at the interface of solid, liquid, and vapor is 0.01 °C on the Celsius scale, which is approximately 32.02 °F on the Fahrenheit scale. Thermometers to be calibrated are placed in the re-entrant well.

The kelvin scale is not for everyday use. Instead, the degree Celsius (°C) and the Celsius scale are used. On the Celsius scale, water freezes at about 0 °C and boils at about 100 °C. The °C is defined as an interval of 1 K, and the Celsius temperature 0 °C is defined as 273.15 K. A one-degree rise in temperature is thus the same on both the kelvin and Celsius scales.

Basic

In changing to the metric system of measurement, the United States along with the rest of the world has adopted the Celsius scale of temperature, symbol °C. This was previously known as centigrade but the name was changed in 1948 by international agreement to avoid confusion with a unit used in some European countries that referred to a fraction of a right angle. In France, the term 'grade' means 1/100 right angle, and 1 centigrade is 1/10 000 right angle.

On the Celsius scale of temperature there are 100 'degree' intervals between the common reference points of freezing water at 0 °C and boiling water at 100 °C. A temperature increase from, say, 20 °C to 25 °C is given as 5 °C and not as 5°C or 5° C, as is found in some books. The relationship of degree Celsius temperatures to kelvin temperatures is as follows:

$$t \, °C = t_k - 273.15$$

On the Celsius scale, water boils at 100 °C (at sea level) and freezes at 0 °C; 20 °C is a pleasant room temperature, and 37 °C is normal body temperature. The following may serve as a rough guide in body temperature:

40 °C is dangerous fever
39 °C is very feverish
38 °C is feverish
37 °C is normal
36 °C is subnormal

The boiling point of water decreases by about 0.03 °C for every 10 metre increase in height above sea level.

The Celsius scale is used extensively in weather forecasting. Some examples of the weather temperature experienced in terms of degrees Celsius are:

AIR TEMPERATURES
DEGREES CELSIUS

Below 0—freezing
0-10—cold
10-20—cool
20-25—mild
25-30—warm
30-40—hot
Over 40—very hot

Temperatures below freezing have a 'minus' sign. For example, -5 °C is a useful danger signal implying frozen radiators and icy roads.

Three rules must be followed when writing temperature information:

1. While the symbol for all units named after famous scientists is a capital letter, the word is not capitalized when written except at the beginning of a sentence. The *degree Celsius* is an exception to this rule and must *always* be written with a capital letter.

2. The degree sign must always be used with the symbol as °C. The reason for this is that capital C by itself is the symbol for coulomb, a derived unit in the SI system used in electricity-electronics.

3. It is normal practice to leave a space between the value and the symbol, such as 10 km or 25 °C. However, in some English-speaking countries no space is used between the amount and the temperature symbol. For example, "We drove 100 kilometres (100 km) in 40 degrees Celsius (40°C) temperature." Note that there is a space between the amount and distance, but not between the amount and the temperature symbol. *Generally in the United States a space will be used. However,* never leave a space between the degree sign and the capital C. For example, the following is *incorrect:* 27° C.

Conversion

There are several methods of converting from Fahrenheit temperature to degrees Celsius and vice-versa. The simplest is to use dual reading thermometer, conversion table, or scales. Fig. 8-2 to 6. An easy way to convert moderate to hot weather temperatures in degrees Celsius to Fahrenheit is as follows: 10 degrees Celsius is equal to 50 degrees Fahrenheit. For every 5 degree rise on the Celsius scale, add 9 degrees on the Fahrenheit scale. For example, 30 degrees Celsius would have four (4) additional 5 degree increments beyond 10 °C. Therefore, 4 x 9 equals 36 and add 50 for a Fahrenheit temperature of 86 degrees. Fig. 8-7.

To change from Fahrenheit to degrees Celsius or vice versa use a simple mathematics formula:

From Fahrenheit to degrees Celsius

$$°C = 5/9 \, (°F - 32)$$
or
$$°C = \frac{°F - 32}{1.8}$$
or
$$°C = (°F - 32) \times 0.556$$

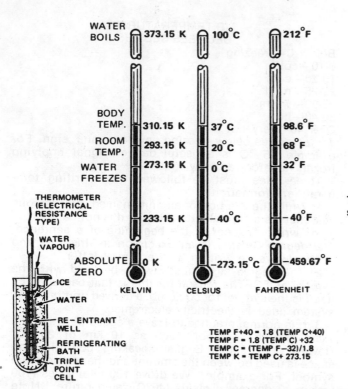

Fig. 8-1a
The relationship of kelvin, Celsius and Fahrenheit scales is shown along with the triple point cell.

TEMP F+40 = 1.8 (TEMP C+40)
TEMP F = 1.8 (TEMP C) +32
TEMP C = (TEMP F−32)/1.8
TEMP K = TEMP C+ 273.15

TEMPERATURE
celsius scale

100	Boiling Point (water)
40	High Fever
37	Normal Body Temperature
30	Quite Warm
22	Air Conditioned Building
20	Mild Spring Day
10	Warm Winter Day
5	Skiing
0	Freezing
−5	Icicles
−30	Bitter Cold

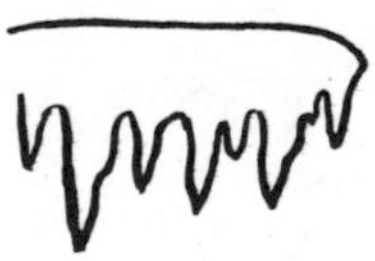

Fig. 8-1b
Some examples of temperatures in degrees Celsius.

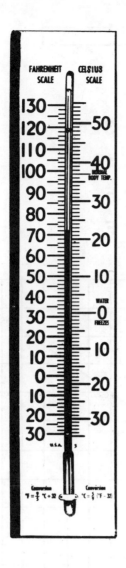

Fig. 8-2
A dual reading Fahrenheit and Celsius thermometer. Note how easy it is to see that 72 degrees Fahrenheit is equal to 22 degrees Celsius.

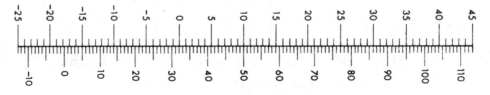

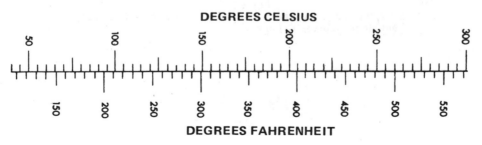

Fig. 8-3
This conversion scale can be used to compute degrees Celsius and degrees Fahrenheit.

TEMPERATURE

degrees Celsius (°C) = 5/9 (F − 32)

Fahrenheit (°F) = 9/5 °C + 32

Water Freezes   0° C   32° F

Water Boils   100° C   212° F

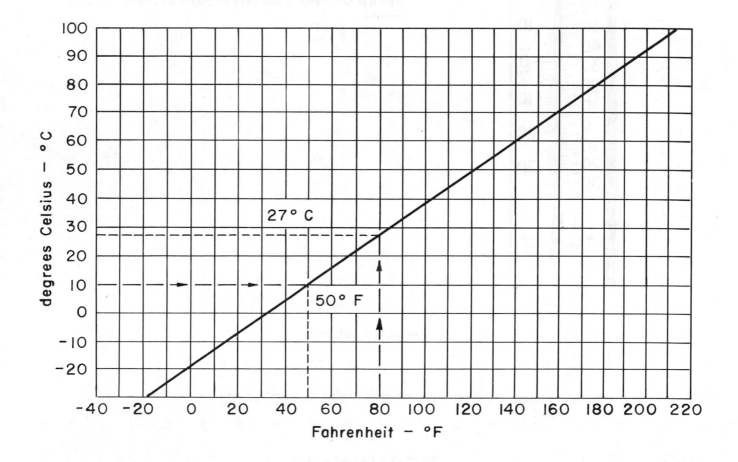

Fig. 8-4
This graph gives you a general idea of the relationship of degrees
Fahrenheit to degrees Celsius.

TEMPERATURE CONVERSION TABLE
—50 to 100

°C		°F	°C		°F	°C		°F
-45.6	-50	-58.0	- 8.3	17	62.6	15.0	59	138.2
-44.4	-48	-54.4	- 7.8	18	64.4	15.6	60	140.0
-43.3	-46	-50.8	- 7.2	19	66.2	16.1	61	141.8
-42.2	-44	-47.2	- 6.7	20	68.0	16.7	62	143.6
-41.1	-42	-43.6	- 6.1	21	69.8	17.2	63	145.4
-40.0	-40	-40.0	- 5.6	22	71.6	17.8	64	147.2
-38.9	-38	-36.4	- 5.0	23	73.4	18.3	65	149.0
-37.8	-36	-32.8	- 4.4	24	75.2	18.9	66	150.8
-36.7	-34	-29.2	- 3.9	25	77.0	19.4	67	152.6
-35.6	-32	-25.6	- 3.3	26	78.8	20.0	68	154.4
-34.4	-30	-22.0	- 2.8	27	80.6	20.6	69	156.2
-33.3	-28	-18.4	- 2.2	28	82.4	21.1	70	158.0
-32.2	-26	-14.8	- 1.7	29	84.2	21.7	71	159.8
-31.1	-24	-11.2	- 1.1	30	86.0	22.2	72	161.6
-30.0	-22	- 7.6	- .6	31	87.8	22.8	73	163.4
-28.9	-20	- 4.0	0.0	32	89.6	23.3	74	165.2
-27.8	-18	- 0.4	.6	33	91.4	23.9	75	167.0
-26.7	-16	+ 3.2	1.1	34	93.2	24.4	76	168.8
-25.6	-14	6.8	1.7	35	95.0	25.0	77	170.6
-24.4	-12	10.4	2.2	36	96.8	25.6	78	172.4
-23.3	-10	14.0	2.8	37	98.6	26.1	79	174.2
-22.2	- 8	17.6	3.3	38	100.4	26.7	80	176.0
-21.1	- 6	21.2	3.9	39	102.2	27.2	81	177.8
-20.0	- 4	24.8	4.4	40	104.0	27.8	82	179.6
-18.9	- 2	28.4	5.0	41	105.8	28.3	83	181.4
-17.8	0	32.0	5.6	42	107.6	28.9	84	183.2
-17.2	1	33.8	6.1	43	109.4	29.4	85	185.0
-16.7	2	35.6	6.7	44	111.2	30.0	86	186.8
-16.1	3	37.4	7.2	45	113.0	30.6	87	188.6
-15.6	4	39.2	7.8	46	114.8	31.1	88	190.4
-15.0	5	41.0	8.3	47	116.6	31.7	89	192.2
-14.4	6	42.8	8.9	48	118.4	32.2	90	194.0
-13.9	7	44.6	9.4	49	120.2	32.8	91	195.8
-13.3	8	46.4	10.0	50	122.0	33.3	92	197.6
-12.8	9	48.2	10.6	51	123.8	33.9	93	199.4
-12.2	10	50.0	11.1	52	125.6	34.4	94	201.2
-11.7	11	51.8	11.7	53	127.4	35.0	95	203.0
-11.1	12	53.6	12.2	54	129.2	35.6	96	204.8
-10.6	13	55.4	12.8	55	131.0	36.1	97	206.6
-10.0	14	57.2	13.3	56	132.8	36.7	98	208.4
- 9.4	15	59.0	13.9	57	134.6	37.2	99	210.2
- 8.9	16	60.8	14.4	58	136.4	37.8	100	212.0

Fig. 8-5

This temperature conversion table can be used to obtain precise conversion temperatures. Look up the temperature to be converted in the middle column. If degrees Celsius, read the Fahrenheit equivalent in the right hand column. If Fahrenheit, read degrees Celsius equivalent in the left hand column. For example, 10 degrees Celsius would equal 50 degrees Fahrenheit, whereas 10 degrees Fahrenheit would equal -12.2 degrees Celsius.

100 to 1000

°C		°F	°C		°F	°C		°F	°C		°F
38	100	212	93	200	392	219	425	797	354	670	1238
39	102	216	94	202	396	221	430	806	357	675	1247
40	104	219	96	204	399	224	435	815	360	680	1256
41	106	223	97	206	403	227	440	824	363	685	1265
42	108	226	98	208	406	229	445	833	366	690	1274
43	110	230	99	210	410	232	450	842	368	695	1283
44	112	234	100	212	414	235	455	851	371	700	1292
46	114	237	102	215	419	238	460	860	374	705	1301
47	116	241	104	220	428	241	465	869	377	710	1310
48	118	244	107	225	437	243	470	878	379	715	1319
49	120	248	110	230	446	246	475	867	382	720	1328
50	122	252	113	235	455	249	480	896	385	725	1337
51	124	255	116	240	464	252	485	905	388	730	1346
52	126	259	119	245	473	254	490	914	391	735	1355
53	128	262	121	250	482	257	495	923	393	740	1364
54	130	266	124	255	491	260	500	932	396	745	1373
56	132	270	127	260	500	263	505	941	399	750	1382
57	134	273	130	265	509	266	510	950	402	755	1391
58	136	277	132	270	518	268	515	959	404	760	1400
59	138	280	135	275	527	271	520	968	407	765	1409
60	140	284	138	280	536	274	525	977	410	770	1418
61	142	288	141	285	545	277	530	986	413	775	1427
62	144	291	143	290	554	279	535	995	416	780	1436
63	146	295	146	295	563	282	540	1004	418	785	1445
64	148	298	149	300	572	285	545	1013	421	790	1454
66	150	302	152	305	581	288	550	1022	424	795	1463
67	152	306	154	310	590	291	555	1031	427	800	1472
68	154	309	157	315	599	293	560	1040	429	805	1481
69	156	313	160	320	608	296	565	1049	432	810	1490
70	158	316	163	325	617	299	570	1058	435	815	1499
71	160	320	166	330	626	302	575	1067	438	820	1508
72	162	324	169	335	635	304	580	1076	441	825	1517
73	164	327	171	340	644	307	585	1085	443	830	1526
74	166	331	174	345	653	310	590	1094	446	835	1535
76	168	334	177	350	662	313	595	1103	449	840	1544
77	170	338	179	355	671	316	600	1112	454	850	1562
78	172	342	182	360	680	319	605	1121	460	860	1580
79	174	345	185	365	689	321	610	1130	466	870	1598
80	176	349	188	370	698	324	615	1139	471	880	1616
81	178	352	191	375	707	327	620	1148	477	890	1624
82	180	356	193	380	716	330	625	1157	482	900	1652
83	182	360	196	385	725	332	630	1166	488	910	1670
84	184	363	199	390	734	335	635	1175	493	920	1688
86	186	367	202	395	743	338	640	1184	499	930	1706
87	188	370	204	400	752	341	645	1193	504	940	1724
88	190	374	207	405	761	343	650	1202	510	950	1742
89	192	378	210	410	770	346	655	1211	516	960	1760
90	194	381	213	415	779	349	660	1220	521	970	1778
91	196	385	216	420	788	352	665	1229	527	980	1796
92	198	388	219	425	797	354	670	1238	532	990	1814
93	200	392							538	1000	1832

TEMPERATURE
BASE UNIT – KELVIN – K

	(F) FAHRENHEIT SCALE	(°C) CELSIUS SCALE	(K) KELVIN SCALE
Surface of the SUN	Approx. 9890°	5476°	5749°
CARBON boils	7592°	4199°	4472°
TUNGSTEN melts	6098°	3370°	3643°
ROCKET exhaust	Approx. 5500°	3037°	3300°
IRON melts	2795°	1535°	1808°
COPPER melts	1981°	1083°	1356°
ALUMINUM melts	1219°	659°	932°
WATER boils	212°	100°	373.2°
U.S. high temperature	134°	57°	330°
HUMAN BODY temperature	98.6°	37°	310°
WATER freezes	32°	0.0°	273.2°
MERCURY freezes	−38°	−38.9°	234.3°
U.S. low temperature	−69.7°	−56.5°	216.7°
DRY ICE	−109.3°	−78.5°	194.7°
WORLD low temperature	−126°	−88°	185.2°
ETHYL ALCOHOL freezes	−202°	−130°	143°
NATURAL GAS liquefies	−258°	−161°	112°
OXYGEN liquefies	−297.4°	−183°	90°
NITROGEN liquefies – freezes	−320.5° −345.8°	−195.8° −209.9°	77.4° 63.3°
OXYGEN freezes	−361.1°	−218.4°	54.8°
HYDROGEN liquefies	−422.9°	−252.7°	20.5°
HELIUM liquefies	−452°	−269°	4°
ABSOLUTE ZERO	−459.7°	−273.2°	0.0°

Fahrenheit scale markings: 10,000 – 9000 – 8000 – 7000 – 6000 – 5000 – 4000 – 3000 – 2000 – 1000 – 200 – 100 – 0 – −100 – −200 – −300 – −400

Fig. 8-6
A comparison of temperatures on the three most commonly used scales.

TEMPERATURE

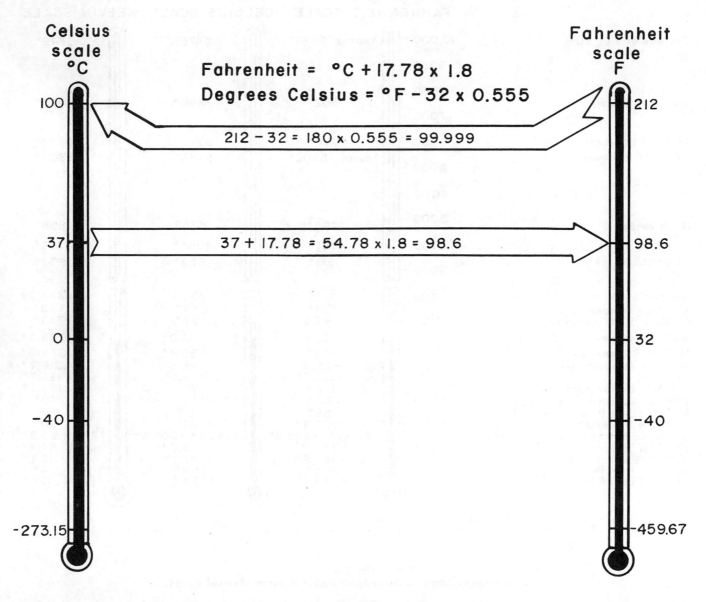

Fahrenheit = °C + 17.78 x 1.8
Degrees Celsius = °F − 32 x 0.555

212 − 32 = 180 x 0.555 = 99.999

37 + 17.78 = 54.78 x 1.8 = 98.6

Fig. 8-8
This conversion method is decimal in approach, since it does not make use of common fractions (which are not commonly used in the metric system).

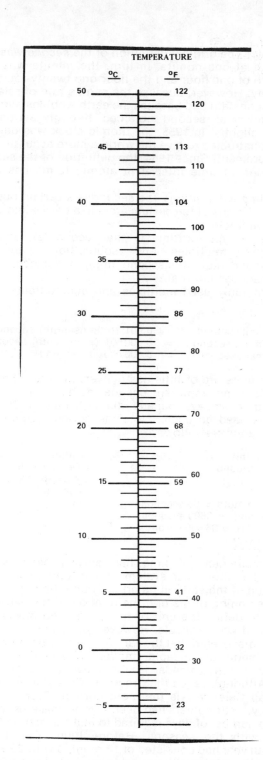

Fig. 8-7
This temperature scale can be very useful in reading weather
reports. Start with 10 degrees Celsius, which is equal to 50
degrees Fahrenheit. For every 5 degree rise in the Celsius scale
there is a 9 degree rise on the Fahrenheit scale. For example, 25
degrees Celsius is equal to 77 degrees Fahrenheit.

A METRIC SUN

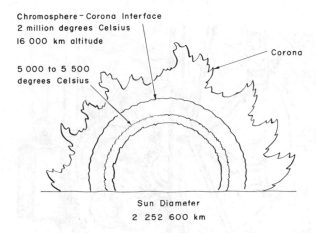

Chromosphere - Corona Interface
2 million degrees Celsius
16 000 km altitude

Corona

5 000 to 5 500
degrees Celsius

Sun Diameter
2 252 600 km

Fig. 8-9
A metric sun shows the intense heat of the sun in degrees
Celsius and the diameter of the sun in kilometers.

UNIT 9
OTHER BASE UNITS AND SUPPLEMENTARY UNITS

The *second, ampere, candela* and *mole* are the four other base units in the SI metric system. These four units are identical in both metric and customary systems. Except for the base unit of time, the second, the other units are not commonly used except for certain technical and scientific work. Fig. 9-1. The two supplementary units, namely, the *radian* and *steradian,* are also not used in daily life.

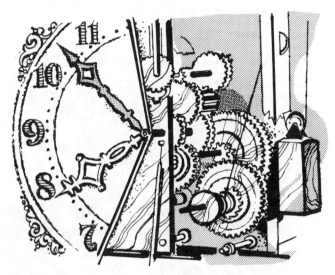

Fig. 9-1
Time is a most important base unit.

Time
word: second
symbol: s
technical definition: The second is defined as the duration of 9 192 631 770 cycles of the radiation associated with a specified transition of the cesium-133 atom. It is realized by tuning an oscillator to the resonance frequency of cesium-133 atoms as they pass through a system of magnets and a resonant cavity into a detector. Fig. 9-2.

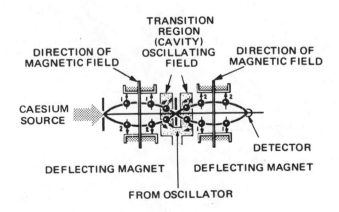

Fig. 9-2
The value of time can be obtained in any good scientific laboratory using the cesium atomic clock.

Basic: The original definition of the *second* was one sixtieth of one minute. In turn, the minute was one sixtieth of one hour and the hour one twenty-fourth of one day. However, because the earth's rate of rotation is not constant and because the earth wobbles slightly, the universal second obtained through astronomy varies slightly. In 1955, the atomic clock was devised and constructed to give the world a more accurate time measurement. Since 1964, the definition of the second as a unit of time interval in atomic terms has been used.

A simple definition: The *second* is a certain number of oscillations of the cesium atom in a device known as an atomic clock.

The SI unit for time is the second (s), and the preferred multiples and submultiples are the kilosecond (ks), millisecond (ms), microsecond (μs) and nanosecond (ns).

Commonly used multiples and submultiples:

ms millisecond	=	0.001 (1 thousandth) second
μs microsecond	=	0.000 001 (1 millionth) second
ns nanosecond	=	0.000 000 001 second

These units are of little use in everyday life. There is, therefore, no important change in the units of time. Such units as day, hour and minute, while not SI units, will be used as usual. Note the correct symbols for these units as follows:

Unit	Symbol
second	s (Don't use the abbreviation sec. for second)
minute = 60 seconds	min
hour = 3600 seconds	h
day = 36 400 seconds	d
year	a

Measurement of time has always been closely related to the solar system and in particular to the rotation of the earth in its orbit around the sun.* From the beginning of history, the rotation of the earth was used to define the unit of time, since no mechanical standard was available. However, early in this century it was discovered that the earth's rate of rotation varies, and a more dependable standard was needed.

Our current calendar is about two thousand years old. Although called the Gregorian Calendar, the name "Julian Calendar" is the more correct. From earliest history, astronomers had been able to make estimates of the number of days required to make a year that is in tune with the seasons. Before Julius Caesar, the Roman year had consisted of 12 months with 29 and 30 days alternately, with one additional day for a total for the year of 355 days. Since it was evident that the year was many days too short, a system was developed of adding an extra month as necessary.

To put an end to such abuses, Julius Caesar established the calendar that now carries his name and which has stood the test of time, with only two minor modifications, for 20 centuries. He changed the beginning of the year to the first day of January instead of March and arranged to have 31 days in each of seven months and 30 days in four months, except for February which had 28 days for three years and 29 days (leap year) every fourth year. The new system began on

*Reproduced by permission of Information Canada

January first, 45 B.C. Therefore, the preceding year was lengthened to 445 days, making 46 B.C. the longest year in history. An error in interpreting Caesar's instructions was corrected in the year 8 B.C. by Augustus Caesar, after whom the ninth month, August, was named. Julius Caesar earlier had the seventh month named after himself (July from Julius).

The Julian Calendar continued unchanged for 15 centuries. However, the cumulative effect of a slight error in the assumption that the year is 365 1/4 days long had become serious. We now know that the true length of the year is 365 days, 5 hours, 49 minutes and 14 seconds. The difference amounts to one day in 128 years. During those 15 centuries, the discrepency between the calendar year and the seasons of the year had become serious. In 1581, Pope Gregory XIII decreed that the day that followed the 5th of October should be considered the 15th of October. Also he ordered that the extra day in February be dropped in every century year except those divisible by 400. This was done to ensure continuing accuracy, so that 1900 was not a leap year although 1600 was.

Pope Gregory was not successful in having his ideas adopted in non-Roman Catholic countries. The change did not take place in Great Britain until 1752 when the error had increased to 11 days.

During the early period of metric change in France, there was some attempt made to develop a decimal time system based on the unit of ten. However, this was soon abandoned.

The 24-Hour Clock

While the 24-hour clock is not necessarily part of metric conversion, it is becoming more universally accepted with the metric system. Most military services have used the 24-hour clock for many years because it eliminates confusion between a.m. and p.m. designations. Many airlines also use this method of designating time. Many clock faces now show the 24-hour designation. Twenty-four-hour clocks are available In two types: the first type moves a full 360 degrees every 12 hours, and is marked on the inside from 1 to 12 and on the outside from 13 to 24; the second type is numbered from 1 to 24 as the hour hand moves in a single full circle (360 degrees) in a 24-hour period. Fig. 9-3 and 4. With the 24-hour time system, the day begins at midnight and ends 24 hours later at midnight. All units starting at one second after midnight are numbered continuously. The hours, minutes, and seconds are counted in the normal way, but written slightly differently:

Conventional system		24-hour clock
7:35 am	=	07:35
12:00 noon	=	12:00
1:00 pm + 12	=	13:00
11:15 pm + 12	=	23:15
12:00 midnight (old day)	=	24:00
12:00 midnight (new day)	=	00:00
12:05 am	=	00:05

Fig. 9-3
This 24-hour clock has an hour hand that moves 360 degrees every 12 hours. The first half of the day is read on the inside portion of the clock and the second half of the day on the outside portion.

Fig. 9-4
This 24-hour clock has an hour hand that makes one complete 360-degree movement in 24 hours.

Instead of breaking the day into two parts each of 12 hours, the hours are numbered all the way through from 1 to 24.

When writing the new time a colon or space (be consistent with either form) separates the hour from the minutes. Some English-speaking countries recommend the colon while others prefer the space. Also there are always four figures in the 24-hour clock system. To designate 9:15 a.m., for example, it is written 09:15.

Electric Current

word: ampere

symbol: A

definition: The ampere is defined as that current which, if maintained in each of two long paralleled wires separated by one metre in free space, would produce a force between the two wires (due to their magnetic fields) of 2 x 10⁻⁷ newton for each metre of length. Fig. 9-5. Commonly used multiples and submultiples are the milliampere (mA) which is one thousandth (0.001) of an ampere, and the microampere (μA) which is one millionth (0.000 001) of an ampere.

The SI unit of voltage is the volt (V).

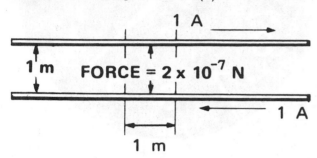

Fig. 9-5
The definition for the ampere is realized by using a current balance.

1 V = 1 W/A or one volt equals one watt divided by one ampere. The volt is the difference of electric potential between two points of a conductor carrying a constant current of one ampere, when the power between these points is equal to one watt.

The SI unit of electric resistance is the ohm (Ω).
1 Ω = 1 V/A or one ohm equals one volt divided by one ampere. The ohm is the electric resistance between two points of a conductor when a constant difference of potential of one volt, applied between these two points, produces in this conductor a current of one ampere, this conductor not being the source of any electromotive force. The other electric and magnetic units are derived from the metre, the kilogram, the second, and the ampere.

Some derived units relating to electricity-electronics include:
inductance - henry - H
magnetic flux - weber - Wb
magnetic flux density - tesla - T
electric charge - coulomb - C
capacitance - farad - F
electric potential - volt - V
electric conductance - siemens - S

Note that all electrical units have names taken from famous scientists. The symbols for these units, except ohm, are the capital letters of the first letter in their last name. To avoid confusion, inductance, named after Henry, uses the symbol H, while hertz, named after Hertz, uses the symbol Hz. Also the watt, named after Watt, uses the symbol W while magnetic flux, named after Weber, uses the symbol Wb. Another unit commonly used in electricity which is based on time is known as frequency. The number of periods or cycles per second is called frequency, and the SI unit is the hertz - Hz. One hertz equals one cycle per second.

Luminous Intensity

word: candela

symbol: cd

definition: The candela is defined as the luminous intensity of 1/600 000 of a square metre of a blackbody at the temperature of freezing platinum (2045 K). Platinum, in this state, is hot and glows. Fig. 9-6.

The SI unit of light flux (amount of light) is the *lumen* (lm). A source having an intensity of 1 candela in all directions radiates a light flux of 4π lumens. A 100-watt light bulb emits about 1700 lumens.

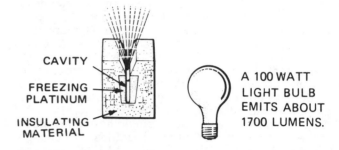

Fig. 9-6a
The primary standard of light is generally constituted by a ceramic tube immersed in molten platinum which is contained in a ceramic crucible and heated by an induction furnace. The heat input is reduced to allow the platinum to solidify slowly, and the photometric observations are made during the period of solidification.

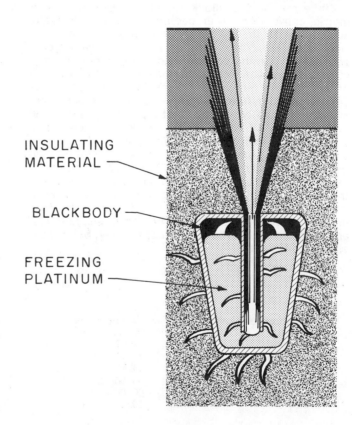

Fig. 9-6b
A blackbody (used in defining the candela) is any object that absorbs all light shined upon it. At a fixed temperature it radiates in accord with Planck's law.

Amount of Substance
word: mole
symbol: mol
definition: The mole is the amount of substance of a system that contains as many elementary entities as there are atoms in 0.012 kilograms of carbon 12. Fig. 9-7.

Fig. 9-7
The mole is used in chemistry and physics.

When the mole is used, the elementary entities must be specified and may be atoms, molecules, ions, electrons, other particles, or specified groups of such particles. This SI unit is usually used only in highly technical and scientific study. The SI unit of concentration (of amount of substance) is the mole per cubic metre (mol/m^3).

Plane Angle
word: radian
symbol: rad
definition: The radian is the plane angle with its vertex at the center of a circle that is subtended by an arc equal in length to the radius. Fig. 9-8.

The recommended SI unit of angular measurement has no significant advantage over using degrees in daily life. The radian is used only in mathematical and engineering calculation. For practical purposes such as in drafting, the angle will be specified in degrees and parts of a degree in one of two methods which are not SI units. The preferred method is to show the angle in degrees *only* using decimals for the parts of a degree. The other method is to show the angle in degrees (°), minutes (') and seconds ("). All sea and air navigation will continue to use the traditional degree, minute and second measurement method.

Unit	Symbol	Value in SI units
degree (of arc)	°	$1° = (\pi/180)$ rad
minute (of arc)	'	$1' = (\pi/10\ 800)$ rad
second (of arc)	"	$1" = (\pi/648\ 000)$ rad

Conversion When you know:	You can find:	If you multiply by: Accurate	Approximate
radians	degrees	57.295 6	57.3
degrees	radians	0.017 45	0.017

Solid Angle
word: steradian
symbol: sr
definition: The steradian is the solid angle with its vertex at the center of a sphere that is subtended by an area of the spherical surface equal to that of a square with sides equal in length to the radius. Fig. 9-9.

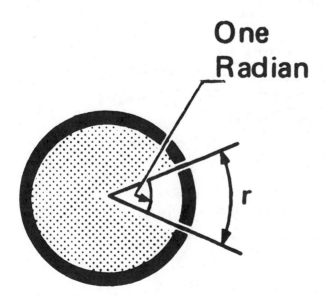

Fig. 9-8
The radian.

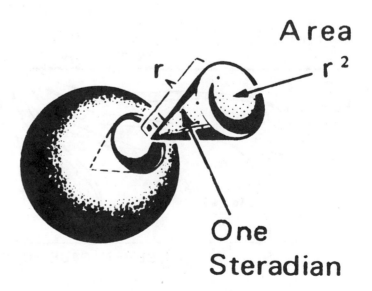

Fig. 9-9
The Steradian.

UNIT 10
DERIVED SI UNITS

The Systeme International d'Unites (SI) is the metric system in its most modern and perfected form. It has the advantage over the other measuring systems in that there is only one SI unit for each physical quantity. This system is simplified even further by the fact that multiples and submultiples of an SI unit are related to the unit by powers of 10 and there is a consistent set of prefixes for naming them.

Calculations are simplified because each derived SI unit is defined in terms of the base units in the most direct way possible, thereby eliminating complicated factors in calculations. A check is provided in that the answer automatically comes out in the correct SI unit.

All units in the SI metric system are known as *derived* units except for the seven base units and the two supplementary units. The word derived means "to originate from," "to draw from" or "to deduce from." This definition describes how these additional SI units are formed. The SI metric system starts by defining a very small number of independent units—called the "base" units plus two supplementary units. Fig. 10-1.

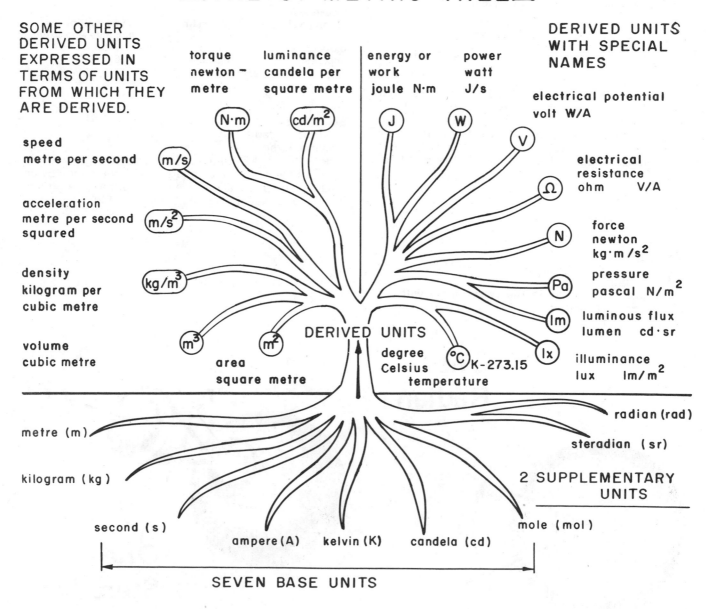

⊏THE SI METRIC TREE⊐

SOME OTHER DERIVED UNITS EXPRESSED IN TERMS OF UNITS FROM WHICH THEY ARE DERIVED.

torque newton - metre

luminance candela per square metre

energy or work joule N·m

power watt J/s

DERIVED UNITS WITH SPECIAL NAMES

electrical potential volt W/A

electrical resistance ohm   V/A

force newton kg·m/s²

pressure pascal N/m²

luminous flux lumen cd·sr

illuminance lux   lm/m²

speed metre per second

acceleration metre per second squared

density kilogram per cubic metre

volume cubic metre

area square metre

degree Celsius temperature °C K-273.15

DERIVED UNITS

radian (rad)

steradian (sr)

2 SUPPLEMENTARY UNITS

metre (m)

kilogram (kg)

second (s)   ampere (A)   kelvin (K)   candela (cd)   mole (mol)

SEVEN BASE UNITS

Fig. 10-1
The SI metric system has its roots in seven base units plus two supplementary units. All other units are derived from (grow out of) these.

From these base units other units are constructed, or derived, by combining the base units together in accordance with basic physical principles. For example, the *newton* (N) is that force, which if applied to a mass of 1 kilogram, gives it an acceleration of 1 metre per second squared. Note that three base units—the *kilogram* the *metre* and the *second*—are all used to define this new unit.

The derived units do not require constants as is so often the case in many of the technical customary units. In addition, no other separately-defined units are needed to define the derived units. Some derived units are based on other derived units. The pascal (Pa), for example, is the pressure produced by a force of 1 newton applied, uniformly distributed, over an area of 1 square metre (m²). The pascal is a combination of one derived unit with a special name—the newton—and one derived unit without a special name—the square metre. A system of units constructed in this way is said to be *coherent.*

The derived units can be divided into two general groups—those with special names and those without special names. Fig. 10-2 & 3. Most of the first group are named after famous scientists and inventors. For this reason the *symbols* for these units use a capital letter.

Commonly Used Derived Units

Of the many derived units used in technical work, only seven (plus the square and cubic metre) are commonly used in daily life. Many of the other derived units such as coulomb, ohm, farad, etc. are employed in specialized fields such as electricity-electronics. A short description of the more commonly used derived units is included. Those readers interested in the more technical aspects of these and other derived units can obtain copies of modern physics or engineering texts in which all units are given in SI metric.

Velocity or Speed

unit word: metre per second

symbol: m/s

definition: The SI unit of velocity or speed is metre per second

Velocity or speed is defined as the distance divided by time. It can be expressed in many ways. Fig. 10-4. In the customary system speed is usually expressed in feet per second or feet per minute. Fig. 10-5a,b. However, for highway travel it is given as miles per hour. Note that the derived unit of velocity or speed in the metric system is metre per second (m/s). Even though the hour is not a coherent SI unit, most speeds including automobile speeds will be expressed in kilometres per hour with the symbol km/h. Fig. 10-6. Thus, roadsigns and speedometers would be marked in this manner—80 km/h. Fig. 10-7. To change miles per hour to kilometres per hour, multiply the miles by 1.609. A speed of 100 km/h is approximately the same as 63 mph and a speed of 60 km/h is equal to about 37 mph. Fig. 10-8.

Typical speeds with the metric number rounded to the closest 5 km/h will be as follows:

	Customary	Metric (rounded)
Top major highway speed	75	120
Major highway speed	70	110
Two lane highway speed	60	95
Controlled highway speed	55	90
Fast "in town" speed	40	65
Medium "in town" speed	30	50
Slow "in town" speed	20	30

Some Other Derived SI Units

Quantity	Unit	Symbol
Area	square metre	m^2
Volume	cubic metre	m^3
Velocity-angular	radian per second	rad/s
Velocity-linear	metre per second	m/s
Acceleration-angular	radian per second squared	rad/s^2
Acceleration-linear	metre per second squared	m/s^2
Density (mass per unit volume)	kilogram per cubic metre	kg/m^3
Moment of force	newton-metre	N·m
Viscosity-dynamic	pascal-second	Pa·s
Thermal conductivity	watt per metre-kelvin	W/(m.K)
Thermal flux density	watt per square metre	W/m^2
Thermal capacity or Entropy	joule per kelvin	J/K
Permeability	henry per metre	H/m
Permittivity	farad per metre	F/m
Luminance	candela per square metre	cd/m^2
Molar entropy	joule per mole-kelvin	J/(mol·K)

Fig. 10-3
Some of the other common derived units. In highly technical areas there are many more.

Derived SI Units Having Special Names

Quantity	Unit	Formula	Symbol
Frequency	hertz	s^{-1}	Hz
Force	newton	$kg·m/s^2$	N
Pressure or Stress	pascal	N/m^2	Pa
Energy or Work	joule	N·m	J
Power	watt	J/s	W
Electric charge	coulomb	A·s	C
Electric potential	volt	W/A	V
Electric resistance	ohm	V/A	Ω
Electric conductance	siemens	A/V	S
Electric capacitance	farad	C/V	F
Magnetic flux	weber	V·s	Wb
Inductance	henry	Wb/A	H
Magnetic flux density	tesla	Wb/m^2	T
Luminous flux	lumen	cd·sr	lm
Illuminance	lux	lm/m^2	lx

Fig. 10-2
Derived units having special names. These are named after famous scientists.

Fig. 10-4
Speed will be given in kilometres per hour in the metric system, although the *knot* may continue to be used for air and sea travel.

There are some who suggest that speed limits should be given in metres per second, since this would impress on people the high velocity at which they are traveling. For example, 35 metres per second is approximately equivalent to 78 miles per hour or 115 feet per second. The velocity of sound in air at sea level is about 330 m/s. The velocity of light in vacuum is about 3×10^8 m/s. What happens in one second is usually more meaningful than what happens in an hour or 3600 seconds (one hour). World-wide sea and air transportation measures speeds and distances in *nautical miles* rather than in kilometres, even though the unit is not part of the SI metric system. A *nautical mile* is equal to 1852 metres or 6076.12 feet. The knot (kn) is defined as one international nautical mile per hour, and is used in specifying speeds of ships and airplanes.

Acceleration

unit words: metre per second squared
symbol: m/s²
definition: The metre per second per second is the acceleration of an object moving in a linear direction, the velocity (speed) of which in one second increases at a uniform rate of one metre per second.

To accelerate means "to move faster" or "to quicken." Fig. 10-9. Acceleration is an increase in the velocity or speed of an object. In the customary system, it is usually stated in inches per second squared or feet per second squared. Fig. 10-10. In order to accelerate the object, inertia must be overcome. Inertia is the tendency to remain at the same speed. The force needed to increase the speed of the object depends on the weight (mass) of the object and the wanted rate of increase. The rate of increase is the measurement of acceleration. If an object is traveling at a rate of 20 metres per second and you wish to increase the speed 5 metres per second every second, the rate of increase is 5 metres per second each second. After one second, the object would be traveling at a speed of 25 metres per second and after two seconds 30 metres per second. The per second on the rate increase means that the listed increase is added onto the speed each second. Acceleration is always shown as a rate of increase. The most common metric unit of acceleration is metres per second squared. Fig. 10-11. Acceleration is a change in velocity either as increasing velocity or as decreasing velocity (deceleration). This is a difficult concept to understand even though people experience this phenomenon everyday when riding in cars or using high speed elevators. Acceleration can either be appreciated by seeing it happen or by feeling the forces that cause it. Quick acceleration in a car will cause a person's body to be jerked back against the seat. Anyone who has watched the astronauts take off can see the effects of dramatic increase in acceleration. The body seems to be literally "left behind" and has to catch up with the space ship. In the process, the distortion of the human face is grotesque, to say the least.

Force

unit word: newton
symbol: N
definition: The SI unit of force is the newton (N). One newton is the force which, when applied to a 1 kilogram mass, will give the kilogram mass an acceleration of 1 metre per second squared.
$$1 \text{ N} = 1 \text{ kg m/s}^2 \qquad \text{Fig. 10-12.}$$
In order to understand *force* it will be helpful to review the meaning of mass and force of gravity. The kilogram is the SI unit of mass. Mass is difficult to define but may be considered to be the matter a body contains. It is a fixed quantity that does not change

VELOCITY SPEED

	metres per second	kilometres per hour	feet per second	miles per hour	nautical miles per hour
1 metre per second	1.	3.6	3.280 840	2.236 936	1.852
1 kilometre per hour	0.277 778	1.	0.911 344	0.621 371	0.451 358
1 foot per second	0.304 8	1.097 28	1.	0.681 818	0.592 495
1 mile per hour	0.447 04	1.609 344	1.466 667	1.	0.868 992
1 knot	0.5144	1.852	1.687 811	1.150	1.

Fig. 10-5a
Table for converting velocity or speed from customary to metric and vice versa.

SPEED (VELOCITY)

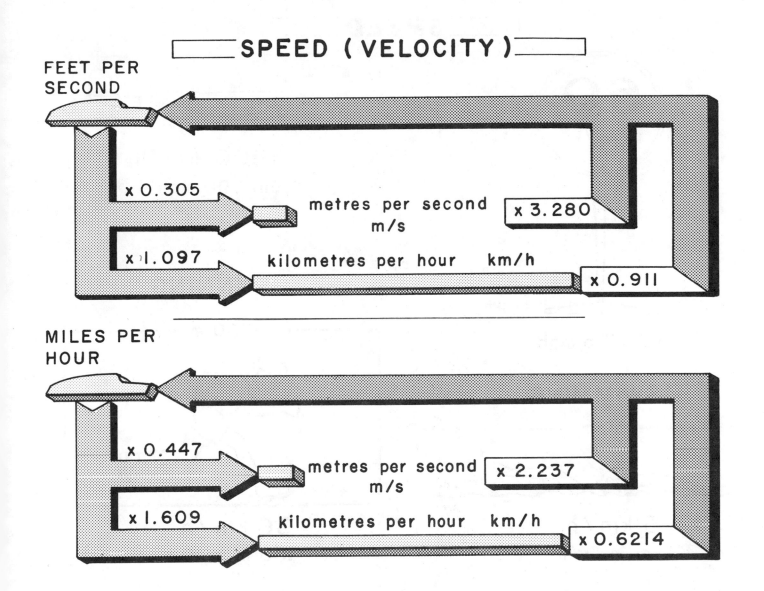

Fig. 10-5b
Use this visual chart for simple conversions.

SPEED

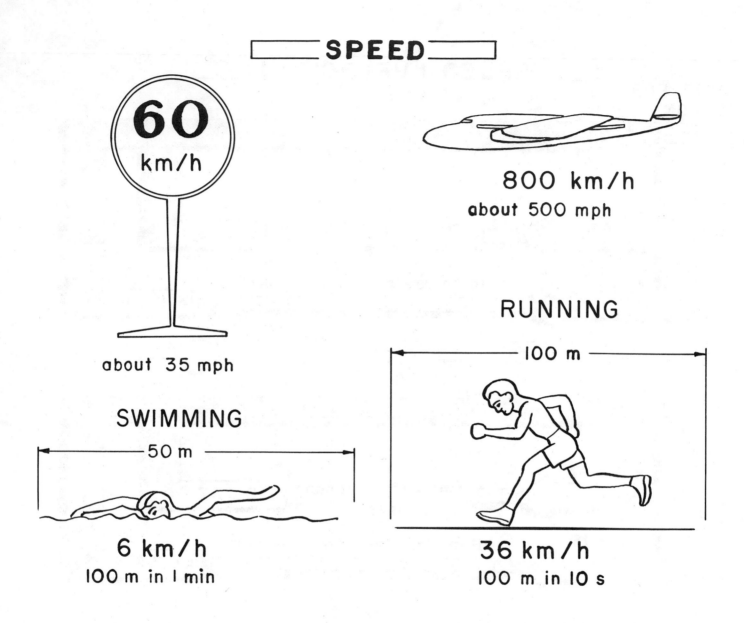

Fig. 10-6
Some examples of speed in metric.

SPEED

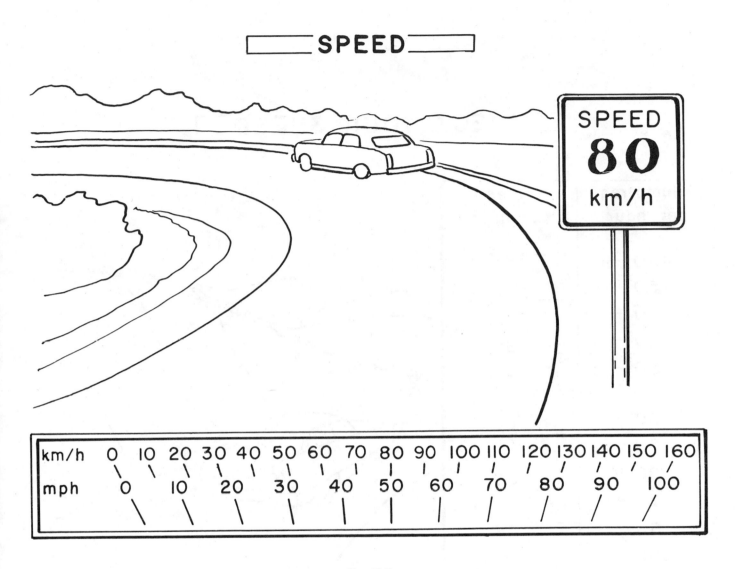

Fig. 10-7
Your speedometer will look like this.

CHECK YOUR SPEED

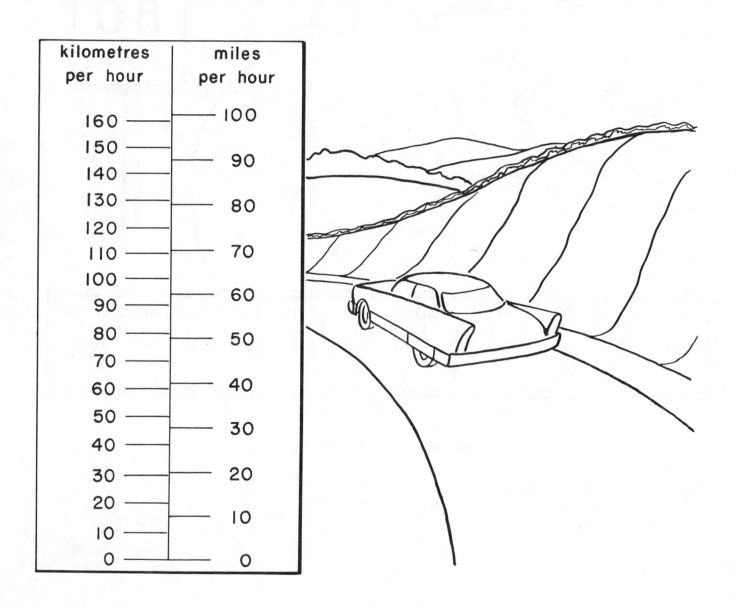

kilometres per hour	miles per hour
160	100
150	
140	90
130	80
120	
110	70
100	
90	60
80	50
70	
60	40
50	30
40	
30	20
20	
10	10
0	0

Fig. 10-8
A small chart can be placed on the dash to check your speed in metric.

Fig. 10-9
A space vehicle accelerates very rapidly in the early stages of liftoff.

From	To	Multiply by	Reciprocal
acceleration			
in/s^2	m/s^2	0.025 4	39.370 1
ft/s^2	m/s^2	0.304 8	3.280 84

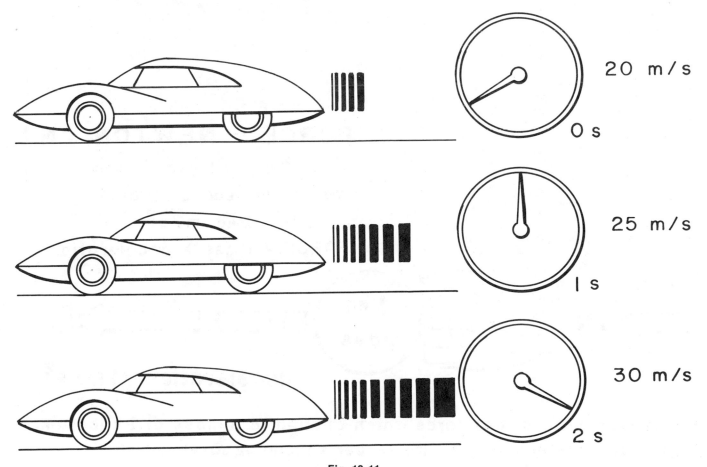

Fig. 10-11
Acceleration is an increase in the speed of an object.

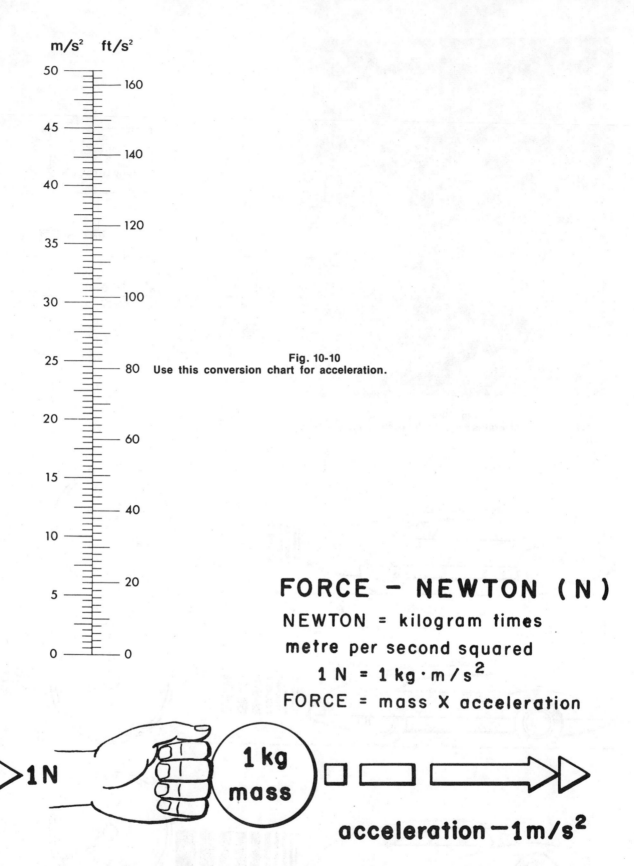

m/s²   ft/s²

50 ——— 160
45 ——— 140
40 ——— 120
35 ——— 100
30 ———
25 ——— 80
20 ———
     —— 60
15 ———
     —— 40
10 ———
     —— 20
5 ———
0 ——— 0

Fig. 10-10
Use this conversion chart for acceleration.

FORCE – NEWTON (N)

NEWTON = kilogram times
metre per second squared
$$1 N = 1 kg \cdot m / s^2$$
FORCE = mass X acceleration

1 N   1 kg mass   acceleration – 1 m/s²

The newton (N) is that force which applied to a mass of 1 kilogram, gives it an acceleration of 1 metre per second squared.

Fig. 10-12
One newton applied to a mass of one kilogram gives an acceleration of 1 metre per second squared.

MORE MASS

MORE MATTER

VOLUME IS THE SAME

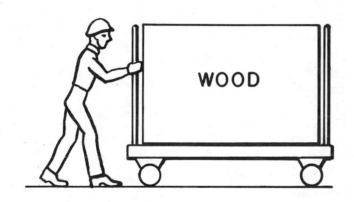

LESS MASS

LESS MATTER

MASS REFERS TO THE INERTIA OF THE OBJECT, OR ITS RESISTANCE TO A FORCE.

THE LARGER THE AMOUNT OF MATTER IN AN OBJECT, THE GREATER IS ITS MASS, EVEN THOUGH THE VOLUME IS THE SAME.

Fig. 10-13
Greater force would be needed to move the object with greater mass.

	From:	To:	Multiply by:	Reciprocals:
force	ounce-force	N	0.278 01	3.596 94
	pound-force	N	4.448 22	0.224 81
	kip	kN	4.448 22	0.224 81
	poundal	N	0.138 25	7.233 01
	dyne	μN	10	0.1
	kilogram-force (kp)	N	9.806 65	0.101 97

Fig. 10-14a
Conversion chart for force.

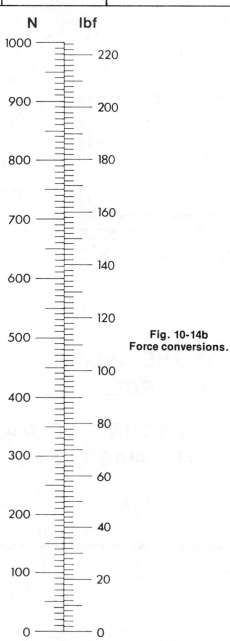

Fig. 10-14b
Force conversions.

10-11

anywhere in the universe. A kilogram of sugar has the same quantity of mass whether it is on earth or on the moon. Mass remains constant so long as the body of material remains the same.

According to Newton's second law of motion, a body, free to move and subjected to a force, experiences an acceleration proportional to force and inversely proportional to the mass. Force, then, is mass times acceleration. Fig. 10-13. Force of gravity is the force with which a body is attracted by gravity to the earth. This pull exerted by the earth is a *force.* When a force acts on a body, the body is accelerated. If there were a way to measure velocity such as with a speedometer, the instrument could be checked every second to find the force. Suppose, for example, a mass of 1 kilogram is pulled towards the earth. The reading one second after applying the force is 9.8 metres per second. Then after another second 19.6 metres per second, etc. Thus the rate of *acceleration* would be 9.8 metres per second squared.

The newton is the unit of force. To find the force of gravity in newtons on an object of known *mass,* the mass must be multiplied by a factor of about 10 (accurate within 2 percent). For example, an average apple with a mass of 100 grams would be subjected to a force of gravity of about one newton. The newton is a very small force. The force of gravity on a body varies about 0.5 percent over the earth's surface. The international standard value of acceleration due to gravity is approximately 9.8 m/s². In SI, therefore, the force of gravity on a mass of 1 kilogram would be 1 x 9.8 kg m/s² or 9.8 newtons at sea level. The force of gravity of this mass at tranquility base on the moon would be only 1.6 newtons.

Before the introduction of SI, force was usually expressed in terms of the local gravitational pull on a known mass (often referred to as "a weight"). Since this pull varies over the earth's surface, the terms "kilogram-weight" and "pound-weight" referring to forces could be used only for low accuracy work. For accuracies greater than 1 percent the variation of force of gravity had to be taken into account. The kilogram-force (called kilopond in some European countries) and pound-force were defined on this basis. The newton will replace obsolete units with the conversions as shown in Fig. 10-14.

Pressure or Stress
    unit word: pascal
    symbol: Pa
    definition—The pascal is the pressure exerted by a force of one newton evenly distributed over an area of one square metre (N/m² or 1 Pa = 1 N/m²). Fig. 10-15.
    Pressure and stress are defined as the force exerted on a unit area. The magnitude of the pressure is determined by the number of newtons on an area of 1 square metre. A person can reduce the danger of his falling through thin ice by lying down on the ice, thereby spreading the force (weight) of his body over a larger area, thus reducing the pressure. The modern hovercraft operates successfully over swamps and water because of the low pressure it exerts over a large surface. The force acting downward, due to the force of gravity on the vehicle, is spread over the entire underside of the vehicle. The air pressure produced by the vehicle is slightly greater than the downward pressure that results from the gravitational force acting on the vehicle so that the vehicle "floats" over the ground. The unit of pressure has a special name in SI called the *pascal.* A pressure of 1 Pa is equal to a force of 1 newton spread over a surface of 1 square metre. The pressure of 1 Pa is a very small unit. To illustrate, one small piece of fruit with a mass of 0.102 kg (102 grams) squashed out evenly on a table that measures 1 square metre exerts a force equal to 1 newton: 0.102 kg x 9.8 m/s² = 1 N. On the 1 square metre table, the pressure on the table is 1 newton per square metre or 1 pascal. The pascal is, therefore, a very small unit. In fact, the atmospheric pressure at sea level is about 100 000 Pa. Therefore, for practical purposes pressure is expressed in kilopascals (1000 Pa) with the symbol kPa or in megapascals (1 000 000 Pa) with the symbol MPa. Stress calculations may yield numerical values significantly larger than would be the case for pressure, and hence the prefix mega or giga may be more commonly associated with stress. Fig. 10-16. It is common practice in the customary system to refer to a pressure as so many psi (pounds per square inch). This is a colloquial expression for "pounds-force per square inch". Tire pressure is expressed in metric in kilopascals instead of pounds per square inch (psi). Once a person becomes accustomed to the idea, it will be just as easy to ask for "195 kPa" as it was to ask for "28 psi." (1 psi equals about 7 kPa.) *Force* in newtons and *pressure* in pascals are not the easiest SI units to understand and get a "feel" for. However, a simple explanation goes something like this:

PRESSURE – PASCAL (Pa)

$$1\ Pa = 1\ N/m^2$$

Pascal = newton per square metre

Pressure = unit force applied to unit area

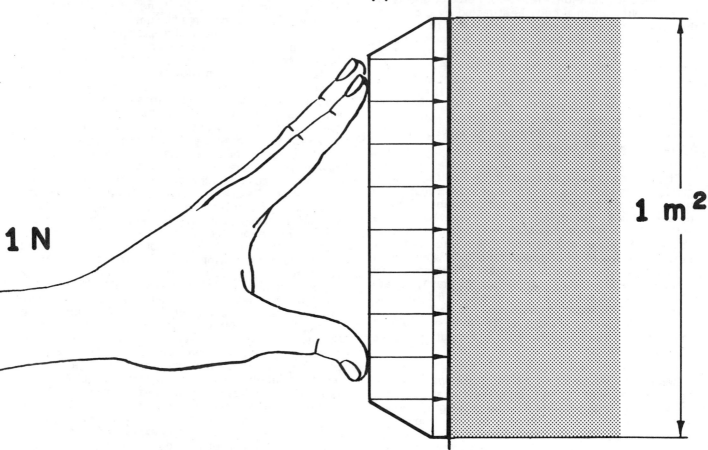

1 N

1 m²

The pascal (Pa) is the pressure produced by a force of 1 newton applied, uniformly distributed, over an area of 1 square metre.

Fig. 10-15

One pascal is the pressure exerted by a force of one newton evenly distributed over an area of one square metre.

	From:	To:	Multiply by:	Reciprocal:
pressure	psi	kPa	6.894 76	0.145 04
	pound-force/ft^2	Pa	47.880 26	0.020 89
	ksi	MPa	6.894 76	0.148 04
	short ton-force/in^2	MPa	13.789 49	0.072 52
	kp/m^2	Pa	9.806 65	0.101 97
	kp/cm^2 technical at.	kPa	98.066 5	0.010 20
	dyn/cm^2	Pa	0.1	10
	bar	Pa	10^5	10^{-5}
stress	psi	MPa	6.894 76^{-3}	145.04

Fig. 10-16a
Conversion chart for pressure and stress.

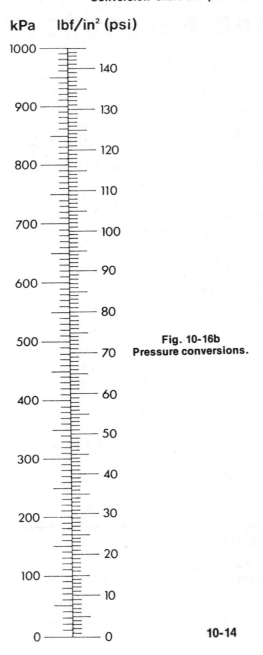

Fig. 10-16b
Pressure conversions.

10-14

An average size apple (about 100 grams in mass) is attracted to the earth by gravity with a force of about 1 newton (N). If the same apple is made into *apple sauce* and spread over an area of one square metre, the pressure exerted would be equal to 1 pascal (1 Pa). Fig. 10-17a.

Another example to illustrate a pressure of one pascal makes use of one hundred one dollar bills. A paper dollar weighs (has a mass of) about one gram and has an area of about one hundredth of a square metre (m²). If these one hundred bills are spread out to form a rectangular area of one square metre, they will exert a pressure of about one pascal. Fig. 10-17b.

In some countries using the SI metric system, the *bar* is used as a unit of gas and liquid pressure even though, like the litre, it is not an SI unit. The bar is a convenient unit because 1 bar is roughly equal to atmospheric pressure at sea level. Therefore, it is most commonly used for atmospheric pressure.

To many people, atmospheric pressure may seem of little concern. People usually worry only whether we are warm or freezing, wet or dry. However, to a large extent, the pressure of air on the earth determines weather. Pressure is measured by an instrument called a barometer, which derived its name from the Greek "baros", meaning weight. The daily weather map is a simple version of the meteorologist's synoptic chart, and shows the distribution of pressure into areas where it is high and low. Generally, a high pressure area indicates fine weather, whereas a low pressure region can have rain and other adverse elements. Lines which join places of equal pressure are called isobars. In metric countries these isobars are labelled in millibars by the meteorologists. Both the pascal and the bar may be used for pressure, but in different areas. *For example:* Atmospheric pressure will be in *kilopascals,* tire pressure will be in *kilopascals* and pressures or stresses in construction will be in *kilopascals* or *megapascals*

Note that:

1 bar = 100 000 Pa = 100 kPa = 0.1 MPa

1 mbar = 100 Pa

Energy and Work

unit word: joule

symbol: J

definition—The *joule* is the work done when the point of application of a force of one newton is

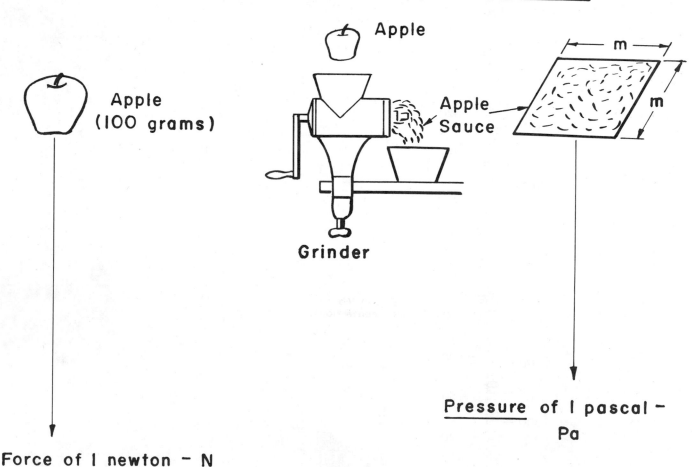

FORCE AND PRESSURE

Apple

Apple (100 grams)

Apple Sauce

Grinder

m

m

Pressure of I pascal – Pa

Force of I newton – N

EARTH

Fig. 10-17a
A visual comparison of one newton and one pascal.

PRESSURE – PASCAL (Pa)

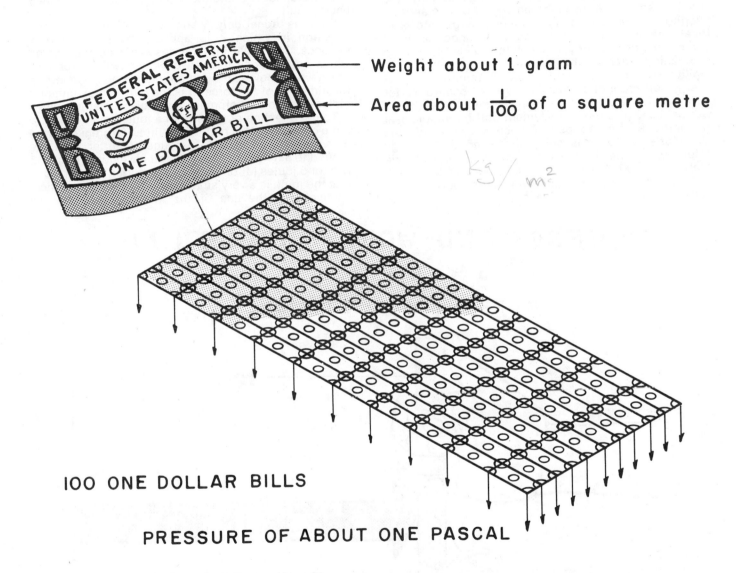

Weight about 1 gram

Area about $\frac{1}{100}$ of a square metre

100 ONE DOLLAR BILLS

PRESSURE OF ABOUT ONE PASCAL

Fig. 10-17b
Another example of a pressure of one pascal.

displaced a distance of one metre in the direction of the force or J = N • m. Fig. 10-18.

Energy is the ability to do work. When work is done on a body, energy is given to the body. Conversely, when energy is released, work is done. Therefore, energy and work are interchangeable and in the SI system the units are the same, namely the joule. To get a better understanding of energy, you must remember that energy exists in many different forms, and that work can be done in many different ways. Today it is possible to change any form of energy directly into virtually any other form of energy. For instance, a telephone is used to change sound energy into electrical energy, a stove is used to change electrical energy into heat energy, a generator is used to change mechanical energy into electrical energy, etc.

With the development of the different forms of energy, different customary units have been used for different forms of energy. The calorie, for example, was selected as a most convenient unit for simple heat calculations for foods; dieticians adopted the kilocalorie, which was soon shortened to the large calorie or Calorie. 1 kilocalorie (kcal) = 1 large Calorie (Cal) = 4.2 kilojoules (kJ). 1000 kilocalories = 4.2 megajoules (MJ). The kilowatt-hour became the suitable measure for electrical energy. The foot-pound-

force or foot-poundal was an obvious unit for mechanical energy in the customary system. The British thermal unit (Btu) was another common unit for *heat* energy. Fig. 10-19. The British thermal unit (Btu) was originally defined as the quantity of heat required to raise one pound of water through one degree Fahrenheit. Unfortunately the energy represented by this definition varies according to the water temperature. If the Btu is used for more precise measurements, it is necessary either to state the water temperature or to relate the Btu to another well defined energy unit.

Work is done *only* when a force moves in the direction in which it is applied. Work = force x distance. The joule may be described as the energy which corresponds to the work done when a force of one newton moves through a distance of one metre in the direction of the force. It is the **only** energy unit and replaces all old customary and non-SI metric units.

To get a feeling of the size of a joule, imagine that a force of nearly 5 N is required to lift a 500 gram package of butter. If you lift this package of butter from the ground to a height of 1 metre, you have done roughly 5 N•m or 5 joules (J) of work on the butter. It is obvious that the joule is a very small unit so, for most practical applications, the use of the kilojoule (kJ) and the

ENERGY AND WORK - JOULE (J)

1 J = 1 N·m

WORK = FORCE X DISTANCE

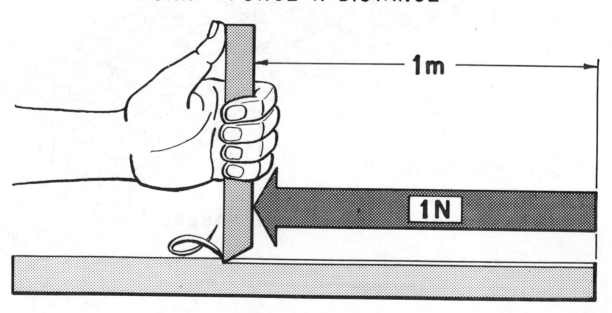

The joule (J) is the work done when the point of application of a force of 1 newton is displaced through a distance of 1 metre in the direction of the force.

Fig. 10-18a

The joule is work done when the point of application of a force of one newton is displaced a distance of one metre in the direction of the force.

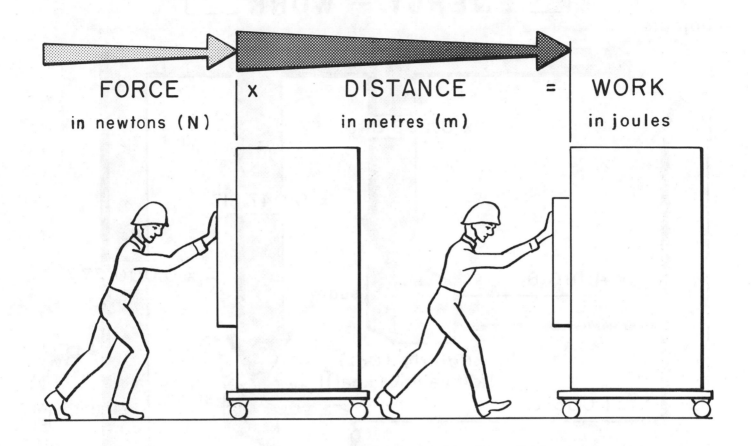

FORCE
in newtons (N)

x

DISTANCE
in metres (m)

=

WORK
in joules

Fig. 10-18b

Note that in metric the force is in newtons, the distance is in metres and the work done is in joules.

ENERGY - WORK

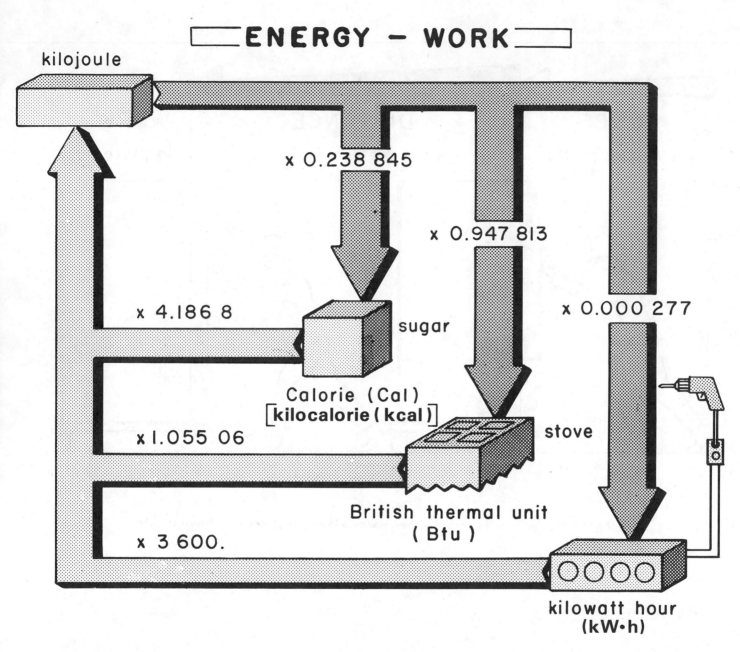

kilojoule

x 0.238 845

x 0.947 813

x 4.186 8

sugar

Calorie (Cal)
[kilocalorie (kcal)]

x 1.055 06

x 0.000 277

stove

British thermal unit
(Btu)

x 3 600.

kilowatt hour
(kW•h)

Fig. 10-19a
Use this visual chart to convert energy units in metrics to customary and vice versa.

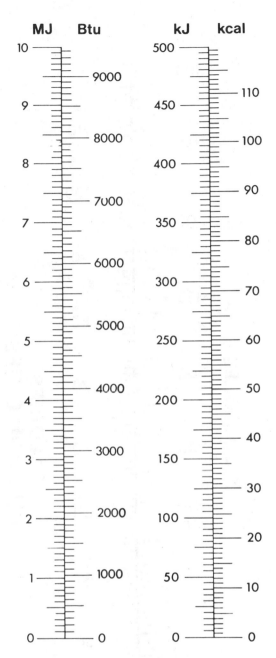

**Fig. 10-19b
Energy conversions.**

megajoule (MJ) is preferred.

1 kJ = 1000 J

1 MJ = 1000 kJ = 1 000 000 J

For example, if it takes 50 newtons to push a car along a highway a distance of 20 metres, then the work done in joules equals 50 x 20, or 1000 joules, or 1 kJ. If a mass of 25 kilograms is moved a distance of 20 metres against the force of gravity, the work done is:

W = force x distance

   = (25 x 9.8) x 20

   = 4900 J or 4.9 kJ

Another example, find the work done to raise a 600 kg steel beam from ground level to the top of a building 20 metres high. Force of gravity in newtons = 600 x 9.8 or 5880 N. Therefore, work done equals 5880 x 20, which is 117 600 joules, or 117.6 kJ.

The practical unit for heat calculations is the kilojoule (kJ) which is the heat needed to raise the temperature of approximately 0.24 kilograms of water through 1 degree Celsius.

In the customary system, the energy unit used in foods and dietetics is actually a kilocalorie, although it is referred to as a calorie. Therefore, the unit should be spelled with a capital C to distinguish it from other kinds of calories. One Calorie (kilocalorie) is equal to 4.1868 kilojoules and can be rounded to 4.2 kJ. Fig. 10-20. Note that the kilojoule is even smaller than a Calorie. For example, a 2000 Calorie daily diet would become a 8400 kilojoule diet or a 8.4 megajoule diet.

Power

  unit name: watt

  symbol: W

  definition—The watt is the power which gives rise to the production of energy at the rate of one joule per second (J/s). Fig. 10-21.

Power is the rate of doing work or expending energy. It can also be defined as the amount of work done in a given amount of time. The watt replaces many different customary and obsolete metric units. Fig. 10-22. In the previous section on energy or work, it was stated that roughly 5 joules of work is done in lifting 500 grams of butter to a height of 1 metre. If this work is done in 2 seconds then the rate of doing the work is 5 J/2 s = 2.5 J/s or 2.5 W. Since the watt is a relatively small unit, the prefixes kilo and mega are often used as follows:

  1 kW = 1000 watts

  1 MW = 1000 kW or 1 000 000 W

In the customary system, power is expressed in foot pound force per second, more commonly reffered to as foot-pounds per second. One horsepower is equal to 550 foot-pounds of work done in one second. The horsepower is as out of place in modern industry as the furlong. For practical purposes it is enough to remember that a horsepower is nearly 75 percent of a kilowatt or 1 hp = 3/4 kW. To convert horsepower to kilowatts, simply multiply by 0.75. For example, a 2.5 hp electric motor would become a 1.875 kW motor. This can be rounded to a 2 kW motor if high accuracy isn't required.

Until the adoption of SI, the watt was applied only to electrical energy. The watt will replace horsepower for automobile power units. The kilowatt (1000 watts) is roughly equal to 1-1/3 horsepower. One hp (horsepower) equals 745.700 W or 0.7457 kW. An 80 horsepower engine in a sub-compact car would become a 59 655 watt power or, rounded, to 60 kW. Using the watt and kilowatt as the units of power in all technical fields will eliminate the need for conversion factors. Fig. 10-23a,b. The kilowatt hour is not an SI unit because it uses the hour (3600 seconds) in the formula. However, it will still apply to measuring the amount of electricity used.

Density (mass per unit volume)

  unit words: kilogram per cubic metre

  symbol: kg/m³

  definition—Density is defined as the mass (weight) per unit volume. Specific gravity is internationally known as relative density.

The most common unit measure is the kilogram per cubic metre—symbol kg/m³. The other measures are the gram per cubic centimetre—symbol g/cm³, and the megagram per cubic metre—symbol Mg/m³. To figure density use one of the following formulas:

density = mass (weight) in kilograms per volume in cubic metres
density = mass (weight) in grams per volume in litres
density = mass (weight) in grams per volume in cubic centimetres
density = mass (weight) in megagrams per volume in cubic metres

The following can be used to illustrate the idea of density. If cubes that measure one decimetre on each side are cut from several materials including plastic foam, balsa wood, hardwood, aluminum, and steel are all painted red, these blocks would have many things in common including color, size, shape and volume. Fig. 10-24. They would differ, however, in one important respect, namely, density. Fig. 10-25. The plastic foam would have the least density while the steel would have the greatest density per unit of volume. The following is the density of common materials:

     gold—19.2   Mg/m³
     steel—7.83   Mg/m³
     aluminum—2.56 Mg/m³
     concrete—2.31 Mg/m³
     water—1.00 Mg/m³
     air at sea level—1.23 kg/m³

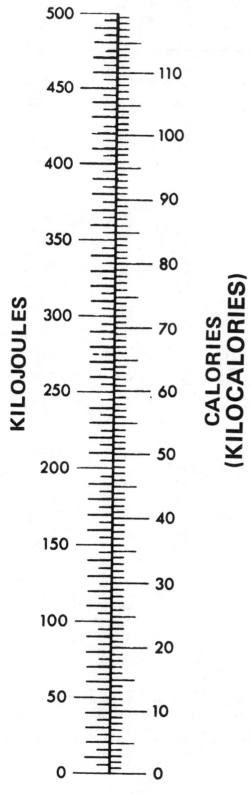

Fig. 10-20
Chart comparing kilojoules with large Calories.

POWER - WATT (W)

$$1 \text{ W} = 1 \text{ J/s} = 1 \text{ N·m/s}$$

POWER = rate of doing work

GAS METER   GAS ENGINE   GENERATOR

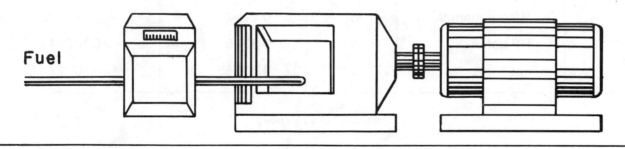

Fuel

HEAT POWER   MECHANICAL POWER   ELECTRICAL POWER

 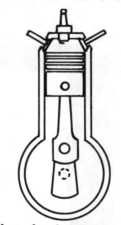 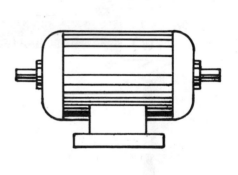

The watt (W) is the power which in 1 second gives rise to energy of 1 joule.

Fig. 10-21
The watt is the power which gives rise to the production of energy at the rate of one joule per second.

	FROM:	TO:	MULTIPLY BY:	RECIPROCAL:
Power	Btu/h	W	0.293 07	3.412 14
	Btu/min	W	1.758 427	0.056 869
	ft • 1bf/h	mW	0.376 62	2.655 22
	ft • 1bf/min	W	0.022 597	44.254
	HP metric	kW	0.735 50	1.359 62
	HP electric	kW	0.746	1.340 48
	HP mechanical	kW	0.745 70	1.341 02
	HP boiler	kW	9.809 5	0.101 94
	kgf • m/s	W	9.806 65	0.101 97

Fig. 10-22
Conversion chart for power.

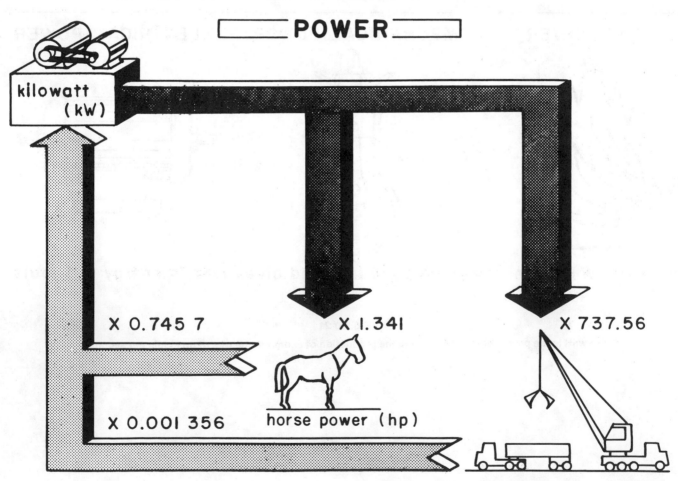

Fig. 10-23a
Visual chart to convert power units in metric to customary
and vice versa.

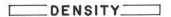

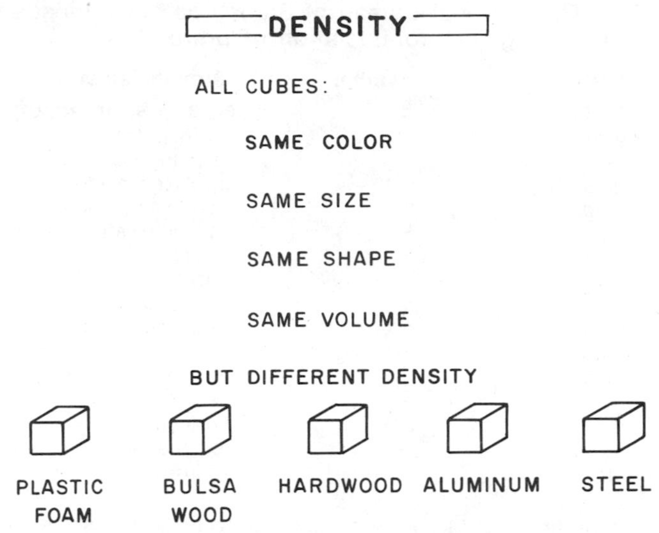
DENSITY
ALL CUBES:
SAME COLOR
SAME SIZE
SAME SHAPE
SAME VOLUME
BUT DIFFERENT DENSITY
PLASTIC FOAM
BULSA WOOD
HARDWOOD
ALUMINUM
STEEL

Fig. 10-24
These cubes differ only in their density.

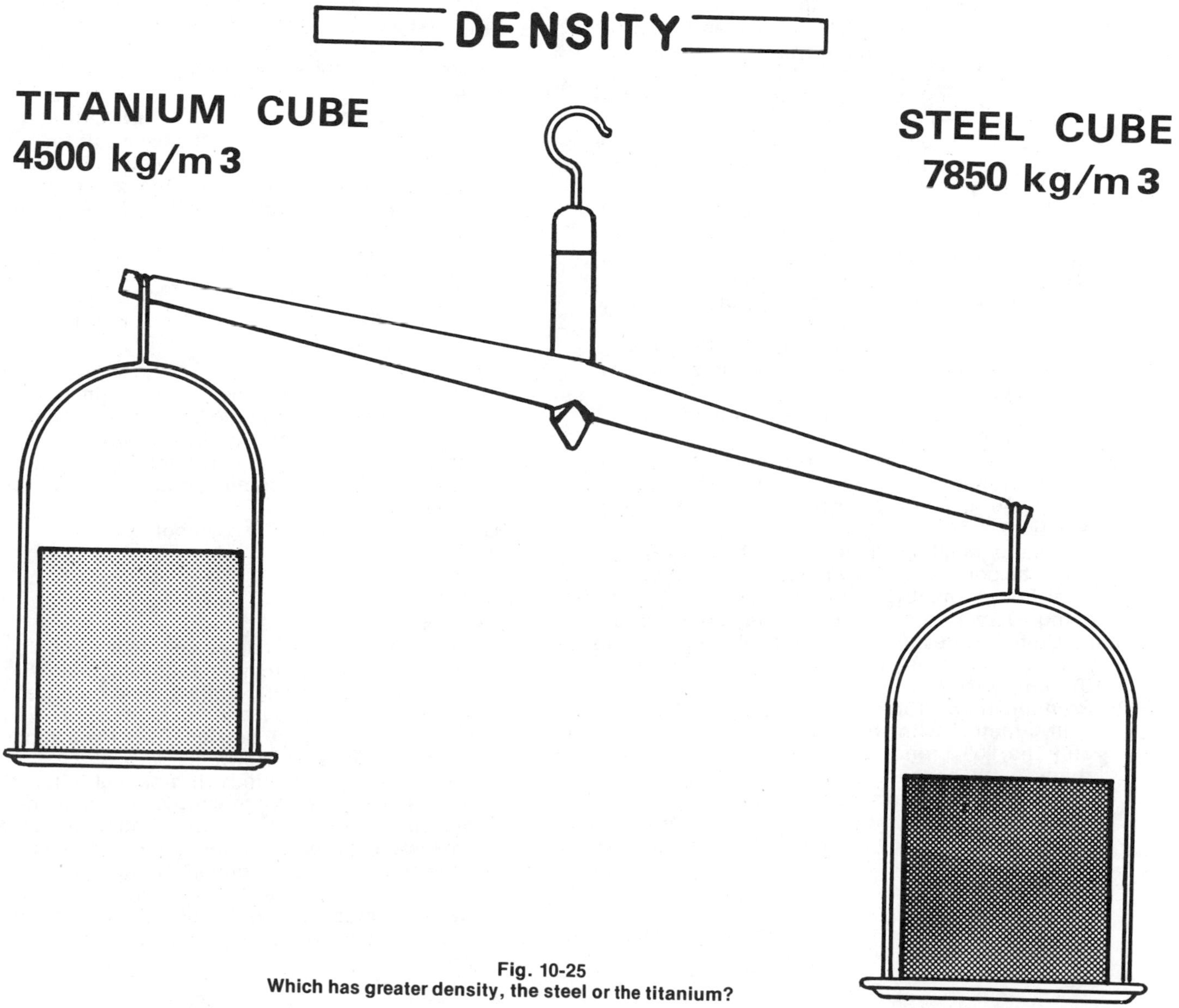
DENSITY
TITANIUM CUBE
4500 kg/m3
STEEL CUBE
7850 kg/m3

Fig. 10-25
Which has greater density, the steel or the titanium?

UNIT 11
RULES WHEN USING SI METRIC UNITS

The rules covered here are based on the bulletin, "The International System of Units (SI)," NBS Special Publication 330, 1974 Edition, and the bulletin, "ISO 1000," 1973, a publication of the International Organization for Standardization (ISO).

Basics

1. *Spelling.* Only two units and one prefix in the SI metric system may cause a spelling problem. The recommended spelling for the unit of length is the *metre* and for fluid volume the *litre.* You will often find the Americanized spelling of these words as meter and liter. Some controversy exists as to which is the correct spelling. Arguments for the *metre* and *litre* spelling are:

a. These are the common international spellings of English-speaking countries.

b. Their use eliminates confusion between the unit of measurement and a measuring instrument. For example, micrometre is a unit of length while micrometer is a measuring instrument.

c. All English-speaking countries now changing to metric including England, South Africa, Australia, New Zealand, Zambia and Canada have approved the *metre* and *litre* spelling.

d. Their use in the United States would promote uniformity of spelling—particularly in the English-speaking countries.

e. Their use will permit multinational companies to produce one set of instructional manuals for all plants.

f. Their use will aid in the smooth conversion to SI metric since metre and litre are closely identified with the modernized metric system.

g. Many American technical societies, industrial corporations and educational groups have adopted these spellings.

Arguments for the *meter* and *liter* spelling are:

a. These spellings have long been established in American English.

b. The other spellings look "foreign" or "technical" to many Americans.

c. These spellings have been in common use in most mathematics and science textbooks.

d. Language experts support and prefer these spellings.

e. The meter spelling when used with a prefix can never be confused with a measuring instrument.

Even though the ISO recommendation for the prefix meaning 10 (or 10 times) is *deca,* the common practice in the United States is to use the spelling *deka.* This is done to avoid confusion with the prefix for tenths (or 1/10), which is *deci.*

2. *Pronunciation.* Kilometre should be pronounced "kill-o-metre" with the accent on the *first* syllable and the "o" pronounced as in "oh". It does *not* rhyme with speedometer. The first syllable of a prefix should always be emphasized.

Pascal, the unit of pressure, should be pronounced "pas" as in "passage" and "cal" as in "local". Preferred "pass'-kal".

Joule—the pronunciation of the *ou* in joule should be like the *oo* in pool.

Candela—The accent is on the second syllable and is pronounced like dell.

Siemens—this is pronounced like seamen's.

The National Bureau of Standards recommends the following for pronunciation of prefixes:

Prefix	Symbol	Pronunciation *
exa	E	ex′a (a as in about)
peta	P	as in petal
tera	T	as in terrace
giga	G	jig a′(a as in about)
mega	M	as in megaphone
kilo	k	as in kilowatt
hecto	h	heck′toe
deka	da	deck′a (a as in about)
deci	d	as in decimal
centi	c	as in centipede
milli	m	as in military
micro	μ	as in microphone
nano	n	nan′oh (an as in ant)
pico	p	peek′oh
femto	f	fem′toe (fem as in feminine)
atto	a	as in anatomy

*The first syllable of every prefix is accented to assure that the prefix will retain its identity. Therefore, the preferred pronunciation of kilometre places the accent on the first syllable, not the second.

3. *Capitals.* The use of capitals in the units and prefixes is covered here and in the next two sections. Avoid the capitalization of unit names and prefixes (except degrees Celsius) unless they start a sentence. Unit symbols derived from proper names are capitalized however.

Example:

CORRECT	INCORRECT
The base unit for length is the metre. The following are the seven base units in the SI metric system:	The base unit for length is the metre. The following are the seven base units in the SI metric system:
metre	Metre
kilogram	Kilogram
second	Second
ampere	Ampere
kelvin	Kelvin
mole	Mole
candela	Candela

Remember, except when a unit (including the multiples and submultiples) is at the beginning of a sentence, the name is always written in small letters, even when the symbol for the unit is a capital letter or a combination of capital letters. Example:

Name	Symbol
hertz	Hz
kilonewton	kN
kilowatt	kW

Symbols

1. The spelling of unit names and their symbols must be exactly as shown in the following table (Fig. 11-1). Symbols for metric units should be lower case, except those named after persons. For example, the unit of force, the newton, uses the symbol N in honor of Sir Isaac Newton.

2. All metric terms begin with a capital letter if they begin a sentence. When written in a sentence, only *degree Celsius* is capitalized. All other metric terms are lower case except if they begin a sentence.

3. *Litre* and *metric ton* (tonne)* are special names for the derived SI units dm³ and Mg.

4. Symbols must always be printed in upright type, never in italics or cursive. For example, m upright, not *m.*

	Symbols in lower case			Symbols with capital letters
metre	m		kelvin	K
square metre	m²		degree Celsius	°C
cubic metre	m³		newton	N
litre	l or L*		pascal	Pa
	litre		joule	J
gram	g		watt	W
second	s		ampere	A
minute	min		volt	V
hour	h		ohm	Ω
metric ton tonne**	t		siemens	S
are	a		coulomb	C
candela	cd		farad	F
lumen	lm		weber	Wb
lux	lx		tesla	T
radian	rad		henry	H
steradian	sr		hertz	Hz
mole	mol			

Fig. 11-1

*The symbol L for litre has been recommended to the General Conference of Weights and Measures.

**The term "tonne" is used instead of megagram (Mg) in England, South Africa. Australia, New Zealand and Canada.

5. The symbol represents the unit and is the same in all languages.

6. The symbol does not change in the plural. For example, the symbol for two kilograms is 2 kg *not* 2 kgs. Remember, the plural "s" is never used with metric symbols.

7. Metric symbols are always written *without a period*. Remember, these are symbols, *not abbreviations* and, therefore, stand by themselves without a *period*.

8. When using the symbols for ohm (Ω)(for omega), micro (μ)(for mu), and other characters of the Greek alphabet, it is preferable to use a typed symbol if available. If not, spell out the word. Hand-drawn symbols may be used when necessary. Avoid use of a lower case u for micro.

   Correct
   μm or micrometre

   Incorrect
   um

9. The litre should be used only for volumes of liquids and gases. There is a problem in typing the symbol for litre since most typewriters use the same character for the lower case "ell" and the figure "one". Therefore, spell out the word litre if there is any chance for error. For example, type 11 litres rather than 11 l. In most other English-speaking countries, the script or italic "ell" is recommended. However, this practice is difficult when typing since the letter must be hand formed. For multiples and submultiples of the litre such as the millilitre and kilolitre, the symbols ml and kl can be typed since there is no chance for confusion.

Prefixes

1. The *name of the unit* (which immediately identifies it as a unit of length, mass, volume, force, etc.), together with a *prefix* (kilo-, milli, etc.) forms the complete word. Each prefix has a fixed meaning, and the same prefix is used for all SI units. The prefix indicates the relationship between the multiples and submultiples and the units. For example, the word kilometre indicates that it is a unit of length (metre) and that it is a thousand times a metre (kilo-) long. The following series of prefixes form larger or smaller units in combination with the unit. Fig. 11-2a,b.

PREFIX	SYMBOL		FACTOR BY WHICH UNIT IS TO BE MULTIPLIED	
exa		E	1 000 000 000 000 000 000	$= 10^{18}$
peta		P	1 000 000 000 000 000	$= 10^{15}$
tera-	Upper	T	1 000 000 000 000	$= 10^{12}$
giga-	Case	G	1 000 000 000	$= 10^{9}$
mega-	Symbols	M	1 000 000	$= 10^{6}$
kilo-		k	1 000	$= 10^{3}$
hecto-		h	100	$= 10^{2}$
deka-		da	10	$= 10^{1}$
deci-		d	0.1	$= 10^{-1}$
centi-	Lower	c	0.01	$= 10^{-2}$
milli-	Case	m	0.001	$= 10^{-3}$
micro-	Symbols	μ	0.000001	$= 10^{-6}$
nano-		n	0.000000001	$= 10^{-9}$
pico-		p	0.000 000 000 001	$= 10^{-12}$
femto-		f	0.000 000 000 000 001	$= 10^{-15}$
atto-		a	0.000 000 000 000 000 001	$= 10^{-18}$

Fig. 11-2a

2. The internationally agreed symbols for prefixes have general rules which apply as follows:

a. Preference is given to the use of prefixes related to the SI unit by powers of 10^{3}, for example: nano (10^{-9}) n, micro (10^{-6})μ, milli (10^{-3}) m, kilo (10^{3}) k, mega (10^{6}) M, and giga (10^{9}) G.

b. This is not a strict rule, however, and there are many times when units such as the centimetre (cm), hectare (ha) and cubic centimetre (cm³) are used.

3. Only the symbols of the five highest prefixes exa-, peta-, tera, giga-, and mega- are written with capital letters. All other prefixes must use lower case.

4. A prefix in combination with the name of the unit forms a single word. For example, the prefix milli- combined with the unit metre is the word millimetre.

PREFIXES, EXPONENTS, and SYMBOLS

Decimal Form	Exponent or Power	Prefix	Pronunciation	Symbol	Meaning
1 000 000 000 000 000 000	$= 10^{18}$	exa	ex´-a	E	quintillion
1 000 000 000 000 000	$= 10^{15}$	peta	pet´-a	P	quadrillion
1 000 000 000 000	$= 10^{12}$	tera	těr´ á	T	trillion
1 000 000 000	$= 10^{9}$	giga	ji´ gá	G	billion
1 000 000	$= 10^{6}$	mega	měg´ á	M	million
1 000	$= 10^{3}$	kilo	kǐl´ ō	k	thousand
100	$= 10^{2}$	hecto	hěk´ tō	h	hundred
10	$= 10^{1}$	deka	děk´ â	da	ten
1					base unit
0.1	$= 10^{-1}$	deci	děs´ ī	d	tenth
0.01	$= 10^{-2}$	centi	sěn´ tǐ	c	hundredth
0.001	$= 10^{-3}$	milli	mǐl ǐ	m	thousandth
0.000 001	$= 10^{-6}$	micro	mī´ krǒ	μ	millionth
0.000 000 001	$= 10^{-9}$	nano	năn´ ǒ	n	billionth
0.000 000 000 001	$= 10^{-12}$	pico	péc ǒ	p	trillionth
0.000 000 000 000 001	$= 10^{-15}$	femto	fěm´ tō	f	quadrillionth
0.000 000 000 000 000 001	$= 10^{-18}$	atto	ăt´ tō	a	quintrillionth

▒ **most commonly used**

11-2b

5. Only one prefix is applied at one time to a given unit. Example: nanometre nm, not millimicrometre m•m.

6. While the base unit for mass, the kilogram, already has a prefix, the prefixes should be applied to the unit gram. In other words, the names of decimal multiples and submultiples of the unit are formed by attaching prefixes to the word gram. For example, the metric ton or tonne is a megagram (Mg) and not a kilokilogram (kkg).

7. While preference is given to prefixes related by powers of 10^3, the following are common exceptions:

centi-   The centimetre is most commonly used for everyday practical measurements including clothing measurements. It is also used for a square centimetre (cm²) and for a cubic centimetre (cm³).

deci-   The decimetre is not normally used as a unit of length except for teaching purposes. However, there is some chance that it might be used as a unit in building materials for such items as floor tile. A 2 decimetre square tile would be close to the current 9" square. The cubic decimetre (dm³) is the equivalent of a litre.

deka-   deka is rarely used except for instructional purposes.

hecto-   hecto is used primarily in hectare (a unit of land measurement).

8. A prefix symbol combined with a unit symbol forms an entirely new unit symbol. For example, the symbol for the unit metre is m while the symbol for unit kilometre is km. The symbol km consists of a prefix symbol k and a unit symbol m. This is an important rule to remember when figuring area and volume. Example: a cube with the dimensions

1 m x 1 m x 1 m

has a volume of

1 m³ or 1 cubic metre.

A cube with the dimensions

1 km x 1 km x 1 km

has a volume of

1 cubic kilometre, which is equal to
1 000 m x 1 000 m x 1 000 m or
1 000 000 000 m³ .

Expressing Numerical Values in SI Metric

1. *Space between value and unit.* A space must always be left between the numerals and the symbol of the unit. In most English-speaking countries converting to the metric system an exception to this rule is made for the symbol for degree Celsius (°C), with no space used between the value and the degree symbol. For example:

Correct	Incorrect
300 ml	300ml
15°C or 15 °C	15 C or 15c
15 g	15g
150 km	150km
30 litres	30l

2. *Decimal marker (or sign).* The decimal point at the bottom of the line will be the accepted method in the United States for the decimal marker, or sign. In countries where the metric system has been in use a long time, the practice is to use a comma as the decimal marker or sign, not the decimal point. The United Kingdom uses a raised British dot as the decimal marker. While the comma is the decimal marker or sign used in the vast majority of traditionally metric countries, it will not be used in the United States. South Africa accepted the comma as the decimal marker in 1971 and Rhodesia in 1972. This will cause no problem in interpretation of information if rule #3 is rigidly adhered to.

3. *Thousandths marker. Do not use the comma to separate large numbers in groups of three.* Instead, always use a space. Groups of three digits before and after the decimal marker should be separated by a small space (a full space in typing and a half space in printing). *No space is required when the numerical value does not exceed four decimal places.* For example 1250 m not 1 250 m. The elimination of the comma as a thousandths marker will make the readings easy to follow regardless of whether a period or comma is used as the decimal marker. For example, 31 547,436 214 or 31 547.436 214 could not be confused. This practice is for tabular material only but not for drafting practice.

4. Always place a zero in front of the decimal point when the numerical value is *less than one.* For example, 0.025 mg is correct while .025 mg is incorrect.

5. Since the metric system is a decimal system, preference should be given to decimal fractions of units rather than simple fractions. Example:

Preferred	Not Preferred
0.25 kg	1/4 kg
500 ml	1/2 litre

6. Use a prefix with the resulting numerical value in the 0.1 to 1 000 range except where certain prefixes have been agreed on for a particular use such as MPa (megapascals). Example:

Preferred	Not Preferred
20 km	20 000 m
45 m	45 000 mm or 0.045 km
5 mm	0.005 m

This usually means that lengths of less than 1 m are expressed as mm while lengths of more than 1000 m are expressed as km. However, the exception to this rule is that, in texts and drawings that are close

together, *do not mix* the prefixes regardless of the size of the unit. For example, if the drawing is to be all in millimetres (as all engineering drawings will be), then the correct unit would be 1250 mm not 1.250 m.

7. Remember, plurals are never used with symbols. For example, 2 kg not 2 kgs. However, when the name of the unit is written out, plurals are used. It should be written as 2 kilograms not 2 kilogram. Another example would be 6 metres per second not 6 metre per second.

8. *Remember that a period is not used after the symbols except at the end of the sentence.* Even then it is preferable to use a space or half space before the period.

9. The preposition per- indicates the ratio or function of division. It should not be used with SI symbols. Instead an oblique fractional stroke or slash is used to indicate division with the symbol to the left as numerator and the symbol to the right as denominator.
   For example:
   speed or velocity: 5 m/s means 5 metres per second
   density: 1 kg/m³ equals 1 kilogram per cubic metre

10. Remember to use the complete correct symbol or write out the unit, but do not mix the two. For example, 60 kilometres per hour or 60 km/h. Do not write 60 kilometres/hour.

11. When compound units are formed by multiplication, always use the product dot (center dot) as a multiplication sign. For example:
    N•m equals newtons times metres. When writing out the name of this unit, a hyphen or space is used but never a center dot. For example, either newton-metre or newton metre is correct.

12. Prefixes should not be used in the denominator of a compound formula except for the kilogram (a base unit). For example, 2 km/s = 2000 m/s (metres per second) rather than 1 m/ms = 1 metre per millisecond. However, use 200 J/kg not 2 dJ/g.

13. The symbols m² and m³ should be used whenever possible in writing square metre and cubic metre in SI metric units. In other words, in all SI metric units, the raised or superior (superscript) 2 and 3 should be used for square and cubic measure. Most typewriters do not have the superior 2 and 3. However, the m² and m³ can be typed by using a special sheet containing these raised numbers. If you do not wish to adjust the machine it is suggested that until such time as the typewriters are modified the name of the unit be written out in full rather than use an incorrect abbreviation such as sq m or cu m.

14. If dual dimensioning is to be used in text material, always show the non-SI units in parentheses. For example, 16 kilograms (35 pounds) or 50.8 mm (2 in).

15. Avoid mixing units, symbols, or words in SI metric.

Examples:

Correct	Incorrect
14.35 m	14 m 350 mm
metres per second	metre/second or metre/s

16. Use only symbols when showing mathematical operation.

Examples:

Correct

$1° = \pi/180$ rad

Incorrect

one degree = π radian ÷ 180

17. Never use slang or obsolete coined words in SI metric.

Examples:

kilos to mean kilograms (write out kilograms or use symbol kg)

cc or c.c. to mean cubic centimetre (In SI cc means centi centi)

metric pound to mean 500 grams or 0.5 kilogram

centigrade to mean degree Celsius

Rules for Computer Use

Using the SI metric system on computers creates several special problems not encountered in other areas. These include:

1. Computers only make printouts with capital letters and, therefore, the correct symbols can't be used for most units. For example, millimetres would printout as MM rather than the correct mm. It would be impossible to tell which prefix is being used for MW for example, Does this mean megawatt (MW) or milliwatt (mW)?

2. Computers can't produce superscript ^{2} and ^{3} as well as the degree sign (°). They can't produce the symbols for the Greek letter mu (μ) for micro or omega Ω for ohm.

3. The number of mathematical units that can be printed on a single line, such as on cost control cards, are limited. For example, if the original numbers are in inches, the equivalent numbers in millimetres will be larger since a millimetre is about 1/25 of an inch. For example, 1 345 274 inches would be 34 169 959 millimetres.

There are several solutions to these problems:

1. Increase the readout capability of the computers.

2. Write the units out in full and don't use symbols

3. Make use of recommended symbols only for use with systems having limited character sets.

Base Units	Proposed Symbol
metre	M
kilogram	KG
second	S
ampere	A
kelvin	K
mole	MOL
candela	CD
Supplementary Units	
radian	RAD
steradian	SR
Derived Units	
hertz	HZ
newton	N
pascal	PA
joule	J
watt	W
coulomb	C
volt	V
farad	F
ohm	OHM
siemens	SIE
weber	WB
tesla	T
henry	H
lumen	LM
lux	LX
Prefixes	
tera	T
giga	G
mega	MA
kilo	K
hecto	H
deca	DA
deci	D
centi	C
milli	M
micro	U
nano	N
pico	P
femto	F
atto	A

UNIT 12
CONVERSION METHODS AND TECHNIQUES

Every effort should be made to "think metric" and avoid conversion. However, you must also know how to make quick and accurate conversions from metric to customary and vice versa. This need for conversion will be greatest during the early stages of metric change-over. There are many reasons why conversion from non-SI metric units to SI metric units and vice versa will always be important.

1. *Conversion of all the major facets of American life to SI metric units will be a long and extended process.* During this conversion period, both systems of measurement will be in common use. Even when the conversion period is completed, SI metric measurement will be the predominant, but not exclusive, measuring system used in the United States.

2. *For many years, products will be assembled of parts that are identical in design and standards, but manufactured in different measuring systems.* Some identical parts will be made in the metric measurement system and others will be produced in the customary measurement system, depending on the sub-contractors' interests and capabilities in using metric measurement. Production drawings that show *dual dimensioning* will allow for this practice, since one manufacturer can use the customary measurements and another can employ the metric measurements to make the identical parts.

3. *Many products will phase in metrically designed and produced parts with existing parts designed and produced in customary units.* Therefore, the metrically designed parts must interface (fit together) with inch designed parts. For example, the telephone is assembled with a combination of parts, some to metric specifications and others to customary specifications. Fig. 12-1.

Fig. 12-1
Many products such as the telephone are assembled of parts, some of which are made to customary standards and others to metric standards.

4. *All measurements having customary units found in books, magazines and newspapers must be converted to metric units.* Everything published prior to the conversion period will be in the customary units.

5. *All inventory records* and other types of records that must be updated will need to be converted to metric units.

There are *five* basic methods of converting from the customary (English or inch-pound) to the metric or vice versa.

1. Manual Computation Using Conversion Formula:

To change from inches to millimetres you would check Fig. 12-2 or 12-3 and find that you must multiply inches by 25.4 to obtain the equivalent in millimetres. For example, 2 inches would equal 2 x 25.4 for a product total of 50.8 mm.

Example
$$\begin{array}{r} 25.4 \\ \times\,2 \\ \hline 50.8 \text{ mm} \end{array}$$

To change from millimetres to inches you must multiply by 0.03937 (a much more difficult job). For example, 25 millimetres would be equal to 0.98425 inch.

Example
$$\begin{array}{r} 0.03937 \\ \times\,25 \\ \hline 19685 \\ 7874 \\ \hline 0.984\,25 \text{ inch} \end{array}$$

(this should be rounded off to 0.984")

To change ounces to grams, you must multiply by 28.35. For example 14 ounces would equal exactly 396.9 g (usually rounded off to 397 grams).

Example
$$\begin{array}{r} 28.35 \\ \times\,14 \\ \hline 113\,40 \\ 283\,5 \\ \hline 396.90 \end{array}$$

2. Using a mechanical slide converter or conversion calculators.

There are a wide variety of plastic and cardboard slide converters that can be used for quick conversion. These are primarily useful for getting the "feel" for metrics. The simpler ones give only approximate results and do not provide accurate conversion figures. Fig. 12-4. Usually the simple converters include length, mass or weight, area, volume (liquid capacity), and temperature. These slide converters are very easy to use and are useful in everyday practice. For example, if you wish to find the number of centimetres in 5 inches, set the slide to 5 and read the results, which is about 12.6 or 12.7 centimetres (the exact equivalent is 12.7 cm). If you wish to find the number of kilograms in 60 pounds, set the slide at 60 under pounds and read the results as approximately 27 kilograms (27.2 kg is closer). The more complicated plastic converters will give very *accurate* readouts to as many as nine decimal places. Some of these technical converters also include conversions for force, torque, pressure and stress, and other derived units. Fig. 12-5.

3. Using Conversion Tables.

Many booklets and books include extensive conversion tables for length, mass or weight, volume and all other units.* These tables printed in tabular form range from relatively simple and limited conversions to very extensive and highly accurate tables. For example, one large booklet covering only *inch to millimetre* conversion tables has 1000 entries per page for 64 pages, making a total of over 64 000 entries. Fig. 12-6. Very extensive tables of this kind are used primarily in engineering. A major problem in using them is the extreme care that must be taken in reading the conversion correctly to avoid errors.

4. Using Mini-calculators.

The ideal instrument to use for converting is the mini-calculator, widely available for homes, offices and businesses in a wide variety of sizes and types. Fig. 12-7. The machine will operate on small batteries, storage batteries that can be charged, standard house current, or a combination of any of these. Some types

*An excellent reference of this type is *Units of Weight and Measure*, U.S. Government Printing Office, NBS Miscellaneous Publication 286.

CUSTOMARY TO METRIC		LENGTH	METRIC TO CUSTOMARY	
1 inch	= 25.40 millimetres - mm		1 millimetre	= 0.03937 inch - in
1 inch	= 2.540 centimetres - cm		1 centimetre	= 0.3937 inch - in
1 foot	= 30.480 centimetres - cm		1 metre	= 39.37 inches - in
1 foot	= 0.3048 metre - m		1 metre	= 3.2808 feet - ft
1 yard	= 91.440 centimetres - cm		1 metre	= 1.0936 yards - yd
1 yard	= 0.9144 metre - m			

CUSTOMARY TO METRIC		AREA	METRIC TO CUSTOMARY	
1 square inch	= 645.16 square millimetres - mm²		1 square millimetre	= 0.00155 square inch - in²
1 square inch	= 6.4516 square centimetres - cm²		1 square centimetre	= 0.1550 square inch - in²
1 square foot	= 929.03 square centimetres - cm²		1 square metre	= 10.7640 square feet - ft²
1 square foot	= 0.0929 square metre - m²		1 square metre	= 1.196 square yards - yd²
1 square yard	= 0.826 square metre - m²			

CUSTOMARY TO METRIC		MASS (Weight)	METRIC TO CUSTOMARY	
1 ounce (dry)	= 28.35 grams - g		1 gram	= 0.03527 ounce - oz
1 pound	= 0.4536 kilogram - kg		1 kilogram	= 2.2046 pounds - lb

CUSTOMARY TO METRIC		VOLUME (Capacity)	METRIC TO CUSTOMARY	
1 pint (liq)	= 0.473 litre = 0.473 cm³		1 litre	= 1000 cm³* = 0.5283 pint (liq)
1 quart (liq)	= 0.9463 litre = 0.9463 dm³**		1 litre	= 1 dm³** = 1.0567 quarts (liq)
1 gallon (liq)	= 3.7853 litre = 3.7853 dm³**		1 litre	= 1 dm³** = 0.26417 gallon (liq)

* cubic centimetre
** cubic decimetre

Fig. 12-2
Common equivalents and conversions.

METRIC UNITS FOR COMMON USE

Quantity	Metric unit and symbol	Conversion Factors (approximate) Customary to Metric Units	Metric to Customary Units
Length	millimetre (mm)	1 in = 25.4 mm*	1 mm = 0.0394 in
	centimetre (cm)	1 in = 2.54 cm*	1 cm = 0.394 in
		1 ft = 30.5 cm	
	metre (m)	1 yd = 0.914 m	1 m = 3.28 ft
	kilometre (km)	1 mi = 1.61 km	1 km = 0.62 mi
Weight (Mass)	gram (g)	1 oz = 28.3 g	1 g = 0.0353 oz
	kilogram (kg)	1 lb = 454 g	1 kg = 2.2 lb
	metric ton or tonne (t)	1 long ton = 1.02 t	1 t = 0.98 long ton
Area	square centimetre (cm²)	1 in² = 6.45 cm²	1 cm² = 0.155 in²
	square metre (m²)	1 ft² = 929 cm²	1 m² = 10.8 ft²
		1 yd² = 0.836 m²	1 m² = 1.2 yd²
	hectare (ha)	1 acre = 0.405 ha	1 ha = 2.47 acres
	square kilometre (km²)	1 mi² = 2.59 km²	1 km² = 0.386 mi²
Volume	cubic centimetre (cm³)	1 in³ = 16.4 cm³	1 cm³ = 0.061 in³
	cubic metre (m³)	1 ft³ = 28 300 cm³	1 m³ = 35.3 ft³
		1 yd³ = 0.765 m³	1 m³ = 1.31 yd³
Volume (liquids and gases)	millimetre (ml)	1 fl oz = 29.6 ml	1 ml = 0.033 8 fl oz
	litre (L or l)	1 liq qt = 0.946 litre	1 litre = 1.057 liq qt
	kilolitre (kl)	1 gal = 3.79 litres	1 kl = 264 gal
Time Interval	second (s) minute (min) hour (h)		
Speed	kilometre per hour (km/h)	1 mph = 1.61 km/h	1 km/h = 0.621 mph
Pressure	kilopascal (kPa)	1 psi = 6.89 kPa	1 kPa = 0.145 psi
Energy	kilojoule (kJ)	1 Btu = 1.06 kJ	1 kJ = 0.948 Btu
		1 kilocalorie* = 4.19 kJ	1 kJ = 0.239 kilocalorie**
Power	kilowatt (kW)	1 hp = 0.746 kW	1 kW = 1.34 hp
Temperature	degree Celsius (°C)	°C = 5/9 (°F-32)	°F = 9/5°C + 32

* Accurate

**kilocalorie, commonly called "Calorie" is a non-SI metric unit

Fig. 12-3
Table for making conversions from metric to non-metric and vice versa.

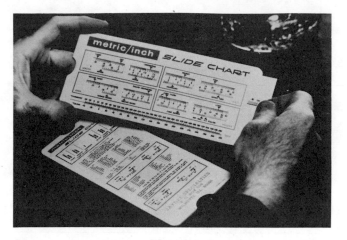

Fig. 12-4
This simple metric inch slide converter will be useful in getting the "feel" for metric units.

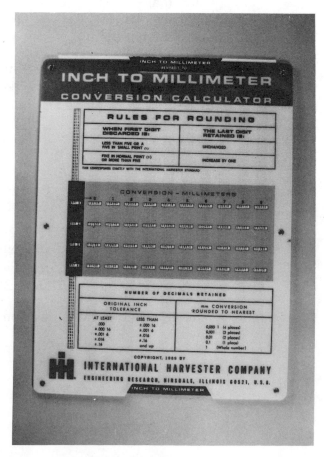

Fig. 12-5
Slide converters that are used in more technical areas give very precise results.

CONVERSION TABLE
in/mm

frac	in	mm	frac	in	mm	frac	in	mm	frac	in	mm	frac	in	mm
	.001	0.0254		.051	1.2954		.101	2.5654		.152	3.8608		.201	5.1054
	.002	0.0508		.052	1.3208		.102	2.5908		.153	3.8862		.202	5.1308
	.003	0.0762		.053	1.3462		.103	2.6162		.154	3.9116		.203	5.1562
	.004	0.1016		.054	1.3716		.104	2.6416		.155	3.9370	13/64	.2031	5.1594
	.005	0.1270		.055	1.3970		.105	2.6670		.156	3.9624		.204	5.1816
	.006	0.1524		.056	1.4224		.106	2.6924	5/32	.1562	3.9687		.205	5.2070
	.007	0.1778		.057	1.4478		.107	2.7178		.157	3.9878		.206	5.2324
	.008	0.2032		.058	1.4732		.108	2.7432		.1575	4.0000		.207	5.2578
	.009	0.2286		.059	1.4986		.109	2.7686		.158	4.0132		.208	5.2832
	.010	0.2540		.060	1.5240	7/64	.1094	2.7781		.159	4.0386		.209	5.3086
	.011	0.2794		.061	1.5494		.110	2.7940		.160	4.0640		.210	5.3340
	.012	0.3048		.062	1.5948		.111	2.8194		.161	4.0894		.211	5.3594
	.013	0.3302	1/16	.0625	1.5875		.112	2.8448		.162	4.1148		.212	5.3848
	.014	0.3556		.063	1.6002		.113	2.8702		.163	4.1402		.213	5.4102
	.015	0.3810		.064	1.6256		.114	2.8956		.164	4.1656		.214	5.4356
1/64	.0156	0.3969		.065	1.6510		.115	2.9210		.165	4.1910		.215	5.4610
	.016	0.4064		.066	1.6764		.116	2.9464		.166	4.2164		.216	5.4864
	.017	0.4318		.067	1.7018		.117	2.9718		.167	4.2418		.217	5.5118
	.018	0.4572		.068	1.7272		.118	2.9972		.168	4.2672		.218	5.5372
	.019	0.4826		.069	1.7526		.1181	3.0000		.169	4.2926	7/32	.2187	5.5562
	.020	0.5080		.070	1.7780		.119	3.0226		.170	4.3180		.219	5.5626
	.021	0.5334		.071	1.8034		.120	3.0480		.171	4.3434		.220	5.5880
	.022	0.5588		.072	1.8288		.121	3.0734	11/64	.1719	4.3656		.221	5.6134
	.023	0.5842		.073	1.8542		.122	3.0988		.172	4.3688		.222	5.6388
	.024	0.6096		.074	1.8796		.123	3.1242		.173	4.3942		.223	5.6642
	.025	0.6350		.075	1.9050		.124	3.1496		.174	4.4196		.224	5.6896
	.026	0.6604		.076	1.9304	1/8	.125	3.1750		.175	4.4450		.225	5.7150
	.027	0.6858		.077	1.9558		.126	3.2004		.176	4.4704		.226	5.7404
	.028	0.7112		.078	1.9812		.127	3.2258		.177	4.4958		.227	5.7658
	.029	0.7366	5/64	.0781	1.9844		.128	3.2512		.178	4.5212		.228	5.7912
	.030	0.7620		.0787	2.0000		.129	3.2766		.179	4.5466		.229	5.8166
	.031	0.7874		.079	2.0066		.130	3.3020		.180	4.5720		.230	5.8420
1/32	.0312	0.7937		.080	2.0320		.131	3.3274		.181	4.5974		.231	5.8674
	.032	0.8128		.081	2.0574		.132	3.3528		.182	4.6228		.232	5.8928
	.033	0.8382		.082	2.0828		.133	3.3782		.183	4.6482		.233	5.9182
	.034	0.8636		.083	2.1082		.134	3.4036		.184	4.6736		.234	5.9436
	.035	0.8890		.084	2.1336		.135	3.4290		.185	4.6990	15/64	.2344	5.9531
	.036	0.9144		.085	2.1590		.136	3.4544		.186	4.7244		.235	5.9690
	.037	0.9398		.086	2.1844		.137	3.4798		.187	4.7498		.236	5.9944
	.038	0.9652		.087	2.2098		.138	3.5052	3/16	.1875	4.7625		.2362	6.0000
	.039	0.9906		.088	2.2352		.139	3.5306		.188	4.7752		.237	6.0198
	.0394	1.0000		.089	2.2606		.140	3.5560		.189	4.8006		.238	6.0452
	.040	1.0160		.090	2.2860	9/64	.1406	3.5719		.190	4.8260		.239	6.0706
	.041	1.0414		.091	2.3114		.141	3.5814		.191	4.8514		.240	6.0960
	.042	1.0668		.092	2.3368		.142	3.6068		.192	4.8768		.241	6.1214
	.043	1.0922		.093	2.3622		.143	3.6322		.193	4.9022		.242	6.1468
	.044	1.1176	3/32	.0937	2.3812		.144	3.6576		.194	4.9276		.243	6.1722
	.045	1.1430		.094	2.3876		.145	3.6830		.195	4.9530		.244	6.1976
	.046	1.1684		.095	2.4130		.146	3.7084		.196	4.9784		.245	6.2230
3/64	.0469	1.1906		.096	2.4384		.147	3.7338		.1969	5.0000		.246	6.2484
	.047	1.1938		.097	2.4638		.148	3.7592		.197	5.0038		.247	6.2738
	.048	1.2192		.098	2.4892		.149	3.7846		.198	5.0292		.248	6.2992
	.049	1.2446		.099	2.5146		.150	3.8100		.199	5.0546		.249	6.3246
	.050	1.2700		.100	2.5400		.151	3.8354		.200	5.0800	1/4	.250	6.3500

Fig. 12-6
Table for conversion of decimal inches to millimetres.

Fig. 12-7
Mini-calculators are available in several different sizes and types that can be used for making conversions.

are completely portable, using batteries when necessary and house current when available. The number of different mathematical functions that can be done on the machine depends on its quality and cost. All mini-calculators can add, subtract, divide and multiply. Others can do percentages, square roots, and other mathematical functions. In buying a mini-calculator for metric conversion work, *be sure that it has a constant or memory key.* This is usually a separate key or switch marked "k" or "m". This key is very important for use in conversion, because once the constant factor has been fed into the machine, a whole series of calculations can be done. The calculator also can be set for the number of decimal places that you wish to carry out for the particular result. Normally, two places beyond the decimal point for the metric result is all that is necessary for most work. In converting inches to millimetres, first turn on the constant key. (1) Feed in 25.4, which will be the constant. (2) Add the times sign. (3) Add the number of inches. For example, if 2 is fed in, the result will be 50.8. (4) Clear the reading, using just the clear (C) button, not the all clear (AC) button. (5) Press 3 and the result will be 76.2. Any number of conversions can be made using the same constant.

Because the mini-calculators function only on the decimal system, it is necessary that all length measurements be in decimals instead of simple fractions. You must change the fractions to decimals before making the conversion. While you can make fraction conversion on the calculator, it is simpler to have a table, Fig. 12-8, that shows the decimal equivalent of common fractions. For example, if the inch dimension 2-5/16" must be converted, find the decimal equivalent for 5/16 on the table, which is 0.3125". Place a 2 in front of it for a total of 2.3125 before feeding into the machine. The result is exactly 58.7375, and this can be rounded to 58.74 mm.

For the common conversion, only the factors shown in Fig. 12-2 will be needed to make conversions. However, for more technical work, use Fig. 12-9 for conversion of customary units to equivalent values in SI metric units.

By using the mini-calculator the chance of errors is very slight. The main error that can creep in is the placement of the decimal point. However, many calculators allow you to feed in the decimal point. For example, in converting 2-1/2 inches (2.5") to metric it is important that the final result be 63.5 mm not 635 mm or 6.35 mm. This is why it is important for the user of the metric system to "think metric." If you have a mental picture that 2 inches is approximately 50 mm, four inches is approximately 100 mm, and 1 foot is approximately 300 mm, then you will be able to sense if the answer is right or wrong. The same is true in converting other measurements such as weight, area and volume.

A mini-calculator designed specifically for metric conversion is available. This calculator/converter has a total of 41 functions: 36 conversion functions as well as addition, subtraction, multiplication and percentage. Fig. 12-10. The unit can be used either as a calculator or for conversion. The 36 metric to non-metric and non-metric to metric conversions include the following:

LENGTH	AREA	VOLUME	MASS	LIQUID
in→cm	in²→cm²	in³→cm³	lb→kg	oz→ml
ft→m	ft²→m²	ft³→m³	oz→gm	qt→litre
yd→m	yd²→m²	yd³→m³	kg→lb	gal→litre
mi→km	mi²→km²	mi³→km³	gm→oz	ml→oz
cm→in	cm²→in²	cm³→in³		litre→qt
m→ft	m²→ft²	m³→ft³	**Temperature**	litre→gal
m→yd	m²→yd²	m³→yd³	°F→°C	
km→mi	km²→mi²	km³→mi³	°C→°F	

Note, however, that there is no inch to millimetre (in→mm) conversion key. This is the function that would be used most frequently in converting drawings and other engineering data in which the customary measurements are in decimal inches.

5. Using a Computer Program.

Most large industries and businesses that have computer time available will use this method for making conversions. Fig. 12-11. A program for metric conversion will be stored in the machine. Any number of customary measurements of the same units, length for example, can be fed into the computer, and the readout will show the metric equivalents arranged in order from largest to smallest (or vice versa). For example, if a drawing is made in the inch system with 25 different dimensions, these can be fed into the computer in any order and the printout will show the equivalents from largest to smallest or the reverse.

Accuracy of Conversion from Non-SI Units to SI Units

The degree of accuracy in converting will depend on the use of the final results. The following are several levels of accuracy: (1) Convert the customary unit to the exact equivalent in SI. To convert 1.475 inches to millimetres, you must multiply by 25.4 for a result of 31.648 4 millimetres. This exact conversion is too

Fractional Inch-Millimetre Equivalents

Fractional Inches							Millimetres	Decimal Inches
Inch	1/2	1/4	1/8	1/16	1/32	1/64		
						1	0.397	0.015 625
					1	2	0.794	0.031 25
						3	1.191	0.046 875
				1	2	4	1.588	0.062 5
						5	1.984	0.078 125
					3	6	2.381	0.093 75
						7	2.778	0.109 375
			1	2	4	8	3.175	0.125 0
						9	3.572	0.140 625
					5	10	3.969	0.156 25
						11	4.366	0.171 875
				3	6	12	4.762	0.187 5
						13	5.159	0.203 125
					7	14	5.556	0.218 75
						15	5.953	0.234 375
		1	2	4	8	16	6.350	0.250 0
						17	6.747	0.265 625
					9	18	7.144	0.281 25
						19	7.541	0.296 875
				5	10	20	7.938	0.312 5
						21	8.334	0.328 125
					11	22	8.731	0.343 75
						23	9.128	0.359 375
			3	6	12	24	9.525	0.375 0
						25	9.922	0.390 625
					13	26	10.319	0.406 25
						27	10.716	0.421 875
				7	14	28	11.112	0.437 5
						29	11.509	0.453 125
					15	30	11.906	0.468 75
						31	12.303	0.484 375
	1	2	4	8	16	32	12.700	0.500 0
						33	13.097	0.515 625
					17	34	13.494	0.531 25
						35	13.891	0.546 875
				9	18	36	14.288	0.562 5

Fig. 12-8

If length measurements are given in fractions of an inch, use this table to convert to decimals; add this amount to the full inch measurements. For example, if the customary measurement is 4 13/32, change this number to 4.40625 and multiply by 25.4 to obtain the result in millimetres.

Fractional Inches							Millimetres	Decimal Inches
Inch	1/2	1/4	1/8	1/16	1/32	1/64		
						37	14.684	0.578 125
					19	38	15.081	0.593 75
						39	15.478	0.609 375
			5	10	20	40	15.875	0.625 0
						41	16.272	0.640 625
					21	42	16.669	0.656 25
						43	17.066	0.671 875
				11	22	44	17.462	0.687 5
						45	17.859	0.703 125
					23	46	18.256	0.718 75
						47	18.653	0.734 375
		3	6	12	24	48	19.050	0.750 0
						49	19.447	0.765 625
					25	50	19.844	0.781 25
						51	20.241	0.796 875
				13	26	52	20.638	0.812 5
						53	21.034	0.828 125
					27	54	21.431	0.843 75
						55	21.828	0.859 375
			7	14	28	56	22.225	0.875 0
						57	22.622	0.890 625
					29	58	23.019	0.906 25
						59	23.416	0.921 875
				15	30	60	23.812	0.937 5
						61	24.209	0.953 125
					31	62	24.606	0.968 75
						63	25.003	0.984 375
1	2	4	8	16	32	64	25.400	1.000 0

MEASUREMENT UNITS AND CONVERSION

ACCELERATION

Unit	Multiply by	to get	Multiply by	to get
foot per second per second (ft/s^2)	3.048 000*E-01	metre per second per second (m/s^2)	3.280 840 E+00	(ft/s^2)
inch per second per second (in/s^2)	2.540 000*E-02	metre per second per second (m/s^2)	3.937 008 E+01	(in/s^2)

ANGULAR MOMENTUM

Unit	Multiply by	to get	Multiply by	to get
pound foot squared per second ($lb \cdot ft^2/s$)	4.214 011 E-02	kilogram metre squared per second ($kg \cdot m^2/s$)	2.373 036 E+01	($lb \cdot ft^2/s$)
pound inch squared per second ($lb \cdot in^2/s$)	2.926 397 E-04	kilogram metre squared per second ($kg \cdot m^2/s$)	3.417 171 E+03	($lb \cdot in^2/s$)
ounce inch squared per second ($oz \cdot in^2/s$)	1.828 998 E-05	kilogram metre squared per second ($kg \cdot m^2/s$)	5.467 475 E+04	($oz \cdot in^2/s$)

AREA

Unit	Multiply by	to get	Multiply by	to get
acre	4.046 856 E+03	square metre (m^2)	2.471 054 E-04	acre
are	1.000 000*E+02	square metre (m^2)	1.000 000*E-02	(a)
square foot (ft^2)	9.290 304*E-02	square metre (m^2)	1.076 391 E+01	(ft^2)
square inch (in^2)	6.451 600*E-04	square metre (m^2)	1.550 003 E+03	(in^2)
square mile ($mile^2$)	2.589 988 E+06	square metre (m^2)	3.861 022 E-07	($mile^2$)
square rod (rod^2)	2.529 285 E+01	square metre (m^2)	3.953 686 E-02	(rod^2)
square yard (yd^2)	8.361 274 E-01	square metre (m^2)	1.195 990 E+00	(yd^2)

BENDING MOMENT AND TORQUE

Unit	Multiply by	to get	Multiply by	to get
dyne centimetre ($dyn \cdot cm$)	1.000 000*E-07	newton metre ($N \cdot m$)	1.000 000*E+07	($dyn \cdot cm$)
kilogram-force metre ($kgf \cdot m$)	9.806 650*E+00	newton metre ($N \cdot m$)	1.019 716 E-01	($kgf \cdot m$)
ounce-force inch ($ozf \cdot in$)	7.061 552 E-03	newton metre ($N \cdot m$)	1.416 119 E+02	($ozf \cdot in$)
pound-force inch ($lbf \cdot in$)	1.129 848 E-01	newton metre ($N \cdot m$)	8.850 748 E+00	($lbf \cdot in$)
pound-force foot ($lbf \cdot ft$)	1.355 818 E+00	newton metre ($N \cdot m$)	7.375 621 E-01	($lbf \cdot ft$)

(BENDING MOMENT AND TORQUE) PER LENGTH

Unit	Multiply by	to get	Multiply by	to get
pound-force foot per inch ($lbf \cdot ft/in$)	5.337 866 E+01	newton metre per metre ($N \cdot m/m$)	1.873 408 E-02	($lbf \cdot ft/in$)
pound-force inch per inch ($lbf \cdot in/in$)	4.448 222 E+00	newton metre per metre ($N \cdot m/m$)	2.248 089 E-01	($lbf \cdot in/in$)

CAPACITY (See Volume)

DENSITY (See Mass per Volume)

ELECTRICITY AND MAGNETISM

Unit	Multiply by	to get	Multiply by	to get
ampere hour ($A \cdot h$)	3.600 000*E+03	coulomb (C)	2.777 778 E-04	($A \cdot h$)
gauss (Gs)	1.000 000*E-04	tesla (T)	1.000 000*E+04	(Gs)
maxwell (Mx)	1.000 000*E-08	weber (Wb)	1.000 000*E+08	(Mx)
mho	1.000 000*E+00	siemens (S)	1.000 000*E+00	mho
oersted (Oe)	7.957 747 E+01	ampere per metre (A/m)	1.256 637 E-02	(Oe)

ENERGY, WORK
(Btu and calorie are International Table)

Unit	Multiply by	to get	Multiply by	to get
British thermal unit (Btu)	1.055 056 E+03	joule (J)	9.478 170 E-04	(Btu)
calorie (cal)	4.186 800*E+00	joule (J)	2.388 460 E-01	(cal)
electron volt (eV)	1.602 19 E-19	joule (J)	6.241 46 E+18	(eV)
erg (erg)	1.000 000*E-07	joule (J)	1.000 000*E+07	(erg)
foot pound-force ($ft \cdot lbf$)	1.355 818 E+00	joule (J)	7.375 621 E-01	($ft \cdot lbf$)
foot poundal ($ft \cdot pdl$)	4.214 011 E-02	joule (J)	2.373 036 E+01	($ft \cdot pdl$)
kilocalorie (kcal)	4.186 800*E+03	joule (J)	2.388 459 E-04	(kcal)
kilowatt hour ($kW \cdot h$)	3.600 000*E+06	joule (J)	2.777 778 E-07	($kW \cdot h$)
watt hour ($W \cdot h$)	3.600 000*E+03	joule (J)	2.777 778 E-04	($W \cdot h$)
watt second ($W \cdot s$)	1.000 000*E+00	joule (J)	1.000 000*E+00	($W \cdot s$)

Fig. 12-9
Conversion factors classified by areas.

MEASUREMENT UNITS AND CONVERSION

FLOW (See Mass per Time or Volume per Time)

FORCE

Unit	Multiply by	to get	Multiply by	to get
dyne (dyn)	1.000 000*E-05	newton (N)	1.000 000*E+05	(dyn)
kilogram force (kgf)	9.806 650*E+00	newton (N)	1.019 716 E-01	(kgf)
kilopond (kp)	9.806 650*E+00	newton (N)	1.019 716 E-01	(kp)
ounce force (ozf)	2.780 139 E-01	newton (N)	3.596 942 E+00	(ozf)
pound force (lbf)	4.448 222 E+00	newton (N)	2.248 089 E-01	(lbf)
poundal (pdl)	1.382 550 E-01	newton (N)	7.233 011 E+00	(pdl)

FORCE PER AREA (See Pressure)

FORCE PER LENGTH

Unit	Multiply by	to get	Multiply by	to get
pound-force per inch (lbf/in)	1.751 268 E+02	newton per metre (N/m)	5.710 148 E-03	(lbf/in)
pound-force per foot (lbf/ft)	1.459 390 E+01	newton per metre (N/m)	6.852 178 E-02	(lbf/ft)

HEAT
(Btu and calorie are International Table)

Unit	Multiply by	to get	Multiply by	to get
Btu/(h·ft·°F) k, thermal conductivity	1.730 735 E+00	watt per metre kelvin W/(m·K)	5.777 893 E-01	Btu/(h·ft·°F)
Btu·in/(s·ft^2·°F) k, thermal conductivity	5.192 204 E+02	watt per metre kelvin W/(m·K)	1.925 964 E-03	Btu·in/(s·ft^2·°F)
Btu·in/(h·ft^2·°F) k, thermal conductivity	1.442 279 E-01	watt per metre kelvin W/(m·K)	6.933 471 E+00	Btu·in/(h·ft^2·°F)
Btu/ft^2	1.135 653 E+04	joule per square metre(J/m^2)	8.805 507 E-05	Btu/ft^2
Btu/(h·ft^2·°F) C, thermal conductance	5.678 263 E+00	watt per square metre kelvin W/(m^2·K)	1.761 102 E-01	Btu/(h·ft^2·°F)
Btu/lb	2.326 000*E+03	joule per kilogram (J/kg)	4.299 226 E-04	Btu/lb
Btu/(lb·°F) c, heat capacity	4.186 800*E+03	joule per kilogram kelvin J/(kg·K)	2.388 459 E-04	Btu/(lb·°F)
Btu/(s·ft^2·°F) C, thermal conductance	2.044 175 E+04	watt per square metre kelvin W/(m^2·K)	4.891 949 E-05	Btu/(s·ft^2·°F)
cal/g	4.186 800*E+03	joule per kilogram (J/kg)	2.388 459 E-04	cal/g
cal/(g·°C) c, heat capacity	4.186 800*E+03	joule per kilogram kelvin J/(kg·K)	2.388 459 E-04	cal/(g·°C)
°F·h·ft^2/Btu R, thermal resistance	1.761 102 E-01	kelvin square metre per watt K·m^2/W	5.678 263 E+00	°F·h·ft^2/Btu

LENGTH

Unit	Multiply by	to get	Multiply by	to get
foot (ft)	3.048 000*E-01	metre (m)	3.280 840 E+00	(ft)
inch (in)	2.540 000*E-02	metre (m)	3.937 008 E+01	(in)
microinch (μin)	2.540 000*E-08	metre (m)	3.937 008 E+07	(μin)
micron (μ)	1.000 000*E-06	metre (m)	1.000 000*E+06	(μ)
mil	2.540 000*E-05	metre (m)	3.937 008 E+04	mil
international nautical mile (n mile)	1.852 000*E+03	metre (m)	5.399 568 E-04	(n mile)
mile (mile)	1.609 344*E+03	metre (m)	6.213 712 E-04	(mile)
rod	5.029 200*E+00	metre (m)	1.988 388 E-01	rod
yard (yd)	9.144 000*E-01	metre (m)	1.093 613 E+00	(yd)

LIGHT

Unit	Multiply by	to get	Multiply by	to get
candle (cd) or candle power	1.000 000 E+00	candela (cd)	1.000 000 E+00	(cd)
foot-candle (fc)	1.076 391 E+01	lux (lx)	9.290 304 E-02	(fc)
foot-lambert (fL)	3.426 259 E+00	candela per square metre (cd/m^2)	2.918 635 E-01	(fL)

MEASUREMENT UNITS AND CONVERSION

MASS

Unit	Multiply by	to get	Multiply by	to get
grain	6.479 891*E-05	kilogram (kg)	1.543 236 E+04	grain
long hundredweight (cwt)	5.080 235 E+01	kilogram (kg)	1.968 413 E-02	(cwt)
short hundredweight (sh cwt)	4.535 924 E+01	kilogram (kg)	2.204 622 E-02	(sh cwt)
kilogram-force second squared per metre (kgf·s^2/m)	9.806 650*E+00	kilogram (kg)	1.019 716 E-01	(kgf·s^2/m)
ounce (oz)	2.834 952 E-02	kilogram (kg)	3.527 397 E+01	(oz)
penneyweight (dwt)	1.555 174 E-03	kilogram (kg)	6.430 149 E+02	(dwt)
pound (lb)	4.535 924 E-01	kilogram (kg)	2.204 622 E+00	(lb)
slug	1.459 390 E+01	kilogram (kg)	6.852 178 E-02	slug
long ton (2240 lb)	1.016 047 E+03	kilogram (kg)	9.842 064 E-04	long ton (2240 lb)
short ton (2000 lb)	9.071 847 E+02	kilogram (kg)	1.102 311 E-03	short ton (2000 lb)
tonne (t)	1.000 000*E+03	kilogram (kg)	1.000 000*E-03	(t)

MASS PER AREA

Unit	Multiply by	to get	Multiply by	to get
ounce per square yard (oz/yd^2)	3.390 575 E-02	kilogram per square metre (kg/m^2)	2.949 352 E+01	(oz/yd^2)
pound per square foot (lb/ft^2)	4.882 428 E+00	kilogram per square metre (kg/m^2)	2.048 161 E-01	(lb/ft^2)

MASS PER CAPACITY (See Mass per Volume)

MASS PER TIME (Includes Flow)

Unit	Multiply by	to get	Multiply by	to get
pound per second (lb/s)	4.535 924 E-01	kilogram per second (kg/s)	2.204 622 E+00	(lb/s)
pound per minute (lb/min)	4.535 924 E-01	kilogram per minute (kg/min)	2.204 622 E+00	(lb/min)
short ton per hour	9.071 847 E+02	kilogram per hour (kg/h)	1.102 311 E-03	short ton per hour

MASS PER VOLUME (Includes Density and Mass Capacity)

Unit	Multiply by	to get	Multiply by	to get
ounce per UK gallon (oz/UK gal)	6.236 021 E+00	kilogram per cubic metre (kg/m^3)	1.603 586 E-01	(oz/UK gal)
ounce per UK gallon (oz/UK gal)	6.236 021 E-03	kilogram per litre (kg/l)	1.603 586 E+02	(oz/UK gal)
ounce per US gallon (oz/US gal)	7.489 152 E+00	kilogram per cubic metre (kg/m^3)	1.335 265 E-01	(oz/US gal)
ounce per US gallon (oz/US gal)	7.489 152 E-03	kilogram per litre (kg/l)	1.335 265 E+02	(oz/US gal)
ounce per cubic inch (oz/in^3)	1.729 994 E+03	kilogram per cubic metre (kg/m^3)	5.780 367 E-04	(oz/in^3)
pound per cubic foot (lb/ft^3)	1.601 846 E+01	kilogram per cubic metre (kg/m^3)	6.242 797 E-02	(lb/ft^3)
pound per cubic inch (lb/in^3)	2.767 990 E+04	kilogram per cubic metre (kg/m^3)	3.612 730 E-05	(lb/in^3)
pound per cubic yard (lb/yd^3)	5.932 763 E-01	kilogram per cubic metre (kg/m^3)	1.685 555 E+00	(lb/yd^3)
pound per UK gallon (lb/UK gal)	9.977 633 E+01	kilogram per cubic metre (kg/m^3)	1.002 242 E-02	(lb/UK gal)
pound per UK gallon (lb/UK gal)	9.977 633 E-02	kilogram per litre (kg/l)	1.002 242 E+01	(lb/UK gal)
pound per US gallon (lb/US gal)	1.198 264 E+02	kilogram per cubic metre (kg/m^3)	8.345 406 E-03	(lb/US gal)
pound per US gallon (lb/US gal)	1.198 264 E-01	kilogram per litre (kg/l)	8.345 406 E+00	(lb/US gal)
slug per cubic foot (slug/ft^3)	5.153 788 E+02	kilogram per cubic metre (kg/m^3)	1.940 320 E-03	(slug/ft^3)
long ton per cubic yard	1.328 939 E+03	kilogram per cubic metre (kg/m^3)	7.524 800 E-04	long ton per cubic yard

MEASUREMENT UNITS AND CONVERSION

MOMENT OF INERTIA

Units	Multiply by	to get	Multiply by	to get
pound foot squared ($lb \cdot ft^2$)	4.214 011 E-02	kilogram metre squared ($kg \cdot m^2$)	2.373 036 E+01	($lb \cdot ft^2$)
pound inch squared ($lb \cdot in^2$)	2.926 397 E-04	kilogram metre squared ($kg \cdot m^2$)	3.417 171 E+03	($lb \cdot in^2$)
ounce inch squared ($oz \cdot in^2$)	1.828 998 E-05	kilogram metre squared ($kg \cdot m^2$)	5.467 475 E+04	($oz \cdot in^2$)

MOMENT OF MOMENTUM (See Angular Momentum)

MOMENTUM

pound foot per second ($lb \cdot ft/s$)	1.382 550 E-01	kilogram metre per second ($kg \cdot m/s$)	7.233 011 E+00	($lb \cdot ft/s$)
pound inch per second ($lb \cdot in/s$)	1.152 125 E-02	kilogram metre per second ($kg \cdot m/s$)	8.679 614 E+01	($lb \cdot in/s$)
ounce inch per second ($oz \cdot in/s$)	7.200 778 E-04	kilogram metre per second ($kg \cdot m/s$)	1.388 739 E+03	($oz \cdot in/s$)

POWER
(Btu is International Table)

Btu per minute (Btu/min)	1.758 427 E+01	watt (W)	5.686 902 E-02	(Btu/min)
Btu per hour (Btu/h)	2.930 711 E-01	watt (W)	3.412 141 E+00	(Btu/h)
erg per second (erg/s)	1.000 000*E-07	watt (W)	1.000 000*E+07	(erg/s)
foot pound-force per hour ($ft \cdot lbf/h$)	3.766 161 E-04	watt (W)	2.655 224 E+03	($ft \cdot lbf/h$)
foot pound-force per minute ($ft \cdot lbf/min$)	2.259 697 E-02	watt (W)	4.425 372 E+01	($ft \cdot lbf/min$)
foot pound-force per second ($ft \cdot lbf/s$)	1.355 818 E+00	watt (W)	7.375 621 E-01	($ft \cdot lbf/s$)
horsepower, 550 foot pound-force per second (hp)	7.456 999 E+02	watt (W)	1.341 022 E-03	(hp)
electric horsepower	7.460 000*E+02	watt (W)	1.340 483 E-03	electric horsepower
metric horsepower in Germany: Pferdestärke (PS) in France: cheval vapeur (CV)	7.354 99 E+02	watt (W)	1.359 62 E-03	metric horsepower
kilogram-force metre per second ($kgf \cdot m/s$)	9.806 65 E+00	watt (W)	1.019 72 E-01	($kgf \cdot m/s$)

PRESSURE OR STRESS (Force per Area)

normal atmosphere (atm)	1.013 25 E+05	pascal (Pa)	9.869 23 E-06	(atm)
bar	1.000 000*E+05	pascal (Pa)	1.000 000*E-05	bar
centimetre of mercury, 0°C (cm Hg)	1.333 22 E+03	pascal (Pa)	7.500 64 E-04	(cm Hg)
centimetre of water, 4°C ($cm\ H_2O$)	9.806 38 E+01	pascal (Pa)	1.019 74 E-02	($cm\ H_2O$)
dyne per square centimetre (dyn/cm^2)	1.000 000*E-01	pascal (Pa)	1.000 000*E+01	(dyn/cm^2)
foot of water, 39.2°F ($ft\ H_2O$)	2.988 98 E+03	pascal (Pa)	3.345 62 E-04	($ft\ H_2O$)
gram-force per square centimetre (gf/cm^2)	9.806 650*E+01	pascal (Pa)	1.019 716 E-02	(gf/cm^2)
inch of mercury, 60°F (in Hg)	3.376 85 E+03	pascal (Pa)	2.961 34 E-04	(in Hg)
inch of water, 60°F ($in\ H_2O$)	2.488 4 E+02	pascal (Pa)	4.018 6 E-03	($in\ H_2O$)
kilogram-force per square centimetre (kgf/cm^2)	9.806 650*E+04	pascal (Pa)	1.019 716 E-05	(kgf/cm^2)
kilogram-force per square metre (kgf/m^2)	9.806 650*E+00	pascal (Pa)	1.019 716 E-01	(kgf/m^2)
kilogram-force per square millimetre (kgf/mm^2)	9.806 650*E+06	pascal (Pa)	1.019 716 E-07	(kgf/mm^2)
millimetre of mercury, 0°C (mm Hg)	1.333 224 E+02	pascal (Pa)	7.500 615 E-03	(mm Hg)

MEASUREMENT UNITS AND CONVERSION

<u>PRESSURE OR STRESS (Force per Area)</u> (Continued)

Units	Multiply by	to get	Multiply by	to get
poundal per square foot (pdl/ft^2)	1.488 164 E+00	pascal (Pa)	6.719 689 E-01	(pdl/ft^2)
pound-force per square foot (lbf/ft^2)	4.788 026 E+01	pascal (Pa)	2.088 543 E-02	(lbf/ft^2)
pound-force per square inch, psi (lbf/in^2)	6.894 757 E+03	pascal (Pa)	1.450 377 E-04	(lbf/in^2)
torr	1.333 22 E+02	pascal (Pa)	7.500 62 E-03	torr

<u>SPECIFIC VOLUME (See Volume per Mass)</u>

SPEED (See Velocity)

STRESS (See Pressure)

<u>SURFACE TENSION (See Force per Length)</u>

<u>TEMPERATURE</u>

Units	Multiply by	to get	Multiply by	to get
degree Celsius (°C)	$t_K = t_C + 273.15$	kelvin (K)	$t_C = t_K - 273.15$	(°C)
degree Fahrenheit (°F)	$t_K = (t_F + 459.67)/1.8$	kelvin (K)	$t_F = 1.8 t_K - 459.67$	(°F)
degree Rankine (°R)	$t_K = t_R /1.8$	kelvin (K)	$t_R = 1.8 t_K$	(°R)
degree Fahrenheit (°F)	$t_C = (t_F - 32)/1.8$	degree Celsius (°C)	$t_F = 1.8 t_C + 32$	(°F)

<u>TEMPERATURE INTERVAL</u>

Units	Multiply by	to get	Multiply by	to get
degree Celsius (°C)	$t_K = t_C$	kelvin (K)	$t_C = t_K$	(°C)
degree Fahrenheit (°F)	$t_K = t_F /1.8$	kelvin (K)	$t_F = 1.8 t_K$	(°F)
degree Rankine (°R)	$t_K = t_R /1.8$	kelvin (K)	$t_R = 1.8 t_K$	(°R)
degree Fahrenheit (°F)	$t_C = t_F /1.8$	kelvin (K)	$t_F = 1.8 t_C$	(°F)

<u>TIME</u>

Units	Multiply by	to get	Multiply by	to get
day (d)	8.640 000 E+04	second (s)	1.157 407 E-05	(d)
hour (h)	3.600 000 E+03	second (s)	2.777 778 E-04	(h)
minute (min)	6.000 000 E+01	second (s)	1.666 667 E-02	(min)
month	2.628 000 E+06	second (s)	3.805 175 E-07	month
year (a)	3.153 600 E+07	second (s)	3.170 979 E-08	(a)

<u>TORQUE (See Bending Moment)</u>

<u>VELOCITY (Includes Speed)</u>

Units	Multiply by	to get	Multiply by	to get
foot per hour (ft/h)	4.466 667 E-05	metre per second (m/s)	2.238 806 E+04	(ft/h)
foot per hour (ft/h)	3.048 000*E-01	metre per hour (m/h)	3.280 840 E+00	(ft/h)
foot per minute (ft/min)	5.080 000*E-03	metre per second (m/s)	1.968 504 E+02	(ft/min)
foot per minute (ft/min)	3.048 000*E-01	metre per minute (m/min)	3.280 840 E+00	(ft/min)
foot per second (ft/s)	3.048 000*E-01	metre per second (m/s)	3.280 840 E+00	(ft/s)
inch per second (in/s)	2.540 000*E-02	metre per second (m/s)	3.937 008 E+01	(in/s)
kilometre per hour (km/h)	2.777 778 E-01	metre per second (m/s)	3.600 000 E+00	(km/h)
international knot	1.852 000*E+00	kilometre per hour (km/h)	5.399 568 E-01	international knot
mile per hour (mile/h)	4.470 400*E-01	metre per second (m/s)	2.236 936 E+00	(mile/h)
mile per hour (mile/h)	1.609 344*E+00	kilometre per hour (km/h)	6.213 712 E-01	(mile/h)
mile per minute (mile/min)	2.682 240*E+01	metre per second (m/s)	3.728 227 E-02	(mile/min)
mile per minute (mile/min)	1.609 344*E+03	metre per minute (m/min)	6.213 712 E-04	(mile/min)
mile per second (mile/s)	1.609 344*E+03	metre per second (m/s)	6.213 712 E-04	(mile/s)

<u>VISCOSITY</u>

Units	Multiply by	to get	Multiply by	to get
centipoise (cP)	1.000 000*E-03	pascal second (Pa·s)	1.000 000*E+03	(cP)
centistokes (cSt)	1.000 000*E-06	square metre per second (m^2/s)	1.000 000*E+06	(cSt)
poise (P)	1.000 000*E-01	pascal second (Pa·s)	1.000 000*E+01	(P)
poundal second per square foot (pdl·s/ft^2)	1.488 164 E+00	pascal second (Pa·s)	6.719 689 E-01	(pdl·s/ft^2)
pound per foot second (lb/ft·s)	1.488 164 E+00	pascal second (Pa·s)	6.719 689 E-01	(lb/ft·s)
pound-force second per square foot (lbf·s/ft^2)	4.788 026 E+01	pascal second (Pa·s)	2.088 543 E-02	(lbf·s/ft^2)
slug per foot second (slug/ft·s)	4.788 026 E+01	pascal second (Pa·s)	2.088 543 E-02	(slug/ft·s)
square foot per second (ft^2/s)	9.290 304*E-02	square metre per second (m^2/s)	1.076 391 E+01	(ft^2/s)
stokes (St)	1.000 000*E-04	square metre per second (m^2/s)	1.000 000*E+04	(St)

MEASUREMENT UNITS AND CONVERSION

VOLUME (Includes Capacity)

Unit	Multiply by	to get	Multiply by	to get
oil barrel (42 US gal)	1.589 873 E-01	cubic metre (m^3)	6.289 811 E+00	oil barrel
oil barrel (42 US gal)	1.589 873 E+02	litre (l)	6.289 811 E-03	oil barrel
US bushel	3.523 907 E-02	cubic metre (m^3)	2.837 759 E+01	US bushel
cubic foot (ft^3)	2.831 685 E-02	cubic metre (m^3)	3.531 466 E+01	(ft^3)
cubic inch (in^3)	1.638 706 E-05	cubic metre (m^3)	6.102 376 E+04	(in^3)
cubic inch (in^3)	1.638 706 E-02	litre (l)	6.102 376 E+01	(in^3)
cubic yard (yd^3)	7.645 549 E-01	cubic metre (m^3)	1.307 951 E+00	(yd^3)
cup	2.365 882 E-04	cubic metre (m^3)	4.226 753 E+03	cup
US fluid ounce (US fl oz)	2.957 353 E-05	cubic metre (m^3)	3.381 402 E+04	(US fl oz)
US fluid ounce (US fl oz)	2.957 353 E-02	litre (l)	3.381 402 E+01	(US fl oz)
Canadian liquid gallon	4.546 090 E-03	cubic metre (m^3)	2.199 692 E+02	Canadian liquid gallon
Canadian liquid gallon	4.546 090 E+00	litre (l)	2.199 692 E-01	Canadian liquid gallon
UK liquid gallon (UK gal)	4.546 092 E-03	cubic metre (m^3)	2.199 692 E+02	(UK gal)
UK liquid gallon (UK gal)	4.546 092 E+00	litre (l)	2.199 692 E-01	(UK gal)
US dry gallon (US dry gal)	4.404 884 E-03	cubic metre (m^3)	2.270 207 E+02	(US dry gal)
US liquid gallon (US gal)	3.785 412 E-03	cubic metre (m^3)	2.641 720 E+02	(US gal)
US liquid gallon (US gal)	3.785 412 E+00	litre (l)	2.641 720 E-01	(US gal)
UK fluid ounce (UK fl oz)	2.841 307 E-05	cubic metre (m^3)	3.519 507 E+04	(UK fl oz)
UK fluid ounce (UK fl oz)	2.841 307 E-02	litre (l)	3.519 507 E+01	(UK fl oz)
US peck	8.809 768 E-03	cubic metre (m^3)	1.135 104 E+02	US peck
US dry pint	5.506 105 E-04	cubic metre (m^3)	1.816 166 E+03	US dry pint
US liquid pint	4.731 765 E-04	cubic metre (m^3)	2.113 376 E+03	US liquid pint
US liquid pint	4.731 765 E-01	litre (l)	2.113 376 E+00	US liquid pint
US dry quart	1.101 221 E-03	cubic metre (m^3)	9.080 829 E+02	US dry quart
US liquid quart	9.463 529 E-04	cubic metre (m^3)	1.056 688 E+03	US liquid quart
US liquid quart	9.463 529 E-01	litre (l)	1.056 688 E+00	US liquid quart
tablespoon	1.478 676 E-05	cubic metre (m^3)	6.762 807 E+04	tablespoon
teaspoon	4.928 922 E-06	cubic metre (m^3)	2.028 841 E+05	teaspoon

VOLUME PER MASS

Unit	Multiply by	to get	Multiply by	to get
cubic foot per pound (ft^3/lb)	6.242 796 E-02	cubic metre per kilogram (m^3/kg)	1.601 846 E+01	(ft^3/lb)
cubic inch per pound (in^3/lb)	3.612 728 E-05	cubic metre per kilogram (m^3/kg)	2.767 991 E+04	(in^3/lb)

VOLUME PER TIME (Includes Flow)

Unit	Multiply by	to get	Multiply by	to get
cubic foot per minute (ft^3/min)	4.719 474 E-04	cubic metre per second (m^3/s)	2.118 880 E+03	(ft^3/min)
cubic foot per minute (ft^3/min)	2.831 685 E-02	cubic metre per minute (m^3/min)	3.531 466 E+01	(ft^3/min)
cubic foot per second (ft^3/s)	2.831 685 E-02	cubic metre per second (m^3/s)	3.531 466 E+01	(ft^3/s)
cubic inch per minute (in^3/min)	2.731 177 E-07	cubic metre per second (m^3/s)	3.661 425 E+06	(in^3/min)
cubic inch per minute (in^3/min)	1.638 706 E-05	cubic metre per minute (m^3/min)	6.102 375 E+04	(in^3/min)
cubic yard per minute (yd^3/min)	1.274 258 E-02	cubic metre per second (m^3/s)	7.847 704 E+01	(yd^3/min)
cubic yard per minute (yd^3/min)	7.645 549 E-01	cubic metre per minute (m^3/min)	1.307 950 E+00	(yd^3/min)
US liquid gallon per minute (US gal/min)	6.309 020 E-05	cubic metre per second (m^3/s)	1.585 032 E+04	(US gal/min)
US liquid gallon per minute (US gal/min)	6.309 020 E-02	litre per second (l/s)	1.585 032 E+01	(US gal/min)
US liquid gallon per minute (US gal/min)	3.785 412 E+00	litre per minute (l/min)	2.641 720 E-01	(US gal/min)
US liquid gallon per second (US gal/s)	3.785 412 E-03	cubic metre per second (m^3/s)	2.641 720 E+02	(US gal/s)
US liquid gallon per second (US gal/s)	3.785 412 E+00	litre per second (l/s)	2.641 720 E-01	(US gal/s)

Fig. 12-10
This mini-calculator is designed specifically for metric conversion.

Fig. 12-11
The computer is the ideal instrument for doing conversion in industry.

precise for most work, and for practical purposes 31.65 would be exact enough. (2) Convert the customary value to the nearest equivalent SI metric value. For example, if the customary rule is divided into 1/16 inch, then a metric rule divided into 1 millimetre divisions would be more precise, since 1 millimetre is approximately 1/25 inch. Therefore, any measurement more accurate than the nearest millimetre would be unnecessary and extremely misleading. For example, for a measurement of 1-11/16", the exact conversion would be 42.862 but should be rounded to 43 mm so that this measurement can be made with the metric rule. Another example occurs when using micrometers and verniers. If the customary micrometer measures to one thousandth of an inch (equal to exactly 0.025 4 mm), then the metric measurement to 0.01 millimetre (1 hundredth of a millimetre) is close enough for most work. Of course, the most accurate equivalents are obtained by multiplying by or with the most accurate conversion factors and then rounding. If a customary reading is in 1/10 000 of an inch such as 0.0013, then the metric reading should be in thousandths of a millimetre or 0.033 mm. Another example, 17' 6" (17.5') converted to metres would be 17.5 x 0.3048 which equals 5.334 metres but could be rounded to 5.33 metres for most work. Naturally a less accurate result would be obtained if a rounded conversion factor is used. For example, 17.5 feet x 0.305 would give a result of 5.3375 metres which should be rounded to 5.34 metres. Another example, assume you wish to convert tire pressures which are normally given in rounded numbers in pounds per square inch (psi). To convert 28 psi to kilopascals (1000 pascals) the number must be multiplied by 6.894 757 for the exact result of 193.053 19 kPa. The rounded number would be 193 kPa. However, only a small amount of precision would be lost by rounding the value to 195 kPa. (3) Convert from customary measurements to SI values and round off to fewer significant digits than the

original value and then label the answer *approximate.* For example, to convert 18 gallons to litres, multiply by 3.785 412 which equals 168.137 416 litres. This should be rounded off to 68.14 litres. However, it might be better to list this as 70 litres *approximately.* Normally rounding the metric results to the same number of digits as with customary units may introduce either too accurate a figure or an excessive error, depending on the accuracy and precision required. (4) When converting, always round the metric unit to the minimum number of significant digits that will maintain the required accuracy—usually one or two beyond the decimal point. In rounding, the following general rules should be considered: (a) If the digit immediately following the last digit to be retained is less than 5, that digit should be dropped off with no other change. For example, 8.524 27 could be rounded to 8.524. (b) When the digit immediately following the last digit to be retained is 5 or greater, it should generally be increased. For example, 2.324 53 could be rounded to 2.325. (c) If the digit to be dropped is exactly 5, and there are no additional digits beyond it, then the last digit retained should be rounded to the nearest *even* digit. For example, 2.365 could be rounded to 2.36 while 6.355 could be rounded to 6.36.

UNIT 13
HISTORIC PERSONS IN SI METRIC

A unique feature of the SI metric system is that it honors many of the famous people of history by naming some of the base units and most of the more commonly used derived units after the persons who made significant contributions. Each one was an interesting person in his own right, and knowing a little about them will give you a better feeling for the units, their definitions, and their symbols.

Fig. 13-2
Lord William Thomson Kelvin

Fig. 13-1
Andre Marie Ampere

Base Units

Andre Marie Ampere, a French physicist (1775-1836) gave private lessons on such scientific subjects as mathematics and chemistry, and he also taught language. Fig. 13-1. He also served as a professor of physics and chemistry and later as a professor of mathematics. His greatest achievement in science was the pioneer work he did in electro-magnetism—the relationship between electricity and magnetism. Ampere developed a mathematical theory which explains in detail the phenomenon of electro-magnetic action. Ampere invented the astatic needle, leading the way to the modern astatic galvanometer.

The *ampere,* or unit of electric current, was named after him—symbol (A).

The unit of temperature used in scientific areas is the kelvin—symbol (K), named after **Lord William Thomson Kelvin** (1824-1907). Fig. 13-2. Of Scotch-Irish ancestry, Lord Kelvin's real name was William Thomson. As a result of his work in thermodynamics, King Edward VII conferred upon him the title of Lord Kelvin, as he is now known throughout the world. After study at the University of Glasgow and at Cambridge, William Thomson worked in a Paris scientific laboratory on the thermo properties of steam. At the

age of 32 he accepted the chair of Natural Philosophy at the University of Glasgow where he remained for 53 years. Thomson met James Joule in 1847, who had interesting views on the nature of heat, and from this meeting in 1848 came Thomson's absolute scale of temperature called Kelvin's scale. During his lifetime William Thomson published 650 papers which appeared in scientific journals.

The common metric unit of temperature is degree Celsius—symbol (°C), commonly used as the everyday metric temperature scale, is named after **Anders Celsius** (1701-1744). Fig. 13-3. Celsius was a Swedish astronomer and inventor who served as professor of astronomy at the University in Uppsala from 1730 until his death. In 1742 he prepared a paper for the Swedish Academy of Sciences in which he described the *centigrade* thermometer. This temperature scale was changed officially to the Celsius in 1948, although it is still often referred to as centigrade.

Derived Units

The unit of force, the newton—symbol (N) was named after **Sir Isaac Newton** (1642-1727). Fig. 13-4. Educated at Trinity College and at Cambridge, Newton later returned to Trinity as a professor of mathematics. His greatest discoveries were in the areas of optics, astronomy, and gravitation. As a very young man he made fundamental discoveries which led to the principles of differential and integral calculus. The unit of force was named after Sir Isaac because of his work in the area of gravitation. He studied the solar system and the relationship of the earth and moon to the sun. It was Sir Isaac who proposed that one and the same force of universal gravitation causes the planets to revolve around the sun in their eliptical paths and the moon to revolve around the earth. Newton took things from common everyday life; his study of gravity is said to be occasioned by the fall of an apple on his head. It

Fig. 13-3
Anders Celsius

Fig. 13-5
Blaise Pascal

is interesting to note that the *newton* as a unit of force is equal to the force with which the earth attracts a medium size apple of approximately 100 grams. Among other accomplishments included discoveries concerning the nature of light, function of the telescope, rotation of the earth, astronomy and mathematics.

Isaac Newton was knighted in 1705 by Queen Mary.

Blaise Pascal (1623-1662), French physicist, mathematician and philosopher, wrote on many subjects including religion, mathematics and science. Fig. 13-5. His lifetime was a wavering between experimentation and religion, which induced the development of an arithmetical machine to do calculations, experiments with characteristics of vacuum and the barometer. He was one of the founders of the science of hydrostatics and hydrodynamics. His work in this field led to the honor of having the unit of pressure and stress named after him, the pascal—symbol (Pa).

The unit of energy is the joule—symbol (J), named after the English scientist, **James Prescott Joule** (1818-1889). Fig. 13-6. Joule was largely a self-taught person in the sciences, although he did have some help from James Dalton. James Dalton (1766-1844) was an English teacher and scientist who proposed the first model to help explain the atom. Joule developed the principle of intraconvertibility of various forms of energy; that is, the first law of thermodynamics. His many contributions to science in heat, electricity and thermodynamics gave him honor during his lifetime. With William Thomson, later known as Lord Kelvin, Joule collaborated on research on the doctrine of correlation and conservation of energy.

The unit of power is the watt—symbol (W), and is named after **James Watt** (1736-1819). Fig. 13-7. Watt was a Scottish engineer who invented the modern

Fig. 13-4
Sir Isaac Newton

Fig. 13-6
James Prescott Joule

condensing steam engine. In his earlier years he made mathematical instruments and developed a considerable knowledge of tools and their uses. It was in 1765 that he conceived of the basic idea for the modern condensing steam engine and soon after built the first steam engine. He made several tests with his engine which proved successful. His first patents were obtained in 1776. His later inventions adapted the steam engine to drive all kinds of machinery. In 1789 he described five different methods of converting reciprocal motion of the piston into rotational motion that could be used for driving any kind of ordinary machine. Watt was the first in Great Britain to suggest decimalization of weights and measures. He tried to decimalize the Imperial System because he was having difficulty comparing the research results with those of French scientists.

Fig. 13-8
Count Alessandro Volta

Fig. 13-7
James Watt

The unit of electrical potential is the volt—symbol (V), named after **Count Alessandro Volta** (1745-1827). Fig. 13-8. Volta, an Italian physicist and chemist, invented the electric battery that provided the first source of direct current. His many other experiments in the electrical science field led to the development of the notion of electrochemical series. He was invited to Paris by Napoleon in 1801 to show his experiments on the generation of electrical current. For most of his life he was a professor of physics at several major schools in Italy. Along with other scientists, Volta's work in electrolysis is credited with man's introduction to the electrical age.

Fig. 13-9
Georg Simon Ohm

Georg Simon Ohm (1789-1854), a professor of physics and mathematics in Germany, made his chief contributions to science in the study of galvanic currents. Fig. 13-9. He discovered the distribution of electromotive force in an electric circuit and showed the relationship between resistance, electromotive force and current strength (Ohm's Law). The unit of electric resistance, the ohm—symbol (Ω), is named after him.

Fig. 13-10
Michael Faraday

Michael Faraday (1791-1867), English physicist, chemist and philosopher, made the discovery of electromagnetic inductance of the laws of electrolysis and of the fundamental relationships between light and magnetism. Fig. 13-10. From his name comes the unit of electrical capacity, the farad—symbol (F). Though he had no training in either mathematics or teaching, his life was a triumph in both areas, which led to many honors including the offer of knighthood, which he refused.

Fig. 13-11
Joseph Henry

Joseph Henry (1797-1878) was a United States physicist and the first secretary of the Smithsonian Institution in Washington, D.C. Fig. 13-11. For many years Henry was a teacher of mathematics and natural philosophy at the Albany Academy and later at Princeton University where he designed relays, which controlled the local circuit of a more powerful magnet. He also used the earth as a return conductor. In recognition of his discoveries of self-induction, the International Congress of Electricians in Chicago in 1893 gave the name of the standard unit of inductive resistance the henry—symbol (H) to which his work was so closely related. He also performed much useful work in weather forecasting, reporting and maps, and helped in establishing several branches of science in the United States.

The unit of quantity of electricity or electric charge is the coulomb—symbol (C) named after **Charles Augustine de Coulomb** (1736-1806). Fig. 13-12. Coulomb, a French physicist, did pioneer work in electrical theory. His principal occupations were first as a military engineer and later he took part in the government's project of a metric system for weights and measures. His work resulted in what is now known as Coulomb's law, which states that electrical force is proportional to the charges and inversely proportional to the square of the distance between them. Because both Coulomb and Celsius are honored with metric units, the symbol for the quantity of electricity is always (C) and the symbol for temperature is (∘C).

During most of his life, **Wilhelm Eduard Weber** (1804-1891) served as a professor at the University of Leipzig and the University of Gottingen. Fig. 13-13. This eminent German physicist made major contributions to the modern system of electrical units. Weber showed that it was theoretically practical to define and measure electrical quantities in terms of units of length, time and mass. In addition, he did extensive research in the theory of magnetism. The derived unit of magnetic flux, the weber—symbol (Wb), is named after Wilhelm Weber.

Werner von Siemens (1816-1892) came from a family of engineers and inventors. Fig. 13-14. The unit of electric conductance, the siemens—symbol (S), is derived from his name. In 1847 he founded a firm to manufacture telegraphic apparatus, but most of his major inventions related to apparatus used in electrical work, including an electroplating process and the electric dynamo. His inventions were also in the realm of printing, open-hearth process of steelmaking, and steam engines.

Fig. 13-12
Charles Augustine de Coulomb

Fig. 13-14
Werner von Siemens

Fig. 13-13
Wilhelm Eduard Weber

The unit of magnetic flux density is the tesla—symbol (T), named after **Nikola Tesla** (1856-1943). Fig. 13-15. Born and educated in Yugoslavia, Tesla came to the United States in 1884 and established his own laboratory in New York City. His major achievement was an effective method of utilizing alternating current. He also patented the induction motor in 1888. He also was responsible for the invention of the principle of the rotary magnetic field. This idea was included in the apparatus used in the transmission of power from Niagara Falls. He is known mostly for his alternating current motors and his famous Tesla coil or transformer.

Heinrich Rudolf Hertz (1856-1894), German physicist, is the man for whom the derived unit of frequency is named—the hertz—symbol (Hz). Fig. 13-16. He served as a professor in a German polytechnic institute and at the University of Bonn. His most important work was his experiments in electricity in which he showed beyond a doubt the electromagnetic nature of light, demonstrating that electromagnetic waves of electricity are transmitted with the same velocity as light. It was because of the Hertzian waves that wireless telegraphy became possible. His research on the discharge of electricity and rarified gases brought him close to the discovery of x-rays, which were actually discovered a few years later by W. C. Rontgen.

Fig. 13-15
Nikola Tesla

Fig. 13-16
Heinrich Rudolf Hertz

SI units named after scientists

Unit	Scientist	Country of birth	Dates
ampere	Ampere, Andre-Marie	France	1775-1836
coulomb	Coulomb, Charles Augustin de	France	1736-1806
degree Celsius	Celsius, Anders	Sweden	1701-1744
farad	Faraday, Michael	England	1791-1867
henry	Henry, Joseph	United States	1797-1878
hertz	Hertz, Heinrich Rudolph	Germany	1857-1894
joule	Joule, James Prescott	England	1818-1889
kelvin	William Thomson, Lord Kelvin	England	1824-1907
newton	Newton, Sir Isaac	England	1642-1727
ohm	Ohm, Georg Simon	Germany	1787-1854
pascal	Pascal, Blaise	France	1623-1662
siemens	Siemens, Karl Wilhelm later Sir William	Germany (England)	1823-1883
tesla	Tesla, Nikola	Croatia (United States)	1856-1943
volt	Volta, Count Alessandro	Italy	1745-1827
watt	Watt, James	Scotland	1736-1819
weber	Weber, Wilhelm Eduard	Germany	1804-1891

UNIT 14
PRECISION METRIC RULES

There are many kinds of metric rules (scales). Common lengths are 150 mm (about 6 inches), 300 mm (about 12 inches), and 1 metre (about 3 feet). Fig. 14-1 & 2. There are also several combinations of *metric* and *customary* (English) rules.

Metric rules are graduated and marked in four different ways. Fig. 14-3. In Type 1, the finest graduations are in one millimetre (1 mm) units, with every tenth line marked in *centimetres* numbered 1, 2, 3, etc.

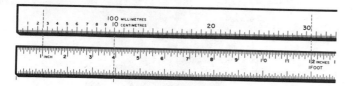

Fig. 14-1
Metric and inch rule to compare length. Note that 12 inches is slightly shorter than 300 millimetres.

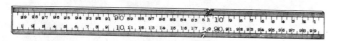

Fig. 14-2
A metre stick with numbered lines marked in centimetres.

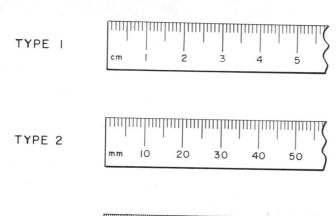

Fig. 14-3
Four types of graduations on metric rules.

Type 2 is exactly the same as Type 1 except that the numbered lines are marked in *millimetres* such as 10, 20, 30, etc.

In Type 3 the finest graduations of the rule are in half millimetres (0.5 mm), with the numbered lines marked in centimetres. There are 20 divisions between the numbered lines, each representing 0.5 mm.

Type 4 is exactly the same as Type 3 except that the numbered lines are marked in millimetres such as 10, 20, 30, etc.

The combination metric and customary scales normally have metric graduations in millimetres or half millimetres and the customary scale in 16ths, 32nds, 64ths, or in decimal equivalents. Fig. 14-4. The numbered lines on the metric rule show either centimetres or millimetres. For example, if the rule is numbered 1, 2, 3, 4, etc., these are *centimetre* divisions with 10 millimetre divisions between each of these numbered lines. If the numbered lines show 10, 20, 30, 40, these indicate *millimetres*. Rules are numbered either left to right or right to left. Fig. 14-5.

For *everyday use* and for more gross measuring such as in building construction, a metric rule marked in centimetres is satisfactory. Fig. 14-6. Each numbered line represents 1 centimetre or 10 millimetres. *However, for drafting and all precision machining, a rule with the numbered lines marked in millimetres should always be selected.* Fig. 14-7. This type is easier to read with less chance of error.

Correct Units

Rulers and measuring tapes must be calibrated in metres (m) and/or submultiples of the metre. The preferred submultiple of the metre is the millimetre (mm). However, the centimetre (cm) is a practical division for measuring tapes used in connection with body dimensions and textiles, and often for woodworking, furniture making, or building construction.

Correct Symbols

If the symbol of a unit appears on an instrument, *it must be the correct symbol*. The correct, internationally recognized symbols for the metre and its acceptable submultiples are:

Unit	Correct symbol	Incorrect symbol
metre	m	M M. m.
centimetre	cm	CM CM. cm. c.m.
millimetre	mm	MM M/M m/m
0.5 millimetre	1/2 mm	1/2 MM

Types of Steel Rules

(1) The *plain* or *tempered steel rule* made in 150 and 300 mm lengths (15 cm and 30 cm) is the most commonly used. Fig. 14-8a,b. The lines are called graduations. Most steel rules are marked or graduated on two or four edges from left to right. One may have divisions in millimetres or half millimetres, and the other in 16ths, 32nds, or 64ths, or tenths of an *inch*. If it is a combination metric and customary rule, the metric measurement may be above or below the customary measurement. With the combination rule it is easy to see that 25 mm is equal to about 1 inch and that 50 mm is equal to about 2 inches.

(2) The *flexible* steel rule is thinner and narrower than the plain rule. Fig. 14-9. Because it is flexible, it can be curved to fit around a curved piece of work. It can also fit into a small space making it easier to use than a wider, thicker plain steel rule.

(3) The *hook* rule has a single or double hook on one end which makes it convenient for measuring both inside and outside workpieces. The hook serves as a reference point from which measurement is taken.

A MILLIMETRE IS ABOUT HALF WAY BETWEEN THE $\frac{1}{32}$" & THE $\frac{1}{16}$".

$\frac{1}{2}$ MILLIMETRE IS ABOUT HALF WAY BETWEEN THE $\frac{1}{32}$" & THE $\frac{1}{64}$".

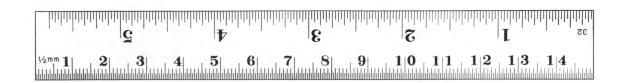

(ENLARGED 10 TIMES ACTUAL SIZE.)

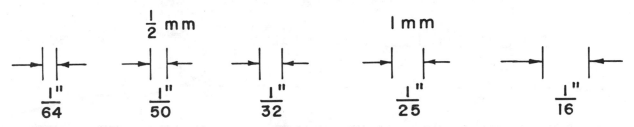

EXACT DIMENSIONAL READING IN INCHES:
0.015625   0.031250   0.062500
          0.019685   0.039370

EXACT DIMENSIONAL READING IN MILLIMETRES:
0.396875   0.793750   1.587500
          0.500000   1.000000

Fig. 14-4

This combination metric and customary rule illustrates the relative sizes of half millimetres (0.5 mm) and millimetres (1 mm) to 1/16, 1/32 and 1/64 inch.

numbered
right to left

Fig. 14-5
The rule at the left (a) is numbered from right to left, and the
rule at the right (b) is numbered from left to right.

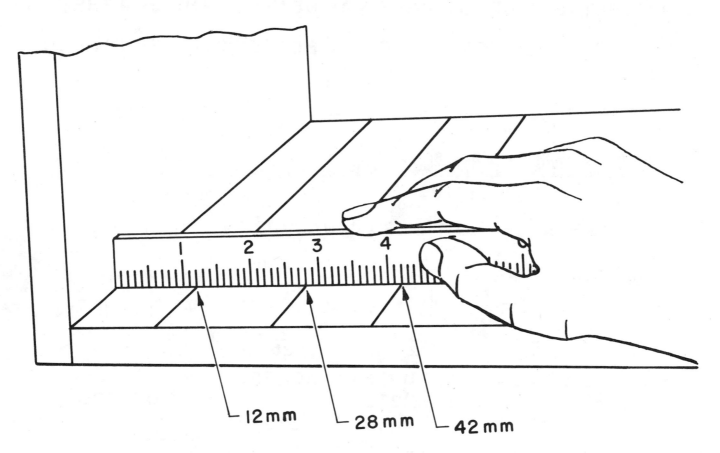

└ 12mm   └ 28mm   └ 42mm

Fig. 14-6
This metric rule has the numbered lines in centimetres.

Fig. 14-7
This combination rule has the numbered lines in millimetres.

Fig. 14-8a
A 150 millimetre rule with the smallest divisions in 1/2 millimetres on one edge and in millimetres on the other edge.

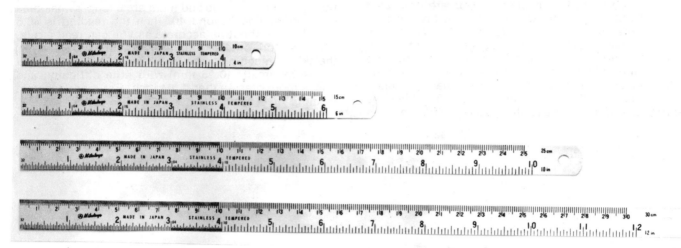

Fig. 14-8b
A 30 centimetre rule with the numbered lines marked in centimetres. Note the incorrect labeling (1 MM) on the rule.

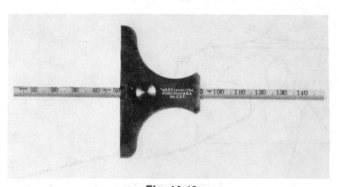

Fig. 14-9
Flexible steel rules in 10, 15, 25 and 30 centimetre lengths.

(4) The *rule depth* gage consists of a steel head or base to which a narrow steel rule fits. This rule is generally graduated in millimetres. A nut provides a means of clamping the rule in place after the measurement has been made. Measurements are quickly and easily made. Simply loosen the nut and push the rule through the head to the required distance. Fig. 14-10.

Fig. 14-11
Steel or flexible rule graduated in centimetres and inches.

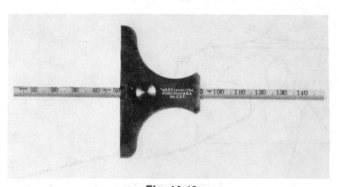

Fig. 14-10
Metric depth rule gage.

(5) The caliper rule, sometimes called the pocket slide caliper, is a handy measuring tool for making both inside and outside measurements. It generally is made in 100 or 300 mm lengths. Two lines of the solid part are marked "in" and "out". An inside measurement must be read from the "in" line and an outside measurement from the "out" line.

(6) The steel tape is commonly used for longer measurement. It is available in 2 and 3 metre lengths. A small catch at the end slips over the end of stock, making it easier to pull out the tape. Fig. 14-11.

Care of Rules

A good steel rule is a precision tool that will serve many years if properly cared for and used. Follow these suggestions:

(1) Always use the right height and/or length of rule.

(2) Keep the rule *away from revolving work or cutting tools.*

(3) Never lay or drop tools or work parts on the steel rule.

(4) Use the rule for measuring or layout only. Never use it as a screw driver, for example.

(5) Don't misuse the rule. You can't measure accurately when a rule is nicked or damaged.

(6) For greater accuracy, learn to make measurements from the 10 mm or 1 cm line rather than from the end.

(7) Occasionally wipe the steel rule with an oiled rag.

(8) Frequently clean the steel rule with fine steel wool. It will be easier to read.

How to Read a Metric Rule

Practice makes it possible for you to read a steel rule accurately and quickly and to be able to visualize metric measurements. Of course, if you are using a combination rule with the metric measurement on one edge and the inch measurement on the other, you will always have a point of reference. When you understand thoroughly the value lines or graduations and can add and subtract without a pencil, you will be skilled in measuring with a steel rule.

First check the rule to determine the smallest graduation that can be read directly and how the numbered lines are marked. Most metric rules are graduated with 1 mm as the smallest division. However, some used in machine shops are graduated in 1/2 mm (0.5 mm) and are so stamped on one end. Let's assume that the rule you are using is graduated in 1 mm with each numbered line marked in centimetres such as 1, 2, etc. If the length from the end of the rule is eight lines beyond the numbered line 2, then the reading is 28 mm. Fig. 14-12. Note that you must mentally change the 2 centimetres into 20 millimetres and then add the 8. There is always a chance for error in

doing this. Therefore, it is always better to select a precision steel rule with the numbered lines marked in millimetres. With this type, if there are four small divisions beyond 40, the reading is 44 mm. Fig. 14-13. The second type of precision rule is graduated in 1/2 millimetres. If there are 20 divisions between each of the numbered lines, then the rule is graduated in 1/2 millimetres (0.5 mm). Note that the 1/2 mm lines are shorter than the 1 millimetre lines. If you are reading this type of metric rule and there are 6 longer lines plus one shorter line beyond 40, then the reading is 46.5 mm. This is about as accurate as you can read a rule, and it is more precise than a 1/32 inch rule. However, the skilled machinist who understands metric can read to 1/4 millimetre (0.25 mm) with little difficulty, and this is more precise than 1/64 inch. For more accurate readings use a micrometer or vernier caliper.

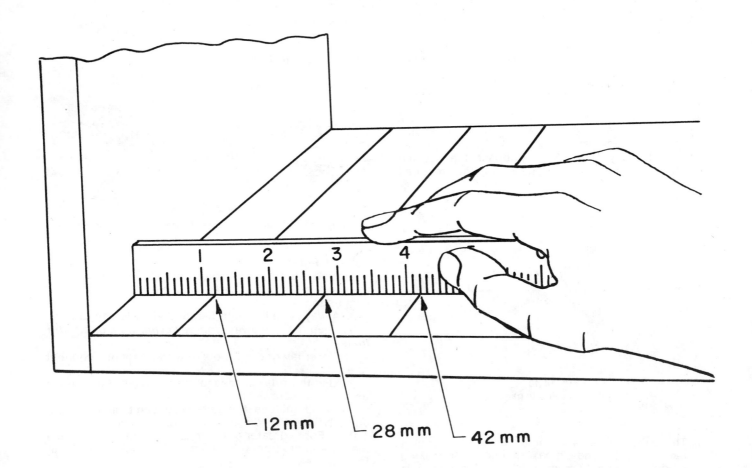

Fig. 14-12
Using a metric rule graduated in centimetres to make measurements. Note that you must mentally convert the centimetre markings to millimetres to obtain the correct measurement. Two graduations past one centimetre equals 12 millimetres.

14-5

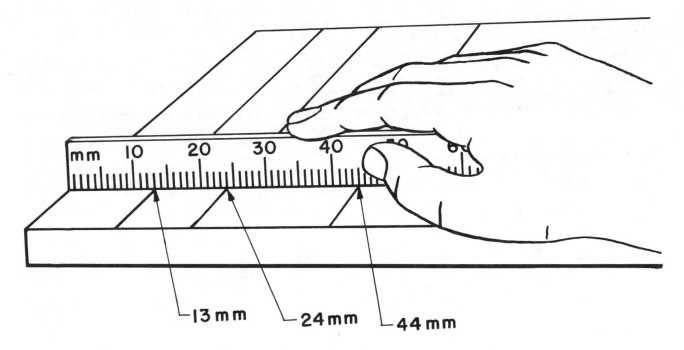

—13mm —24mm —44mm

Fig. 14-13
It is much easier to use a rule graduated in millimetres. Merely add the number of divisions beyond the numbered line to obtain the total.

Combination Set

The *combination set* consists of three separate tools (square head, bevel protractor, and center head) and a steel rule that may be used in each. The rule is either 300 mm (30 cm), 450 mm (45 cm), or 600 mm (60 cm) long. The square head and rule is called a *combination square.* Fig. 14-14. The combination set is useful for general work which does not require great accuracy.

Fig. 14-14
A combination set.

The combination square head has both a 45-degree angle face and a 90-degree angle face. Because a 45-degree angle is so commonly used, this square is most useful. The combination square also contains a spirit level for checking the levelness of a workpiece. It is not a precision level, however, and should not be used where extreme precision is required.

For laying out dimensions or lines to full or half millimetres, the combination square is best. The rule can be set a given distance from the head, and lines scribed at the end of the rule. The head is always held firmly against the surface from which the measurement is taken. Fig. 14-15 shows several other applications.

The center head (sometimes called a *center square*) is a useful tool for finding the center on the end of a round shaft.

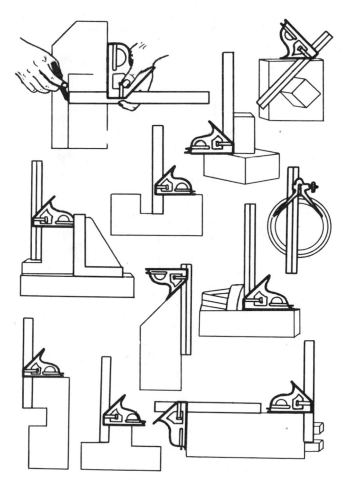

Fig. 14-15
Common uses for the combination square.

Scribers and Other Marking Tools

The *scriber* is a slender steel rod about 200 to 300 mm long with a sharp point on one or both ends. Sometimes one end is bent at a right angle. The scriber is used to scribe or scratch lines on most metal surfaces. For marking on metal plate, a *soapstone crayon* is good because it shows up well. For marking bend lines on sheet metal, a *pencil* is used.

Measuring and Marking Out

To measure the thickness of a piece of metal, *hold the rule on edge* with one edge of the metal on the 10 mm line. The line above the other edge will show the thickness.

Measure the width the same way.

There are no strict rules for measuring and marking out in all instances. Here are a few suggestions:

(1) Make sure the end of the workpiece from which the marking is done is square.

(2) Hold the rule on edge in contact with the surface of the workpiece. Fig. 14-16. If the end of the rule is worn, hold the 1 cm or 10 mm mark over the edge of the workpiece.

(3) Make sure the rule is kept parallel to the workpiece, so that the exact length can be obtained.

(4) Mark the exact length shown on the rule with a scriber.

(5) Hold a square firmly against the side of the workpiece. Mark a line across the workpiece. Turn the scriber at a slight angle, so that the point will draw along the lower edge of the rule.

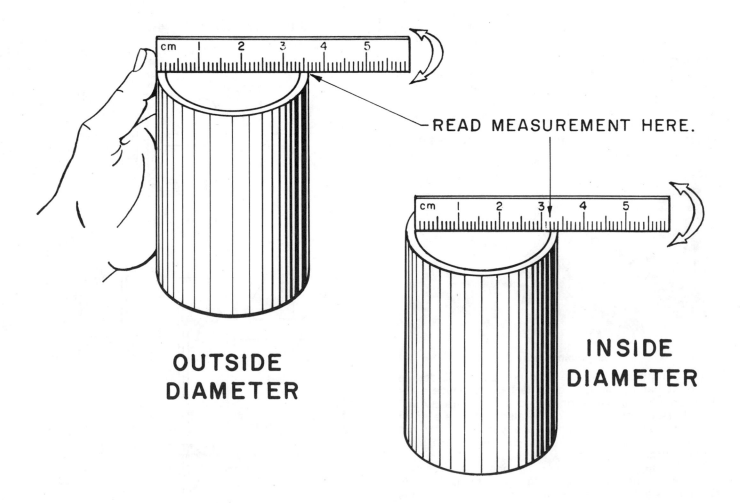

READ MEASUREMENT HERE.

OUTSIDE DIAMETER

INSIDE DIAMETER

Fig. 14-16
Note how the thumb is used to line up the rule with the outer edge of the pipe. Then swing the rule back and forth in an arc until the diameter can be read accurately.

UNIT 15
METRIC MICROMETERS

Metric micrometers are available in a variety of styles and sizes similar to those used in the customary system. A micrometer or "mike" as it is often called, is a precision measuring instrument. A machinist, toolmaker or other skilled worker who uses a metric micrometer *only* will find it relatively easy to read and use. However, if one uses both the metric and the inch micrometer, or a combination micrometer, he must be very careful taking readings. Fig. 15-1. You must remember that *one hundredth* of a millimetre is not at all the same as *one hundredth* of an inch. In fact, 0.01 (one hundredth) of a millimetre is equal to 0.000 394 of an inch. Fig. 15-2 & 3. There is a good deal of difference between reading a micrometer and knowing how to use one. Only through constant use can a person acquire what is known as "feel" (just the right amount of pressure needed to get an accurate reading). You must be able to measure workpieces quickly and accurately without making mistakes.

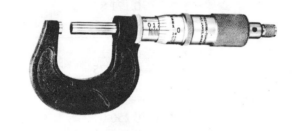

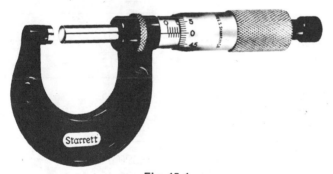

Fig. 15-1
Can you tell which is the customary (inch) and which is the metric micrometer?

Kinds and Sizes of Micrometers

The most common kinds and sizes of micrometers are: (1) the *outside micrometer* used to measure the thickness of material and parts and the diameter of workpieces. These are available in sizes ranging from 0-25 mm, 25-50 mm, 50-75 mm, etc., up to 275-300 mm. Fig. 15-4. The most common is one that measures from 0-25 mm. Fig. 15-5. (2) The *inside micrometer* is used for measuring the diameter of holes. There are two types. The caliper-type inside micrometer is available in ranges from 5-25 mm and 25-50 mm, and the straight inside micrometers have ranges from 25-50 mm to 50-300 mm. (3) The *depth micrometer* is used to measure the depth of holes and slots, and the depth of shoulders and projections. The common types range in size from 0-100 mm to 0-150 mm. (4) The *micrometer head* can be used with various measuring holders to make accurate measurements. Fig. 15-6.

Parts

A standard micrometer has a U-shaped *frame,* an anvil, a *spindle,* a *sleeve, hub,* and a *thimble.* Fig. 15-7. The spindle is threaded and attached to the thimble. Many micrometers have a *ratchet* or *ratchet stop* at the end of the thimble. The ratchet stop enables you to obtain uniform pressure for accurate readings until you develop the sense of feel so necessary to measure accurately. The *lock ring* or *nut* is used to lock the spindle after the setting is made.

Kinds of Metric Micrometers

Type 1—Standard metric micrometer with metric measurement on sleeve and spindle. All micrometers use the screw thread principle to obtain measurement. Unlike the familiar 40 threads per inch customary spindle, the metric micrometer spindle has 50 threads per 25 mm. Consequently, it takes 50 complete revolutions to advance the metric spindle from 0 to 25 mm. Fig. 15-8a. One revolution, therefore, advances (or retracts) the spindle 0.5 mm, or one half of a millimetre. On the sleeve (barrel sleeve as it is sometimes called) there is an *index line* parallel to the axis. This long horizontal line is sometimes called the *datum line.* When the micrometer is closed, the line on the thimble marked "0" coincides with this line. The sleeve is graduated by lines perpendicular to the horizontal line. Those above the horizontal line (on the upper sleeve) represent one millimetre (1 mm) units and every fifth one is numbered 5, 10, 15 etc. to aid in reading the results. Those below the horizontal line (on the lower sleeve) represent one half millimetre (0.5 mm) units or the amount the thimble moves with each complete revolution of the thimble. The bevelled edge on the thimble is divided into 50 equal divisions, each division representing 1/100 millimetre or 0.01 mm (equivalent to 0.004"). Fig. 15-8b. The metric micrometer has three reading parts:

(1) the *upper sleeve* which reads from 0 to 25 mm with each division representing 1 mm

(2) the *lower sleeve* which subdivides each 1 mm into halves or 0.5 mm

(3) the thimble which further subdivides 0.5 mm into 50 equal parts to give the final reading of 1/50 or 0.5 mm or 0.01 mm (one/hundredth of a millimetre).

EXAMPLE: Fig. 15-9.

(1) Note that the thimble has stopped at a point beyond 7 on the upper sleeve (7.00 mm)

(2) Note, too, that it also shows that it is beyond the half-point mark (0.5 mm)

(3) The line "44" on the thimble meets the center line of the sleeve (0.44 mm). By adding the above three readings, the total reading is:

(1)	Upper Sleeve	7.00 mm
(2)	Lower Sleeve	0.50 mm
(3)	Thimble reading	0.44 mm
	Total reading	7.94 mm

Fractional Inch-Millimetre Equivalents

Fractional Inches							Millimetres	Decimal Inches
Inch	1/2	1/4	1/8	1/16	1/32	1/64		
						1	0.397	0.015 625
					1	2	0.794	0.031 25
						3	1.191	0.046 875
				1	2	4	1.588	0.062 5
						5	1.984	0.078 125
					3	6	2.381	0.093 75
						7	2.778	0.109 375
			1	2	4	8	3.175	0.125 0
						9	3.572	0.140 625
					5	10	3.969	0.156 25
						11	4.366	0.171 875
				3	6	12	4.762	0.187 5
						13	5.159	0.203 125
					7	14	5.556	0.218 75
						15	5.953	0.234 375
		1	2	4	8	16	6.350	0.250 0
						17	6.747	0.265 625
					9	18	7.144	0.281 25
						19	7.541	0.296 875
				5	10	20	7.938	0.312 5
						21	8.334	0.328 125
					11	22	8.731	0.343 75
						23	9.128	0.359 375
			3	6	12	24	9.525	0.375 0
						25	9.922	0.390 625
					13	26	10.319	0.406 25
						27	10.716	0.421 875
				7	14	28	11.112	0.437 5
						29	11.509	0.453 125
					15	30	11.906	0.468 75
						31	12.303	0.484 375
	1	2	4	8	16	32	12.700	0.500 0
						33	13.097	0.515 625
					17	34	13.494	0.531 25
						35	13.891	0.546 875
				9	18	36	14.288	0.562 5

Fig. 15-2
Fractions and their decimal and metric equivalents.

Fractional Inches							Millimetres	Decimal Inches
Inch	1/2	1/4	1/8	1/16	1/32	1/64		
						37	14.684	0.578 125
					19	38	15.081	0.593 75
						39	15.478	0.609 375
			5	10	20	40	15.875	0.625 0
						41	16.272	0.640 625
					21	42	16.669	0.656 25
						43	17.066	0.671 875
				11	22	44	17.462	0.687 5
						45	17.859	0.703 125
					23	46	18.256	0.718 75
						47	18.653	0.734 375
		3	6	12	24	48	19.050	0.750 0
						49	19.447	0.765 625
					25	50	19.844	0.781 25
						51	20.241	0.796 875
				13	26	52	20.638	0.812 5
						53	21.034	0.828 125
					27	54	21.431	0.843 75
						55	21.828	0.859 375
			7	14	28	56	22.225	0.875 0
						57	22.622	0.890 625
					29	58	23.019	0.906 25
						59	23.416	0.921 875
				15	30	60	23.812	0.937 5
						61	24.209	0.953 125
					31	62	24.606	0.968 75
						63	25.003	0.984 375
1	2	4	8	16	32	64	25.400	1.000 0

DECIMAL EQUIVALENTS OF MILLIMETRES

mm	in	mm	in	mm	in	mm	in	mm	in	mm	in	mm	in	mm	in
0.1	0.00394	2.3	0.09055	4.5	0.17716	6.7	0.26377	8.9	0.35039	11.0	0.43307	13.1	0.51574	16.0	0.62992
0.2	0.00787	2.4	0.09448	4.6	0.18110	6.8	0.26771	9.0	0.35433	11.1	0.43700	13.2	0.51968	16.5	0.64960
0.3	0.01181	2.5	0.09842	4.7	0.18503	6.9	0.27165	9.1	0.35826	11.2	0.44094	13.3	0.52362	17.0	0.66929
0.4	0.01575	2.6	0.10236	4.8	0.18897	7.0	0.27559	9.2	0.36220	11.3	0.44488	13.4	0.52755	17.5	0.68897
0.5	0.01968	2.7	0.10629	4.9	0.19291	7.1	0.27952	9.3	0.36614	11.4	0.44881	13.5	0.53149	18.0	0.70866
0.6	0.02362	2.8	0.11023	5.0	0.19685	7.2	0.28346	9.4	0.37007	11.5	0.45275	13.6	0.53543	18.5	0.72834
0.7	0.02756	2.9	0.11417	5.1	0.20078	7.3	0.28740	9.5	0.37401	11.6	0.45669	13.7	0.53936	19.0	0.74803
0.8	0.03149	3.0	0.11811	5.2	0.20472	7.4	0.29133	9.6	0.37795	11.7	0.46062	13.8	0.54330	19.5	0.76771
0.9	0.03543	3.1	0.12204	5.3	0.20866	7.5	0.29527	9.7	0.38188	11.8	0.46456	13.9	0.54724	20.0	0.78740
1.0	0.03937	3.2	0.12598	5.4	0.21259	7.6	0.29921	9.8	0.38582	11.9	0.46850	14.0	0.55118	20.5	0.80708
1.1	0.04330	3.3	0.12992	5.5	0.21653	7.7	0.30314	9.9	0.38976	12.0	0.47244	14.1	0.55511	21.0	0.82677
1.2	0.04724	3.4	0.13385	5.6	0.22047	7.8	0.30708	10.0	0.39370	12.1	0.47637	14.2	0.55905	21.5	0.84645
1.3	0.05118	3.5	0.13779	5.7	0.22440	7.9	0.31102	10.1	0.39763	12.2	0.48031	14.3	0.56299	22.0	0.86614
1.4	0.05512	3.6	0.14173	5.8	0.22834	8.0	0.31496	10.2	0.40157	12.3	0.48425	14.4	0.56692	22.5	0.88582
1.5	0.05905	3.7	0.14566	5.9	0.23228	8.1	0.31889	10.3	0.40551	12.4	0.48818	14.5	0.57086	23.0	0.90551
1.6	0.06299	3.8	0.14960	6.0	0.23622	8.2	0.32283	10.4	0.40944	12.5	0.49212	14.6	0.57480	23.5	0.92519
1.7	0.06692	3.9	0.15354	6.1	0.24015	8.3	0.32677	10.5	0.41338	12.6	0.49606	14.7	0.57873	24.0	0.94488
1.8	0.07086	4.0	0.15748	6.2	0.24409	8.4	0.33070	10.6	0.41732	12.7	0.50000	14.8	0.58267	24.5	0.96456
1.9	0.07480	4.1	0.16141	6.3	0.24803	8.5	0.33464	10.7	0.42125	12.8	0.50393	14.9	0.58661	25.0	0.98425
2.0	0.07874	4.2	0.16535	6.4	0.25196	8.6	0.33858	10.8	0.42519	12.9	0.50787	15.0	0.59055	25.5	1.00393
2.1	0.08267	4.3	0.16929	6.5	0.25590	8.7	0.34251	10.9	0.42913	13.0	0.51181	15.5	0.61023	26.0	1.02362
2.2	0.08661	4.4	0.17332	6.6	0.25984	8.8	0.34645								

Fig .15-3
Decimal equivalents of millimetres.

Fig. 15-4
A complete set of outside micrometers is available in a variety of sizes.

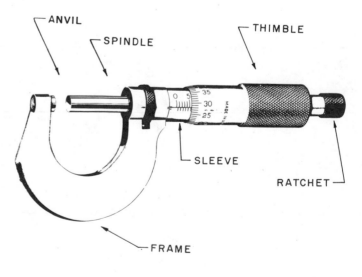

Fig. 15-5
A standard metric micrometer with a range of 0 to 25 millimetres.

15-4

Fig. 15-6
A metric micrometer head that can fit into a variety of holders. This unit can be used for a depth micrometer and for many other uses.

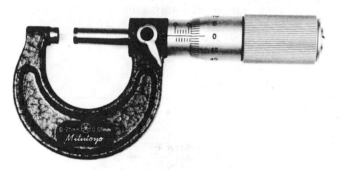

Fig. 15-8a
A standard 0 to 25 millimetre micrometer with the smallest reading of 0.01 millimetre. This micrometer does not have a ratchet or ratchet stop.

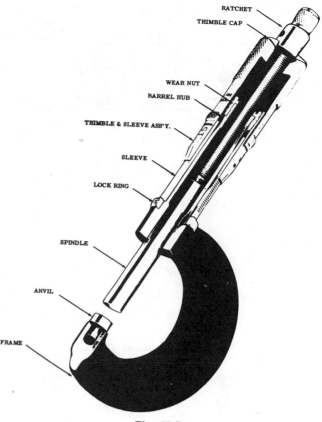

RATCHET
THIMBLE CAP
WEAR NUT
BARREL HUB
THIMBLE & SLEEVE ASS'Y.
SLEEVE
LOCK RING
SPINDLE
ANVIL
FRAME

Fig. 15-7
Parts of a micrometer.

METRIC MICROMETER
TYPE 1-METRIC ON SLEEVE AND THIMBLE

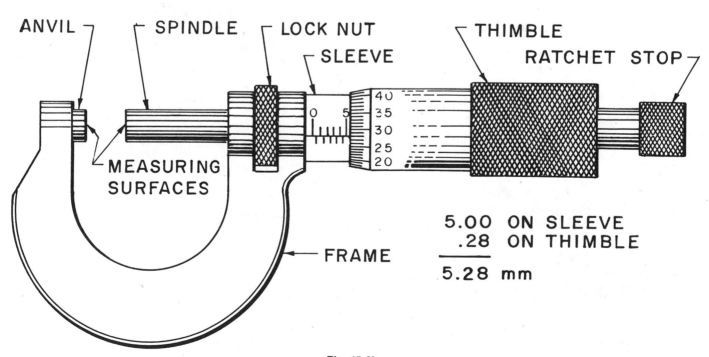

ANVIL   SPINDLE   LOCK NUT   THIMBLE
SLEEVE   RATCHET STOP

MEASURING SURFACES

FRAME

5.00 ON SLEEVE
.28 ON THIMBLE
―――――
5.28 mm

Fig. 15-8b
A standard metric micrometer with the parts named, including a ratchet stop.

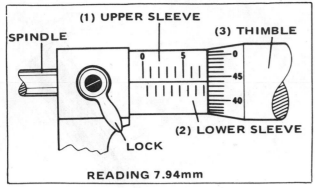

READING 7.94mm

Fig. 15-9
The complete reading is 7.94 mm.

(1)	Upper Sleeve	7.00 mm
(2)	Lower Sleeve	0.50 mm
(3)	Thimble reading	0.06 mm
	Total reading	7.56 mm

EXAMPLE: Fig. 15-10.

(1) Note that the thimble has stopped at a point beyond 5 on the upper sleeve.

(2) Note, also, it shows that it is beyond the half-point mark (0.5 mm).

(3) The line 28 on the thimble meets the center line on the sleeve. By adding the above three readings, the total reading is:

Reading a metric micrometer graduated in thousandths of a millimetre. For greater accuracy, a micrometer that reads in thousandths of a millimetre can be used. Metric micrometers graduated in thousandths of a millimetre have an additional vernier scale. They are read the same way as those graduated in hundredths except for the extra vernier reading. The thousandth reading which is obtained from a vernier is added to the hundredth reading. The thousandth reading is obtained by checking which lines on the vernier coincide with the line on the thimble. Note that the vernier is marked with numbers indicating thousandths (0.001 mm), and the graduations are closer to each other than those on the English vernier. The vernier scale is used when a graduation on the thimble does not line up exactly with the datum line. EXAMPLE: Fig. 15-12.

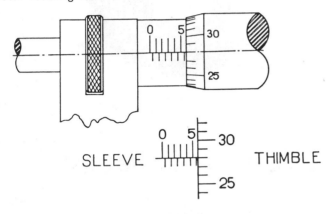

READING 5.78mm

Fig. 15-10
This reading is 5.78 mm.

(1)	Upper Sleeve	5.00 mm
(2)	Lower Sleeve	0.50 mm
(3)	Thimble reading	0.28 mm
	Total reading	5.78 mm

Another type of standard metric micrometer has a digital counter that shows the same reading as on the sleeve spindle.
EXAMPLE: Fig. 15-11.

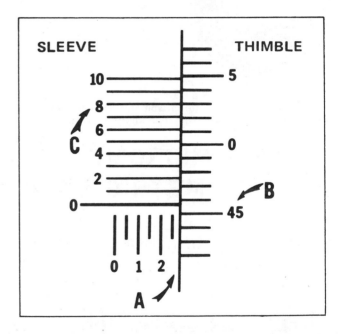

Fig. 15-12
Note that to read in thousandths of a millimetre you must match the line on the vernier scale with the line on the thimble. In this case the line marked 8 exactly coincides.

(1)	Sleeve reading	2.500 mm
(2)	Thimble reading	0.450 mm
(3)	Vernier reading	0.008 mm
	Total reading	2.958 mm

Fig. 15-11
A metric micrometer with digital readout window. The reading can be made either on the sleeve and spindle or on the digital counter (readout window). This is one of the easiest micrometers to use since there is a cross-check on each reading.

Type 2—Metric micrometer with the reading in full millimetres on the sleeve and the direct reading to thousandths of a millimetre as a direct reading on the thimble. On this type the full millimetre reading is shown by the exposed number on the sleeve. For example, in Fig. 15-13a,b, the number 5 or 5.000 mm is visible. Two numbers appear on the direct reading thimble—the first is in tenths of a millimetre (0.1 mm) and the second is in hundredths of a millimetre (0.01 mm). Note that 19 is showing, indicating that there are 19 hundredths of a millimetre more (0.190 mm). In addition, the reading shows four units (each equalling 2 thousandths millimetre or 0.002 mm) beyond the 19 for an additional reading of 0.008 mm. By adding the above readings, the total reading is:

Fig. 13-a
This metric micrometer shows the readings in full millimetres on the sleeve and a direct reading in tenths, hundredths and thousandths of a millimetre on the clear plastic opening on the thimble.

Sleeve reading	5.000 mm
Direct reading on the Thimble	0.190 mm
Scale on the Thimble	0.008 mm
Total reading	5.198 mm

**METRIC MICROMETER
TYPE 2 – READING ON SLEEVE AND
DIRECT READING THIMBLE**

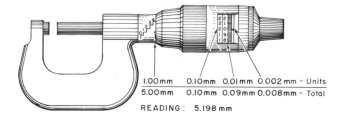

1.00mm	0.10mm	0.01mm	0.002mm – Units
5.00mm	0.10mm	0.09mm	0.008mm – Total

READING: 5.198 mm

Fig. 15-13b
The units and total for the complete reading of 5.198 mm.

Another example is shown in Fig. 15-14.

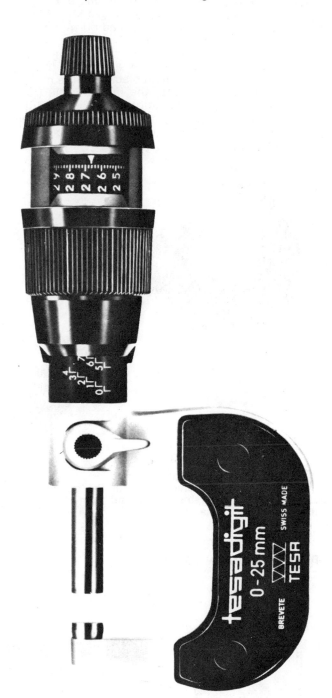

Fig. 15-14
Can you see how the reading in thousandths is made? Note that each of the smallest divisions on the direct reading thimble represents 0.002 millimetres.

Sleeve reading	7.000 mm
Direct reading on the Thimble	0.260 mm
Scale on the Thimble	0.006 mm
Total reading	7.266 mm

Dual Reading Micrometers

Type1—Metric on sleeve and thimble in red and customary (English or inch) on sleeve and thimble in black. Fig. 15-15a,b. This dual reading micrometer is the most difficult type to read without error. There are two scales on the sleeve and two on the thimble. The metric scales are in red with a vertical (or angle) reading; the inch scales are in black with the horizontal readings. To accommodate the metric scale (red) on the thimble, the inch graduations are slightly different from those encountered on a conventional micrometer. The correct method of reading the metric and inch scales is shown in Fig. 15-16.

Fig. 15-15a
A combination micrometer with both the metric and the customary reading on the sleeve and thimble. This is a difficult kind of "mike" to use.

DUAL READING MICROMETER
TYPE I - METRIC IN RED
CUSTOMARY IN BLACK

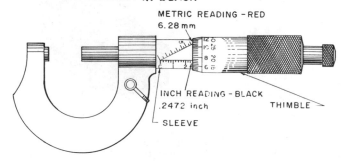

Fig. 15-15b
The two readings, 6.28 mm or 0.2472 inch, are equal.

Type 2—Customary on sleeve and thimble, metric in digital counter. The easier dual reading or combination micrometer to use reads the decimal inches on the spindle while its equivalent in millimetres is read in the window. Fig. 15-17a,b. Since the average user will be familiar with the customary (inch) micrometer he will have little difficulty with this type. The sleeve and **spindle reading in thousandths of an inch are read** exactly the same as the conventional or customary inch "mike".
EXAMPLE:

Numbered line on Sleeve	2.00"
2 extra lines (each 0.0250)	0.50
Thimble reading	0.00
Total reading	2.50"

or
6.35 mm on the window

Fig. 15-17a
This is a combination micrometer that has the customary or English reading on the spindle and thimble and the metric reading on the digital counter (readout window). This type might be useful if the drawings are made with dual dimensioning so that either measurement could be checked.

A few other typical readings are shown in the chart.

Straight Reading Metric Micrometer (Straight readings to 0.01 mm).

The sleeve on this micrometer is divided into 25 divisions or graduations from zero to 25 mm. In other words, the pitch of the thread used is one full millimetre. There are 100 clearly engraved 0.01 mm graduations or divisions on the thimble. Fig. 15-18a. Therefore, one complete turn of the thimble moves the micrometer one millimetre on the sleeve. Reading the straight reading micrometer is a two step process.

First, read the full millimetres on the sleeve. *Second,* add the number of divisions on the thimble to obtain the complete reading. For example, if there are 9 divisions (9.00 mm) showing on the sleeve plus 10 divisions (0.10 mm) on the thimble, the complete reading is 9.10 mm. Fig. 15-18b.

Another example, if there are 5 divisions (5.00 mm) showing on the sleeve and 12 divisions (0.12 mm) on the thimble, the complete reading is 5.12. Fig. 15-19.

Because there are 100 divisions around the edge of the thimble, this part is usually made slightly larger than the thimble on the standard metric micrometer.

METRIC SCALES (----) VERTICAL READING.

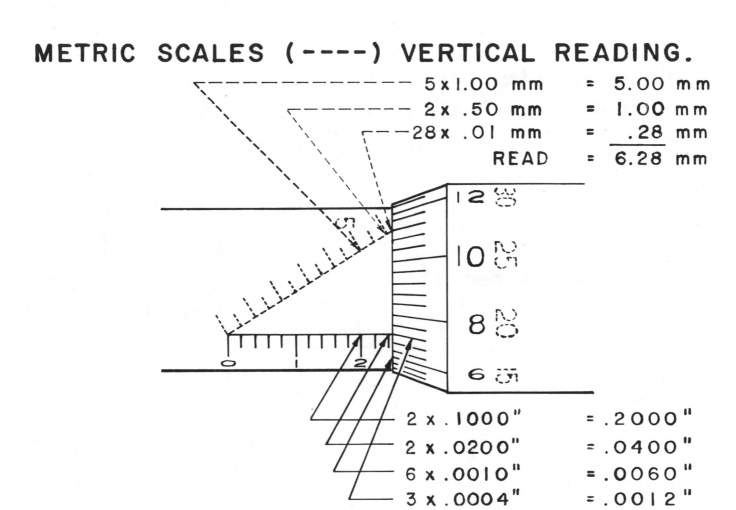

5 x 1.00 mm	=	5.00 mm
2 x .50 mm	=	1.00 mm
28 x .01 mm	=	.28 mm
READ	=	6.28 mm

2 x .1000"	=	.2000"
2 x .0200"	=	.0400"
6 x .0010"	=	.0060"
3 x .0004"	=	.0012"
READ	=	.2472"

INCH SCALES (——) HORIZONTAL READING.

Fig. 15-16
How to read the micrometer in inches and in millimetres.

DUAL READING MICROMETER
TYPE 2 – CUSTOMARY ON SLEEVE AND THIMBLE METRIC IN DIGITAL COUNTER.

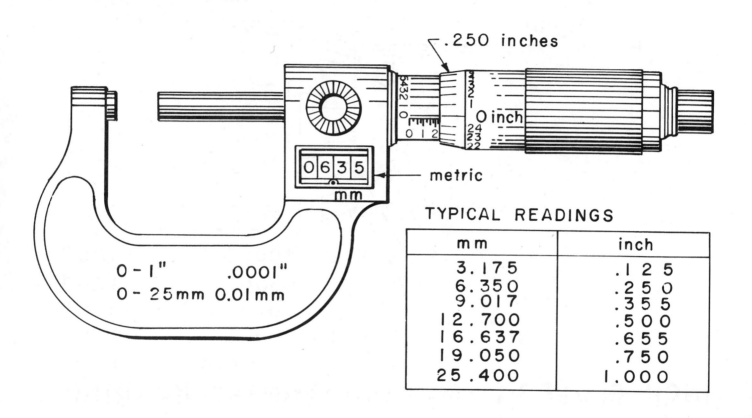

TYPICAL READINGS

mm	inch
3.175	.125
6.350	.250
9.017	.355
12.700	.500
16.637	.655
19.050	.750
25.400	1.000

Fig. 15-17b
An example of the combination (in-mm) micrometer with some typical readings.

Fig. 15-18a
This is a straight reading external metric micrometer. Note that the divisions or graduations on the sleeve are in full millimetres and there are 100 divisions or graduations around the thimble.

STRAIGHT READING METRIC MICROMETER

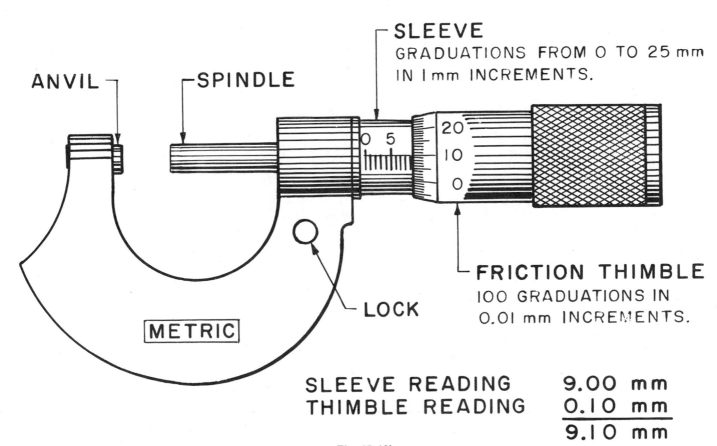

ANVIL

SPINDLE

SLEEVE
GRADUATIONS FROM 0 TO 25 mm IN 1 mm INCREMENTS.

LOCK

FRICTION THIMBLE
100 GRADUATIONS IN 0.01 mm INCREMENTS.

METRIC

SLEEVE READING   9.00 mm
THIMBLE READING   0.10 mm
   9.10 mm

Fig. 15-18b
The straight reading micrometer with the parts named.

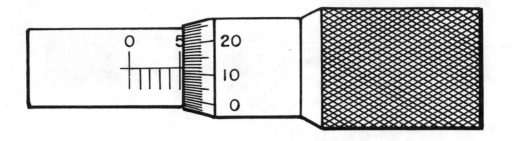

SLEEVE   5.00
THIMBLE   0.12
          ————
          5.12

Fig. 15-19
A reading of 5.12 mm. Note that you can see the 5 (5.00 mm) on the sleeve and 12 divisions (0.12 mm) on the thimble for a total reading of 5.12 mm.

UNIT 16
VERNIER CALIPER, HEIGHT AND DEPTH GAGE

A vernier caliper consists of an L- or T-shaped member with a scale engraved on the long shank. A sliding member is free to move on the bar and carries a jaw which matches the arm on the L or T. The vernier scale is engraved on a small plate that is attached to the sliding member. These useful calipers apply the principle of the difference between two scales—the *main* scale and the *vernier* scale—which have divisions that are almost but not quite equal. The vernier principle is simply the measurement of the fractional part of a subdivision by the addition of another (vernier) scale. Pierre Vernier invented the sliding scale which bears his name and is in use today.

Look, for example, on the main scale and vernier scale in Fig. 16-1a. The 50 graduations on the vernier scale cover a distance equal to 49 graduations on the main scale. Therefore, 1 graduation on the vernier scale will equal 49 divided by 50. The decimal equivalent of 49/50 is 0.98 so that 1 vernier scale graduation equals 0.98 mm. The difference, therefore, between 1 graduation on the main scale (equal to 1mm) and 1 graduation on the vernier scale (equal to 0.98) is 0.02 mm. Therefore, a metric vernier with 50 graduations on the vernier scale will read to an accuracy of 0.02 mm.

The combination customary/metric vernier caliper has been in use for a long time. Fig. 16-1b. The major improvements consist of clearer graduations made by increasing the length of vernier scales.

There are many makes and models to choose from. Some of the more common types are described in this unit.

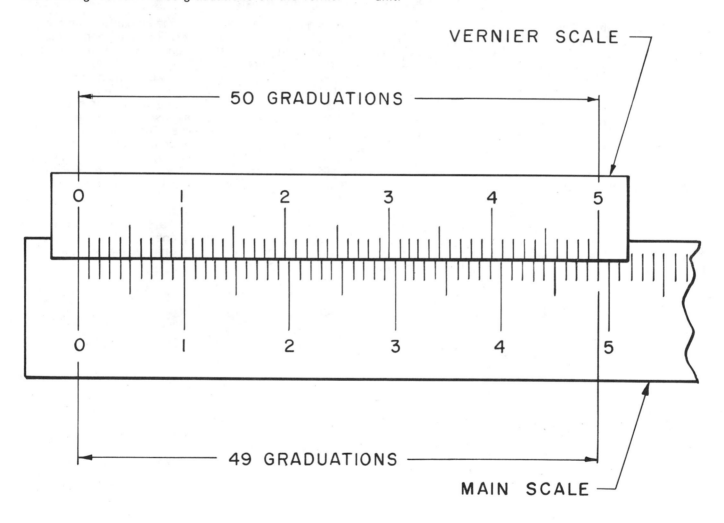

Fig. 16-1a
Note that 50 graduations on the vernier scale equal 49 graduations on the main scale.

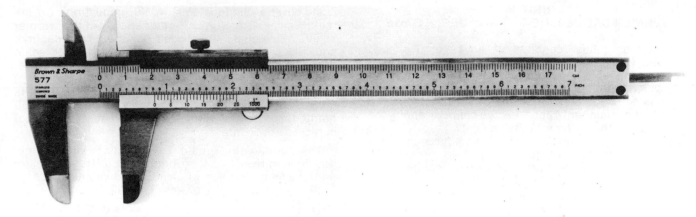

Fig. 16-1b
A combination customary-metric vernier caliper.

Care of the Vernier Scale

1. The inside faces of the jaws and the outside of the tips must be treated with great care. If they become worn or the jaws bent, the tool will no longer accurately read amounts.

2. Vernier calipers can be adjusted when they are not accurate. Always follow the manufacturer's recommendation for this adjustment.

3. Keep vernier calipers lightly oiled to prevent rust; keep them stored away from heavy tools.

Kinds and Styles of Vernier Calipers

Vernier calipers differ in several ways so that the operator must check carefully to be sure he knows how to use the particular design and kind.

Design. Many vernier calipers have an L-shaped main bar with a sliding bar opposite it with both the inside and outside readings using the same but opposite jaws. Fig. 16-2. On this kind of design, the outside reading is read from one side of the instrument and the inside from the other. The instrument is clearly stamped *inside* or *internal* on one side and *outside* or *external* on the other.

A second type has a T-shaped main bar with a sliding bar that also protrudes above and below the main bar. On this one, outside measurements are made using the lower jaws; inside measurements are made using the upper jaws. The readings for both inside and outside are made from the same side of the instrument. In addition, this type is also designed to make depth measurements and step measurements, eliminating the need for a separate depth gage. Fig. 16-3a,b.

Kinds of Scales. Many of the calipers that have been on the market for sometime have dual scales with the customary (English) along one edge and the metric along the other. Others have only the metric scales and verniers. Fig. 16-4.

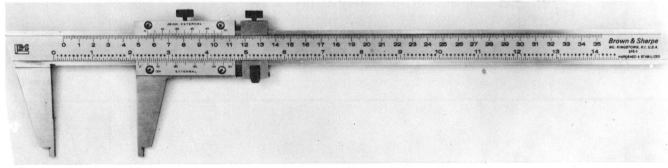

Fig. 16-2
An L-shaped design combination caliper. The same set of jaws is used for both internal and external measurement. However, the readings are made from opposite sides of the tool.

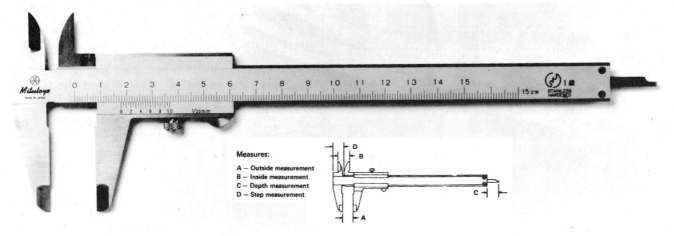

Fig. 16-3a
A metric vernier caliper that can be used for four different types of measurements.

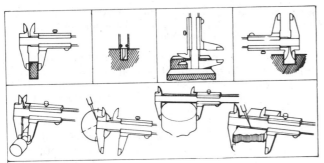

Fig. 16-3b
Using the vernier caliper shown in Fig. 16-3a for various kinds of measurements.

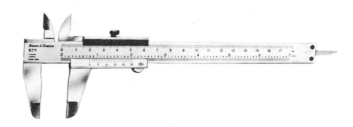

Fig. 16-4
The most common vernier calipers have both customary (English) and metric scales, measuring in inches and millimetres.

Precision of Vernier Scale and Main Scale

There is no uniformity in the graduations either on the main scale or the vernier scale so the graduations of scales must be carefully checked before attempting to read each instrument. Here are some of the more common types:

Type 1—the *main* scale is divided into *millimetres* with the number lines marked in *cm* or *mm*. The vernier scale has 20 divisions that equal a length of 19 mm on the main scale. Fig. 16-5. Therefore, 1 mm on the main scale is divided into 1/20 millimetre or 0.05 mm. Note, however, that the vernier is only marked to 10, even though there are 20 divisions between the 0 and 10. Fig. 16-6 shows 32 mm on the main scale and 0.45 mm (9 divisions of 0.05 mm) on the vernier scale. Adding the two readings together, the total reading is 32.45 mm.

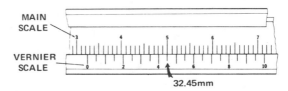

Fig. 16-6
Note that you can read directly two graduations past number 3 on the main scale, or 32 millimetres. Since each graduation on the vernier scale represents 0.05 millimetre and there are 9 divisions to the line marked with an arrow, the vernier scale would represent 0.45 millimetre (0.05 x 9) for a total of 32.45 millimetres.

Type 2—the main scale is divided in *millimetres* with the number lines marked in *cm* or *mm*. The vernier scale has 50 divisions that equal 49 mm on the main scale. Therefore, the readings can be made to an accuracy of 0.02 mm. Fig. 16-7a,b,c. Remember each small graduation on the vernier is equal to 0.02 mm. The numbered lines are marked every 5th or 10th division as 5, 10, 15, 20, 25, 30, etc. to 50. For example, in Fig. 16-7a the vernier is numbered every 5th division. Fig. 16-7b shows the same type of vernier numbered every 10th division. Fig. 16-7c shows the vernier numbered every 5th division as 1, 2, 3, etc. Regardless of the way the verniers are marked, *each small graduation on the vernier equals 0.02 mm.* Therefore, if there are 8 small divisions from 0, the reading is 8 x 0.02 or 0.16 mm. The reading in Fig. 16-7b shows the zero line of the vernier 2 lines past 2 on

Fig. 16-5
Note that there are 20 graduations on the vernier scale between 0 and 10. Each numbered line on the vernier scale represents 0.20 millimetre.

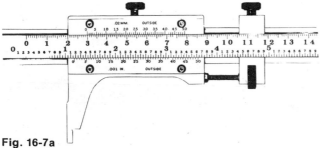

Fig. 16-7a
The vernier scale is divided into 50 equal parts, each graduation representing 0.02 millimetre (0.02 mm). (Note the incorrect way the vernier scale is stamped—MM—using capital letters instead of lower case letters.)

HOW TO READ 50-DIVISION VERNIER with ENGLISH/METRIC GRADUATIONS

METRIC READING
Use the upper Vernier and Beam Scales
Each Beam graduation is 1mm; each Numbered Beam graduation equals the number times 10 (numeral 1 = 10mm, 2 = 20mm, etc.); Vernier shows each .02mm and has numbered graduations by 10's (thus, 5 x .02 = .1mm, 10 x .02 = .2mm etc.)
Read External Measurements directly:
Example in photo: 20 plus 2 Beam graduations = 22mm, plus Vernier Reading of line which coincides with Beam line, 5 x .02 = .10mm.
Total External Reading — 22.10mm
For Internal Measurement read as above and add 7.62mm (width of Nibs) to the reading.
Example: 22.10mm + 7.62mm = 29.72mm

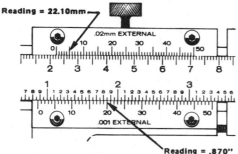

ENGLISH READING
Use the lower Vernier and Beam Scales.
Each Beam graduation is .050"; each Numbered Beam graduation between inches is .100"; Vernier shows each .001" and has numbered graduations by .010".
Read External Measurements directly as described above.
Example in photo: .850" + .020" (Vernier reading) = .870"
For Internal Measurement, read as above and add .300" (width of Nibs) to the reading.
Example: .870" + .300" = 1.170"

Fig. 16-7b
This vernier scale reads to 0.02 millimetre, although it is numbered slightly different from 7a.

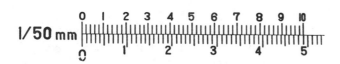

Fig. 16-7c
This vernier scale reads to 0.02 millimetre, although it is numbered differently from the previous two illustrations.

the main scale or 22.00 mm with 5 divisions (graduations) on the vernier scale for 0.10 (5 x 0.02) mm for a total reading of 22.10. Fig. 16-8 shows a vernier scale that reads to 0.02 mm with the vernier scale number every 5 divisions 1, 2, 3, etc. The "0" line is 2 graduations past the 10 mm (1 cm) graduation on the main scale. On the vernier scale the numbered lines represent 0.1 mm while the subdivisions represent 0.02 mm. The line on the vernier that aligns with the main scale is 1 unit beyond 6 or 0.62 mm (31 divisions x 0.02 mm). The total reading is 12.62 mm.

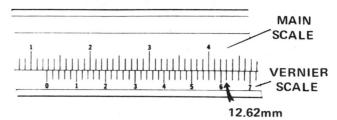

Fig. 16-8
Can you see how this vernier scale is read? The illustration shows a reading of 12 millimetres on the main scale and 0.62 millimetre on the vernier scale.

Type 3—the main scale is divided into 1/2 millimetres (0.50 mm) with the vernier scale graduated into 25 equal parts. Each graduation on the vernier scale gives a reading of 1/50 millimetre (1/25 of a half millimetre) or 0.02 mm.

For example, in Fig. 16-9a the zero on the vernier scale has moved past the 4 centimetres (40.00 mm) graduation. Add to this one full millimetre (1.00 mm) and one half millimetre (0.50 mm) for a total reading of 41.50 mm on the main scale. The ninth graduation on the vernier scale coincides with a line on the main scale, and this is indicated by the star. Therefore, 9 x 0.02 mm is 0.18 mm which is added to the reading on the main scale. The total reading is 41.50 plus 0.18 for a total reading of 41.68. In Fig. 16-9b the total reading is 3.16 mm.

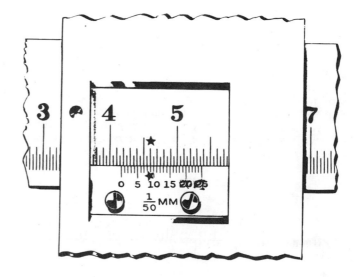

Fig. 16-9a
The main scale of this vernier caliper is divided into 1/2 millimetres (0.50 mm).

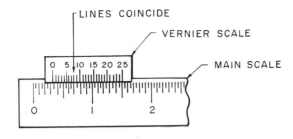

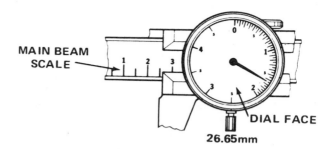

Fig. 16-11
Another type of dial indicator vernier caliper. The smallest graduation on the main scale is 5 mm, and every numbered line represents 1 centimetre or 10 millimetres.

3.00 mm ON THE MAIN SCALE
.02 x 8 OR 0.16 mm ON THE VERNIER SCALE
3.16 mm total

Fig. 16-9b

Note that 3 mm is shown between "0" on the main scale and "0" on the vernier scale. The 8th line on the vernier coincides with a line on the main scale. Since each graduation equals 0.02 mm, the vernier reading is 0.16 mm.

Type 4—the main scale is divided into millimetres with every 10th graduation marked in centimetres. The dial face is divided into 50 equal parts (marked from 0 to 100), each graduation representing 0.02 mm. For example, the main scale in Fig. 16-10 shows 19.00 mm and the dial face shows 0.50 mm for a total reading of 19.50.

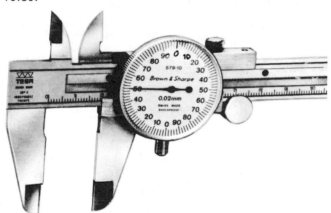

Fig. 16-10

Reading to 0.02 mm is shown on the dial of this vernier caliper.

Type 5—the main scale is divided into 5 millimetre graduations with every other line marked in centimetres as 1, 2, 3, etc. The smallest reading of the main scale is 5 mm and it coincides with one complete revolution of the dial hand. Since one complete revolution of the dial hand represents 5 mm, the dial face is divided into 5 numbered graduations, each equal to 1 mm. Numbers marked on the dial face represent 0 to 1 mm - 2 mm - 3 mm - 4 mm. 1 mm is further divided into 20 equal divisions, thus reading to 1/20 mm or 0.05 mm. For example in Fig. 16-11:
(1) The reading on the main beam scale is ...25.00 mm
(2) The reading on the dial face..............1.65 mm
Complete reading ....26.65 mm

Type 6—the main scale is divided into 10 millimetre units and is marked as such. The dial face divides the 10 millimetres into 1 mm units, plus 10 divisions between each 1 mm for 0.1 mm units. For example, Fig. 16-12, the main scale shows a 10 mm plus reading and the dial face shows 7.7 mm for a total reading of 17.7 mm.

Other Kinds of Vernier Measuring Tools

In addition to the vernier caliper, machinists find wide use for the following measuring tools:

1. The *vernier height gage* is a precision instrument used on a surface plate or another flat surface for laying out, checking, or inspecting work. It consists of a *base,* an *upright bar,* a *sliding jaw* containing the vernier scale, and a *sliding clamp* connected to the sliding jaw for making fine adjustments. Fig. 16-13. The sliding jaw has a clamp that holds a flat scriber or a dial indicator gage. The upright bar is graduated the same as a vernier caliper and is read in the same way.

2. The *vernier depth gage* is for the same purpose as a micrometer depth gage. It is somewhat easier to use and, therefore, many machinists perfer it. These tools are ordinarily provided with 22 to 30 cm length blades. The blade is graduated and read in the same manner as a vernier caliper. The blade slides in a slot in the base. The base contains the vernier scale. Fig. 16-14.

Fig. 16-13
A metric surface height gage.

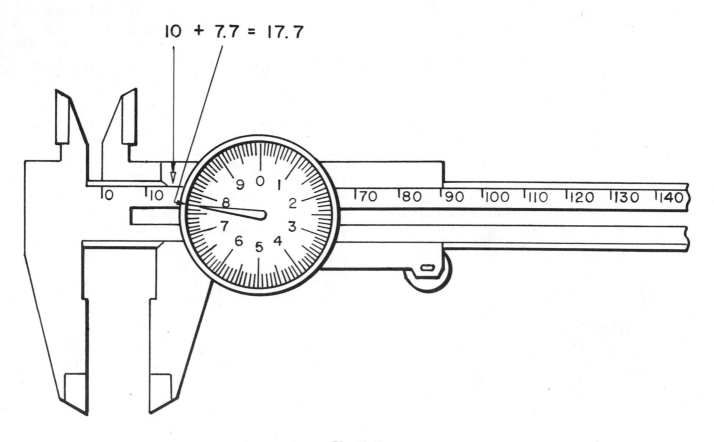

Fig. 16-12
Another type of vernier caliper with a dial indicator that reads in tenths (0.1) of a millimetre.

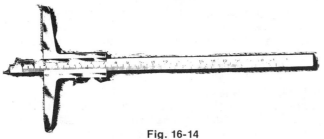

Fig. 16-14
A metric vernier depth gage.

Using Vernier Measuring Tools

Follow correct procedure when using vernier tools to obtain accurate readings and measurements:

1. Use a magnifying glass to avoid errors and prevent eyestrain.

2. Always locate or hold a vernier tool so that the light shines directly on the part you are reading.

3. To set a vernier tool for a given dimension, loosen both clamp screws first. Then slide the movable jaw to the approximate position on the main scale, using the zero on the vernier as the index line. Always grasp the movable jaw by placing your fingers on each side of the main scale. Never pull on the end of the movable jaw. Tighten the screw on the sliding clamp. Set to correct reading by turning the adjusting screw. Then tighten the clamp screw on the movable jaw just snug enough to prevent its moving.

4. Always hold the vernier so that the main beam is parallel to the surface to be measured. Fig. 16-15.

5. Never hold the vernier at an angle to the work. This would result in an incorrect reading.

6. Never force the jaws out of alignment by applying too much pressure when measuring.

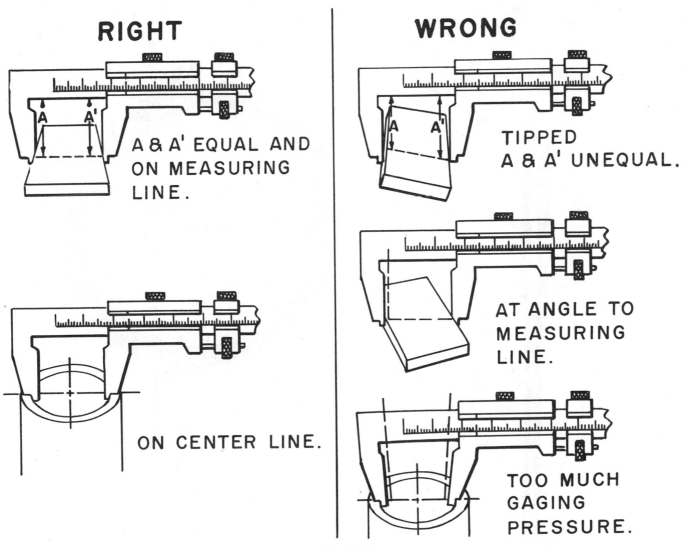

RIGHT

A & A' EQUAL AND ON MEASURING LINE.

ON CENTER LINE.

WRONG

TIPPED A & A' UNEQUAL.

AT ANGLE TO MEASURING LINE.

TOO MUCH GAGING PRESSURE.

Fig. 16-15
Correct and incorrect methods of using a vernier caliper.

UNIT 17
OTHER PRECISION MEASURING TOOLS

Other precision metric measuring tools and gaging equipment are needed, particularly in machining and manufacturing activities including:

Dial Indicating Gages

Metric dial indicating gages are available in the smallest scale graduations of 0.001, 0.002, 0.01 or 0.02 millimetres in various reading ranges from 0.5 millimetre to 50 millimetres. Before using a dial indicator, select the correct type and range. The *continuous* type reads in one direction only. A revolution counter (inner scale) is often included in this type of dial in order to register the number of revolutions made by the larger hand of the indicator. This smaller hand usually reads in full millimetres. Fig. 17-1. The *balance* type can indicate measurements in either direction from zero. Balance dial indicators are useful for checking plus or minus variations on a workpiece. Fig. 17-2.

Before using the dial indicator check for its range and for the values of the graduations. For example, Fig. 17-3 shows a dial indicator with a range of 0.5 millimetres with the smallest graduations equal to 0.002 millimetre. In contrast, Fig. 17-4 shows a dial indicator that has a range of 10 millimetres, with each graduation equal to 0.01 millimetre.

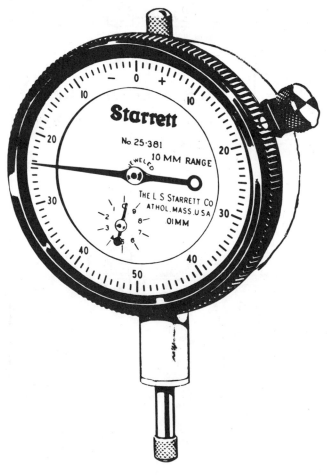

Fig. 17-2
A dial indicator of the balance type. Each small division is 0.01 mm.

Fig. 17-1
A continuous-reading dial indicator.

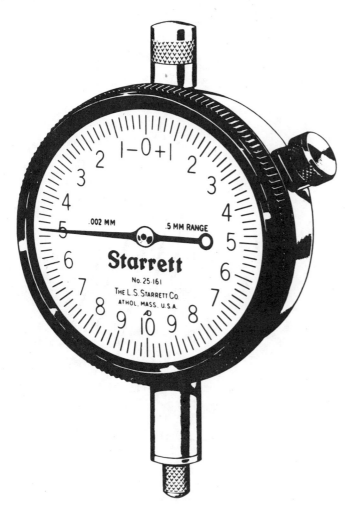

Fig. 17-3
A balance type with a maximum range of 0.5 mm.

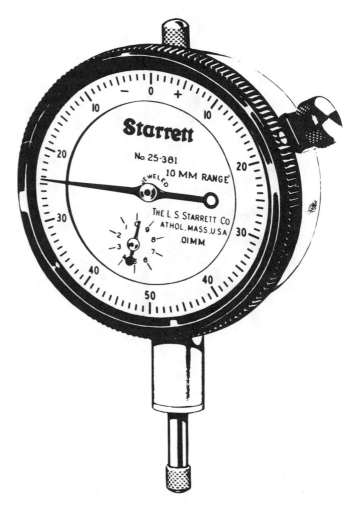

Fig. 17-4
This dial indicator has a maximum range up to 10 mm.

Using a Dial Indicator

The hand of the dial is actuated by a plunger that is in contact with the workpiece. A tracer pin is usually attached to the end of the plunger. Place the tracer pin against the workpiece until the hand of the dial moves. This is called pre-loading the indicator. Now turn the dial face until the "0" line coincides with the hand. The tracer pin can move freely in or out so that the hand will move clockwise (+) or counterclockwise (—). If there is only a small difference in size, such as a bearing that is out-of-round, use a balance type with a small range. The large dial hand will show the plus and minus variation of the work. If there is to be a continuously larger difference, a continuous type dial indicator with a smaller inner scale should be used. Each time the large hand makes one continuous revolution, this will register on the inner scale.

Thickness Gages

Metric thickness gages are available in combinations from a set with as few as 10 or 12 leaves to as many as 28 leaves. Fig. 17-5. For average work, in automechanics for example, a set with 10 leaves ranging from 0.05 to 0.25 millimetres by 0.05 millimetre steps and from 0.30 to 0.80 millimetres by 0.1 millimetre steps is all that would be required. Fig. 17-6. For more accurate machine shop work, a set with as many as 28 leaves may be needed in ranges from 0.05

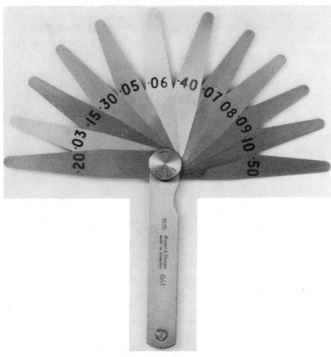

Fig. 17-5
This set of thickness gages has 10 blades.

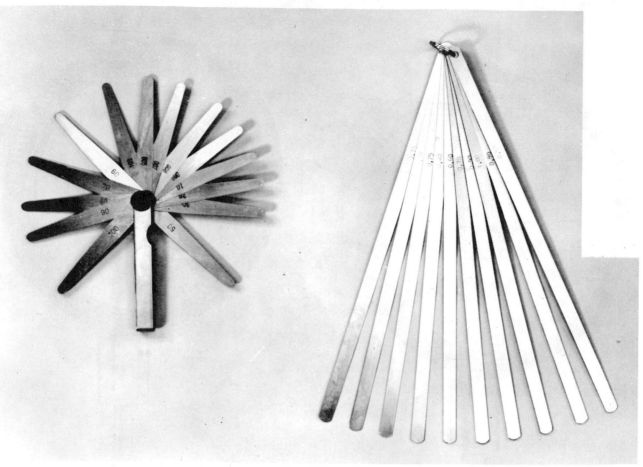

Fig. 17-6
Thickness gages are available with long or short blades in a variety of thicknesses.

to 0.14 millimetre by 0.1 millimetre steps and from 0.15 to 1.00 millimetres by 0.5 millimetre steps. By combining two or more leaves, different thicknesses in millimetres can be obtained. A wide variety of other combinations is made by various manufacturers in either short or long lengths.

Radius Gages

Radius gages are used for checking concave and convex surfaces. These are available in various ranges and different steps. Fig. 17-7. One manufacturer, for example, has sets available as follows:

    1 to 2 mm by 0.25 steps
    3.5 to 7 mm by 0.5 steps
    7.5 to 15 mm by 0.5 steps
    15.5 to 20 mm by 0.5 steps
    21 to 25 mm by 0.1 steps

Another manufacturer has two sets available. One set checks radii from 0.75 to 13 mm in steps of 0.25 mm; another set checks radii from 5.5 to 13.0 mm in steps of 0.5 mm.

Fixed Gages

Fixed gages are used to tell whether dimensions of a workpiece fall within certain limits. All fixed gages must be replaced with those graduated in metric measurements. These include such gages as ring, snap and plug gages. Fig. 17-8.

Fig. 17-7
Radius gages are useful for layout work and for checking radii. Gages consist of 18 or more leaves for checking both concave and convex radii.

17-3

RING GAGE

PLUG GAGE

SNAP GAGE

Fig. 17-8
All types of fixed gages are used for checking parts to metric dimension.

Adjustable Gages

Adjustable gages do not have to be replaced since they can be recalibrated with gage blocks to any metric setting. For example, adjustable snap gages can be set to check the limits of parts machined to metric standards.

Metric Height Master

The metric height master basically consists of two major parts: (1) the measuring column, of stacked and permanently wrung 10 mm gage blocks; and (2) the micrometer head with 500 equal divisions on its thimble.

One complete revolution of the micrometer head moves the measuring column 0.5 mm. Fig. 17-9. Since the head has 500 equal divisions on its thimble, each of the smallest divisions of the thimble represents 0.001 mm or 1 micrometre (μm). The digital counter is designed to eliminate possible reading errors and to permit speedy height transfer operations. The first digit on the digit counter is in millimetres, the second is in tenths of a millimetre, and the last digit is in hundredths. The larger dimensions (exceeding 9.99 mm) are to be relayed to the vertical scale marked by the measuring column. A sample reading is shown in Fig. 17-10. The reading of 7.85 indicated by the digital counter is actually 7.85 mm. The thimble has made 15 complete revolutions for 7.50 mm plus the reading on the thimble which indicates 0.35 mm for a total of 7.85 mm. This is shown on the digital counter. To read to the thousandth, find the line on the thimble which coincides with the zero point scribed on the lower ring. In the example illustrated above, the second line beyond 35 coincides. Each of these small graduations equals 0.001 mm. Therefore, the completed reading is 7.852 mm. To read to the thousandth, find the line on the thimble which coincides with the zero point scribed on the lower ring. In the example illustrated above, the second line beyond 35 coincides. Each of these small graduations equals 0.001 mm. Therefore, the completed reading is 7.852 mm.

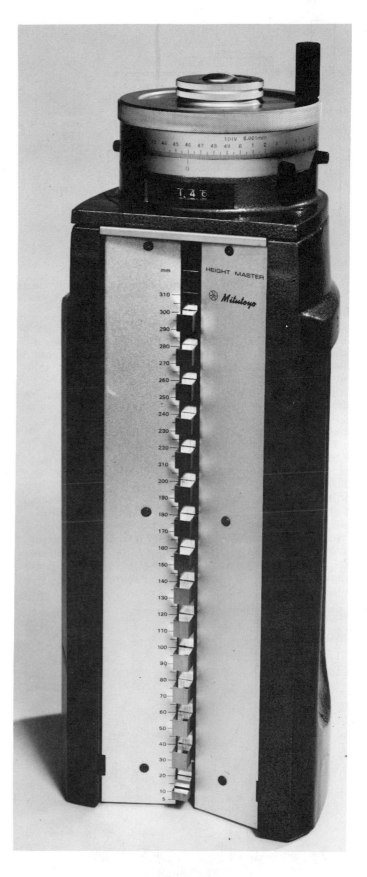

Fig. 17-9
This metric master height gage is a very precise type of instrument.

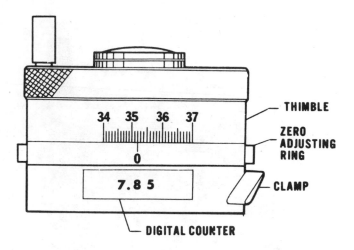

Fig. 17-10
The total reading shows 7.85 mm on the digital counter plus 0.002 mm on the thimble for a complete reading of 7.852 mm.

Sine Bars

Sine bars do not have to be replaced since a metric measurement can be given to them. For example, a 5 inch sine bar would become a 127.00 millimetre bar and the 10 inch sine bar would become a 254.00 millimetre bar. All calculations to find the sine of the angle can be done in the same way as in the inch system, except for the change in the length of the sine bar itself.

Electronic Gage

Electronic gages are available in a wide variety of sizes from the small hand-held type to very large production types. The gage head, similar to the plunger on a dial indicator gage, is fastened into the unit and can be used for the same general purposes as dial indicator gages. Fig. 17-11 illustrates one with a range in micrometres from plus or minus 3 micrometres to plus or minus 300 micrometres, with a range setting of 3, 10, 30, 100 and 300. An electronic height and marking gage with a digital readout unit will show dimensions in either decimal inches or millimetres. Fig. 17-12.

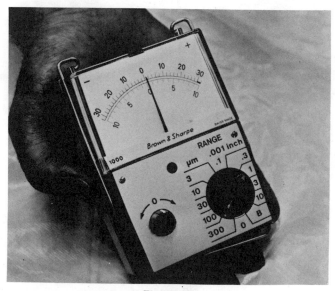

Fig. 17-11
A hand-held electronic gage.

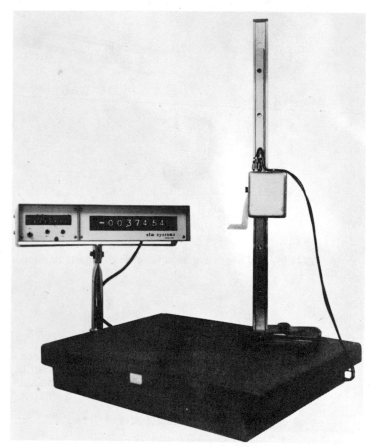

Fig. 17-12
This electronic height gage has a digital readout unit. The reading can be changed from decimal inches to millimetres with a flick of the switch.

Gage Blocks

Gage blocks are the industrial standards of length used for the following purposes: (1) calibrating **precision measuring instruments such as micrometers** and vernier calipers; (2) verifying the accuracy of inspection gages such as snap gages; (3) checking accuracy of tools; (4) setting gages in tools; (5) laying out for making tools and fixtures. Gage blocks are made of hard, stable material with measuring or gaging surfaces or faces on either end. The measuring faces are ground and lapped to an overall dimension with the tolerance as close as plus or minus 0.001 millimetre or 0.1 micrometre. Precision gage blocks are made of tool steel, chrome plated steel, stainless steel, chrome, carbide and tungsten steel. They are often called "Jo" blocks after C. J. Johansson, the first to develop an accurate set of blocks. Johansson's patent contained 102 hard steel metric blocks of different known sizes. With these different blocks it was possible to build up any size required between 1 and 201 millimetres (mm) in steps of 0.01 millimetre. Today a wide range of combinations is available in different qualities. Fig. 17-13. Gage blocks are made to several grades or degrees of accuracy to meet Federal specifications as shown in Fig. 17-14. Generally, grade 1 is used to control the accuracy of an entire manufacturing operation. Their major use is to certify the accuracy of other gage blocks. Grade 2 are the working blocks used in the shop for checking instruments. Grade 3 are often used directly for inspection work. The permissible deviation

Fig. 17-13

Size (mm)	Size (mm)	Size (mm)
0.5	1.26	5.50
1.00	1.27	6.00
1.001	1.28	6.50
1.002	1.29	7.00
1.003		7.50
1.004	1.30	8.00
1.005	1.31	8.50
1.006	1.32	9.00
1.007	1.33	9.50
1.008	1.34	
1.009	1.35	10.00
	1.36	11.00
1.01	1.37	12.00
1.02	1.38	13.00
1.03	1.39	14.00
1.04		15.00
1.05	1.40	16.00
1.06	1.41	17.00
1.07	1.42	18.00
1.08	1.43	19.00
1.09	1.44	
1.10	1.45	20.00
1.11	1.46	21.00
1.12	1.47	22.00
1.13	1.48	23.00
1.14	1.49	24.00
		25.00
1.15	1.50	30.00
1.16	1.60	40.00
1.17	1.70	50.00
1.18	1.80	60.00
1.19	1.90	70.00
	2.00	75.00
1.20	2.50	80.00
1.21	3.00	90.00
1.22	3.50	100.00
1.23	4.00	
1.24	4.50	
1.25	5.00	

Fig. 17-13
Common sizes of metric gage blocks.

	Federal Specification GGG-G-15B Tolerances on length for Metric Gage Blocks					
	Tolerance grade					
Nominal size	1 (formerly grade AA)		2 (formerly grade A+)		3 (compromise between former grades A and B)	
	Plus	Minus	Plus	Minus	Plus	Minus
mm	Tolerances in micrometres (0.001 mm)					
10 or less	0.05	0.05	0.10	0.05	0.20	0.10
over 10 thru 25	.08	.08	.15	.08	.30	.15
over 25 thru 50	.10	.10	.20	.10	.40	.20
over 50 thru 75	.13	.13	.25	.12	.45	.22
over 75 thru 100	.15	.15	.30	.15	.60	.30

Fig. 17-14
Three qualities of metric gage blocks that are available. Note that tolerance is shown in microns which is an obsolete term for micrometres.

in the size of a 25 mm block of finest quality is $\pm$ 0.000 05 mm or 0.05 μm. To illustrate how fine this is, the average thickness of a hair is about 0.05 millimetre. If this were divided into a thousand equal units across its thickness, the resultant thickness would be larger than the permissible deviation of the best grade of gage blocks.

Assembling Metric Gage Blocks

Common metric gage blocks consist of sets of 41, 47, 56 or 87 pieces. Fig. 17-15. Assume that you wish to assemble a set of blocks for checking the length of 43.21 millimetres. First select a block that is 40.00 millimetres in length. Next select a combination of blocks for a total of 3.21 millimetres. For example, you might use blocks in sizes 1.01 + 1.06 + 1.14 millimetres for a total of 3.21 millimetres. These three blocks plus the 40 millimetre block would total 43.21 millimetres. Fig. 17-16.

Number of Blocks	Grade	No.	Blocks in set
87 Pcs.	2 (A+)	516-946	9 Blocks — 1.001mm thru 1.009mm(step of 0.001mm) / 49 Blocks — 1.01mm thru 1.49mm(step of 0.01mm)
87 Pcs.	3 (A&B)	516-947	19 Blocks — 0.5mm thru 9.5mm(step of 0.5mm) / 10 Blocks — 10mm thru 100mm(step of 10mm)
56 Pcs.	2 (A+)	516-954	1 Block — 0.5mm / 9 Blocks — 1.001mm thru 1.009mm(step of 0.001mm) / 9 Blocks — 1.01mm thru 1.09mm(step of 0.01mm) / 9 Blocks — 1.1mm thru 1.9mm(step of 0.1mm)
56 Pcs.	3 (A&B)	516-955	24 Blocks — 1mm thru 24mm(step of 1mm) / 4 Blocks — 25mm thru 100mm(step of 25mm)
47 Pcs.	2 (A+)	516-958	1 Block — 1.005mm / 9 Blocks — 1.01mm thru 1.09mm(step of 0.01mm) / 9 Blocks — 1.1mm thru 1.9mm(step of 0.1mm)
47 Pcs.	3 (A&B)	516-959	24 Blocks — 1mm thru 24mm(step of 1mm) / 4 Blocks — 25mm thru 100mm(step of 25mm)

Fig. 17-15a
Several combinations of gage block sets.

Using the Gage Blocks

Before using the blocks, follow these steps: (1) With a clean chamois, cleaning tissue, and some non-corrosive cleaning fluid such as kerosene and naphtha, remove the rust-preventative coating on the blocks. Remember, gage blocks should never be allowed to rub together for any extended period as this can interfere with their accuracy. (2) Always use the blocks in an atmosphere that is as completely dirt-free as possible. Controlled temperature and humidity are important when using the best quality blocks. The presence of dirt, dust, filings, moisture, or other foreign matter will damage or corrode the blocks. (3) Keep all blocks in a case when not in use. (4) Remember that heat will affect the length of the block. Therefore, they must be handled with great care. Handling the blocks excessively will cause an expansion from 3 to 10 micrometres in length. (5) After the blocks have been cleaned, they must be wrung together. The wringing process, which refers to the adhesive force that binds the two blocks together, is illustrated in Fig. 17-17.

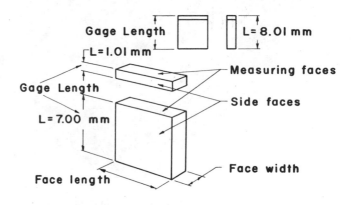

Fig. 17-16
The measuring faces are clearly indicated. These should be joined together to obtain the length wanted.

First overlap the blocks about 4 mm, then slide together with a slight pressure. They should begin to adhere. Once the wringing begins, the blocks should be oscillated until resistance ceases to increase.

Gage blocks can be placed in holders of various types so that they can be used for checking, inspecting and gaging. After gage blocks have been used they should be carefully cleaned, oiled, and replaced in the trays.

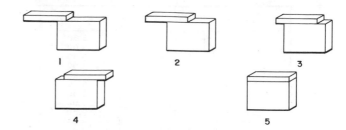

Fig. 17-17
The wringing process. Once the blocks have been joined together they will adhere so tightly that two persons, each weighing 60 kilograms, couldn't pull them apart.

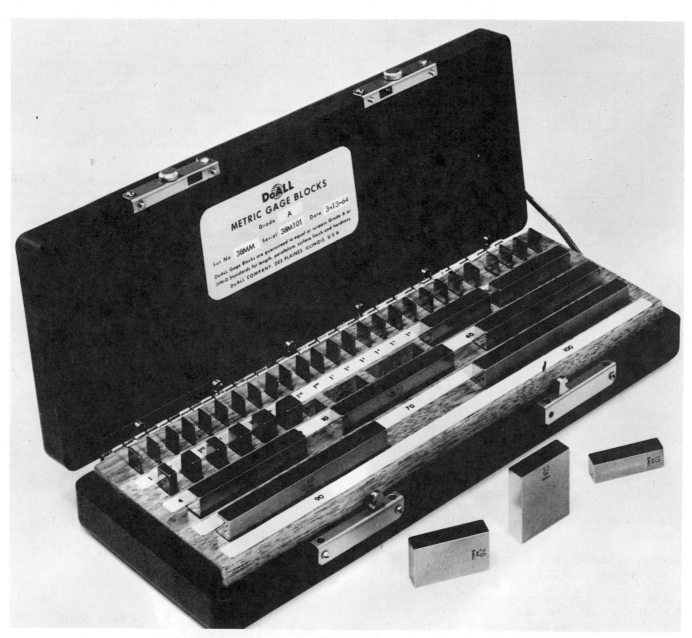

Fig. 17-15b
This is a *Grade A* set of gage blocks consisting of 41 blocks of various lengths.

UNIT 18
NATIONAL AND INTERNATIONAL ENGINEERING STANDARDS

Adoption of the *SI metric system* of measurement is frequently confused with the acceptance of *metric engineering standards*. This leads to misunderstanding about metric conversion. SI metric is an international measurement system *only*. It is totally *independent* and *separate* from any industry, national or international engineering standards.

An adequate understanding of the distinction between a change to metric measurement and acceptance of international engineering standards depends on two things: an appreciation of what engineering standards are and the role they play in our industrial economy.

Broadly speaking, engineering standards are agreements that specify characteristics of things or ways to do things. These apply to almost anything that can be measured or described and cover an enormous range, for example, the diameter of wire, the length and width of paper, the sizes of screw threads, the purity of aspirin, the fire resistance of clothing, the meat content of frankfurters, the symbols on highway signs, the way to test for sulphur in oil, the technical basis for local building codes, the strength of a safety belt, the wattage of light bulbs, the weight of a nickel.

Many years ago, before national and international engineering standards came into being, each firm, or industry, developed its own standards with the result that there was little or no nationwide uniformity. For example, before standardization, many companies developed their own thread standards. If an individual customer wished to replace a bolt or nut, he had to order one from the original manufacturer. Even today, after many years of standardization, there are over 108 different thread forms (the shape of the thread) used throughout the world. For example, even though the ISO inch (unified) thread series and the ISO metric thread series use the same thread form or profile (a 60 degree V), the threads are *not interchangeable.*

Engineering standards serve as both a dictionary and a recipe book for industry. Without them we would have chaos, inconvenience, and higher costs for almost everything. Mass production would not be possible if there were no assurance that two parts, such as a nut and a bolt, would fit together. Electric clocks would all keep different time if household current did not alternate precisely 60 times in a second.

Indeed, where standards have not been established, or when two different standards exist, life in all aspects is much more complicated. In Europe standard household current is 220 volts, 50 hertz (cycles per second); in the U.S. it is 115 volts, 60 hertz. An American-made electric razor does not work on European current. For that matter, it could not even be plugged in because the receptacles are different.

History of Standardization

Standardization is not new. It is an indispensable part of any civilization. In fact, the basic concept is as old as Nature and evidenced by such things as the structure of the atom, the movement of the planets, and the lines of latitude and longitude. Man himself is a highly standardized product, each with two arms, two legs, two ears, one nose, ten toes and a full complement of standardized organs. Yet no one considers his essential individuality in any way restricted by that basic standardization. There has always been a need for standardized products and methods:

- The Stone Age potter did not fashion a new shape in clay every time; to save time and effort, he specialized in a limited number of patterns, with specified dimensions.
- The pyramids of Egypt were constructed of standardized elements.
- The famous Roman water pipes had standardized dimensions: on the basis of the pipe diameter, the authorities were able to calculate the consumption—and bill the user accordingly.
- In the year 1502, the Sultan of Turkey established a standard for the manufacture of carpets.

Today, standardization is a much more sophisticated operation, but the aims are the same: to simplify, to clarify, to diminish the risk of errors, and to capitalize on lessons already learned. The principal change in standard needs is a geographical one. The Stone Age potter could not envisage a widespread distribution of his products. His customers were generally limited to the people living in the same village, since transport outside the village was time-consuming and hazardous. Today, the situation has changed radically. New transportation methods have made it possible to transport almost any goods over large distances. Improvements in communications mean, in turn, faster technological development. While an invention like the wheel took thousands of years to reach into every corner of our planet, the electronic computer has become an accepted universal tool within a generation.

In each phase of the history of standards, there has been an attempt to gain agreements on the widest possible basis. At the beginning of this century, this meant the national level. The British Standards Institution (BSI), the first national standards body, was created in 1901. A great number of other industrialized countries founded their own national institutes around 1920. International standardization began in the electrotechnical field by creation of the International Electrotechnical Commission (IEC) in 1906.

On October 14, 1946, 64 delegates from 25 countries met in London to consider the establishment of a new international organization "whose object shall be to facilitate the international coordination and unification of industrial standards." Discussions led to the setting up of ISO (International Organization for Standardization), and the first provisional General Assembly of the new body took place in London on October 24, 1946. Fig. 18-1. The ISO Constitution and Rules of Procedure were unanimously adopted by the General Assembly and it was decided that ISO should begin to function on an official basis as soon as the provisions had been ratified by 15 national standards bodies. The 15th ratification was received by the provisional Central Secretariat on February 23, 1947. At the same time, IEC was affiliated to ISO and, while preserving its autonomy, functioned henceforth as the Electrical Division of ISO.

Concern for international standardization was originally restricted largely to the manufacturing industry. Today, however, governmental authorities, research institutes, consumer associations and other international organizations are involved in standards.

1, rue de Varembé, 1211 Genève 20

Tel. 34 12 40   Cable: Isorganiz   Telex: 23 88 7 ISO CH

Fig. 18-1
ISO logo and address

The old idea that standardization is primarily a matter of screw threads and nuts and bolts is further than ever from the truth. About twenty percent of the ISO standards produced fall within the *mechanical* field. The most comprehensive results of ISO have been achieved in the *chemical* field, where some 600 standards—equal to thirty percent of the output—have been published. The areas of *metals* and *agriculture* each account for some ten percent. Other areas of activity are expected to account for a larger proportion of ISO work in the future. Particularly important is the field of *transportation* where standards for automobiles, aircraft, ships, containers, and packaging will facilitate the exchange of goods and services. *Building* and *information processing* are also fields where increasing international trade and interdependence make world standards imperative.

Traditionally, international standardization work has been concentrated on three aspects: *terminology, dimensions* and *test methods.*

The overwhelming majority of all ISO standards is concerned with at least one of these aspects. For example, some 10,000 defined terms are to be found in published and draft ISO standards, and a great many more are under study. Many of these terms have been translated into other languages for direct incorporation into national standards, thus reinforcing their utility as an evolving multilingual dictionary of great importance.

A common technical language is a basic requirement for international understanding. An ISO activity of special significance is, therefore, the development of international standards for units, symbols and drawing practice. Methods of testing materials and products constitute another cornerstone in international standardization. More than fifty percent of all ISO standards include the testing aspect.

Supplementing the three basic aspects is a fourth category of *performance standards,* including questions of safety and quality. An international standard for protective helmets, for example, should enable one to compare helmets from different countries. Likewise, an engineer looks to ISO for an objective, universally recognized standard to compare the performance of lifting chains from different manufacturers.

The need for international standardization first became apparent in Western Europe, and for many years other regions played only a relatively minor role in the ISO work. As late as the 1950's, almost all ISO meetings were held in Europe, and Western European countries held practically all the ISO technical secretariats. In recent years, however, ISO has developed into a truly international organization. Fig. 18-2. One significant outcome is the composition of the 1972 ISO Council which is charged with the operation and administration of the Organization between meetings of the General Assembly. France, Germany, Italy, Norway and the United Kingdom are members of the Council, but a healthy balance of interest and geographical location is provided by the presence of such member countries as Australia, Brazil, Canada, India, Iran, Japan, Romania, U.S.A. and U.S.S.R.

How Standards Develop

Engineering standards are developed by many organizations or groups at different levels: a single firm, a national group such as a trade association, or an international group. A company may develop its own standards for products it makes. A local government issues codes and regulations for building construction, driving, highways. In either case, their standards may not be in agreement with those issued by other companies or other governments.

For things generally used such as television, national standards are essential if the system is to function. For example, a television set must be able to receive programs on all channels, and television stations must broadcast in a prescribed way. The development of standards for such a complex system can be costly and time consuming; it took 10 million engineering man hours to develop national standards for color television.

The Department of Defense and the General Services Administration have issued, for government use, about 40,000 procurement standards encompassing most industrial products, food, clothing, and other consumer goods. This is about twice the number of standards issued by private groups. In the absence of a standard issued by a private group, the government's procurement standard may be used as a national standard.

Private voluntary groups, numbering in the hundreds, have issued about 20,000 standards. About one-fifth of these standards are recognized as national standards by a voluntary national coordinating body called the American National Standards Institute (ANSI) which represents the U.S. in international groups.

The American National Standards Institute does not write or develop standards. Instead standards are developed by various industry groups. Fig. 18-3. The *American National Standards Institute* approves, issues and distributes these standards. In fact, all national standards from all countries, such as those from the British Standards Institute, must be purchased through the American National Standards Institute. All *international standards,* including those

AAMA	Architectural Aluminum Manufacturers Association
AAR	Association of American Railroads
AASHO	American Association of State Highway Officials
AATCC	American Association of Textile Chemists and Colorists
ACI	American Concrete Institute
ADA	American Dental Association
AFBMA	Anti-Friction Bearing Manufacturers Association, Inc.
AGMA	American Gear Manufacturers Association
AHAM	Association of Home Appliance Manufacturers
AIA	American Institute of Architects
AIEE	American Institute of Electrical Engineers; name changed to Institute of Electrical and Electronics Engineers (IEEE)
API	American Petroleum Institute
ARI	Air-Conditioning and Refrigeration Institute
ASAE	American Society of Agricultural Engineers
ASCE	American Society of Civil Engineers
ASHRAE	American Society of Heating, Refrigerating and Air-Conditioning Engineers
ASLE	American Society of Lubricating Engineers
ASME	American Society of Mechanical Engineers
ASQC	American Society for Quality Control
ASSE	American Society of Sanitary Engineers
ASTM	American Society for Testing and Materials
AWS	American Welding Society
AWWA	American Water Works Association
BHMA	Builders Hardware Manufacturers Association
BMIC	U.S. Bureau of Mines Information Circular
BMTP	U.S. Bureau of Mines Technical Paper
CEE	International Commission on Rules for the Approval of Electrical Equipment
CEMA	Conveyor Equipment Manufacturers Association
CGA	Compressed Gas Association
CISPR	International Special Committee on Radio Interference
CS	Commercial Standard
DCDMA	Diamond Core Drill Manufacturers Association
EEI	Edison Electric Institute
EIA	Electronic Industries Association
FSPT	Federation of Societies for Paint Technology
ICC	Interstate Commerce Commission
IEEE	Institute of Electrical and Electronics Engineers
IES	Illuminating Engineering Society
IFI	Industrial Fasteners Institute
IME	Institute of Makers of Explosives
IP	Institute of Petroleum (London)
IPCEA	Insulated Power Cable Engineers Association
IRE	Institute of Radio Engineers; name changed to Institute of Electrical and Electronics Engineers (IEEE)
ITE	Institute of Traffic Engineers
MPTA	Mechanical Power Transmission Association
NBS	National Bureau of Standards
NEMA	National Electrical Manufacturers Association
NFPA	National Fire Protection Association
NFPA	National Fluid Power Association
NLGI	National Lubricating Grease Institute
RETMA	Radio-Electronics-Television Manufacturers Association; name changed to Electronic Industries Association (EIA)
RWMA	Resistance Welder Manufacturers Association
SAE	Society of Automotive Engineers
SAMA	Scientific Apparatus Makers Association
SPR	Simplified Practice Recommendation
TAPPI	Technical Association of the Pulp and Paper Industry
UL	Underwriters' Laboratories

Fig. 18-3
Organizations that are members of the American National Standards Institute.

of IEC and ISO must be obtained from the participating organization in each country. For example, in the U.S. the standards are available from American National Standards Institute while in Canada the Standards Council of Canada is the official source.

International Agreement

The leading international groups are the International Organization for Standardization (ISO) and the International Electrotechnical Commission (IEC), in which all major nations are represented. IEC is concerned with the standardization of electrical and electronic equipment; ISO is responsible for all other fields.

ISO as the international specialized agency for standardization was comprised in 1975 of the national standards bodies of 80 countries. The work of ISO is aimed at world-wide agreement on *International Standards* with a view to the expansion of trade, the improvement of quality, the increase of productivity and the lowering of prices. The work is carried out through some 1,200 technical bodies.

U.S. participation is voluntary and is not supported directly by the Government. The U.S. participates in all IEC technical committees and most of the ISO technical committees. After member countries of IEC or ISO reach a consensus, an ISO international standard is published for adoption by any country as its national standard.

Participants in international standards negotiations need to be adept in the use of metric units, for the International Metric System is the official measurement language of both IEC and ISO.

Increasingly, countries are adopting IEC and ISO standards instead of developing their own national standards. At the same time existing national standards can form a basis for agreement on international standards. In addition to the national and international standard groups, there are also certain regional standard organizations. One of great concern in the United States is the Pacific Area Standards Congress (PASC). It is composed of the countries of Canada, Japan, Australia, New Zealand, and the United States. This group works with the ISO and IEC to participate effectively in international standards.

Only about 2,500 international standards have been adopted by IEC and ISO. Of these about 150 are in the SI metric measurement language. Of course, many of the international standards do not require measurement. World trade needs somewhere between 20,000 and 30,000 standards to function effectively. Of these, about 11,000 must be metric *industrial standards* for items like threads, roller bearings, chains, gears, pumps and thousands of other items. The industrial powers of the world recognize the urgency of this need and are producing international engineering standards at an ever-increasing rate. Most of the required international standards will be developed in the next 10 years.

ISO member bodies

Albania/Albanie	BSA	Byroja e Standarteve Prane Komisionit te Planit te Shtetit
Australia/Australie	SAA	Standards Association of Australia
Austria/Autriche	ON	Österreichisches Normungs institut
Bangladesh	BDSI	Bangladesh Standards Institution
Belgium/Belgique	IBN	Institut belge de normalisation
Brazil/Brésil	ABNT	Associação Brasileira de Normas Técnicas
Bulgaria/Bulgarie	KKCM	Committee for Quality, Standardization and Metrology at the Council of Ministers
Canada	SCC	Standards Council of Canada
Chile/Chili	INN	Instituto Nacional de Normalización
Colombia/Colombie	ICONTEC	Instituto Colombiano de Normas Técnicas
Cuba	NC	Instituto Cubano de Normalización, Metrologia y Control de la Calidad
Czechoslovakia/Tchécoslovaquie	CSN	Urad pro normalizaci a mereni
Denmark/Danemark	DS	Dansk Standardiseringsraad
Egypt, Arab Rep. of/Egypte, Rep. Arabe d'	EOS	Egyptian Organization for Standardization
Ethiopia/Ethiopie	ESI	Ethiopian Standards Institution
Finland/Finlande	SFS	Suomen Standardisoimisliitto r.y.
France	AFNOR	Association française de normalisation
Germany/Allemagne	DNA	Deutscher Normenausschuss
Ghana	GSB	Ghana Standards Board
Greece/Grèce	NHS	Hellenic Republic Ministry of Industry Standardization Division
Hungary/Hongrie	MSZH	Magyar Szabványügyi Hivatal
India/Inde	ISI	Indian Standards Institution
Indonesia-/Indonésie	YDNI	Yayasan Dana Normalisasi Indonesia
Iran	ISIRI	Institute of Standards and Industrial Research of Iran Ministry of Industries and Mines
Iraq	IOS	Iraqi Organization for Standards
Ireland/Irlande	IIRS	Institute for Industrial Research and Standards
Israel/Israël	SII	Standards Institution of Israel
Italy/Italie	UNI	Ente Nazionale Italiano di Unificazione
Jamaica/Jamaïque	JBS	Bureau of Standards
Japan/Japon	JISC	Japanese Industrial Standards Committee
Korea, Dem. P. Rep. of/Corée, Rép. Dém. P. de	CSK	Committee for Standardization of the Democratic People's Republic of Korea
Korea, Rep. of/Corée, Rép. de	KBS	Bureau of Standards Industrial Advancement Administration
Lebanon/Liban	LIBNOR	Institut libanais de normalisation
Malaysia/Malaisie	SIM	Standards Institution of Malaysia
Mexico/Mexique	DGN	Dirección General de Normas
Morocco/Maroc	SNIMA	Service de normalisation industrielle marocaine — Direction de l'industrie — Ministère du commerce, de l'industrie, des mines et de la marine marchande
Netherlands/Pays-Bas	NNI	Nederlands Normalisatie-Instituut
New Zealand/Nouvelle-Zélande	SANZ	Standards Association of New Zealand
Nigeria	NSO	Federal Ministry of Industries, Nigerian Standards Organization
Norway/Norvège	NSF	Norges Standardiseringsforbund
Pakistan	PSI	Pakistan Standards Institution
Peru/Pérou	ITINTEC	Instituto de Investigación Tecnológica Industrial y de Normas Tecnicas
Philippines	KP	Bureau of Standards of the Philippines
Poland/Pologne	PKNiM	Polski Komitet Normalizacji i Miar
Portugal	IGPAI	Repartição de Normalização
Romania/Roumanie	IRS	Institutul Român de Standardizare
Saudi Arabia/Arabie Saoudite	SASO	Saudi Arabian Standards Organization
Singapore/Singapour	SISIR	Singapore Institute of Standards and Industrial Research
South Africa, Rep. of/Afrique du Sud, Rép. d'	SABS	South African Bureau of Standards
Spain/Espagne	IRANOR	Instituto Nacional de Racionalización y Normalización
Sri Lanka	BCS	Bureau of Ceylon Standards
Sudan/Soudan	OSS	Sudanese Organization for Standards Specifications
Sweden/Suède	SIS	Sveriges Standardiseringskommission
Switzerland/Suisse	SNV	Association suisse de normalisation
Thailand/Thaïlande	TISI	Thai Industrial Standards Institute
Turkey/Turquie	TSE	Türk Standardlari Enstitüsü
United Kingdom/Royaume-Uni	BSI	British Standards Institution
USA	ANSI	American National Standards Institute
USSR/URSS	GOST	Gosudarstvennyj Komitet Standartov Soveta Ministrov S.S.S.R.
Venezuela	COVENIN	Comisión Venezolana de Normas Industriales
Yugoslavia/Yougoslavie	JZS	Jugoslovenski zavod za Standardizaciju
Zambia/Zambie	ZSI	Zambian Standards Institute

ISO correspondent members

Algeria/Algérie	Institut algérien de normalisation et de propriété industrielle
Barbados/Barbade	Barbados National Standards Institution
Cameroon/Cameroun	Direction de l'industrie (Service de normalisation) - Ministère du développement industriel et commercial
Cyprus/Chypre	The Ministry of Commerce and Industry of the Republic of Cyprus
Ecuador/Équateur	Instituto Ecuatoriano de Normalización
Hong Kong	Federation of Hong Kong Industries
Iceland/Islande	Industrial Development Institute
Ivory Coast/Côte d'Ivoire	Bureau ivoirien de normalisation - Ministère du Plan
Jordan/Jordanie	Directorate of Standards. Ministry of National Economy
Kenya	Kenya Bureau of Standards
Kuwait/Koweit	The Ministry of Commerce and Industry
Liberia	Ministry of Commerce, Industry and Transportation
Libya/Libye	The Standards and Specifications Section, Department of Industrial Organization Ministry of Industry
Madagascar	Ministère des Mines, de l'Industrie, du Commerce et du Ravitaillement - Service du Conditionnement
Malta/Malte	Department of Industry
Syria/Syrie	Industrial Testing and Research Centre
Trinidad and Tabago/Trinité-et-Tobago	Trinidad and Tobago Bureau of Standards Ministry of Industry and Commerce
Tunisia/Tunisie	Ministère de l'Economie Nationale

Fig. 18-2
ISO membership

Summary

ISO (the International Organization for Standardization) is the international specialized agency for standardization, comprising the national standards bodies of 80 countries.

The ISO work covers a wide range of topics: from containers to dental equipment, from computer languages to materials testing, from automobile safety to paper sizes, from machine tools to environmental pollution—to mention just a few of the areas in which ISO is engaged. ISO is the largest international organization for industrial and technical collaboration, and brings together in its technical bodies the interest of producers, users (including consumers), government and the scientific community.

The results of ISO technical work are published as *International Standards,* which represent a global consensus of opinion.

- The technical work of ISO is carried out through 1,400 technical committees, sub-committees and working groups.

- The secretariats of the technical committees are located in 27 countries, served by some 400 people.

- The work is planned and coordinated by the Central Secretariat in Geneva, with a staff of 85 people drawn from 20 countries.

- Eight ISO meetings take place, on average, every working day of the year. A total of 20,000 experts from all over the world take part each year in ISO meetings.

- In a year, more than 10,000 different working documents are circulated to the participants in ISO work.

UNIT 19
PAPER STANDARDS

The knowledge explosion of the last 30 years is a direct result of our ever-increasing emphasis on technological developments. In addition, governments at all levels have increased in complexity. The result is a paperwork explosion that has literally inundated the world with printed materials of all types. Each year thousands of new books are published. Over 50 000 journals and magazines are printed on a regular basis. Add to this the forms, tables, and reports published by the government plus all of the paperwork needed for our "credit card" economy. This has not only caused a serious paper shortage, but more serious problems in storage of printed materials. One only has to glance at the bookshelves in a library or bookstore to see what a difficult job it is to store books of hundreds of different sizes and shapes.

Under our present customary system, paper sizes have developed for the convenience of the publisher and printer. There are no standards in book sizes, and many publishers attempt to attract attention to their books by printing them in an odd size that is very difficult to store. Much of the storage of printed material must be done in a very inefficient manner, simply because there are so many sizes and shapes. Even the *microfilming* of printed materials is difficult, because there is no standard size or shape that must be reproduced.

The only standardization of any type is the correspondence paper used in the United States, and this, too, is not one size. For industry and everyday use, the 8-1/2" x 11" paper size is normal. However, for federal government use the official size is 8" x 10-1/2". In addition, there is an 8-1/2" x 14" size sometimes called "foolscap" used for legal work. Fig. 19-1. These three sizes were introduced shortly after World War I, and have become standard for industry and government. Apparently the reason for the discrepancy between industry and government correspondence paper size was one of beaurocratic indecision. Former President Hoover, when he was Secretary of Commerce, established by decree on March 28, 1921 that his department would use 8" x 10-1/2" letter size paper. This eventually became standard throughout the government. An attempt was made during a government-industry conference to work out the difference in sizes. However, no decision was reached on a single paper size for correspondence, and the discrepancy has continued.

Because of the three correspondence paper sizes it is necessary to have at least two different sizes of filing cabinets. Also, different sizes of notebook covers or binders are needed for correspondence size paper and legal size paper. To cite one example, before conversion to ISO paper sizes, the Ontario government used over 80 different paper sizes. With the change to international standards, this has been reduced to only 6 or 8 standard sizes.

History of Paper Standardization

The first evidence of any attempt to standardize paper sizes is found in a French legal document dated November 3, 1798. It is important to note that this date was just five years after the metric system was first conceived. This French law established paper sizes that were very similar to those developed much later as international standards. National standard paper sizes were first established in Germany in 1922 by their standards organization, which is now called Deutchen Normenausschuss (DNA). These standard sizes received international recognition when they were incorporated into the ISO standards by the International Organization for Standardization, created in 1947. Since 1922 when Germany first established paper sizes as national standards, they have become the official standards in all metric countries including those converting to the metric system of measurement.

Current Paper Sizes

In the customary system paper sizes and weights are complex subjects because there are so many kinds and sizes with no relationship between sizes and weights. Some of the more common customary sizes of paper available are shown in Fig. 19-2. Note that the basic size of bond paper is 17" x 22", but it is also available in several other sizes. The *basis* weight for a particular kind of paper is its weight in pounds per 500 sheets (a ream). For example, if a package is marked *bond* 17" x 22"-16-32/M, it means that the paper has a basis weight of 16 pounds and that the weight of 1000 sheets is 32 pounds, indicated by 32/M (M means 1000). Because the weight of paper bears a certain relationship to thickness, and because different kinds of paper have a different basic size and different basis weight for approximately the same thickness of material, it is difficult, for example, to compare the thickness of bond paper and some other kinds of printing paper. While one ream might be marked *bond—40 pound* and another *book—40 pound*, it would be almost impossible to compare actual thickness of each sheet. In contrast, in the international paper sizes, weights and thicknesses of paper can be compared very easily, since all weights are based on grams per square metre (g/m^2).

ISO Paper Sizes

The ISO paper sizes are based on a rectangle whose sides are in a ratio of 1 to the square root of 2 (1 to $\sqrt{2}$), or 1 to 1.414 with an *area equal* to exactly 1 square metre (m^2). Fig. 19-3. With this unique relationship the sheet can be folded in half as many times as desired, and the subdivisions will always be in the same proportion. The basic standard sheet A0 measures 841 x 1189 mm (33.1" x 46.8"). Fig. 19-4. Each smaller size is half the next larger size and all are in the same proportion. Fig. 19-5. Each size is always slightly narrower and a little longer than a square, which is considered to be in good design proportion. Fig. 19-6.

The ISO A series is the main series used for general printing, including stationery, magazines and various other kinds of periodicals. It should be used whenever possible. It is available in sizes for normal trim and also for bleed work or extra trim. Fig. 19-7. The AO series is the standard size, and when it is halved so that it becomes two pieces, these two are exactly equal to the previous piece. The number after the A indicates the halving of the previous piece. Thus, A1 (594 x 841 mm) is one half of A0, which is 841 x 1189 mm. Note also that the longer side of the halved piece is the same as the shorter side of the previous piece. For example, the short side of A3 paper is 297 mm while the long side of A4 paper, which is 1/2 as large, is 297 mm.

The ISO B series paper is a secondary series that is used primarily for posters and other printed items such

STANDARD PAPER SIZES:

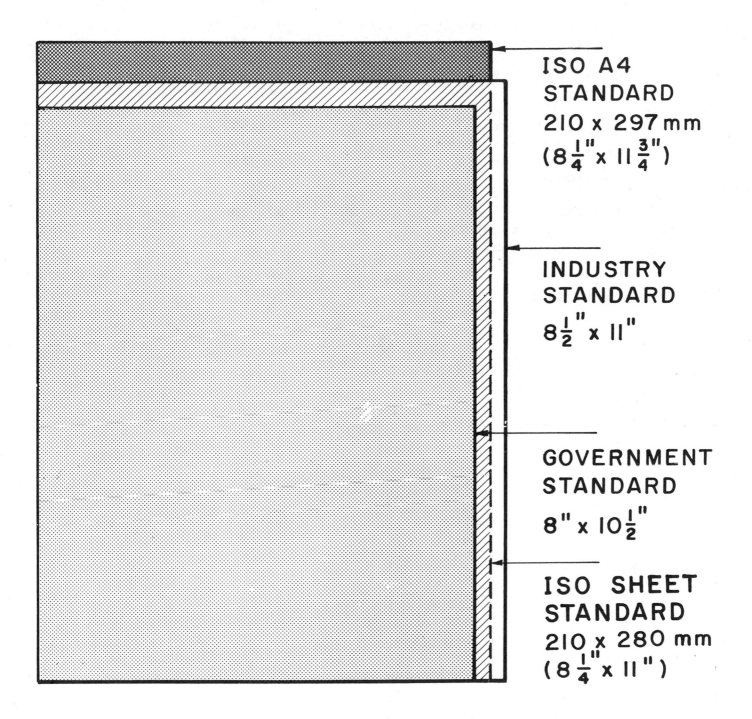

ISO A4
STANDARD
210 x 297 mm
($8\frac{1}{4}$" x $11\frac{3}{4}$")

INDUSTRY
STANDARD
$8\frac{1}{2}$" x 11"

GOVERNMENT
STANDARD
8" x $10\frac{1}{2}$"

ISO SHEET
STANDARD
210 x 280 mm
($8\frac{1}{4}$" x 11")

Fig. 19-1
Comparison of the two common customary standards for stationery in relationship to the metric sizes.

Kind	General Uses	Basic Size (Inches)	Substance Weights (pounds)	Other Common Sizes (Inches)
Bond	Letterheads, Documents, office forms	17 x 22	9, 13, 16 20, 24	17 x 28, 19 x 24
Index	Index cards, folders	25½ x 30½	90, 110, 140, 170	20½ x 24 3/4 22½ x 28 1/2
Book	General printing Books and halftones Calendered for halftones	25 x 38	50, 60, 70, 80, 90, 100	17½ x 22½, 19 x 25, 23 x 29, 28 x 42, and multiples
Cover	Covers. Enameled for covers with halftones	20 x 26	50, 60, 65, 80	23 x 35, 28 x 40
Label	Labels. Coated – for varnishing	25 x 38	50, 60, 70	

Fig. 19-2
Common packaged sizes of paper available in the customary system.

Paper sizes   *Golden Rectangle*

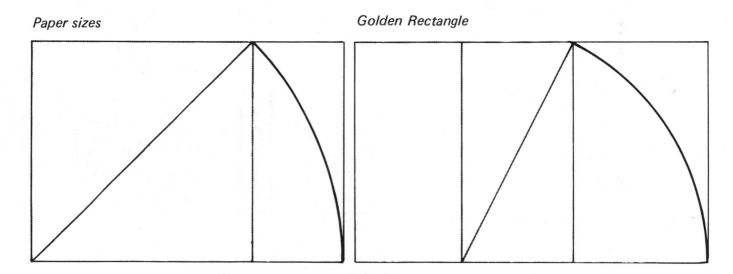

Fig. 19-3
A comparison of international paper size based on a proportion of 1:√2 or 1:1.414 and the golden rectangle commonly used in design which has a proportion of 1:1.618. The international paper sizes have a proportion that is maintained whenever the sheet is folded in half. The golden rectangle is constructed in such a way that when the shaded area is removed the area remaining is also a golden rectangle.

COMPARISON CHART - A SIZE PAPER

ISO-sizes	METRIC-millimetres	CUSTOMARY-inches
2A	1189 x 1682	46.81 x 66.22
A0	841 x 1189	33.11 x 46.81
A1	594 x 841	23.39 x 33.11
A2	420 x 594	16.54 x 23.39
A3	297 x 420	11.69 x 16.54
A4	210 x 297	8.27 x 11.69
A5	148 x 210	5.83 x 8.27
A6	105 x 148	4.13 x 5.83
A7	74 x 105	2.91 x 4.13
A8	52 x 74	2.05 x 2.91
A9	37 x 52	1.46 x 2.05
A10	26 x 37	1.02 x 1.46

Fig. 19-4
A comparison of the common A size papers.

ISO - A SIZE PAPER

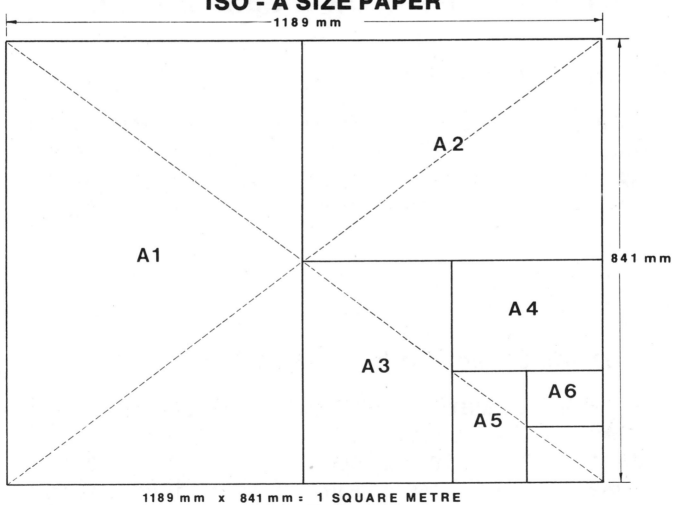

1189 mm x 841 mm : 1 SQUARE METRE

Fig. 19-5

A graphic representation of the affect of doubling or halving the size of the A size paper. Any size in the A series can be obtained by enlarging and reducing, and it will still retain the same proportion.

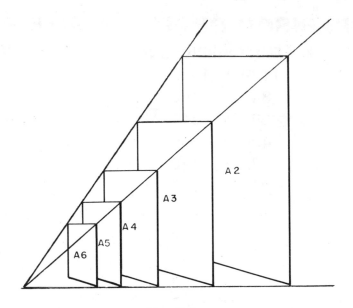

Fig. 19-6
Note that all ISO paper sizes have exactly the same proportion.

STOCK SIZES - FOR A SERIES PAPER

Sizes for Normal Trims

ISO - size	METRIC - millimetres	CUSTOMARY - inches
RAO	860 x 1220	33.86 x 48.03
RA1	610 x 860	24.02 x 33.86
RA2	430 x 610	16.93 x 24.02

Sizes for Bleed Work or Extra Trims

ISO - size	METRIC - millimetres	CUSTOMARY - inches
SRAO	900 x 1280	35.43 x 50.39
SRA1	640 x 900	25.20 x 35.43
SRA2	450 x 640	17.72 x 25.20

Fig. 19-7
Common ISO sizes used in printing when the sheets must be trimmed.

as wall charts. The B series is exactly intermediary between various A sizes. Therefore, this series is used where the difference in size of the larger sizes in the A series represents too large a jump. Fig. 19-8. The B series is derived from rational metric dimensions with both the basic B0 and B1 size having one side that measures exactly 1 metre (1000 mm). The basic B0 size is called B0 and measures 1000 x 1414 mm(the 1 to 1.414 relationship is retained exactly as in the A series).

The ISO C series is for envelopes, and also for folders and postcards. Fig. 19-9. The relationship between the A, B and C series is illustrated in Fig. 19-10. International envelope sizes are designed to be used with the ISO series of paper sizes. The most commonly used international envelope sizes are in the C series, and are designed to accommodate the A series of paper sizes folded in various ways. Fig. 11-1a,b,c,d. The C series envelopes will fit into the B series envelopes with the same numbers. Therefore, the B series are normally intended to be used when it is necessary to mail an envelope within another envelope.

In addition to the ISO A, B, and C sizes, two additional sheet sizes have been approved.

A. A sheet size that measures 210 x 280 mm, which is equal to 8.27 inches by 11.02 inches. This size is exactly the same in width as the A4 size. Therefore, ISO metric size envelopes can be used. However, this size is slightly shorter than the A4 and almost exactly the same length as the 8-1/2 x 11" size; so that all existing filing and duplicating equipment can be used. This size is recommended primarily for correspondence but not to replace the A4 size for drafting and other uses.

B. The second size is the 210 x 198 mm, which is exactly 2/3 the size of the A4. This size can be used as an intermediate size between the A4 and A5 paper.

Weight of ISO Paper

In the ISO system, paper substance or basis weight is calculated on the weight in grams of a standard area of 1 square metre of one sheet of paper. The symbol for this is g/m^2 but the French word "gramme" is sometimes used to express this factor. In the A series the basic size A0 has an area of exactly 1 square metre. Therefore, if the paper has a weight of 80 grams per square metre (g/m^2), one sheet of size A4 paper which is 1/16 of an A0 sheet would weigh exactly 5 grams. Remember that a gram is a very small amount since there are 454 grams in a pound. With this system, calculation of all paper weights will be greatly simplified. Since paper substance (basis weight), measured in g/m^2, does not vary with paper size but rather is determined by the weight of a standard area, comparisons of substance of various qualities of paper can be made instantly. Such easy calculation makes it easy to figure the weight of the contents of a letter or the approximate weight of a book.

If it is necessary to convert from customary paper weights to metric weights, this can be done either by using a table, such as in Fig. 19-12 or by a formula. As a rule of thumb, to change the basis weight of *book* paper from pounds per ream to grams per square metre multiply by 1.5. For example if *book* paper has a basis weight of 30 pounds per ream this equals about 45 g/m^2. To change the basis weight of bond paper from pounds per ream to grams per square metre, multiply by 3.75. For example, if *bond* paper has a basis weight

of 20 pounds this is equal to about 75 g/m^2. Any paper weight can be converted from customary to metric by using the formula:

$$\frac{\text{basis weight x 1406}}{\text{square inches per sheet}} = g/m^2 .$$

For example, to find the weight in grams per square metre (g/m^2) of 17" x 22"—20 pound bond the formula would be

$$\frac{20 \times 1406}{374}$$

which equals 75.18 g/m^2, rounded to 75 g/m^2.

There is a preferred range for the substances (weights) of ISO paper based on the Renard number series R20. Fig. 19-13. Using this series as a base would provide the graphic designer, printer and consumer with ideal choices of paper substances.

The thickness of paper in metric will be measured in micrometres (μm) instead of thousandths of an inch or mils, as in customary paper.

Advantages of ISO Paper Sizes

1. Their use will reduce the wide variety of paper sizes now in common use. The Ontario provincial government has approved the use of ISO paper sizes, and in the process has reduced the number of paper sizes used from 80 to 6 or 8.

2. Their use will streamline office application, since there will be a limited number of sizes of paper to be stored and used. Since each smaller A size paper is 1/2 the next larger size, paper of different sizes can be stacked efficiently. For example, an A4 size normally used for letter writing and an A5 size commonly used for notes can be stacked one above the other, since two packages of A5 size paper placed side by side will be exactly equal to one package of A4 paper.

3. Since A4 paper is slightly narrower and just a little longer than 8-1/2" x 11" paper, it will provide for at least two additional double (four single spaced) lines of typing on the average letter.

4. All of the smaller sizes of A paper can be cut from the basic A0 size without scrap and, therefore, no waste.

5. Use of international standards in offices will provide for much greater efficiency and economy since there will be fewer sizes of paper and, therefore, reduced costs.

6. There will be better utilization of storage facilities.

7. It will improve the handling of mail by automatic postal equipment. International postal standards will give preference to certain ISO paper sizes and envelopes.

8. Filing will be simplified because fewer sizes and shapes of paper will be handled.

9. Microfilming will be simplified. One of the great advantages of the ISO paper sizes is that both the A and B series are in the same proportion and have a ratio of the shorter to the longer side of 1 to the square root of 2. Any size in either of the series can be reduced to microfilm size with the same proportions. Only the camera length needs to be changed, and each of the A size papers will fill up the film without any great waste. The standard microfiche is 105 x 148 mm which is equal to the ISO paper A6 size.

COMPARISON CHART - B SIZE PAPER

ISO-sizes	METRIC-millimetres	CUSTOMARY-inches
B0	1000 x 1414	39.37 x 55.67
B1	707 x 1000	27.83 x 39.37
B2	500 x 707	19.68 x 27.83
B3	353 x 500	13.90 x 19.68
B4	250 x 353	9.84 x 13.90
B5	176 x 250	6.93 x 9.84
B6	125 x 176	4.92 x 6.93
B7	88 x 125	3.46 x 4.92
B8	62 x 88	2.44 x 3.46
B9	44 x 62	1.73 x 2.44
B10	31 x 44	1.22 x 1.73

Fig. 19-8
The B size papers are usually used for posters and other printed matter such as wall charts.

COMPARISON CHART - C SIZE ENVELOPE

ISO - size	METRIC - millimetres	CUSTOMARY - inches
C4	229 x 324	9.02 x 12.76
C5	162 x 229	6.38 x 9.02
C6	114 x 162	4.49 x 6.38
DL	110 x 220	4.33 x 8.66

Fig. 19-9
The C sizes are used for envelopes.

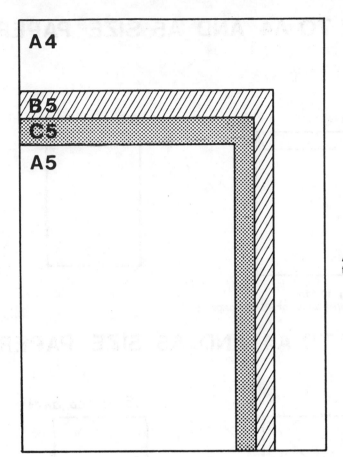

Fig. 19-10
A comparison of A5, B5 and C5 paper with the A4 size used for stationery.

COMPARING C4 ENVELOPE TO A4 AND A3 SIZE PAPER

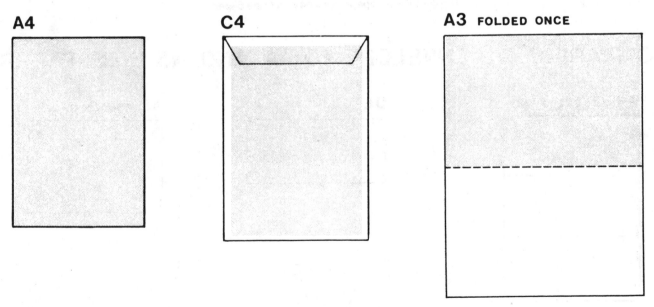

A4   **C4**   **A3** FOLDED ONCE

Fig. 19-11a
Using a C4 envelope with A4 or A3 size paper.

COMPARING C5 ENVELOPE TO A4 AND A5 SIZE PAPER

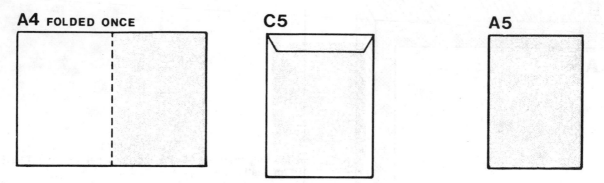

Fig. 19-11b
Using a C5 envelope with an A4 or A5 size paper.

COMPARING C6 ENVELOPE TO A4 AND A5 SIZE PAPER

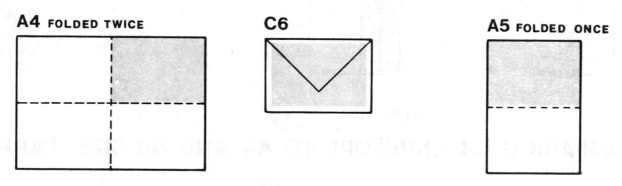

Fig. 19-11c
Using a C6 envelope with an A4 or A5 size paper.

COMPARING DL ENVELOPE TO A4 AND A5 SIZE PAPER

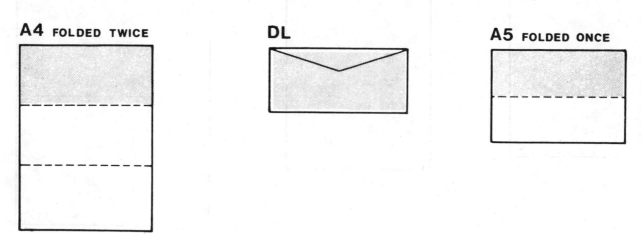

Fig. 19-11d
Using a DL envelope with an A4 or A5 size paper. The DL size is the standard commercial envelope size.

Relationship
of
Ream Weights and g/m²

Book 25 x 38"		Bond and Ledger 17 x 22"	
lbs	g/m²	lbs.	g/m²
30	44	12	45
33	49	13	49
40	59	16	60
45	66	18	68
50	74	20	75
60	89	24	90
70	104	28	105
80	118	32	120
90	133	36	135
100	148	40	150
110	163	44	165

Fig. 19-12
Customary and metric weight relationships. Using the metric equivalent, note how closely the weight of *70 pound book* and *28 pound bond* compare.

R20 SERIES OF PAPER WEIGHTS AND EQUIVALENT WEIGHTS

'R' series	Bond 17 x 22 432 x 559 mm	Cover 20 x 26 508 x 660 mm	Index 25½ x 30½ 648 x 775 mm	Newsprint 24 x 36 610 x 914 mm	Book 25 x 38 635 x 965 mm
g/m²	lb/ream	lb/ream	lb/ream	lb/ream	lb/ream
20.0	5.32	7.39	11.00	12.29	13.51
22.4	5.95	8.28	12.39	13.77	15.13
25.0	6.65	9.24	13.83	15.36	16.89
28.0	7.44	10.35	15.49	17.21	18.92
31.5	8.37	11.65	17.43	19.36	21.28
45.0	11.97	16.64	24.89	27.66	30.40
50.0	13.30	18.49	27.66	30.73	33.78
56.0	14.89	20.71	30.98	34.42	37.84
63.0	16.75	23.30	34.85	38.72	42.57
71.0	18.88	26.26	39.28	43.63	47.97
85.0	22.61	31.45	46.90	52.27	57.46
100.0	26.60	36.98	55.32	61.46	67.57
112.0	29.79	41.42	61.96	68.83	75.68
140.0	37.24	51.78	77.45	86.04	94.60
180.0	47.88	66.57	99.58	110.62	121.63
200.0	53.20	73.97	110.64	122.91	135.14
250.0	66.50	92.46	138.30	153.64	168.93
400.0	106.41	147.95	221.29	245.83	270.29

Fig. 19-13
The R20 series of paper weights in grams per square metre with comparative weights in various customary papers.

Disadvantages of ISO Paper Sizes

1. Most paper manufacturing equipment used in the United States produces paper rolls that are not designed for efficient cutting to metric sizes. It has been estimated that there may be as much as ten percent increase in paper wastage if A size papers are cut from standard rolls of paper currently manufactured.

2. Use of A4 size paper as standard for school and business purposes may require changes in related stationery items used.

a. While A4 paper can be stored in standard letter files, it is slightly longer than the 8-1/2" x 11" size. Therefore, a slightly wider filing cabinet would be better.

b. An entirely different notebook cover or ring binder is required for A4 size paper. The cover is longer and has four rings instead of three.

c. A different paper punch is needed for use with A4 size paper.

3. A4 size paper cannot be cut from customary paper package without very great waste.

Stationery Supplies for ISO Paper Sizes

A change to A4 letter size paper from the current 8-1/2" x 11" (216 x 279 mm) would cause some difficulties. Therefore the metric letter size (210 x 280 mm) will be used in most offices. The A4 size paper is 6 mm narrower than the 8-1/2" x 11" and 18 mm longer. Some factors to consider are as follows:

1. *Filing cabinets and folders.* The standard letter filing cabinet has an inside width of from 307 to 312 mm. Therefore, the slightly longer A4 sheets can be filed with little difficulty. However, if hanging file folders are used, these are normally about 295 mm wide or slightly narrower than the length of the A4 sheet. If standard manila file folders are used, these are approximately 300 mm wide, or slightly wider than the length of the A4 sheet. It is recommended that the manila folders for A4 letter size should measure 220 x 315 mm. These would be slightly larger in both directions than the current manila folders. If legal size cabinets and folders are used, there will be no problem since the A4 size is considerably smaller. However, there will be waste of space by using legal size cabinets with A4 paper.

2. *Ring binders.* While three ring binders can be used with A4 size paper, the four ring binder is more commonly used in international practice. The four ring binder requires a different paper punch. The advantage of the four ring binder is that it is very convenient to hold both the A4 size and two sheets of the A5 size in the same binder. The outside diameter of the four ring binder should be about 38 x 250 x 310 mm for wide rings of 30 mm diameter. The outside diameter should be 20 x 240 x 310 mm for the narrow rings of 15 mm diameter. Standard three ring binder can be used with the metric letter size of paper.

3. *Duplicating equipment.* Most duplicating equipment will accommodate A4 size paper with some difficulty. If there is a very small margin on the top and bottom of a typing on A4 size paper, it may not completely reproduce on an 8-1/2" x 11" sheet. This will not be a problem with the metric letter size of paper.

4. *Ruled paper.* If ruled paper is used in a ring binder, the paper normally has the ruled lines spaced 5, 7 or 9 mm apart. The 9 mm spacing is the most common.

5. *Paper cutters.* Paper cutters can be easily converted to cutting both customary and international paper sizes by changing the metal tape that gives the readout for depth of cut. A dual reading tape can be added to replace the existing inch tape so cutting can be conveniently done.

6. *Conversion to ISO paper sizes.* It is unlikely that the paper industry will convert all customary sizes to ISO sizes. Perhaps the first conversion will be a soft one from the customary system. In addition, some of the more common ISO sizes may be available, particularly the A4 for correspondence, A5 for notes and the letter size that measures 210 x 280 mm.

When ISO paper sizes are available, suggested practical applications of the A series are shown in Fig. 19-14.

USES FOR ISO PAPER SIZES

	A0	A1	A2	A3	A4	A5	A6	A7	A8	A9
1. Books, standard size						x				
2. Books, paperback							x			
3. Business, Credit Cards									x	
4. Calendars, wall			x	x	x					
5. Candy wrappers								x	x	
6. Carbon paper					x	x				
7. Catalogs					x	x				
8. Checks							x			
9. Directories					x	x				
10. Facial Tissues					x					
11. Forms					x	x	x	x		
12. Gift Wrap	x	x								
13. Greeting Cards						x	x	x		
14. Index Cards						x	x			
15. Invoices					x	x	x			
16. Labels						x	x	x	x	x
17. Letterheads					x	x				
18. Magazines					x	x				
19. Newspapers			x	x						
20. Postcards							x			

Fig. 19-14
Common uses for various sizes of ISO paper.

UNIT 20
THREAD STANDARDS

The first known practical application of the screw thread was developed by Archimedes over 2000 years ago, but the screw thread did not become important in commerce until the industrial revolution. A screw thread is a ridge in the form of a helix on the external or internal surface of a cylinder or cone. It is essentially a spiral inclined plane or wedge whose mechanical advantage is used to increase the applied force.

Screw threads have many uses. They *hold or fasten* parts such as nuts and bolts together. Fig. 20-1. They *transmit motion,* as on a lathe lead screw. Fig. 20-2. They are used as *measuring* instruments, as on a micrometer or camera. They increase *torque* such as in raising a heavy building with a screw jack. Screw threads also serve many other functions such as connectors or couplings, gas and liquid seals, and translators of motion and power. Threaded fasteners are a most important element of today's technology. In fact, a study of manufacturing time in all of American industries indicates that about *half of all production time* is spent in assembling parts. While adhesive bonding and welding are increasingly used in permanent fastening, threaded fasteners are unmatched in fastening and disassembling parts.

The *screw* is one of six simple machines; the others being the *lever and fulcrum, wheel and axle, pulley, inclined plane,* and *wedge.* Of these, the screw is the most complex and difficult to standardize in order to achieve interchangeability. The standardization problem stems from the numerous forms or shapes of screw threads in use. A book on world screw thread standards lists over 200 thread forms and shapes. In the United States alone it is estimated that over 2 million different *kinds* of threaded fasteners are used, based on such factors as thread form, head shape, kind of material, diameter, pitch, length, and many other factors.

Most of the thread forms are modifications of the 55 degree V-thread proposed in 1841 by Sir Joseph Whitworth in England and the 60 degree V-thread proposed by Mr. William Sellers of the Franklin Institute, Philadelphia, in 1864. The Whitworth thread was adopted as a British Standard in 1905, and its use became widespread in countries that adopted British technology. The Sellers thread was adopted by many industries in the United States, but it was not standardized nationally when World War I started. However, during the next 30 years this thread form became the basis for our national standard and was known as the American National thread form. It included two basic series: the National fine (NF) and the National coarse (NC) and several special series.

Fig. 20-1
Most types of metal products are assembled with threaded fasteners.

Fig. 20-2
There are many types of threads on a lathe. The thread on the lead screw makes it possible for the engine lathe to cut threads of many types.

International Standardization

The use of different national standards for threads by the Allied Nations during World War II, particularly the Whitworth thread in the United Kingdom and the American National thread in the United States, caused many difficulties since no threaded parts could be interchanged.

In 1948, Great Britain, Canada, and the United States agreed on a thread form known as the Unified form. This thread form has a 60 degree angle. The crest of the external thread may be either flat or rounded. The rounded or flat root of the external thread may be made intentionally or be the result of a worn tool. The internal thread has a flat crest and a rounded or flat root. This makes it possible to interchange the Unified thread form with the American National thread form. Since the American National thread form and the Unified thread form are interchangeable, they can be thought of as one system, the Unified National. There are minor differences between the two systems, but these differences are so technical that they do not need to concern the average machinist. Most threaded fasteners made by industry use one of the Unified National thread forms.

About the same time a metric bureau developed a System International metric thread. However, the metric thread did not specify diameters and pitches so that different metric countries developed their own *national standards* of diameters and pitches. Because thread standardization is such an important topic, during the early days of the ISO organization much of

the time was devoted to the establishment of standards for thread forms. In 1949 the first technical committee of the ISO agreed to adopt the basic profile of the Unified thread as the common profile for all ISO threads and fasteners. Fig. 20-3. This basic profile is used in five accepted series: (1) *ISO metric coarse pitch,* (2) *ISO metric fine pitch,* (3) *ISO metric constant pitch,* (4) *ISO inch* (*Unified*) *coarse pitch,* and (5) *ISO inch* [*Unified*] *fine pitch.* Fig. 20-4. While all of these thread series share the same thread form, they are not interchangeable. In comparing the thread diameters and pitches of ISO metric and ISO inch threads, it will be noted that most of the sizes, particularly in the coarse series, are very close in diameter and number of threads per inch. Lack of interchangeability is clearly obvious to the thousands of owners of automobiles produced outside the United States and many owners of compact American cars. The owner soon learns two basic facts: (a) that a different set of wrenches (called spanners in some countries) is needed—one for the ISO metric thread series and one for the ISO inch series, (b) that while the threads may appear very similar in size and shape, *they are not interchangeable.* For example, while a bolt with an ISO thread M10x1.5 may look almost identical to a bolt with a UNC thread 3/8-16, they are not interchangeable. Fig. 20-5.

In the world at large, the ISO metric thread is the one most commonly used for general fastening purposes. Most English-speaking countries converting to the metric measurement system, such as the United Kingdom, are also converting to the ISO metric thread

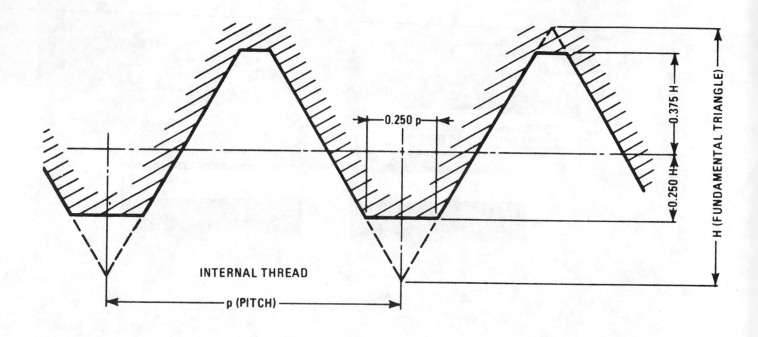

INTERNAL THREAD

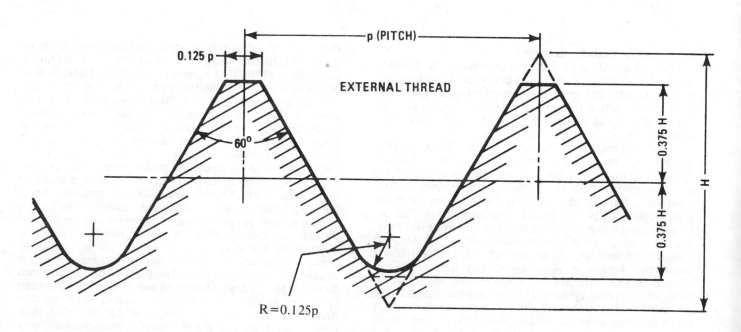

EXTERNAL THREAD

Fig. 20-3
A simplified illustration of the thread form used by both the ISO metric and the ISO inch (Unified) series.

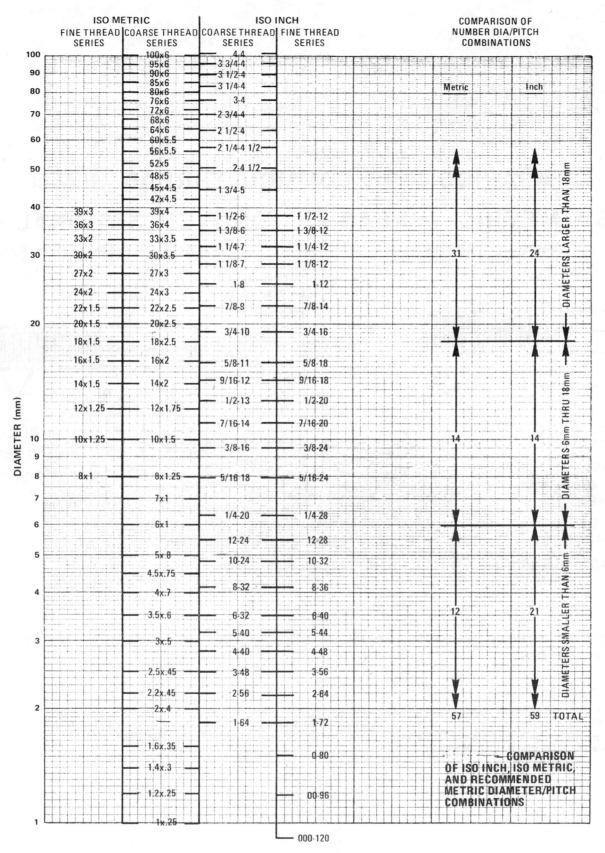

Fig. 20-4
Note the large number of diameters and pitches in the ISO metric and inch series. Together they total 116.

COMPARISON OF COMMON THREAD SIZES
ISO METRIC THREAD
THREAD SERIES
UNIFIED NATIONAL
COARSE THREAD SERIES

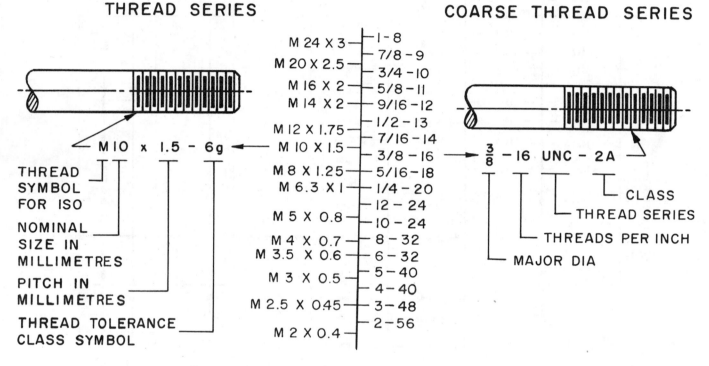

M 24 X 3	1-8
M 20 X 2.5	7/8 - 9
	3/4 - 10
M 16 X 2	5/8 - 11
M 14 X 2	9/16 - 12
	1/2 - 13
M 12 X 1.75	7/16 - 14
M 10 X 1.5	3/8 - 16
M 8 X 1.25	5/16 - 18
M 6.3 X 1	1/4 - 20
	12 - 24
M 5 X 0.8	10 - 24
M 4 X 0.7	8 - 32
M 3.5 X 0.6	6 - 32
	5 - 40
M 3 X 0.5	4 - 40
M 2.5 X 0.45	3 - 48
	2 - 56
M 2 X 0.4	

M 10 x 1.5 - 6g

THREAD SYMBOL FOR ISO

NOMINAL SIZE IN MILLIMETRES

PITCH IN MILLIMETRES

THREAD TOLERANCE CLASS SYMBOL

3/8 - 16 UNC - 2A

CLASS

THREAD SERIES

THREADS PER INCH

MAJOR DIA

NOTE -
THE METRIC THREAD ILLUSTRATED IS A LITTLE LARGER IN DIAMETER THAN 3/8"
AND HAS ALMOST 17 THREADS PER INCH.

Fig. 20-5
While ISO metric threads may appear to be similar in diameter and pitch, they are not interchangeable with the ISO inch,
commonly known as the Unified National.

standards. Of course, even countries that have always used metric threads have had to make some adjustments in the diameter and pitch series to conform with the ISO standards. This is true because when metric threads were first used, each country established its own metric thread standards. Therefore, the Japanese metric threads were not compatible with the German metric threads. Only the United States and Canada operate on the dual system of ISO metric threads and ISO inch (Unified) threads, with the ISO inch thread predominant by a wide margin.

Here it is well to point out again that there is a great difference between converting to metric measurement system and converting to ISO standards. Some large American corporations have made a decision to convert to the metric measurement system but, at the same time, to continue to use the ISO inch fastener system. Other American companies are converting to metric measurement and are also changing to ISO metric threads or OMFS threads.

ISO Metric Screw Threads

Information concerning ISO screw threads is covered in a series of ISO standards that are available from the American National Standards Institute. Much of this is highly technical material that is useful only to the engineer. However, the following is the basic information that is needed by anyone who is to utilize the threads: The ISO metric basic profile is shown in Fig. 20-6. As has been indicated earlier, the ISO screw threads come in three standards: coarse, fine and constant pitch. However, only the ISO coarse pitch series is in common use. The ISO metric fine pitch is used in special precision tools and certain instruments. The ISO constant pitch series is used primarily for machine parts and not for fasteners. However, the metric thread on all sparkplugs is in the constant pitch series. Fig. 20-7.

In countries using the ISO metric series, approximately 90 percent of all the threaded fasteners used for manufacturing are in the coarse thread series in the 12 diameter as follows: 2, 2.5, 3, 4, 5, 6, 8, 10, 12, 16, 20, and 24. Fig. 20-8. The ISO fine thread series is used primarily in precision instruments, and threaded fasteners in this system are not commonly available. Fig. 20-9.

Basic Designation

ISO metric threads are designated by the capital letter M followed by the nominal size in millimetres and the pitch in millimetres separated by the sign x. For example, M12x1.75 Fig. 20-10. However, for coarse threads only, the capital letter M and the nominal size

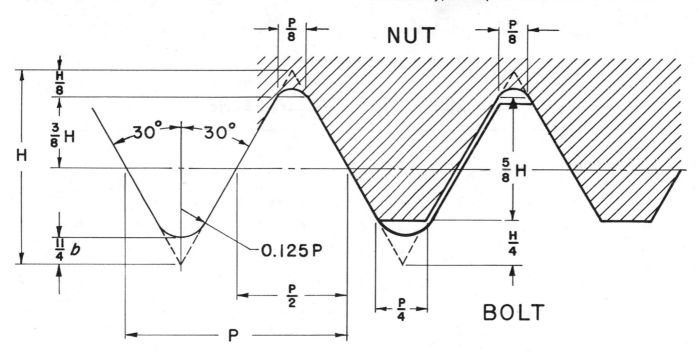

Same basic thread profile for both ISO metric and ISO inch "UNIFIED".

However threads are NOT INTERCHANGEABLE.

Fig. 20-6
A more detailed illustration of the thread profile used for both ISO metric and ISO inch.

Fig. 20-7
Spark plugs all have metric threads in the constant series.

ISO Metric Thread—Coarse Series

Diameter	2	2.5	3	4	5	6	8	10
Pitch	0.4	0.45	0.5	0.7	0.8	1.0	1.25	1.5
Basic effective diameter ...	1.740	2.208	2.675	3.545	4.480	5.350	7.188	9.026
Depth of thread in screw	0.25	0.28	0.31	0.43	0.49	0.61	0.77	0.92
Area of Root dia. (mm^2) ...	1.79	2.98	4.47	7.75	12.7	17.9	32.8	52.3
Diameter of tapping drill	1.6	2.05	2.5	3.3	4.2	5.0	6.8	8.5

Diameter	12	16	20	24	30	36	42	48
Pitch	1.75	2.0	2.5	3.0	3.5	4.0	4.5	5.0
Basic effective diameter ...	10.863	14.701	18.376	22.051	27.727	33.402	39.077	44.752
Depth of thread in screw	1.07	1.23	1.53	1.84	2.15	2.45	2.76	3.07
Area of Root dia. (mm^2) ...	76.2	144	225	324	519	759	1050	1380
Diameter of tapping drill	10.2	14.0	17.5	21.0	26.5	32.0	37.5	43.0

Fig. 20-8
The most common sizes of ISO metric threads used in the coarse series. By far the largest percentage of thread fasteners used are in sizes from 2 to 24.

ISO Metric Thread—Fine Series

Diameter	8	10	12	14	16	18	20
Pitch	1.0	1.25	1.25	1.5	1.5	1.5	1.5
Basic effective dia. ...	7.350	9.188	11.188	13.026	15.026	17.026	19.026
Depth of thread in screw	0.61	0.77	0.77	0.92	0.92	0.92	0.92
Area of Root dia. (mm²) ...	36.0	56.3	86.0	116	157	205	259
Diameter of tapping drill	7.0	8.8	10.8	12.5	14.5	16.5	18.5

Diameter	22	24	30	36	42	48
Pitch	1.5	2.0	2.0	3.0	3.0	3.0
Basic effective diameter ...	21.026	22.701	28.701	34.051	40.051	46.051
Depth of thread in screw	0.92	1.23	1.23	1.84	1.84	1.84
Area of Root dia. (mm²) ...	319	365	586	820	1210	1540
Diameter of tapping drill	20.5	22.0	28.0	33.0	39.0	45.0

Fig. 20-9
The ISO metric threads in the fine series are not commonly used.

THREADS: INTERNAL

EXTERNAL

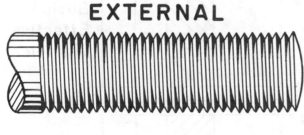

M 12 X 1.75 — 6g

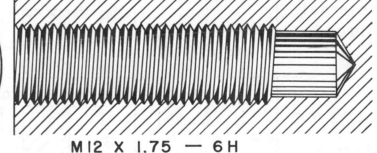

M 12 X 1.75 — 6H

SCREWS & BOLTS NUTS

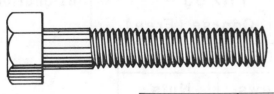

M 12 — 6g

M 12 — 6H

CLASS OF FIT	TOLERANCE CLASS	
	Bolts & Screws	Nuts
Medium	6g	6H

Fig. 20-10

Note the correct symbol to use in identifying a thread. While it is correct to show only the diameter and tolerance class for the coarse series, it is better to add the pitch for better identification.

in millimetres is needed. For example, M16 indicates a 16 mm diameter thread having a 2 millimetre pitch. While the ISO standards require only the diameter size designation, the common practice by many U.S. companies is to include the pitch symbol, even for the coarse pitch series. The inclusion of the pitch symbol will not cause any special problems to the user and will help to identify the thread.

Thread Tolerance

For average commercial use, only three classes of fits were used with ISO threads as follows: fine fit (4h-5H), medium fit (6g-6H), and coarse fit (8g-7H). Fig. 20-11 was used only for precision work. The medium fit is the general commercial grade, and is the one that is most commonly used. The coarse fit was primarily used where very easy assembly is required after the threads are dirty or slightly damaged. Note that the

numbers used for tolerance show a smaller grade number for smaller tolerances and a larger grade number for larger tolerances. *A lower case letter indicates the tolerances on the bolt and a capital letter is used for the nut.*

Optimum Metric Fastener System (OMFS)

In April 1971 the American National Standards Institute appointed a special committee to study the development of an optimum metric fastener system. The work was done by Industrial Fasteners Institute, supported by U.S. manufacturers of industrial fasteners. The object of the study was to develop a total system of metric modular mechanical fasteners that would serve U.S. industries using the fewest possible number of different sizes, series, grades, types and styles of fasteners. Since that time a tremendous amount of work was done to accomplish this goal.

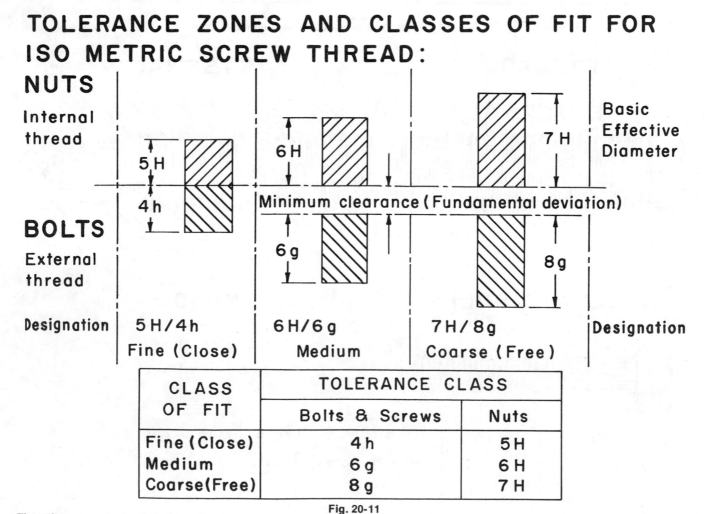

Fig. 20-11
The tolerance zones and classes of fit for ISO metric threads most commonly used. This gives a pictorial representation of the three most common combinations.

CLASS OF FIT	TOLERANCE CLASS	
	Bolts & Screws	Nuts
Fine (Close)	4 h	5 H
Medium	6 g	6 H
Coarse (Free)	8 g	7 H

The major problem with the original ISO metric and inch series was the large number of diameters and pitches available. For example, in the ISO inch system there are 59 different standard combinations of nominal diameters and pitches in the coarse and fine series from sizes number 000 (0.034 in) to 4 in. In the ISO metric thread series there are 57 different combinations of pitches and diameters in the fine and coarse series ranging in sizes from 1 mm diameter to 100 mm diameter.

On the basis of a complete and thorough study based on computer analysis an optimum metric fastener system (OMFS) was developed that included only 25 diameter-pitch combinations in a single series in sizes ranging from M1.6 through M100. Fig. 20-12. These 25 sizes are completely compatible with ISO metric coarse thread series, except for size M6.3x1.

(This size has about 25 threads per inch and is about halfway between the UNC 1/4-20 and the UNF 1/4-28 in coarseness of thread.) There were, however, several other differences between the Optimum Metric Fastener thread and the ISO. The Optimum Metric Fastener thread profile had a slightly increased root for the internal thread to improve its strength property, and the distance from the pitch line to the bottom of the root was slightly different. The only change in the external thread was a slight difference in the root radius. These changes in no way affect compatibility with the equivalent sizes of ISO metric threads. In addition, the Optimum Metric Fastener System developed a much more simplified method of describing the thread without any loss in completeness. The definition is based on the boundary or envelope concept. The system also has recom-

NOMINAL SIZE	INTERNAL THREAD MINOR DIA		TAP DRILL DIA	NOMINAL SIZE	INTERNAL THREAD MINOR DIA		TAP DRILL DIA
	Max	Min			Max	Min	
1.6P0.35	1.350	1.250	1.25	16P2	14.375	14.000	14.0
2P0.4	1.712	1.600	1.6	20P2.5	17.950	17.500	17.5
2.5P0.45	2.175	2.050	2.05	24P3	21.500	21.000	21.0
3P0.5	2.640	2.500	2.5	30P3.5	27.060	26.500	26.5
3.5P0.6	3.060	2.900	2.9	36P4	32.600	32.000	32.0
4P0.7	3.480	3.300	3.3	42P4.5	38.170	37.500	37.5
5P0.8	4.400	4.200	4.2	48P5	43.710	43.000	43.0
6.3P1	5.536	5.300	5.3	56P5.5	51.250	50.500	50.5
8P1.25	7.015	6.750	6.8	64P6	58.800	58.000	58.0
10P1.5	8.800	8.500	8.5	72P6	66.800	66.000	66.0
12P1.75	10.585	10.250	10.3*	80P6	74.800	74.000	74.0
14P2	12.375	12.000	12.0	90P6	84.800	84.000	84.0
				100P6	94.800	94.000	94.0

NOTES:

All dimensions are in millimetres.

* Not presently in agreement with the drill sizes recommended in ISO 2306.

Fig. 20-12

The diameter and pitch series for fasteners is the OMFS. There are great savings in assembly operations using these 25 sizes. This is now called the modified ISO (OMFS) series.

mendations for a simplified method of checking the sizes and diameters with a single "go" gage and two "no-go" gages. In addition, the OMFS system recommended slightly different standards for material grades.

In the OMFS series the class of thread fit and thread designation was somewhat different from the ISO threads. The OMFS series had two classes of fits. One class designated 6H/5g6g for general purpose application approximates Unified class 2A/2B. The closer thread fit class approximates the tolerance of Unified class 3A/3B with the addition of an allowance. OMFS metric threads were designated by the letter P between the nominal size (the basic measure diameter) in millimetres and pitch in millimetres. For example, a thread marked 10P1.5 indicates that the thread has a nominal size of 10 millimetres and a pitch of 1.5 millimetres. For a detailed study of the Optimum Metric Fastener System the reader is referred to the Industrial Fasteners Institute, 1505 E. Ohio Building, 1717 E. 9th Street, Cleveland, Ohio.

Revised ISO Standards

In 1975 a series of international meetings were held to resolve the differences between the ISO standards for metric screw threads and those developed by the Industrial Fasteners Institute as part of the Optimum Metric Fastener System. As a result of these meetings a compromise developed that made it unnecessary to have a separate United States standard for the Optimum Metric Fastener System. The following agreements were reached, which are incorporated in revised ISO standards.

There will be two thread systems, the "J" thread profile for all aerospace fasteners and a series for all commercial and industrial fasteners. The commercial series is described in this unit.

All commercial and industrial fasteners will have a minimum root radius of 0.125P on all external threaded part.

The base thread depth for all commercial and industrial fasteners will be 0.54127P.

There will be two classes of thread tolerance for all external threads, namely 6g for general purpose and 5g6g for close tolerance threads. There will be only one tolerance class for internal threads--6H.

There will be a common designation system using the designator "M" as currently practiced by ISO. This means the "P" designator used to identify the modified ISO (OMFS thread) will not be used.

National standards can describe and dimension threads in any appropriate way providing that interchangeability of manufactured parts is maintained. This decision permits the United States standard to take advantage of the more sophisticated dimensioning technique developed through the OMFS study.

M6.3 x 1.0 is added to ISO as a standard diameter/pitch combination. Fig. 20-13.

Whereas ISO had traditionally had a progression of 5, 6 and 8 mm diameters, and 7 mm as a second choice, the OMFS had an M6.3x1 size as a replacement of both the 6 and 7 mm sizes. The ISO committee agreed to recommend the 6.3 variant as a third-choice size, and expressed hopes that it would eventually also be adopted in Europe. Failing this, and if M6.3 x 1 fasteners appeared alongside the 6 mm size, some cases of serious mismatching may occur.

NOMINAL SIZE	INTERNAL THREAD MINOR DIA		TAP DRILL DIA	NOMINAL SIZE	INTERNAL THREAD MINOR DIA		TAP DRILL DIA
	Max	Min			Max	Min	
M1.6x0.35	1.321	1.221	1.25	M16x2	14.210	13.835	14.0
M2x0.4	1.679	1.567	1.6	M20x2.5	17.744	17.294	17.5
M2.5x0.45	2.138	2.013	2.05	M24x3	21.252	20.752	21.0
M3x0.5	2.599	2.459	2.5	M30x3.5	26.771	26.211	26.5
M3.5x0.6	3.010	2.850	2.9	M36x4	32.270	31.670	32.0
M4x0.7	3.422	3.242	3.3	M42x4.5	37.799	37.129	37.5
M5x0.8	4.334	4.134	4.2	M48x5	43.297	42.587	43.0
M6.3x1	5.553	5.217	5.3	M56x5.5	50.796	50.046	50.5
M8x1.25	6.912	6.647	6.8	M64x6	58.305	57.505	58.0
M10x1.5	8.676	8.376	8.5	M72x6	66.305	65.505	66.0
M12x1.75	10.441	10.106	10.2	M80x6	74.305	73.505	74.0
M14x2	12.210	11.835	12.0	M90x6	84.305	83.505	84.0
				M100x6	94.305	93.505	94.0

Fig. 20-13
The new ISO series of 25 selected sizes that will be used by North American manufacturers. Compare this chart with the obsolete OMFS standard shown in Fig. 20-12.

UNIT 21
OTHER METRIC STANDARDS

While paper sizes and screw threads are important and commonly used metric standards, they represent only two of the thousands of standards that must be developed in order to have the true international standards needed for world trade. Some of the other areas in which ISO standards are available include steel, nonferrous metals, plastics, rubber, anti-friction bearings, building construction, building materials, and pipe and tubing. Currently there are about 150 to 200 ISO standards in which the SI metric measurement is used. A few examples of these international standards available in selected areas are listed in Fig. 21-1. Anyone interested in securing copies of the individual standards should refer to the current catalog of the American National Standards Institute, 4130 Broadway, New York, New York 10018. This organization is the only official source for all standards issued by either ISO or IEC as well as any of the other countries' standard organizations.

During the next 10 years about 11,000 metric industrial standards will need to be developed. As they are published by ISO, these standards will be available from the American National Standards Institute. Before 1967 the principal engineering standards were issued in the following units: traditional metric units, Imperial units, and U.S. customary units. These units are not mutually exclusive since most Imperial and U.S. Customary units are the same, except for some volume and liquid capacity. For example, the Imperial gallon is larger than the U.S. gallon. On the other hand, some U.S. customary units are the same as customary metric units. For example, most electrical units used in the U.S. are based on IEC recommendations. The use of the international system of units (SI) is now required by both IEC and ISO for all new international standards. Any future national standards which do not include SI units will not be given consideration for development as international standards. It must be remembered that dimensional specifications used in different metric countries for their national standards are frequently as incompatible in metric units as they are between inch units and metric units. *Therefore, a change to metric units itself does not make standards compatible.* The only compatible standards are those developed on a cooperative basis by all countries utilizing SI units as the standard measuring system.

Non-metric International Standards

Not all international standards will be in metric units, although they will be the predominant ones. In areas where United States industry has developed and held the lead throughout the world, many of the basic international standards will be based on the inch system. For example, the spacing of holes in computer printout sheets is exactly 1/2 inch even though in metric countries these spaces are listed as 12.7 mm. All pipes and threads for oil drilling, a very specialized area, utilize the inch system and will probably continue to do so since this is the predominant area of American industrial expertise. A few of the world-wide international standards based on the inch-pound units are shown in Fig. 21-2.

Items	Some examples of Nominal Values
ATHLETICS & SPORTS	
Shots, in track & field	16 lb.
Weights, track & field	35 lb
Tennis courts	36 x 78 ft
Tennis court nets	30 + 36 in
AUTOMOTIVE	
Tires	6 x 16; 7.50 x 15 in
Tire valves, caps	5/16 x 32/in
Tire valves, stems	#8 x 36/in
BOTTLES	
Soft drink & beer crowns	1 in (not 25 mm)
Coke	6.5 oz
ELECTRONICS	
Racks, "relay"	19 in
FLYING, SAILING	
Speed	knots
OFFICE	
Typewriters horizontal spacing	10/in, 12/in
Typewriters vertical spacing	1/6 in
PHOTOGRAPHY	
Slides, 35 mm film	2 x 2 in
Prints, still film	2-1/4 x 3-1/4 in
RAZOR BLADES	
Size	7/8 x 1-11/16 in
Mounts	1 in
RECORDERS	
Tape speed	3.5, 1.75 in/sec

Fig. 21-2
Common standards based on the inch-pound system that are used on a world-wide basis.

R14-1955 Straight-Sided Splines (for Cylindrical Shafts), Nominal Dimensions in Millimetres
R15/1-1968 Rolling Bearings, Radial Bearings, Boundary Dimensions, General Plan, Diameter Series 8, 9, 0, 1, 2, 3 and 4, including Amendment 1-1971
R15/11-1970 Rolling Bearings, Radial Bearings, Boundary Dimension, General Plan, Part II: Diameter Series 7
R22-1956 Widths of Flat Transmission Belts and Corresponding Pulleys
R50-1957 Steel Sockets Screwed in Accordance with ISO Recommendation R7 Minimum Lengths
R53-1957 Basic Rack of Cylindrical Gears for General Engineering (B6. 1-1968)
R54-1966 Modules and Diametral Pitches of Cylindrical Gears for General Engineering and for Heavy Engineering
R64-1971 Steel Tubes—Outside Diameters
R68-1969 General Purpose Screw Threads, Basic Profile (B1. 1-1960 and B1.10-1958)
R104-1966 Rolling Bearings: Thrust Bearings with Flat Seats, Boundary Dimensions
R221-1971 Steel Tubes—Wall Thicknesses
ISO 235/11-1972 Core Drills With Paralleled Shanks and Morse Taper Shanks—Recommended Stocked Sizes
R336-1971 Plain End Steel Tubes, Welded or Seamless, General Table of Dimensions and Masses per Unit Length
ISO 582-1972 Rolling Bearings: Metric Series Bearings, Chamfer Dimension Limits and Maximum Shaft and Housing Fillet Radius
R1340-1971 Cylindrical Gears—Information To Be Given To The Manufacturer by the Purchaser In Order to Obtain The Gear Required
R1341-1971 Straight Bevel Gears—Information To Be Given to The Manufacturer by the Purchaser in Order to Obtain the Gear Required
R1234-1971 Split Pins—Metric Series
R1755-1971 Photography—Projector Slides—Dimensions (PH3.43-1969)
ISO 2133-1972 Duplicators—Minimum Overprint on Duplicating Stencils
ISO 2157-1972 Dental Burs and Cutters—Nominal Sizes and Designation of Working Parts
ISO 2194-1972 Wire Screens and Plate Screens For Industrial Purposes—Nominal Sizes of Apertures
ISO 2235-1972 Abrasive Sheets and Discs, Dimensions
ISO 2236-1972 Assembly Tools For Screws and Nuts—Forged and Tubular Socket Wrenches—Metric Series—Maximum Outside Dimensions
ISO 2250-1972 Finishing Reamers For Morse and Metric Tapers, With Parallel and Morse Taper Shanks (B94.2-1971)
ISO 2257-1972 Office Machines and Printing Machines Used For Information Processing—Widths of Fabric Printing Ribbons on Spools
ISO 2264-1972 Rolling Bearings—Bearings With Spherical Outside Surface and Extended Inner Ring Width
ISO 2265-1972 Rolling Bearings—Bearings With Locating Snap Ring—Inner Diameter of Snap Ring
ISO 2283-1972 Long Shank Machine Taps With Nominal Diameters From 3 to 24 mm and 1/8 to 1 in
ISO 2284-1972 Hand Taps for Pipe Threads For Parallel and Taper Threads—General Dimensions and Marking
ISO 2296-1972 Metal Slitting Saws With Fine and Coarse Teeth—Metric Series
ISO 2306-1972 Drills For Use Prior To Tapping Screw Threads
ISO 2324-1972 End Mills With 7/24 Taper Shanks—Standard Series and Long Series
ISO 2336-1972 Hand and Machine Hacksaw Blades—Dimensions for Lengths Up to 450 mm and Pitches Up to 6.3 mm
ISO 2338-1972 Parallel Pins, Unhardened—Metric Series
ISO 2340-1972 Clevis Pins—Metric Series
ISO 2341-1972 Clevis Pins With Heads—Metric Series
ISO 2342-1972 Slotted Headless Screws—Metric Series
ISO 2343-1972 Hexagon Socket Set Screw—Metric Series
ISO 2351-1972 Screwdriver Bits, For Slotted Head Screws, With Male Hexagon Drive
ISO 2352-1972 Spiral Ratchet Screwdriver Ends
ISO 2358-1972 Prevailing Torque-Type Hexagon Locknuts—Dimensions—Metric Series
ISO 2380-1972 Screwdriver Blades For Slotted Head Screws
ISO 1006-1973 Modular Co-ordination—Basic Module
ISO 1040-1973 Modular Co-ordination—Multimodules for Horizontal Co-ordinating Dimensions

Fig. 21-1
A selected list of ISO standards.

National Metric Engineering Standards

In addition to the international metric standards developed by ISO, national metric engineering standards are being developed by committees and sector groups working under the direction of the American National Metric Council.

These committees and sector groups include:

A. Building and Construction Committees
1. Builders Sector
2. Design Sector
3. Product Sector
4. Client Sector
5. Standards and Codes Sector
6. 4 x 8 Panel Task Force
7. Metric Units for Building and Construction Task Force
8. Structural Building Products Task Force

B. Consumer Products Committee
1. Food and Grocery Products Sector
2. Apparel and Household Furnishings Sector
3. Commercial and Consumer Measurement Practices Sector
4. Textiles Sector

C. Engineering Industries Committee
1. Marine Sector
2. Highway Vehicle Sector
3. Offroad Vehicle Sector
4. Rail Sector
5. Aerospace Sector
6. Computer and Office Equipment Sector
7. Electronic Equipment and Components Sector
8. Machinery Sector
9. Instruments Sector

D. Materials Committee
1. Metal Products Sector
2. Chemical and Allied Products Sector
3. Petroleum and Natural Gas Sector
4. Lumber and Wood Products Sector
5. Mined and Mineral Products Sector
6. Silicone Task Force

These national metric standards may or may not be completely compatible with similar international metric standards.

Some typical national metric standards available include:

A. From Industrial Fasteners Institute

IFI-500	Screw Threads for Metric Series Mechanical Fasteners
IFI-501	Mechanical and Material Requirements for Metric Series Externally Threaded Steel Fasteners
IFI-502	Slotted and Recessed Hand Tapping Screws—Metric Dimensions
IFI-503	Thread Rolling Screws—Metric Dimensions
IFI-504	Steel Self-Drilling Tapping Screws—Metric Dimensions
IFI-505	Standard for Metric Series Break Mandrel Blind Rivets
IFI-509	Metric Series Break Mandrel Closed End Blind Rivets

B. From the American National Standards Institute

ANSI B 32.3 Preferred Thicknesses and Widths for Flat Metal Products

ANSI B 32.4 Preferred Metric Sizes for Round, Square and Hexagon Metal Products

UNIT 22
METRICS IN THE DESIGN STAGE

A major goal of "going metric" is to make the change with a minimum of cost and inconvenience. However, the metric change also provides a great challenge to industry and education, not only to adopt the SI units but also to rationalize the number of sizes and to improve the design and quality of products produced. **Fig. 22-1**

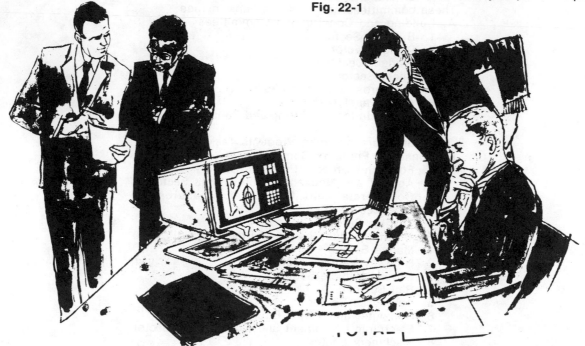

Fig. 22-1
Designing in metric is the first step to converting an industry to metric.

It provides a chance for industry to do some much needed "house cleaning" and to reduce unnecessary varieties of sizes. The metric fastener system developed by the IFI (Industrial Fasteners Institute) is an example of increasing efficiency by reducing the variety of products. In the original ISO thread series there are two pitches (fine and coarse) in the metric series and two pitches (fine and coarse) in the inch series for a total of 139 different thread diameters and pitches. **Fig. 22-2**

The preferred metric fastener system recommended for use in the United States reduces the number of diameters to 25 in a single pitch series. This is only one way in which changing to the metric system can reduce cost and increase efficiency by reducing the number and variety of sizes that need to be stocked. There are very few companies or schools that could not benefit by a critical reexamination of their designs, manufacturing processes and products. In other words, changing to metric measuring units also provides industries and education with an opportunity to "think metric" and "think again." "Going metric" provides a unique opportunity to select rational sizes and to reduce the wide variety of duplication.

Three Kinds of Metric Conversion
1. Soft conversion is the simplest and least efficient method, since it makes no change whatsoever *except* in the measuring language. Soft conversion is just a question of converting inches to millimetres, pounds to kilograms, ounces to grams, and quarts to litres *with no change in the size of things*. Soft conversion from customary to metric always results in odd sizes in

Fig. 22-2
Many different kinds of metal fasteners are manufactured based on diameter, thread profile, pitch, and other factors.

metric. For example, a 4 inch measurement becomes 101.6 millimetres, and a 10 ounce cereal box becomes a 283.5 gram box. A soft conversion is of *no help* in improving standardization or in rationalizing sizes.

2. *Hard conversion with metric engineering standards* is one in which all of the designing is done in preferred metric sizes using metric standards such as metric threads.

3. *Metric modules in rational sizes without metric standards.* Many products can be redesigned to even metric modules or sizes without the use of any metric engineering standards. For example, packaging of products can be done in this manner. Toothpaste may be produced in rounded millilitre sizes based on increments of 25 millilitres, the smallest being 25 millilitres, then 50, 75, 100, and so forth.

Both the second and third kinds of conversion provide industry with an excellent opportunity to rethink their total product lines.

Problems In Designing Metric Sizes

Some of the basic problems to consider before designing in metric are the following:

1. *Availability of basic components and materials from which parts are to be made.* For example, while it might have been very desirable to select the ISO metric paper sizes in the A range, it may not be possible to obtain these sizes from the paper mill without extra cutting cost. The widths of current paper-making machines are such that ISO A size paper cannot be cut efficiently from the standard widths produced. However, this extra cost might be offset by reducing the number and variety of paper sizes that are used in the particular industry or government unit. For example, when the Ontario government changed to the ISO paper sizes, it reduced the number of commonly used paper sizes from about 80 to a mere 8. Most concerns will want to use the ISO letter or sheet size that is 210 x 180 mm.

2. *Availability of basic stock sizes.* Manufacturers of any products must depend on the producer of the basic materials to provide desired metric sizes. For example, many small manufacturers of metal products may not obtain (without extra cost) preferred metric thicknesses and diameters of flats, rounds, and so forth. Large producers can always obtain any sizes desired.

3. *Number of sizes in the product line.* A major problem many manufacturers face is that there is a proliferation of sizes that they produce and stock. Many of these sizes are rarely purchased, resulting in efficiency and increased costs. Originally the manufacturer produced sizes which he thought would sell best. Then he continued to add sizes customers seemed to want until the total number got out of hand. Many producers are locked into a wide variety of sizes, since traditionally they have always produced these. Frequently 90 percent of the business is done in 20 to 30 percent of the sizes produced. The others are manufactured for the convenience of a few customers, or because tradition has always indicated that they should be produced. Frequently an analysis will indicate that many of the odd or unusual sizes could be dropped in converting to metric.

4. *Storage.* The fewer sizes of parts or products, the easier the storage problem and the more efficient the ordering, billing, and office practice. There is always much less chance for error. Therefore, in converting to metric, if 10 sizes will do the job as well as the 60 older sizes, there will be a great increase in efficiency and an actual financial savings in converting to metric measurement. During the transition period many concerns will need to keep a dual inventory of customary and metric sizes.

Preferred Numbers

History. Colonel Charles Renard, commissioner of aerial communications in France, was an avid balloonist. He found that the French army used 425 different sizes of ropes and cords for mooring balloons. Renard was determined to reduce this number and at the same time provide for maximum safety. In 1870 he came up with the idea of determinimg desirable diameters of ropes on the basis of geometric progression. Renard used this new idea to reduce the number of ropes and cord sizes from 420 to 17 standard sizes. Later, in 1877, he enlarged and developed these ideas further into a series of preferred numbers that have become commonly known as the *Renard* series. The basic idea behind this preferred numbers series is that man naturally prefers a geometric progression rather than an arithmetic progression in determining a series of graded sizes.

Fig. 22-3

PREFERRED NUMBERS

ARITHMETIC SERIES

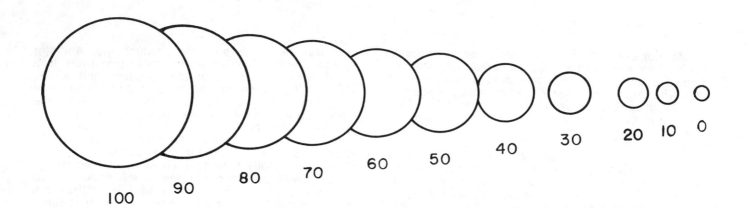

100 90 80 70 60 50 40 30 20 10 0

GEOMETRIC SERIES

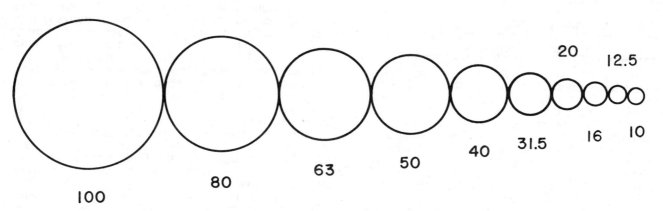

100 80 63 50 40 31.5 20 16 12.5 10

Fig. 22-3
In the *arithmetic* series there is an overlapping of sizes, while
in the *geometric* series there is a logical progression of sizes.

With preferred numbers anyone can quickly establish a standard series for any kind of part or product. In the past the preferred series has not been employed to maximum effectiveness simply because there appears to be a mystery about the mathematical development of this series. The designer, however, can use the preferred numbers series without any understanding of the mathematical development.

While it isn't necessary to know the theoretical basis for the preferred numbers, it may be well to understand how they were developed. Preferred numbers are conveniently rounded off to numbers of a geometric series using the integral power of 10. Starting with 10 as the first number of the series, the other exact numbers are obtained by multiplying the number of the series by a constant factor. These factors are as follows:

For the 5 series, $5\sqrt{10}$, or 1.5849

For the 10 series, $10\sqrt{10}$, or 1.2589

For the 20 series, $20\sqrt{10}$, or 1.1220

For the 40 series, $40\sqrt{10}$, or 1.0593

The same numbers can be obtained by starting with the 40-series and then taking every other number to form the 20-series, every fourth number to form the 10-series, and every eighth number to form the 5-series.

1. Uses of the preferred series. In using the *Renard numbers* the first step is to decide on how many sizes are to be provided between the largest and smallest in the total range. As you can see, there are four basic series, namely R5, R10, R20, and R40. There is also a fifth and less used series R80. **Fig. 22-4**

BASIC SERIES OF PREFERRED NUMBERS

1	2	3	4	5
SERIAL NUMBER	Basic Series			
	R5	R10	R20	R40
0	1.00	1.00	1.00	1.00
1				1.06
2			1.12	1.12
3				1.18
4		1.25	1.25	1.25
5				1.32
6			1.40	1.40
7				1.50
8	1.60	1.60	1.60	1.60
9				1.70
10			1.80	1.80
11				1.90
12		2.00	2.00	2.00
13				2.12
14			2.24	2.24
15				2.36
16	2.50	2.50	2.50	2.50
17				2.65
18			2.80	2.80
19				3.00
20		3.15	3.15	3.15
21				3.35
22			3.55	3.55
23				3.75
24	4.00	4.00	4.00	4.00
25				4.25
26			4.50	4.50
27				4.75
28		5.00	5.00	5.00
29				5.30
30			5.60	5.60
31				6.00
32	6.30	6.30	6.30	6.30
33				6.70
34			7.10	7.10
35				7.50
36		8.00	8.00	8.00
37				8.50
38			9.00	9.00
39				9.50
40	10.00	10.00	10.00	10.00

R80 SERIES
OF
PREFERRED
NUMBERS
FOR
EXCEPTIONAL
USE

1	2	3	4
1.00	1.80	3.15	5.60
1.03	1.85	3.25	5.80
1.06	1.90	3.35	6.00
1.09	1.95	3.45	6.15
1.12	2.00	3.55	6.30
1.15	2.06	3.65	6.50
1.18	2.12	3.75	6.70
1.22	2.18	3.87	6.90
1.25	2.24	4.00	7.10
1.28	2.30	4.12	7.30
1.32	2.36	4.25	7.50
1.36	2.43	4.37	7.75
1.40	2.50	4.50	8.00
1.45	2.58	4.62	8.25
1.50	2.65	4.75	8.50
1.55	2.72	4.87	8.75
1.60	2.80	5.00	9.00
1.65	2.90	5.15	9.25
1.70	3.00	5.30	9.50
1.75	3.07	5.45	9.75

Fig. 22-4
There are four series of preferred numbers in the basic series
and one series of preferred numbers for exceptional use.

Note in the R5 that there are five intervals between 1 and 10 making a total of six altogether. In the R10 there are 11 sizes, in R20 21 sizes and in R40 41 sizes. For example, suppose the decision is to design a product with 10 preferred sizes; then the R10 series would be used. Each increase in size would be the tenth root of 10 or 1.2589.

Using this method of determining the preferred sizes will result in some relatively odd sizes. Therefore, rounding off is permitted as shown in the table of preferred sizes.

The R10 series is rounded off so that the 11 sizes starting at the smallest would be 1, 1.2, 1.6, 2.0, 2.5, 3.15, 4.0, 5.0, 6.3, 8.0, and 10.0. The percentage increase in sizes is as follows: (a) In the R5 series, each size is increased by about 60 percent (actual 58 percent); (b) in the R10, each size is increased by about 25 percent (actual 26 percent); in the R12, each size is increased by 12 percent; (d) in the R40, each size is increased by 6 percent; (e) in the R80, each size is increased by 3 percent. **Fig. 22-5**

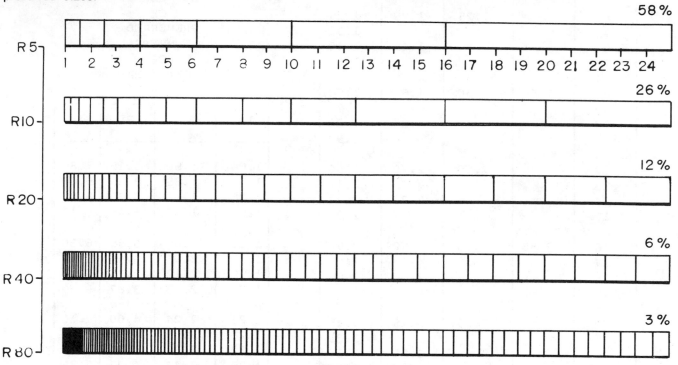

Fig. 22-5
The Renard system of preferred numbers shown in a graphic representation.

Each of the other series has 10, 20, 40 and 80 steps between 1 and 10 or 10 and 100. Note that any of the series can be used for any range of sizes. For example, if preferred numbers below 10 are needed, merely divide the number by 10, 100, 1000, and so forth. The preferred numbers above 100 can be formed by multiplying the numbers 10, 100, 1000 and so forth. The numbers at the top of the table indicate the number of values there are in the series. It must be remembered that the recommended sizes of preferred numbers should be used as a guide, and not necessarily as the final answer to exact sizes. Of course, the advantage of this type of rationalization is that the products designed by different companies would match in size. The only objection some designers have to using the Renard series is that the steps in the upper end of the range are relatively large and may not be suitable for a particular product.

The preferred series can be used in a number of ways to simplify the number and sizes of parts or products produced. They may include the following: (a) The sizes of basic materials. Many of the ISO standards for materials are based on the Renard numbers.
Fig. 22-6

Bore Sizes for Rubber Hose

ISO*		Conventional	
mm	inch	inch**	mm***
3.2	0.126	1/8	3.5
4	.157	5/32	
5	.197	3/16	5
6.3	.248	1/4	6 (6)
8	.315	5/16	8
10	.394	3/8	10 (9)
12.5	.492	1/2	12 (13)
16	.630	5/8	15 (16)
20	.787	3/4	20 (19)
25	.984	1	25 (25)
31.5	1.24	1 1/4	30 (32)
40	1.57	1 1/2	40 (38)
50	1.97	2	50 (50)
63	2.48	2 1/2	60 (63)
80	3.15	3	75 (75)
100	3.94	4	100 (100)
125	4.92	5	125
160	6.30	6	150
200	7.87	8	200
250	9.84	10	250
315	12.40	12	300

*The millimetre values correspond to R10 series of preferred numbers.
**Countries using English units.
***Countries using metric units; values in parentheses were used in some metric countries.

Fig. 22-6
The bore size of rubber hose illustrates the use of preferred numbers. International agreement between metric and nonmetric countries was achieved by the use of the R10 series of preferred numbers. Shown here is a comparison of the ISO and the conventional bore sizes used in both metric and nonmetric countries.

Linear dimensions of parts such as lengths, diameters, areas, volume, etc. can be based on these numbers. (b) Rating of equipment in standard units. (c) Sizes and relationships of figures of all kinds. The designer planning any kind of product, therefore, only has to decide on how many units must be included in the series. Based on this he can use any of the basic series available. One of the best examples of how preferred numbers have simplified sizes produced is in the rating of electric motors. Before employing preferred numbers, manufacturers used a variety of sizes with no two manufacturers producing the same sizes. However, the National Electrical Manufacturers Association established standards using the R10 series so that products are available in sizes of 10, 12.5, 16, 20, 25, 31.5, 40, 50, 80. Common electric light bulbs follows the R5 series. The ideal time to use a preferred number series is when the designer is determining the various sizes of the units to be produced. If there is agreement in a particular trade association for using a selected series, then all manufacturers will produce the same sizes, therefore providing for great economy and interchangeability. Preferred numbers can be used to produce raw materials, parts and complete sets of equipment.

2. Preferred metric sizes for engineering. Many countries and companies have developed preferred metric sizes for engineering that are adaptions of the Renard series. The preferred metric basic sizes for engineering are shown in **Fig. 22-7**. Note that whenever possible the first choice should be used in each of the series. For preferred basic sizes above 300 mm and up to 1000 mm, use sizes equal to 10 times the corresponding sizes from 10 mm to 100 mm. For sizes above 1000 mm, use sizes equal to 1000 times 1 mm to 10 mm. The first choice, for example, would be 100 mm, 1200 mm, 1600 mm, 2000 mm, and so forth.

PREFERRED METRIC SIZES FOR ENGINEERING

SIZES 1 mm to 10 mm

CHOICE 1st	CHOICE 2nd	CHOICE 3rd
1		
	1.1	
1.2		
		1.3
	1.4	
		1.5
1.6		
		1.7
	1.8	
		1.9
2		
	2.2	2.1
		2.4
2.5		
		2.6
	2.8	
3		
		3.2
	3.5	
		3.8
4		4.2
	4.5	
		4.8
5		5.2
	5.5	
		5.8
6		
		6.5
	7	
		7.5
8		
	8.5	
	9	
		9.5
10		

SIZES 10 mm to 100 mm

CHOICE 1st	CHOICE 2nd	CHOICE 3rd
10		
	11	
12		
		13
	14	
		15
16		
		17
	18	
		19
20		
	22	21
		23
		24
25		
		26
	28	
30	32	
	35	34
		36
40	38	
	42	
	45	44
		46
50	48	
	52	
	55	54
		56
60	58	
		62
	65	
	70	68
		72
	75	
80		78
		82
	85	
	90	88
		92
	95	
		98
100		

SIZES 100 mm to 1000 mm

CHOICE 1st	CHOICE 2nd	CHOICE 3rd
100		
110		105
120		115
	130	125
140		135
	150	145
160		155
	170	165
180		175
	190	185
200		195
220	210	
	230	
	240	
250		
	260	
280		270
300	320	290
350		340
400	380	360
	420	
450		440
500	480	460
	520	
550		540
600	580	560
	620	
	650	640
700	680	660
	720	
	750	740
800	780	760
	850	820
900		880
	950	920
1000		980

Fig. 22-7
Preferred metric sizes that can be used in engineering.

22-6

3. Other sizing methods. Many factors will determine the metric sizes to use. These include such items as (a) functional requirement of the product, (b) availability of stock materials, (c) choice of range sizes, (d) demand for product, (e) manufacturing problems, and (f) storage problems. Efficiency and economic production demand the use for as few as possible sizes of tools and materials to reduce cost. This is true not only for the base materials, such as sheet, rod and strip stock, but also for using such tools as drills, reamers, taps, and gages. Since there are a large number of standards for preferred sizes, it will be necessary for individual industries to give serious consideration to the sizing most desired for their products. For example, increasing sizes by a factor of 10 may be best. If the first size is 2, then the next sizes should be 20, 200, and so forth. Another method is to use sizes that are rounded off in full metric modules. For example, 3 is preferable to 3.2, 30 is preferable to 32, 35 is preferable to 36, and so forth. Another method is to design the product or part in preferred sizes, rising by units of 5, 10, 20, or 50. **Fig. 22-8**

METRIC LINEAR SIZES

Preferred basic millimetre sizes for engineering

	Rising by 5	Rising by 10	Rising by 20	Rising by 50
1	20	80	200	300
1.2	25	90	220	350
1.6	30	100	240	400
2	35	110	260	450
2.5	40	120	280	500
3	45	130	300	550
4	50	140		600
5	55	150		650
6	60	160		700
8	65	170		750
10	70	180		800
12	75	190		850
16	80	200		900
20				950
				1000

Fig. 22-8
Recommended preferred basic millimetre sizes for engineering, rising by units of 5, 10, 20 and 50.

4. Sizing for packaging. The use of modular sizes in packaging standards will make it simpler for the consumer in buying materials and reducing the number and variety of sizes. The cosmetic industry in Canada, for example, has based all toothpaste on a 25 millilitre module.

There are two basic range sizes for packaging, namely the rational dimensional range and the alternate half range. The rational dimensional range is to be preferred. For liquids the units are the litre and millilitre. **Fig. 22.9**

Rationalized Decimal Range	Alternate Halved Range
10 kg	10 kg
5 kg	5 kg
2 kg	2.5 kg
1 kg	1 kg
500 g	500 g
200 g	250 g
100 g	125 g or 100 g
50 g	62.5 g or 50 g
20 g	25 g
10 g	12.5 g or 10 g

Fig. 22-9
Two methods by which packaging sizes can be arranged. The preferred method is to use the rationalized decimal range.

Designing Practices

In designing in metric, the design engineer and/or designer must have a "feel" for the metric system in terms of design characteristics and size relationships. Some of the points to keep in mind in any design activity are the following:

1. *Metric is a decimal system based on the unit of 10.* Therefore the base unit can only be divided evenly *once*. In other words, 10 can be divided into 5 as a whole number. After that there are no other divisions except those that involve the use of decimals. For example, if 5 is divided, it becomes 2.5. If 2.5 is divided it becomes 1.25, and if 1.25 is divided again it becomes 0.625. Note that the second division is in tenths (one decimal place), the third in hundredths (2 decimal places), and the fourth division in thousandths (3 decimal places). Normally, in metric, this *halving principle* is not used since this idea is based largely on the old customary system. If 10 is to be divided into a metric series of sizes, then the logical rounded units would be 2, 4, 6, 8, and 10 not 0.625, 1.25, 2.5, 5.0, and 10.

2. *Designing for accuracy.* It must be remembered that a millimetre is approximately 1/25 of an inch. Therefore, much greater accuracy is obtained by carrying a millimetre measurement out to the same number of decimal places. For example, if the average tolerance in the inch system is 0.010 (10 thousandth) then the equivalent tolerance in millimetres would be 0.254 rounded to 0.25 mm (25 hundredths). Normally if a tolerance is given to *three* decimal places in the inch system, then only *two* decimal places should be used in the metric system. In other words, if the normal tolerance is 0.005 in, then the equivalent tolerance in metric would be 0.13 mm.

3. *If graph paper is used for design in metric, it should have 10 squares to the unit [not 8 or 12].* Each square could represent a square millimetre, centimetre, decimetre, metre, and so forth.

4. *If the design is to be in metric and is to be accurate to one place beyond the decimal point, use the even numbers beyond the decimal point rather than the odd.* For example, it is preferable to have such units as 0.2, 0.4, and 0.6 rather than 0.1, 0.3, 0.5, etc. The only exception to this rule is when only one smaller division is used below the even millimetre. Then 0.5 mm (1/2 millimetre) could be used. Many millimetre rules and scales are divided in 1/2 millimetres (0.5 mm) as the smallest reading graduation. Therefore, 0.5 mm is a convenient division to use in making designs and layouts.

5. *Other metric design problems.* In the forseeable future, the designer will always be making compromises when designing in the metric system. It will be rare, indeed, to be able to design a total product using metric modules or preferred numbers with all metric standards. Until all raw materials and components are available in metric sizes and until all metric engineering standards have been developed and approved, designing in metric will involve many compromises. For example, during the early stages of conversion, many of the raw materials may be available only in inch sizes and, therefore, it will not be possible to specify a 12 mm or 25 mm thickness when the material available will be 12.7 mm and 25.4 mm in thickness.

6. *Parts that must interface.* Frequently some parts used in a complete product are designed and manufactured in the metric system while other parts are designed and manufactured in the inch system. As a result, there must be an *interface* (fitting together) between the metric parts and the inch parts. The telephone is a good example of a product in which both metric and customary parts are used. In a product where two measurement languages are used, it is important that there be no mismatch between the parts. The ultimate example of an interface between parts designed and manufactured in the inch system and parts designed and manufactured in the metric system is the lock system used with the hook-up between the American and the Russian astronauts. This is called the ASTP docking approach between the Apollo and Soyuz space crafts.

Fig. 22-10

This complicated system was built in two sections, one half in the United States to inch standards and the other half in Russia to metric standards. The interlocking sections are as complicated as a bank vault, one half the door and the other half the frame, yet the match fits perfectly.

7. *Use of metric engineering standards.* The use of metric standard materials such as nuts, bolts, splines, and other items will depend on whether or not a standard is available, and whether the materials for making the parts are readily available. For example, some manufacturers may decide to use the metric measurement language but continue to specify United National (ISO inch) threads. Other designers will want to utilize the ISO metric threads.

8. *Conversion of inch limits to millimetres.* There are two methods for converting tolerance limits from inches to millimetres. Both use the table shown below to determine the number of decimal places to be used in the converted figures:

ORIGINAL TOLERANCE IN INCHES		NUMBER OF DECIMAL PLACES FOR ROUNDING TO mm
At least but	Less than	
.00001	.0001	0.000 01
.0001	.001	0.000 1
.001	.01	0.001
.01	.1	0.01
.1	1.0	0.1

First Method

This method guarantees that even in the most difficult cases, the inch-limits will not be exceeded nor diminished by more than two per cent of the value of the tolerance.

1. Establish the maximum and minimum limits in inches.

2. Convert the limits exactly into millimetres using the conversion factor: 1'' = 25.4 mm.

3. Applying the original inch-tolerance to the above table, round each millimetre limit to the correct number of decimal places. The result is the completed conversion.

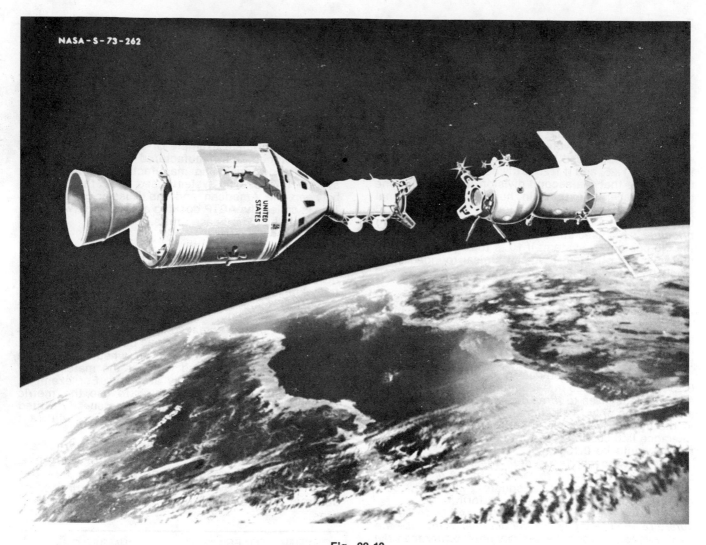

Fig. 22-10
The AST docking system. The United States section is built to customary standards and the Russian section is built to metric standards.

Example:

Dimensions in inches	2.950 ± 0.16	
1. Limits in inches	2.934	
2. Limits in millimetres	75.3364 to 74.5236	
3. Original inch-tolerance	.032 (0.01 in table)	
Rounded millimetre limits	75.34 to 74.52	
Tolerance	0.82 mm	
Dimension in metric	74.93 ± 0.41 mm	

Second Method

This method is used when the original outside limits may not be violated. It is used on parts which must be accepted by original gages or mated with other parts. In extreme cases, this method may alter the upper and lower limits a maximum of four per cent of the tolerance.

1. Establish the maximum and minimum limits and the tolerances in inches.

2. Convert the limits exactly into millimetres using the conversion factor: 1'' = 25.4 mm.

3. Applying the original inch-tolerance to the table shown, round each millimetre limit to the correct number of decimal places.

4. Round each limit toward the interior of the tolerance . . . to the next lower value for the upper limit . . . to the next higher value for the lower limit.

The result is the completed conversion.

Example:

Dimension in inches	2.950 ± 0.16	
1. Limit in inches	2.966 to 2.934	
2. Limits in millimetres	75.3364 to 74.5236	
3. Original inch-tolerance	.032 = (0.01 in table)	
Rounded to millimetre limits	75.34 to 74.52	
4. Rounded toward inter.:	75.33 to 74.53	
Tolerance:	0.80 mm	
Dimension in metric	74.93 ± 0.40 mm	

Note the tolerance difference obtained by the two conversion methods: First = 0.82 mm; Second = 0.80 mm.

UNIT 23
DRAFTING EQUIPMENT AND SUPPLIES

A minimum amount of extra equipment and supplies is needed to do metric drafting. All of the standard drafting equipment, with the exception of scales and templates, can be retained. However, such supplementary tools as micrometers and vernier calipers must be available either in all metric or in dual reading measurements. Needs to be considered in converting drafting facilities to produce metric drawings are as follows:

Drafting Table or Work Station

The drafting table or work station can remain *as is* since it does not affect the method by which a drawing is made. Eventually, however, the tops of drawing tables will be made to standard A sizes to be compatible with ISO metric paper sizes. Generally the boards on the drafting table will be available in two sizes: A1 size which measures 650 x 920 mm and A2 size which measures 470 x 650 mm. **Fig. 23-1**

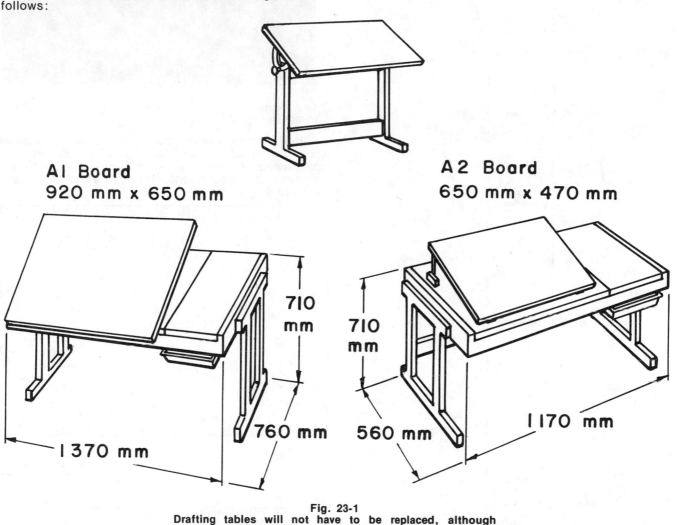

**A1 Board
920 mm x 650 mm**

**A2 Board
650 mm x 470 mm**

710 mm

710 mm

760 mm

1370 mm

560 mm

1170 mm

**Fig. 23-1
Drafting tables will not have to be replaced, although eventually new drafting tables will be made with the board in standard A sizes.**

Scales

Scales are made with three kinds of graduations, namely: (a) in inches and fractions of an inch, (b) in tenths of an inch and (c) in millimetres. Metric scales are available in a variety of shapes, the most common of which are the flat, oval or triangular. **Fig. 23-2**

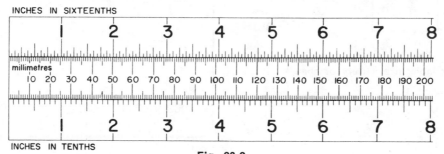

INCHES IN SIXTEENTHS

millimetres

INCHES IN TENTHS

**Fig. 23-2
Comparison of the three types of scales in common use.**

While the shape is not too significant, the ratios on the scale are extremely important. The ratios for all metric scales should be a factor of 10 relationship for both reductions and enlargements. **Fig. 23-3a Fig. 23-3b**

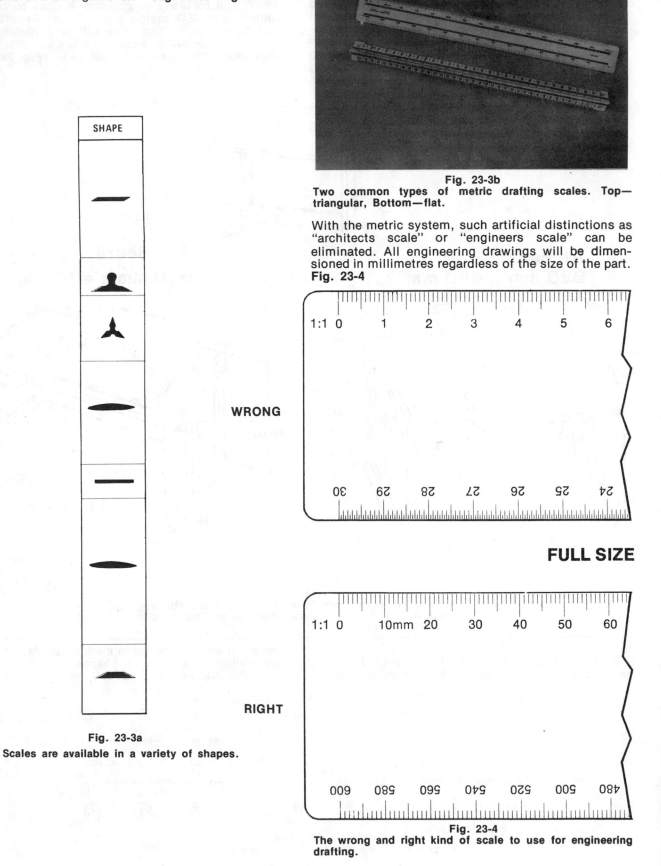

Fig. 23-3b
Two common types of metric drafting scales. Top—triangular, Bottom—flat.

With the metric system, such artificial distinctions as "architects scale" or "engineers scale" can be eliminated. All engineering drawings will be dimensioned in millimetres regardless of the size of the part. **Fig. 23-4**

SHAPE

WRONG

1:1 0   1   2   3   4   5   6

30 29 28 27 26 25 24

FULL SIZE

1:1 0   10mm 20   30   40   50   60

600 580 560 540 520 500 480

RIGHT

Fig. 23-3a
Scales are available in a variety of shapes.

Fig. 23-4
The wrong and right kind of scale to use for engineering drafting.

Therefore, a drafting scale should be marked in millimetres rather than in centimetres as is sometimes found. For example, for a *full size* drawing with a scale of 1:1, the number lines should be 10, 20, 30, etc. rather than 1, 2, 3, 4, etc. Never select a drafting scale marked in centimetres. The ISO (International Organization for Standardization) has recommended the basic reduction ratios of 1:2, 1:5, and 1:10.

Fig. 23-5a,b

Common Drafting Scales

Customary Inch		Nearest ISO Metric Equivalent (mm)*
1:2500	(1 in = 200 ft)	1:2000
1:1250	(1 in = 100 ft)	1:1000
1:500	(1/32 in = 1 ft)	1:500
1:192	(1/16 in = 1 ft)	1:200
1:96	(1/8 in = 1 ft)	1:100
1:48	(1/4 in = 1 ft)	1:50
1:24	(1/2 in = 1 ft)	1:20
1:12	(1 in = 1 ft)	1:10
1:4	(quarter size) (3 in = 1 ft)	1:5
1:2	(half size) (6 in = 1 ft)	1:2
1:1	(full size) (12 in = 1 ft)	1:1

*Based on scales recommended in ISO R1047.

Fig. 23-5a
Preferred metric scales. Note that all metric scales have a factor of 1:10 relationship. Reduction scales above 1:10 are used primarily in architectural drafting.

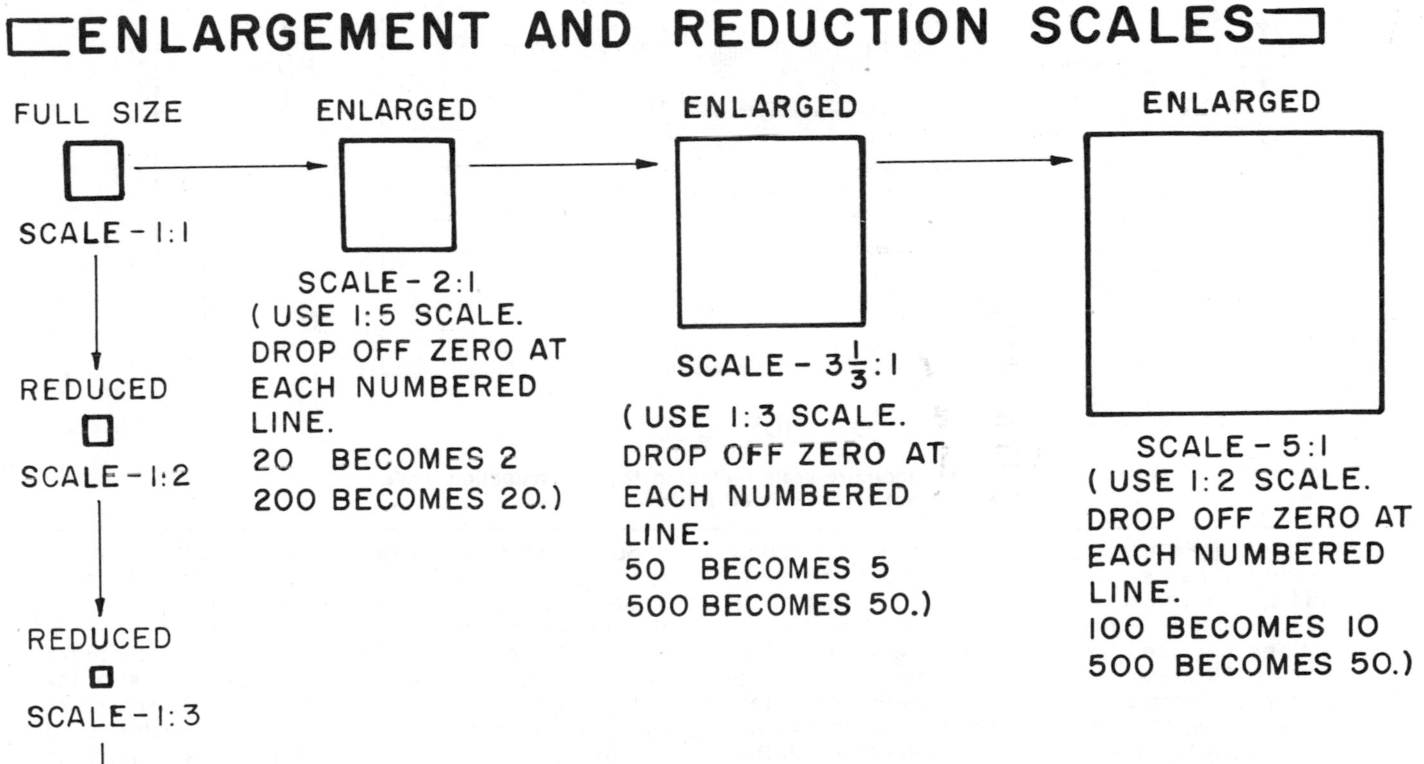

⊏ENLARGEMENT AND REDUCTION SCALES⊐

FULL SIZE

SCALE – 1:1

REDUCED

SCALE – 1:2

REDUCED

SCALE – 1:3

REDUCED

SCALE – 1:5

ENLARGED

SCALE – 2:1
(USE 1:5 SCALE.
DROP OFF ZERO AT
EACH NUMBERED
LINE.
20 BECOMES 2
200 BECOMES 20.)

ENLARGED

SCALE – $3\frac{1}{3}$:1
(USE 1:3 SCALE.
DROP OFF ZERO AT
EACH NUMBERED
LINE.
50 BECOMES 5
500 BECOMES 50.)

ENLARGED

SCALE – 5:1
(USE 1:2 SCALE.
DROP OFF ZERO AT
EACH NUMBERED
LINE.
100 BECOMES 10
500 BECOMES 50.)

USUAL METRIC SCALES ARE:			
FULL SIZE	1:1		
ENLARGEMENT	2:1	$3\frac{1}{3}$:1	5:1
REDUCTION	1:2	1:3	1:5

Fig. 23-5b
Enlargement and reduction scales. Note that the same scale can be used to reduce the object to a scale of 1:2 and to enlarge it to a scale of 5:1.

For engineering use, then, at least these three scales, namely 1:1, 1:2, and 1:5 should be shown on three edges of the measuring tool. **Fig. 23-6**

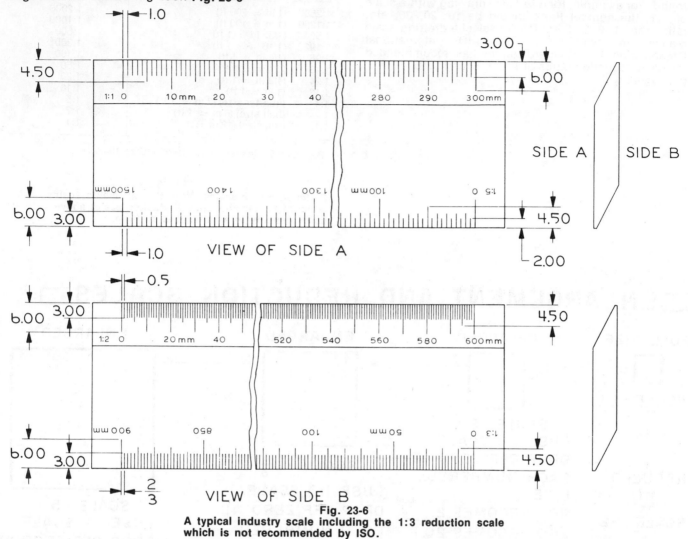

VIEW OF SIDE A

VIEW OF SIDE B

Fig. 23-6
A typical industry scale including the 1:3 reduction scale which is not recommended by ISO.

For all *full size* drawings use the 1:1 ratio. To reduce the drawing to *half size* a scale of 1:2 should be used. This same scale can also be used for a 5:1 enlargement scale. For example, to make the reduction drawing, the graduations are used exactly as they appear on the scale itself. However, for an enlargement of 5:1 the layout is made using the numbered lines that show ten times the values. Drop off the last zero when placing the dimensions on the drawing. For example, if the part calls for a line 24 mm in length with a reduction scale of 1:2, mark off a distance from zero and of 4 graduations past the 20 mm. The line itself would actually be 12 mm in length, but the dimension would be shown as *24 mm.* From the enlargement of 5:1 the line would be laid out from 0 to 240 on the 1:2 scale; however, the dimension would be shown as *24 mm.* The difference, then, between a 1:2 reduction scale and a 5:1 enlargement scale is by a factor of 10. The same relationship exists between the 1:5 reduction scale and the 2:1 enlargement scale. Therefore, with a scale that has the ratios of 1:1, 1:2, and 1:5, the draftsman has all possible reductions and enlargements commonly used for *engineering drawings.*

Some industries use a metric scale with one reduction ratio of 1:3. *This is not an ISO recommended scale but many industries feel they need such a ratio to fill the large gap between 1:2 and 1:5.* The 1:3 reduction approximates a 3/8 size in the customary system. If the 1:3 is used as the reduction ratio, then the enlargement ratio should be 3 1/3:1. The reason for this is that there should be a factor of 10 relationship between all enlargement and reduction scales. If the enlargement scale were made 3:1 this would not be true. A number of additional reduction scales such as 1:10, 1:20, 1:50, 1:100, etc. are needed for architectural drafting. Many countries that use metric in building construction show all floor plan sizes in millimetre dimensions and only site and plot plans in metre dimensions. Because the millimetre and metre differ by a factor of 1000, a single scale can be used for either millimetre and metre measurements. For example, the first numbered line on a reduction scale of 1:5 would show 100 mm while the same numbered line for a reduction scale of 1:50 would show 1 m. The scales on a drafting machine can be converted to metric by replacing either the plastic blades or by adding metric marked pressure sensitized tape to cover the customary scale. **Fig. 23-7.**

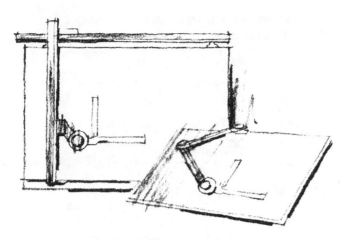

Fig. 23-7
Only the plastic scales of the drafting machine need to be replaced for metric drafting.

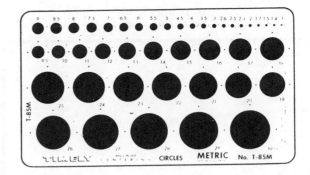

Templates

All types and designs of templates are available in metric measurements including circles, elipses, squares, hexagons, triangles, and many other specialized types. **Fig. 23-8**

Check carefully to make sure that the templates are marked in millimetres. For example, for metric designs, a hole template should be marked in the full millimetre sizes such as 1, 2, 3, 4, 5, 6, etc. up through 30 mm plus half millimetres up to ten. These templates are used in designing and drawing parts that are in rounded or full millimetre measurements. When dual dimensioning in which only a soft conversion is being done, the existing customary templates or conversion templates should be used with the correct metric dimensions added to the template. For example, if the hole template has a 1 inch size, both 1.000 in or 25.4 mm should be stamped next to it. The template used to draw the hexagonal bolt heads and nuts for ISO threads should be marked in common metric sizes such as M6, M8, M10, etc.

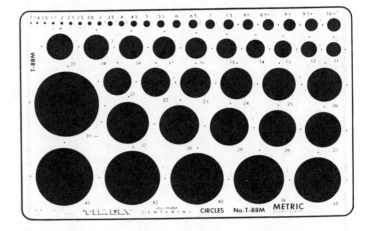

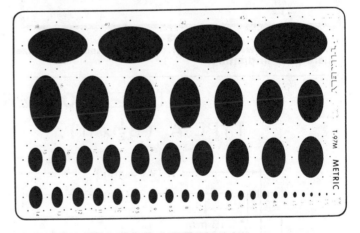

Drafting Paper and Film

Drafting paper, velum and polyester drafting film will eventually be available in both customary inch sizes and ISO metric sizes. See Paper Standards. For example, an A4 size paper is approximately equivalent to the customary 8 1/2" x 11" size.
Fig. 23-9a   Fig. 23-9b

If the drafting room is anticipating converting to A size papers or if the drawings are used in other countries in which international standard paper sizes are used, it is recommended that the border line be in proportion to the A4 paper size rather than the 8 1/2" x 11" or 9" x 12" paper size. **Fig. 23-10**

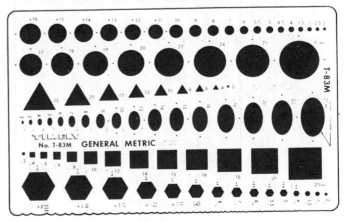

Fig. 23-8
Typical shapes of metric templates.

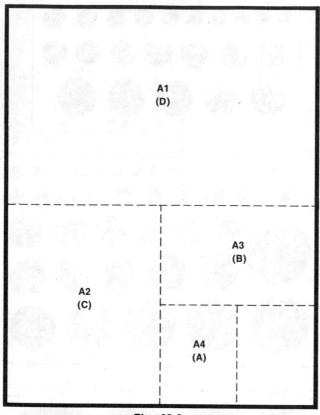

TOTAL SHEET "A0"
TOTAL SHEET "E"

A1
(D)

A3
(B)

A2
(C)

A4
(A)

Fig. 23-9a
Comparison between common customary and metric size papers used in drafting.

STANDARD DRAWING SIZE
ISO STANDARD

SIZE	MILLIMETERS	INCHES
A0	841 x 1189	33.11 x 46.81
A1	594 x 841	23.39 x 33.11
A2	420 x 594	16.54 x 23.39
A3	297 x 420	11.69 x 16.54
A4	210 x 297	8.27 x 11.69

AMERICAN STANDARD

SIZE	INCHES	MILLIMETERS
E	34 x 44	863.6 x 1117.6
D	22 x 34	558.8 x 863.6
C	17 x 22	431.8 x 558.8
B	11 x 17	279.4 x 431.8
A	8½ x 11	215.9 x 279.4
E	36 x 48	914.4 x 1219.2
D	24 x 36	609.6 x 914.4
C	18 x 24	457.2 x 609.6
B	12 x 18	304.8 x 457.2
A	9 x 12	228.6 x 304.8

Fig. 23-9b
This chart shows millimetre sizes and the customary inch equivalent sizes of ISO papers.

BORDER LINES

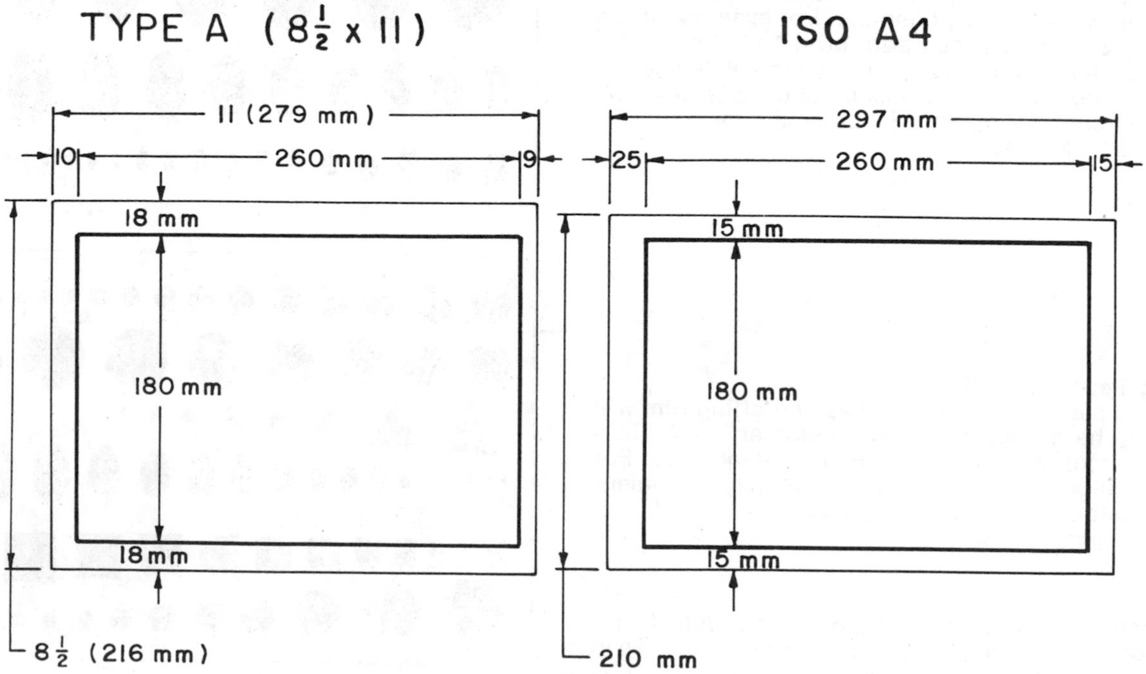

TYPE A (8½ x 11)

11 (279 mm)
260 mm
10 ⊢ ⊣ 9
18 mm
180 mm
18 mm
8½ (216 mm)

ISO A4

297 mm
260 mm
25 ⊢ ⊣ 15
15 mm
180 mm
15 mm
210 mm

Fig. 23-10
If metric drawings are to be made on inch size papers, it is desirable to have the inside dimensions in millimetres, the same as if ISO A4 size paper were used.

If larger size is used, such as 11" x 17", then the borders should be in proportion to the A3 size. This will facilitate microfilming of the drawings that can then later be reproduced on A4 size paper. For example, the border line for type A4 paper would have an inside dimension of 180 x 260 mm.

Some companies are producing drafting paper, velum or polyester film in A sizes with a very light blue overprint covering the entire surface divided into small 1 mm squares and with slightly darker blue lines for the 10 millimetre squares. This light overprint does not show up in the final reproduction yet aids the draftsman in making layouts. The correct method of folding A sized papers is shown in **Fig. 23-11**.

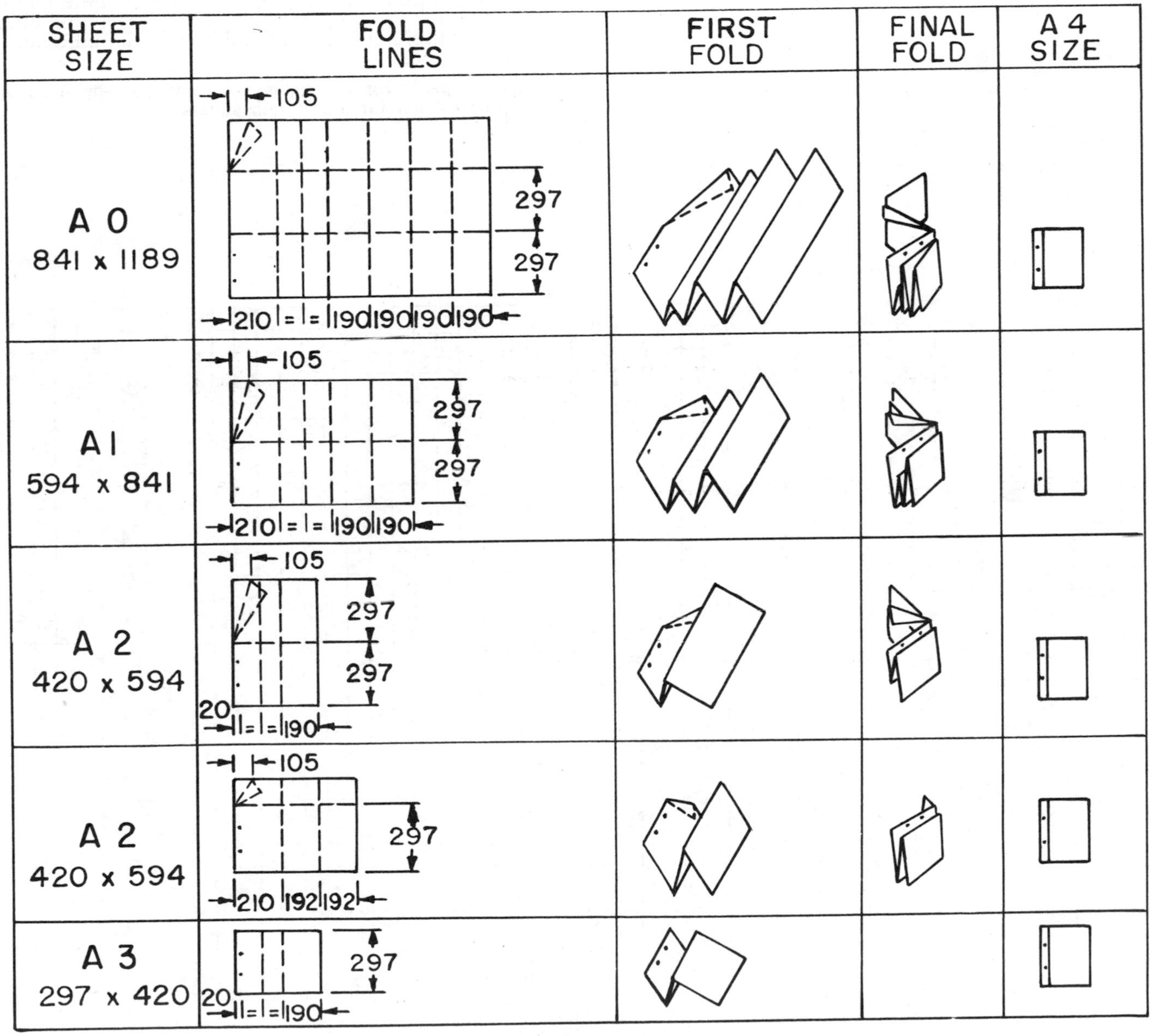

SHEET SIZE	FOLD LINES	FIRST FOLD	FINAL FOLD	A4 SIZE
A 0 841 x 1189				
A 1 594 x 841				
A 2 420 x 594				
A 2 420 x 594				
A 3 297 x 420				

Fig. 23-11
Correct method of folding A0 to A3 size papers so that the folded size will be equal to A4 size paper.

Squared Paper

Squared paper to millimetre dimensions is commonly used in freehand drawing and also for architectural work. Each small square represents 1 millimetre. **Fig. 23-12**

This grid can be used for a variety of ratios. For example, if the ratio is 1:1, each square equals 1 mm; if the ratio is 1:5 each square equals 5 mm. In architectural work each square could represent a very large dimension such as 200 mm. The squares could also be used to represent metres for extremely large scale drawings. Metric isometric grid paper is available to speed making an isometric sketch or drawing. **Fig. 23-13**

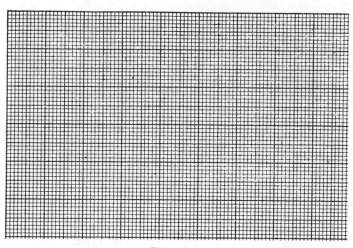

Fig. 23-12
Squared paper for making metric sketches. The lines are slightly heavier for the 10 mm squares.

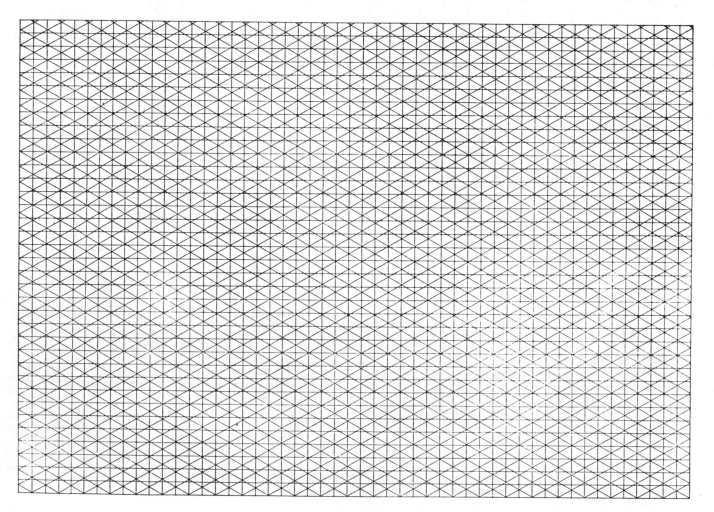

Fig. 23-13
Isometric paper with the diagonal squares 5 mm.

UNIT 24
DRAFTING METHODS AND STANDARDS

There are only a few international metric standards for drafting. Most drafting practices are common within a specific country or company and, therefore, each company develops its own set of drafting standards. The exact methods of adding dimensions to drawings vary somewhat from industry to industry and company to company. Two basic standards related to drafting practices are ISO/R128 Engineering Drawing Principles and Presentation, and ISO/R129 Engineering Drawing Dimensions. There are other ISO standards for limits and fits, surface roughness, and tolerances. **Fig. 24-1**

```
DRAFTING, DESIGN, AND TOLERANCE DATA


ISO  R128-1959  Engineering Drawing, Principles
of Presentation (Y14.2-1957 and Y14.3-1957).....
ISO  R129-1959  Engineering Drawing, Dimension-
ing (Y14.5-1966).................................
ISO  R286-Part 1-1962  System of Limits and
Fits Part 1:  General, Tolerances and Deviations
(supersedes ISA 25)  (B4.1-1967)................
ISO  R370-1964  Conversion of Toleranced
Dimensions from Inches into Millimetres and
Vice Versa. (B48.1-1933) (R1947)................
ISO  R406-1964  Inscription of Linear and Angu-
lar Tolerances. (Y14.5-1966)....................
ISO  R468-1966  Surface Roughness  (B46.1-1962).
ISO  R1101-1969  Tolerances of Form and of
Position, Part 1:  Generalities, Symbols, Indica
tions on Drawings, including Amendment 1-1971...
ISO  R1219-1970  Graphical Symbols for Hydraulic
and Pneumatic Equipment and Accessories for
Fluid Power Transmission  (Y32.10-1967).........
ISO  R1302-1971  Technical Drawings, Method of
Indicating Surface Texture on Drawings..........
ISO  R1660-1971  Technical Drawings -- Toler-
ances of Form and of Position -- Part III:
Dimensioning and Tolerancing of Profiles........
ISO  R1661-1971  Technical Drawings  -- Toler-
ances of Form and of Position -- Part IV:
Practical Examples of Indications on Drawings...
ISO  R1829-1970  Selection of Tolerance Zones
for General Purposes............................
ISO  R1938-1971  ISO System of Limits and Fits
-- Part II:  Inspection of Plain Workpieces.....
```

Fig. 24-1
ISO standards relating to drafting, design and tolerance data.

A basic document for drafting practices used by most U.S. industries is *Dimensioning and Tolerancing, ANSI Y14.5-1973.* All of these standards are available on request from the American National Standards Institute.

This short unit cannot possibly describe all the variations in practices or the details involved in metric drafting. Interested individuals should obtain a specific company's drafting standards to determine the exact practices used by that company. The general practices used by certain types of industries are similar. For example, the drafting standards of automobile companies vary somewhat from the standards of off-the-road vehicle industries.

International Variations
Some of the variations in international drafting

practices include the following:

Projection. In accordance with ISO/R128, either first or third angle projection may be used in drafting. Third angle projection, commonly referred to as American projection, is used in the United States and many countries throughout the world. **Fig. 24-2a,b.**

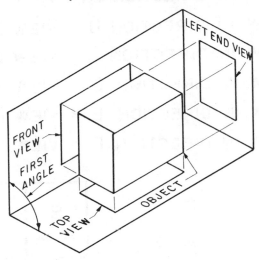

FIRST ANGLE PROJECTION

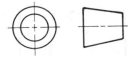

THIRD ANGLE PROJECTION

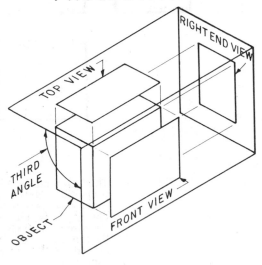

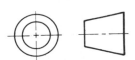

Fig. 24-2a
Two projection methods.

In drawing an object with this system the object can be assumed to be enclosed in a glass container. Each view represents that which is seen when looking perpendicular at each face of the box. The principal views are the front, top and right side. If each view were projected perpendicular to the box faces and the box were then opened - hinged along the top and right side of the front face - the third angle projection would be obtained. In first angle projection, known as European, the object is drawn as having been rolled over to either side so that the right side of the object is drawn to the left of the front view. **Fig. 24-2c**

VIEW IN DIRECTION A = VIEW FROM THE FRONT.

VIEW IN DIRECTION B = VIEW FROM ABOVE.

VIEW IN DIRECTION C = VIEW FROM THE LEFT.

VIEW IN DIRECTION D = VIEW FROM THE RIGHT.

VIEW IN DIRECTION E = VIEW FROM BELOW.

VIEW IN DIRECTION F = VIEW FROM THE REAR.

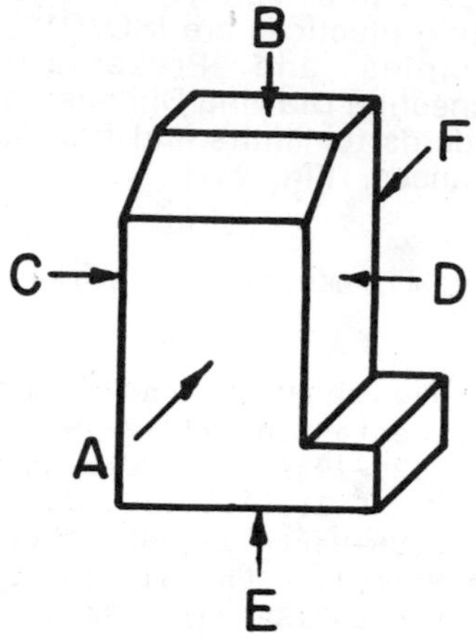

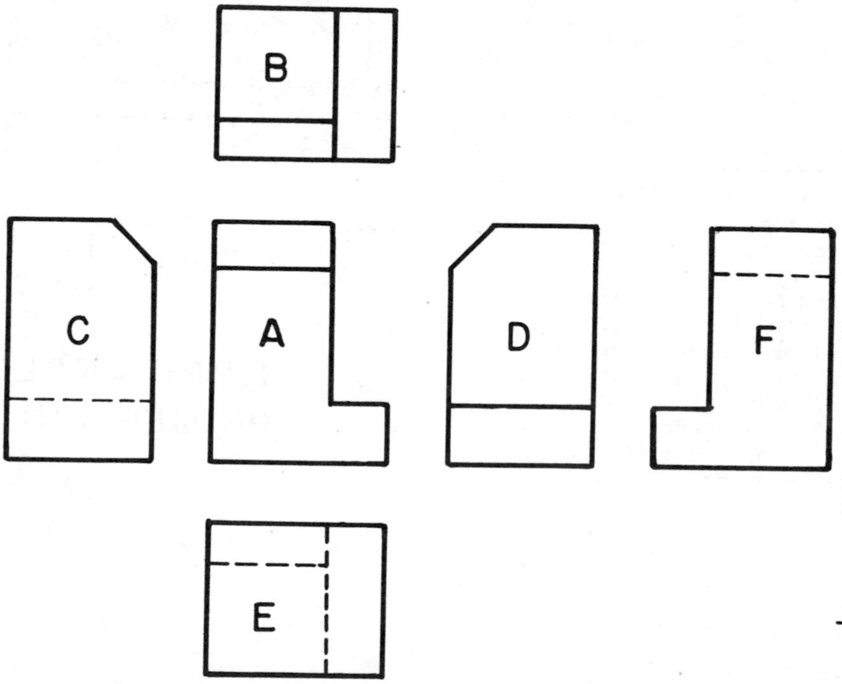

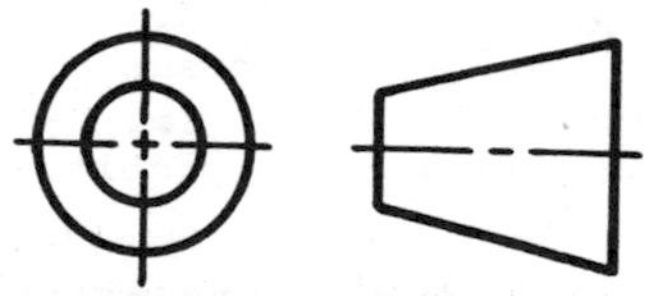

THIRD ANGLE

Fig. 24-2b
This method is known as the American or third angle projection. Note that with reference to the front view the other views are arranged as follows: the view from above is placed above, the view from below is placed underneath, the view from the right is placed to the right, and the view from the left is placed to the left. The view for the rear can either be placed on the left or on the right, as determined by convenience.

VIEW IN DIRECTION A = VIEW FROM THE FRONT.
VIEW IN DIRECTION B = VIEW FROM ABOVE.
VIEW IN DIRECTION C = VIEW FROM THE LEFT.
VIEW IN DIRECTION D = VIEW FROM THE RIGHT.
VIEW IN DIRECTION E = VIEW FROM BELOW.
VIEW IN DIRECTION F = VIEW FROM THE REAR.

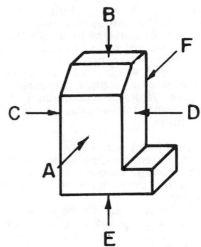

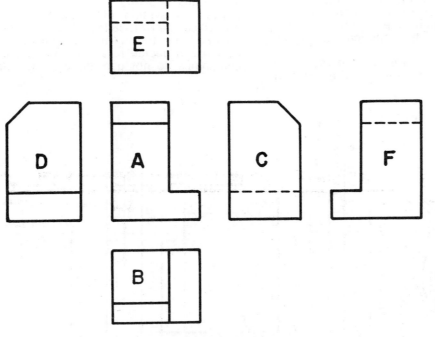

Fig. 24-2c
The first angle or European method. In relationship to the front view the other views are arranged as follows: the view from above is placed beneath, the view from below is placed above, the view from the left is placed to the right, the view from the right is placed to the left.

FIRST ANGLE

In other words, the difference between first and third angle projection is that in first angle the object is viewed as projected onto the drawing surface while in *third* angle the object is drawn *as viewed.* The projection system used should be indicated by means of the ISO symbol, which is a small drawing showing two views of a conical detail. While projection is not a part of metric conversion, it is important for the draftsman to understand the two projection systems.
Decimal marker. The decimal marker in the United States will be a dot or point on the line. **Fig. 24-3**

AMERICAN SYSTEM

13 240.00
a

13240.00
b

EUROPEAN SYSTEM

13 240,00
c

Fig. 24-3
Three methods of indicating dimensions. (a) The typical method used in many company standards. (b) the method recommended by ANSI Y14.5-1973. (c) the method used in most European countries.

However, in many European, African and South American countries the comma is used as the decimal marker. Because of these different practices *it is very important not to use the comma* as a divider between groups of three numbers.

Angles. Angles will be shown in degrees with minutes and seconds expressed in decimal parts of a degree. While SI recommends the use of radians and steradians for angles, these will not be used on drawings.

Basic Limits and Fits.

To understand the system of limits, tolerances and fits used in modern manufacturing, you must first learn the definitions of these and related terms as follows:

Nominal size. The nominal size is the designation used for purposes of general identification.

Basic size. The basic size of a dimension is the theoretical size from which the limits for that dimension are derived, by the application of the allowance and tolerance.

Limits of size. These limits are the maximum and minimum sizes permissible for a specific dimension. It is the largest and smallest size of the part that can still function successfully.

Tolerance. The tolerance on a dimension is the total permissible variation in its size. The tolerance is the difference between the maximum and minimum limits of a size. The tolerance may be *unilateral* in which the tolerance is in one direction only or *bilateral* in which the tolerance is in two directions from the basic size.

Allowance. An allowance is an intentional difference in correlated dimensions of mating parts.

Fit. The fit between two mating parts is the relationship existing between them with respect to the amount of clearance or interference which is present when they are assembled. For example, in some parts, a shaft must revolve in a hole while in other parts the shaft is made to fit very tightly in the hole.

ISO Limits and Fits.

The ISO system of limits and fit described in ISO/R286 and R/1938 includes a full set of definitions relating to limits and fits. Companies or industries may or may not decide to accept this system. Most U.S. companies do not use this system. **Fig. 24-4**

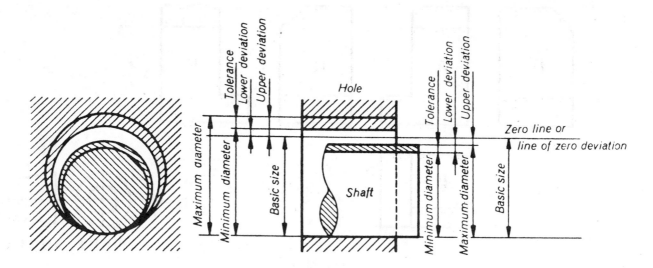

FIG. 1

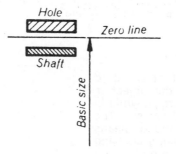

Fig. 24-4
The definitions used in the ISO system of limits and fits.

The system is based on a series of standard tolerances and deviations covering sizes up to 3150 mm. The system consists of these essentials:

Basic size is a size without tolerance much like a basic dimension in true position tolerance.

Fundamental deviation is designated by a letter. When applied to holes, the letter is upper case while the lower case is for forshafts. This value added to the basic size gives one limit of size, that of least clearance, or least interference depending on the letter specified.

Tolerance grade is designated by a number. The value of the tolerance grade added to the fundamental deviation and the basic size provides the other limit of size.

Eighteen tolerance grades are included. The system also provides 27 different fundamental deviations for sizes up to and including 500 mm and 14 for larger sizes to give different types of fits ranging from coarse clearance to heavy interference.

For detail information on ISO limits and fits, ISO/R128 gives guidance for preferred tolerances for shafts and holes to be used in determining fits.

Geometric Dimensioning and Tolerancing

The subject of geometric dimensioning and tolerancing is too complicated to be described in any detail in this publication. However, the engineer, draftsman, and machinist should be aware of the fact that many companies are not only changing to the metric measuring system but also are using geometric dimensioning and tolerancing on drawings to replace or supplement more conventional coordinate dimensioning. **Fig. 24-5a,b,c,d**

		CHARACTERISTIC	SYMBOL	NOTES
INDIVIDUAL FEATURES	FORM TOLERANCES	STRAIGHTNESS	—	1
		FLATNESS	▱	1
		ROUNDNESS (CIRCULARITY)	○	
		CYLINDRICITY	⌭	
INDIVIDUAL OR RELATED FEATURES		PROFILE OF A LINE	⌒	2
		PROFILE OF A SURFACE	⌓	2
RELATED FEATURES		ANGULARITY	∠	
		PERPENDICULARITY (SQUARENESS)	⊥	
		PARALLELISM	//	3
	LOCATION TOLERANCES	POSITION	⊕	
		CONCENTRICITY	◎	3,7
		SYMMETRY	≡	5
	RUNOUT TOLERANCES	CIRCULAR	↗	4
		TOTAL	↗	4,6

Note: 1) The symbol ⌣ formerly denoted flatness.

The symbol ⌒ or — formerly denoted flatness and straightness.

2) Considered "related" features where datums are specified.

3) The symbol || and ◉ formerly denoted parallelism and concentricity, respectively.

4) The symbol ↗ without the qualifier "CIRCULAR" formerly denoted total runout.

5) Where symmetry applies, it is preferred that the position symbol be used.

6) "TOTAL" must be specified under the feature control symbol.

7) Consider the use of position or runout.

Where existing drawings using the above former symbols are continued in use, each former symbol denotes that geometric characteristic which is applicable to the specific type of feature shown.

Fig. 24-5a
Geometric characteristic symbols used for geometric tolerancing.

In more conventional *coordinate dimensioning,* limits of tolerances are measured along the x and y axes so that the overall limits take the form of a square. With this method, the tolerance across the diagonal of the square is greater than along either the x or y axis. While this diagonal is greater than the tolerance limit, it is still considered to be within the tolerance zone. In the geometric tolerancing system this square is replaced with a true positioned tolerancing which gives a circular tolerance zone. The diameter of this circular tolerance zone is exactly the same as the diagonal across the square of the more conventional coordinate tolerance zone. **Fig. 24-5b**

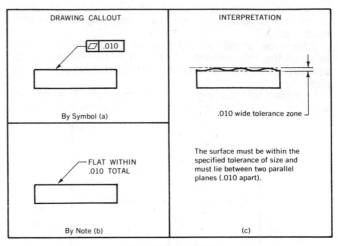

SPECIFYING FLATNESS

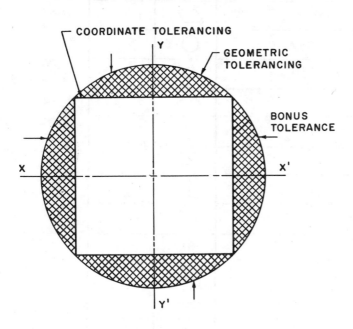

Fig. 24-5b
Note the difference between the tolerancing used in the coordinate system and that used in geometric tolerancing.

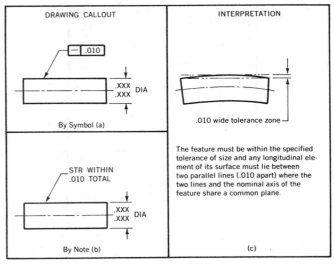

SPECIFYING STRAIGHTNESS

Fig. 24-5c
Two examples of tolerancing showing the geometric system above and the coordinate system below.

Since all points on the same circle are the same distance from the true center, this allows greater latitude in locating the position of the hole. This is an example of *tolerance position.* There are also *tolerances of form* including thickness, flatness, roundness, cylindricity, and others. **Fig. 24-5c**

24-6

In the more conventional coordinate dimensioning system, many of these details must be described by notes or notations; in the geometric dimensioning and tolerancing system symbols are used. The result is

AMERICAN NATIONAL STANDARD DIMENSIONING AND TOLERANCING

that the drawing is much neater, less cluttered, and cleaner. It should be noted that some of the geometric symbols have changed slightly from earlier standards.
Fig. 24-5d

ANSI Y14.5—1973

ASME   American Society of Mechanical Engineers

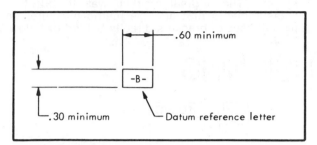

FIG. 74   DATUM IDENTIFYING SYMBOL

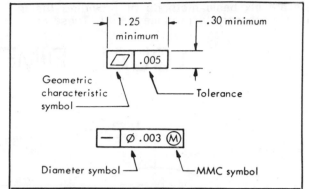

FIG. 78   FEATURE CONTROL SYMBOLS

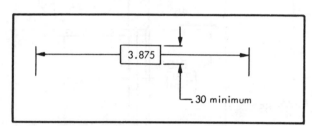

FIG. 75   BASIC DIMENSION SYMBOL

TERM	ABBREVIATION	SYMBOL
Maximum Material Condition	MMC	Ⓜ
Regardless of Feature Size	RFS	Ⓢ
Diameter	DIA	∅
Projected Tolerance Zone	TOL ZONE PROJ	Ⓟ
Reference	REF	(1.250)
Basic	BSC	3.875

FIG. 76   OTHER SYMBOLS

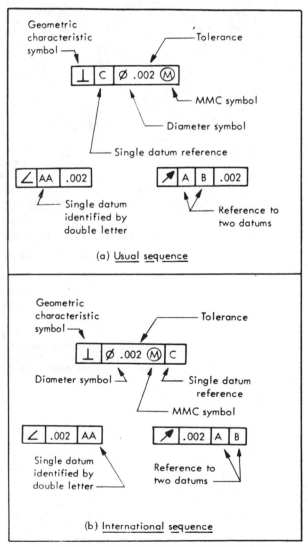

(a) Usual sequence

(b) International sequence

FIG. 79   FEATURE CONTROL SYMBOLS INCORPORATING DATUM REFERENCES

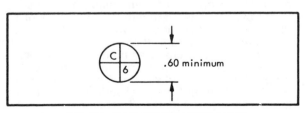

FIG. 77   DATUM TARGET SYMBOL

Fig. 24-5d
Other common symbols.

Readers interested in the details of this system should obtain a copy of **Dimensioning and Tolerancing, ANSI Y14.5-1973** and the book, **Geometric Dimensioning and Tolerancing, A Working Guide,** by O. L. Foster, published by Addison-Wesley Publishing Company, Reading, PA 08167.

Methods of Dimensioning a Drawing

There are six basic methods of providing the information necessary to produce a part. These are:

Dual dimensioning using the dimension line method. The dual dimensioning practice was the original method for dimensioning engineering drawings with both metric and inch units shown on the same drawing. This method is used to give a drawing dual capabilities, that is, the drawing could be used for manufacturing a part in either the customary or metric system. The original practice was to put the inch measurements first and the metric measurements in parentheses or brackets directly behind or below. **Fig. 24-6.**

DUAL DIMENSIONING

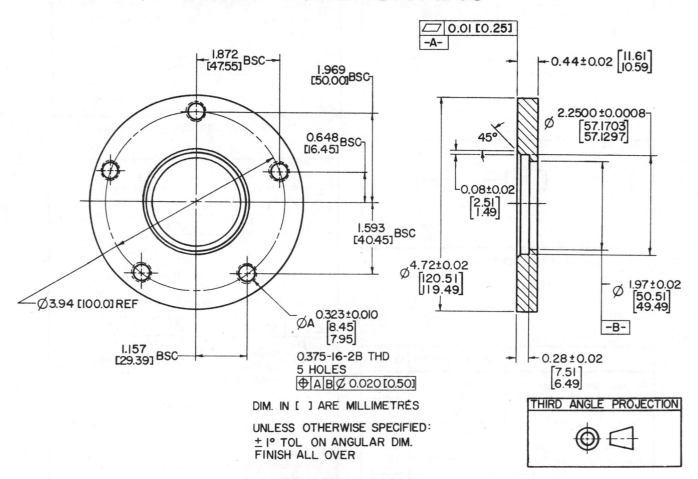

DIM. IN [ ] ARE MILLIMETRES

UNLESS OTHERWISE SPECIFIED:
± 1° TOL ON ANGULAR DIM.
FINISH ALL OVER

Fig. 24-6
Dual dimensioning using the bracket method with the inch dimensions above and the metric dimensions below. This is the traditional dual dimensioning method.

The SAE metric advisory committee formulated SAE Standard J390 dual dimensioning as the first standardized dual dimensioning procedure to be published in the United States. Many other industries produced their own dual dimensioning standards.

In the early stages of conversion the United Kingdom dual dimensioned all drawings. However, it was soon found that the plant worker ignored the metric dimensions and continued to use the inch dimensions. Dual dimensioning is the most complicated method of adding the necessary technical information. As a result, it is rapidly being replaced by other drafting practices. The amount of time and energy necessary to

dual dimension a drawing and the extra complexities of the drawing after it is complete have made this a less desirable method of dimensioning. The average draftsman spends approximately one half of his time dimensioning drawings. It was also found in the dual dimensioning system that errors in manufacturing were greater and scrap was higher. If it is necessary to dual dimension a drawing for manufacturing, the linear dimensions to establish the *design* should be in the metric system and then converted to obtain the inch measurement. The metric dimensions should establish the fits and limits. It is important to add to the title block an indication of the system of measurement used, namely, linear measurement - millimetre/inch. The best practice (called position method) is to put the metric dimensions on the drawing above the dimension or leader line and the inch dimension below.

Some companies use the *bracket* method with recommendations that the inch dimensions be enclosed in parentheses. **Fig. 24-7**

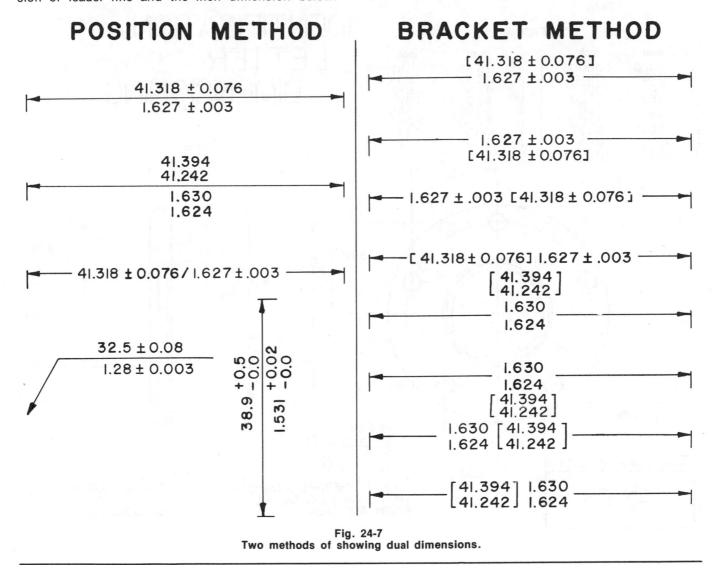

POSITION METHOD

41.318 ± 0.076
1.627 ±.003

41.394
41.242
1.630
1.624

41.318 ± 0.076 / 1.627 ±.003

32.5 ± 0.08
1.28 ± 0.003

38.9 +0.5 -0.0
1.531 +0.02 -0.0

BRACKET METHOD

[41.318 ± 0.076]
1.627 ±.003

1.627 ±.003
[41.318 ± 0.076]

1.627 ±.003 [41.318 ± 0.076]

[41.318 ± 0.076] 1.627 ±.003
[41.394]
[41.242]
1.630
1.624

1.630
1.624
[41.394]
[41.242]

1.630 [41.394]
1.624 [41.242]

[41.394] 1.630
[41.242] 1.624

Fig. 24-7
Two methods of showing dual dimensions.

Whenever possible, callouts should be expressed as a ratio so that they will be equal in both systems. For example, taper 0.006:1 would mean a taper of 0.006 inch per inch or 0.006 millimetres per millimetre.

Dual dimensioning may be preferred for the following reasons: (1) the same part will be manufactured using the two different measuring systems; (2) because of the nature of the part, it may be manufactured in both metric and customary systems for an extended period of time; (3) metric parts that are to be introduced into the total product slowly must interface with existing parts and, therefore, (a) the dual dimensioned parts will help with checking the interface dimensions, (b) subcontractors may want to produce the part in either the metric or the customary system, and (c) numerical control machines that are designed in the inch system will require the customary information until the machine is converted to dual capabilities or is replaced by an all-metric machine.

If an inch-designed part must be used in a metric product, it should be drawn as follows:
1. Convert inch dimensions to metric values without rounding off.
2. Use the established tolerance and/or fit relationships.
3. Using the information in (1) and (2), establish the mating part dimensions in metric units with the inch units in brackets.
4. Inch-designed parts should have dual dimensioning shown on the drawing for convenience in manufacturing.

Dimensioning with letters or tabular method. Another drafting technique that has had limited use is to letter all dimensions (A, B, C, etc.). Then a tabular chart is added showing the metric and inch equivalent for each of the letters. For example, **A** might show 0.500 under the inch column and 12.7 under the metric column. **Fig. 24-8**

IDENTIFICATION LETTER DIMENSIONING

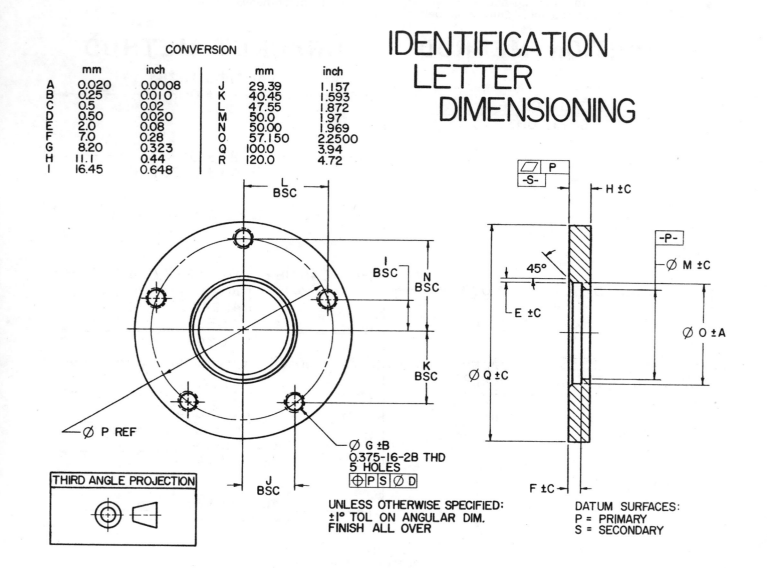

CONVERSION

	mm	inch		mm	inch
A	0.020	0.0008	J	29.39	1.157
B	0.25	0.010	K	40.45	1.593
C	0.5	0.02	L	47.55	1.872
D	0.50	0.020	M	50.0	1.97
E	2.0	0.08	N	50.00	1.969
F	7.0	0.28	O	57.150	2.2500
G	8.20	0.323	Q	100.0	3.94
H	11.1	0.44	R	120.0	4.72
I	16.45	0.648			

THIRD ANGLE PROJECTION

Ø P REF

L BSC

I BSC

N BSC

K BSC

J BSC

Ø G ±B
0.375-16-2B THD
5 HOLES
⊕ P S Ø D

UNLESS OTHERWISE SPECIFIED:
±1° TOL ON ANGULAR DIM.
FINISH ALL OVER

P / -S-

H ±C

-P-

45°

Ø M ±C

E ±C

Ø O ±A

Ø Q ±C

F ±C

DATUM SURFACES:
P = PRIMARY
S = SECONDARY

Fig. 24-8
Dimensioning a drawing using letters or by the tabular method.

This method is confusing and requires a great deal of care in print reading, since the user must first look at the letter on the drawing and then find the measurement on the chart. Frequently the worker will write in the needed dimension after the letter, adding to clutter on the drawing.

Another problem is that there could be a conflict between the letter designating a dimension and the geometric tolerance. This method is not common and, therefore, of little importance.

Metric dimensioning with customary readout chart, or the chart method. With this method the design is made to metric modules and only metric dimensions are placed on the drawing itself. **Fig. 24-9**

METRIC DIMENSIONING
(WITH CUSTOMARY READOUT CHART)

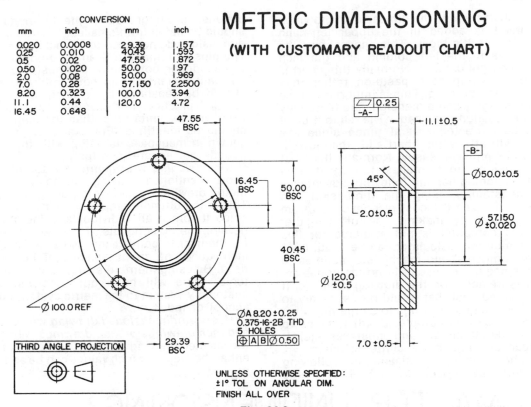

CONVERSION

mm	inch	mm	inch
0.020	0.0008	29.39	1.157
0.25	0.010	40.45	1.593
0.5	0.02	47.55	1.872
0.50	0.020	50.0	1.97
2.0	0.08	50.00	1.969
7.0	0.28	57.150	2.2500
8.20	0.323	100.0	3.94
11.1	0.44	120.0	4.72
16.45	0.648		

UNLESS OTHERWISE SPECIFIED:
±1° TOL ON ANGULAR DIM.
FINISH ALL OVER

Fig. 24-9a
Metric drawing with customary readout chart. This is commonly known as the chart method.

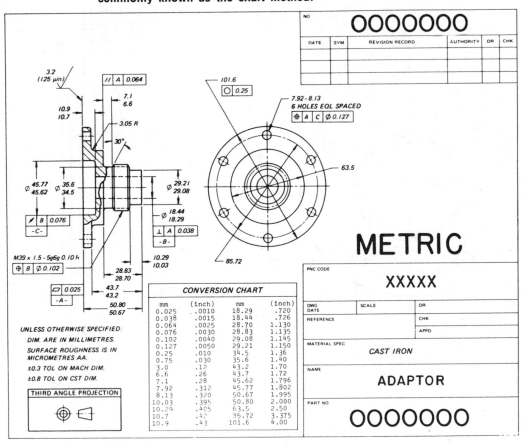

Fig. 24-9b
The conversion chart on this drawing is placed near the title block.

CONVERSION CHART			
mm	(inch)	mm	(inch)
0.025	.0010	18.29	.720
0.038	.0015	18.44	.726
0.064	.0025	28.70	1.130
0.076	.0030	28.83	1.135
0.102	.0040	29.08	1.145
0.127	.0050	29.21	1.150
0.25	.010	34.5	1.36
0.75	.030	35.6	1.40
3.0	.12	43.2	1.70
6.6	.26	43.7	1.72
7.1	.28	45.62	1.796
7.92	.312	45.77	1.802
8.13	.320	50.67	1.995
10.03	.395	50.80	2.000
10.29	.405	63.5	2.50
10.7	.42	85.72	3.375
10.9	.43	101.6	4.00

UNLESS OTHERWISE SPECIFIED:
DIM. ARE IN MILLIMETRES.
SURFACE ROUGHNESS IS IN MICROMETRES AA.
±0.3 TOL ON MACH DIM.
±0.8 TOL ON CST DIM.

CAST IRON
ADAPTOR
METRIC

Then a readout chart for only the dimensions shown on the drawing itself is added in the upper left-hand corner or next to the title block. This chart shows the metric dimensions in the left column and the inch equivalents in the right column. Normally this chart is attached to the drawing as a paste-on rather than added directly on the drawing. This is important in the early stages of design when dimensions are frequently changed as modifications are made. The readout chart may need to be corrected several times since any design change will affect this chart and, therefore, it must be able to be replaced easily. Normally the chart will show dimensions from smallest to largest. This method of dimensioning has the following advantages over dual dimensioning using the dimension line method: (a) It minimizes the cost of conversion from metric to customary by making use of computer capabilities. If a computer is not available for this conversion, a small mini-calculator can be used. (b) It speeds up the engineers' and machinists' abilities to "think metric" since all the user will normally see are the metric measurements on the drawing itself. (c) It eliminates the added cost that would be necessary to convert dual dimensioned drawings to all metric, when total metric conversion is completed. (d) It helps to eliminate minunderstandings and mistakes. (e) It provides a clean drawing, not a cluttered one.

When the chart method is used, the following practices should be observed: (1) The metric dimensions should be in the left-hand column and should be listed from smallest to largest. (2) Duplicate dimensions do not need to be included in the chart. (3) The plus and minus tolerances on dimensions should be included in both metric and customary dimensions. (4) Limit dimensions in both millimetres and inches should be separated by a slash or by other recommended practice. For example, 51.5/49.5. (5) All information for units other than the millimetre and inch should be identified. For example, pressure may be shown in megapascals (MPa) with the equivalents in pounds per square inch (psi).

Dimensioning with metric measurements only. The above mentioned drawing can be converted to an all metric drawing by merely removing the readout chart. This is the ultimate step in a "think metric" campaign since it forces all individuals using the drawing to develop metric concepts. If it is absolutely necessary for the user to convert the metric measurement to its inch equivalent, an inexpensive mini-calculator can be used. By using metric drawings and metric measuring tools, there will be a quick conversion from the customary system to the metric system throughout the school or industry.

Master undimensioned drawing with separate metric and inch drawings or dual drawings. With this method the master drawing is done without dimensions so either the metric or inch values can be added.
Fig. 24-10a,b,c,d

MASTER UNIDIMENSIONING

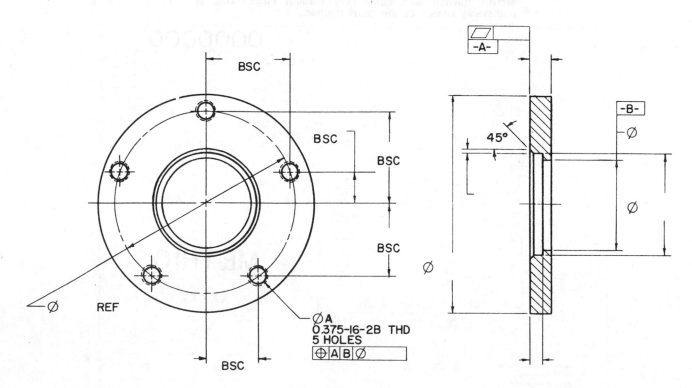

UNLESS OTHERWISE SPECIFIED:
±1° TOL ON ANGULAR DIM.
FINISH ALL OVER
Fig. 24-10a
A master undimensioning. Once the prints are made, metric measurements can be added to one drawing and inch dimensions to the other.

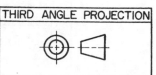

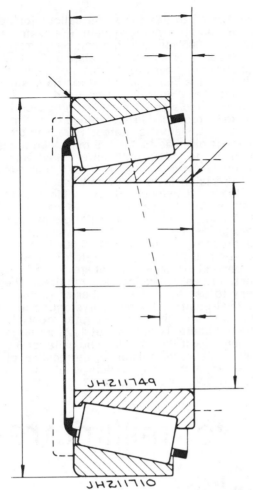

Fig. 24-10b
An undimensioned master drawing.

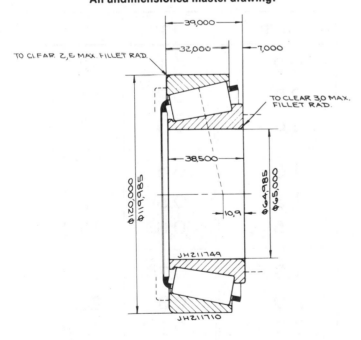

BRR = 4180 KG
BTR = 2420 KG

Fig. 24-10c
The metric dimensions have been added. Note that the comma (European practice) is used as a decimal marker.

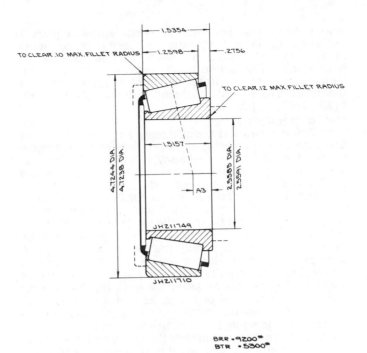

BRR = 9200 lb
BTR = 5300 lb

Fig. 24-10d
The inch dimensions have been added.

Once the drawing itself is produced, a photographic print is made of the master drawing. The metric dimensions are added to one drawing and the inch dimensions to the other. An advantage to this system is that the notes and other details can be added in whatever language is needed to manufacture the part. Also, variations in company or country practices with regard to the use of the decimal marker can be observed. For example, if the drawing is to be used in most European countries or South Africa, the decimal marker can be a comma. As a result, the master drawing can be used to produce the kind of drawing needed for world-wide manufacture. Some companies, however, do not permit the use of dual drawings because of the possibility that one or the other of the drawings will have changes made on it so that the two are no longer compatible.

Using a metric grid. In architectural drawing a metric grid can also be used for making plans. **Fig. 24-11** shows a metric grid in which each small square equals 1 millimetre on a side or 1mm^2. The 1:1 ratio (full size)

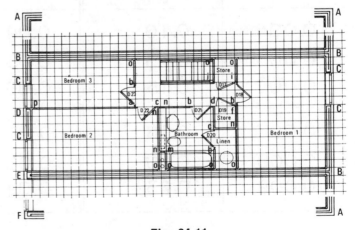

Fig. 24-11
This metric grid is commonly used for sketching and to do architectural drawings.

would mean that the side of each square equals 1 millimetre while a 1:10 ratio (reduction ratio) would mean that the side of each square equals 10 millimetres. The proportions can also be used for centimetres or metres. In architectural drafting practices, some of the common ratios would be 1:10, 1:20, 1:50, 1:100, etc.

Metric Practices

1. *Think metric.* The draftsman and designer must know how to use metric units properly and must begin to "think metric." The tendency to think and design in the familiar inch-pound system and then convert to the metric system must be avoided.

2. *Metric units.* The metric unit for linear dimensions will be the millimetre. This will be used for *all* engineering drawings regardless of size. With the millimetre, some value numbers will be quite large since there are 25.4 millimetres in an inch. For example, a 36-inch dimension is a 914.4 millimetre dimension. Other units frequently used on drawings are the kilogram for mass or weight; the newton for force; the kilopascal or megapascal for pressure and stress; the newton metre for torque; the square millimetre, the square centimetre and the square metre for area; the cubic millimetre, the cubic centimetre and the cubic metre for volume; the millilitre, the litre and the kilolitre for liquid capacity; the joule for energy and work; the watt for power; and degree Celsius for temperature.

3. *Units common to either system.* Measurements such as taper can use the same callout for both the inch-pound and the metric system. For example, 0.005 per inch or 0.005 mm per mm can be expressed as a ratio of 0.005:1 or as a note, taper 0.005:1. Angular dimensions in degrees and decimals of degrees are the same in both the inch-pound and metric systems. The radian and steradian will not be used.

4. *Implied precision.* The implied precision to which a part is to be produced is determined by the manner in which the dimension is stated. For example, if the dimension is given as 45.3 ± 0.5 mm, then the implied precision is to 1/10 millimetre. However, if the dimension is given as 45.30 ± 0.01 mm, then the implied precision is to 1/100 millimetre.

5. *Metric dimensioning.* (a) Most millimetre dimensions will be shown to one or two decimal places. This means that there will be only one or two numbers to the right of the decimal point. It must be remembered that 0.1 mm is about 0.004 inch while 0.01 mm is about 0.0004 inch. Therefore, three or more figures beyond the decimal point are needed only when extremely critical tolerances are required. There is a tendency to use the same number of figures beyond the decimal point in the metric system as in the inch system. The draftsman and designer must remember that the millimetre is only about 1/25 as large as the inch. Therefore, if the inch drawing calls for 0.010 inch or a ten thousandths tolerance, the equivalent metric tolerance is 0.254 mm, which would normally be rounded to 0.25 mm. **Fig. 24-12**

Decimals of an inch to millimetres (rounded values)

in	mm	in	mm	in	mm
0.001	0.02	0.01	0.2	0.1	2.5
0.002	0.05	0.02	0.5	0.2	5.1
0.003	0.08	0.03	0.8	0.3	7.6
0.004	0.10	0.04	1.0	0.4	10.2
0.005	0.13	0.05	1.3	0.5	12.7
0.006	0.15	0.06	1.5	0.6	15.2
0.007	0.18	0.07	1.8	0.7	17.8
0.008	0.20	0.08	2.0	0.8	20.3
0.009	0.23	0.09	2.3	0.9	22.9

Fig. 24-12
General rounding methods used in converting from inches to millimetres.

(b) Whenever possible, dimensions should be specified to even millimetres. For more precise work, specify to the 0.5 millimetre since this is the most accurate measurement found on the machinist's rule. A millimetre value that is less than one must always show a zero to the left of the decimal point. For example, 0.3 *not* .3.

(c) There should always be shown at least one zero to the right of the decimal point, even when millimetres are in even numbers. For example, when the value measure is a rounded untoleranced number, it should be shown as 25.0 not 25.

(d) When limit dimensions are used with either maximum or minimum dimensions to the right of the decimal point, the rounded value should have zero added for uniformity.

For example, $\dfrac{24.0}{23.6}$ not $\dfrac{24}{23.6}$

If the drawing uses a *unilateral* tolerance with metric dimensions where either the plus or minus tolerance is zero, the dimensions should be expressed by zeros to exactly the same number of digits as that required for the tolerance.
For example:

$43.00 \begin{array}{l} +0.00 \\ -0.03 \end{array}$ not 43.0-0.03   or

$37.00 \begin{array}{l} +0.04 \\ -0.00 \end{array}$ not 37.00+0.04.

If bilateral tolerancing is employed where a millimetre dimension contains an unequal plus and minus tolerance, both the maximum and minimum tolerances must have the same number of decimal places, using zeros if necessary.
For example:

$42.00 \begin{array}{l} +0.25 \\ -0.10 \end{array}$ not $42.00 \begin{array}{l} +0.25 \\ -0.1 \end{array}$

6. *Decimal marker.* The decimal marker for millimetre dimensions is exactly the same as that used for inch dimensions, namely, the dot or period on the line. However, the draftsman may frequently find drawings from other countries in which the decimal marker is a comma. It is for this reason that the next rule must be rigid. *Commas must never be used to designate thousands either in the inch or metric value*, because users of the drawing may confuse this with a decimal marker.

Many company standards recommend that a space be used where the comma would normally be found. *However, ANSI Y14.5-1973 specifically rules out the use of either the comma or the space to denote thousands.* This standard makes the point that on engineering drawings a space might be interpreted as a missing decimal point or number, particularly when prints are made from an original drawing.

7. *Drawing identification.* Identify all metric drawings with a stamp or sticker prominently displayed (normally at a slight angle) near the title block with the word METRIC. Use all capital letters that are a minimum of 8 mm in height. On an all-metric drawing include the general note, "UNLESS OTHERWISE SPECIFIED DIM. ARE IN MILLIMETRES." Some companies use colored (yellow) paper for metric drawings to distinguish them from customary drawings. Another method is to add a note just above the title block to indicate the system of measure.
LINEAR MEASURE:

$\dfrac{mm}{IN}$, mm/IN or $\dfrac{mm}{(in)}$, mm/in

8. *General rounding off rules.* (a) Inch to millimetre. When converting decimal inch to millimetre dimensions, multiply the inch dimensions by 25.4 and then round off to one less digit than the inch value, following the standard rounding off procedures. For example, if the dimension expressed in inches is 1.282, multiply 1.282 by 25.4 for a result of 32.562 8 mm. This should be rounded off to 32.56 and shown as such on the drawing.

(b) Millimetre to inch. In changing millimetre dimensions to decimal inch dimensions, divide the millimetre dimensions by 25.4 or multiply this by 0.039 370, then round off to one more digit than the millimetre value. In most cases if the drawing is designed in metric, the decimal inch dimensions are used for reference only. For example, if the metric dimension is 47.67 mm, then the inch dimension is 1.876 771 6. This should be rounded off to 1.877.

9. *Rounding for toleranced dimensions.* The tolerance is a good indicator of the precision required to produce a specific part. Therefore, in converting metric to customary tolerances or vice versa, follow this procedure:

(a) Use one of the following tables to determine the number of decimal places to retain in converting values. **Fig. 24-13a,b**

INCH TO MILLIMETRE		
Original Tolerance INCH		Millimetre Conversion Rounded to the Nearest:
at least	less than	
0	±0.000 16	0.000 1 (4 places)
±0.000 16	±0.001 6	0.001 (3 places)
±0.001 6	±0.016	0.01 (2 places)
±0.016	±0.16	0.1 (1 place)
±0.16	and up	1 (whole number)

MILLIMETRE TO INCH		
Original Tolerance MILLIMETRE		Inch Conversion Rounded to the Nearest:
at least	less than	
0	±0.008	0.000 01 (5 places)
±0.008	±0.08	0.000 1 (4 places)
±0.08	±0.8	0.001 (3 places)
±0.8	±8	0.01 (2 places)
±8	and up	0.1 (1 place)

Fig. 24-13a
This is one recommended method for changing from inches to millimetres and millimetres to inches when greater precision is required.

ORIGINAL TOLERANCE, in		FINENESS OF ROUNDING, mm
At Least	Less Than	
0.000 01	0.000 1	0.000 01
0.000 1	0.001	0.000 1
0.001	0.01	0.001
0.01	0.1	0.01
0.1	1	0.1

ORIGINAL TOLERANCE, mm.		FINENESS OF ROUNDING in
At Least	Less Than	
0.0005	0.005	0.000 001
0.005	0.05	0.000 01
0.05	0.5	0.000 1
0.5	5	0.001
5	50	0.01

Fig. 24-13b
This is from another company standard. Note that it is similar but slightly different from the previous standard.

(b) Convert the dimensions to the exact conversion, carrying the conversion to at least two more decimal places than the number of places to be retained.

(c) Then round off the tolerances using the rules given in 9..

(d) For example, to convert 71 ± 0.5 mm to an inch dimension, change 71 mm to 2.795 270 and round to 2.795 in. Change ± 0.5 mm to ± 0.019 68 in and round to 0.020 in. Customary equivalent is 2.795 ± 0.020.

10. *Rounding off procedures.* The following is the correct method of rounding off.

(a) The last digit to be retained is unchanged if it is followed by a number less than 5.

(b) The last digit to be retained is increased by one if it is followed by a number greater than 5.

(c) The last digit to be retained is unchanged if it is even, and is followed by exactly 5. For example, 0.075 in = 0.190 5 mm rounded to 0.190.

(d) The last digit to be retained is increased by one if it is odd and is followed by exactly 5: 0.0025 in = 0.063 5 mm rounded to 0.064.

11. *Conversion of units other than linear.* In converting units other than linear, round off the value so that it is consistent with the original accuracy. For example, to change psi to MPa multiply by 0.006894757. For example, 28 psi would equal 0.19 MPa or 193 kPa. For less accurate work, such as tire pressure the metric unit could be rounded to 190 kPa.

12. *Screw threads.* Each company must decide whether to use the ISO metric or to retain the ISO inch (Unified National) threads. If the *ISO inch threads* are used on a metric drawing, no change is to be made in the way the threads are designated on the drawing. *Do not change the customary measurement of screw threads to a "soft" conversion in metric.*

If ISO metric threads are used, these are to be defined by the nominal size (basic major diameter) and pitch expressed in millimetres. An "M" indicates that it is an ISO thread and this precedes the nominal size. An "x" separates the nominal size from the pitch.

Fig. 24-14

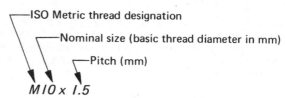

Fig. 24-14
The correct method of indicating a metric thread.

If length is specified, this should be separated from the pitch by an additional x. **Fig. 24-15**

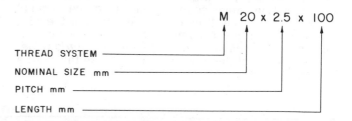

Fig. 24-15
This gives the additional information as to the length of the thread.

According to ISO standards, the pitch for coarse series need not be added so the thread could be shown as follows: M10. However, most U.S. companies will include the pitch in the designation to help in the recognition of ISO threads. A complete designation for an ISO metric screw thread includes an addition to the basic designation, an identification for the tolerance grade. The tolerance grade designation for general purpose applications is "6g" for external threads and "6H" (the only one) for internal threads. These grades are comparable to the Unified thread classes 2A and 2B, respectively.

The other designation "5g6g" is used for closer tolerance external threads. For general purpose threads, only the basic designation such as M4x0.7 is required on the drawing. For a close tolerance thread, add a capital "C" after the basic designation. The correct designation on the drawing for a close tolerance thread that is M6.3x1 would be M6.3x1C.

13. *Gears.* With the exception of the term "MODULE," which will be used on metric drawings instead of "DIAMETRAL PITCH," specification for gears will be unaffected by metric conversion. All values will be soft converted and gear data dimensions now expressed in inches will be dimensioned in millimetres on the face of the drawing. The only change in terminology on metric gear drawings will be the use of the term "MODULE" in place of "DIAMETRAL PITCH."

14. *Surface texture.* Average roughness height is expressed in micrometres (0.000 001 metre) instead of in microinches (0.000 001 in). See ISO R468 and R1302. **Fig. 24.16**

SURFACE TEXTURE — ROUGHNESS, WAVINESS AND LAY

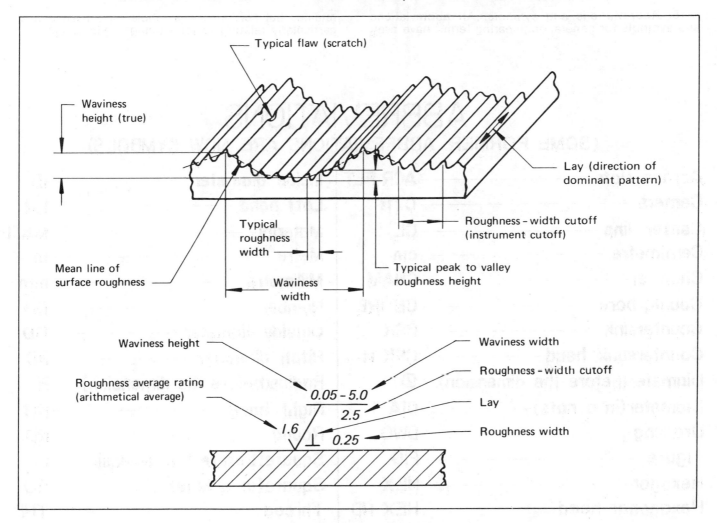

RECOMMENDED ROUGHNESS AVERAGE RATING VALUES MICROMETRES, μm (MICROINCHES, μin)*							
μm	μin	μm	μin	μm	μin	μm	μin
0.025	(1)	0.25	(10)	1.25	(50)	**6.3**	**(250)**
0.050	**(2)**	0.32	(13)	**1.6**	**(63)**	8.0	(320)
0.075	(3)	**0.40**	**(16)**	2.0	(80)	10.0	(400)
0.100	**(4)**	0.50	(20)	2.5	(100)	**12.5**	**(500)**
0.125	(5)	0.63	(25)	**3.2**	**(125)**	15.0	(600)
0.15	(6)	**0.80**	**(32)**	4.0	(160)	20.0	(800)
0.20	**(8)**	1.00	(40)	5.0	(200)	25.0	(1000)
*Boldface values preferred							

Fig. 24-16
Recommended values for surface texture.

15. *Abbreviations and symbols.* All abbreviations and symbols for general engineering terms have been retained but several new symbols have been added, particularly relating to tolerancing. **Fig. 24-17**

ABBREVIATIONS
(SOME FORMER ABBREVIATIONS ARE NOW SYMBOLS)

Across flats	ACR FLT	Inside diameter	ID
Centers	CTR	Left hand	LH
Center line	CL	Material	MATL
Centimetre	cm	Metre	m
Chamfer	CHAM	Millimetre	mm
Counterbore	CBORE	Number	NO
Countersink	CSK	Outside diameter	OD
Countersunk head	CSK H	Pitch diameter	PD
Diameter(before the dimension)	Ø	Radius(before the dimension)	R
Diameter(in a note)	DIA	Right hand	RH
Drawing	DWG	Round	RD
Figure	FIG	Square(before the dimension)	□
Hexagon	HEX	Square(in a note)	SQ
Hexagonal head	HEX HD	Thread	THD

Fig. 24-17
Abbreviations.

UNIT 25
BEGINNING DRAFTING PRACTICES

All metric activities involved in designing and producing a product begin in the drafting room. If the product is presently designed and dimensioned in the inch system, there is usually no good reason for changing the dimensions to the metric system. Don't convert inches to millimetres without some good purpose. However, for all new designs the metric system should be considered. The extent to which all dimensions can be in rounded metric units will depend on the availability of metric sizes of materials including metric fasteners.   **Fig. 25-1a,b**

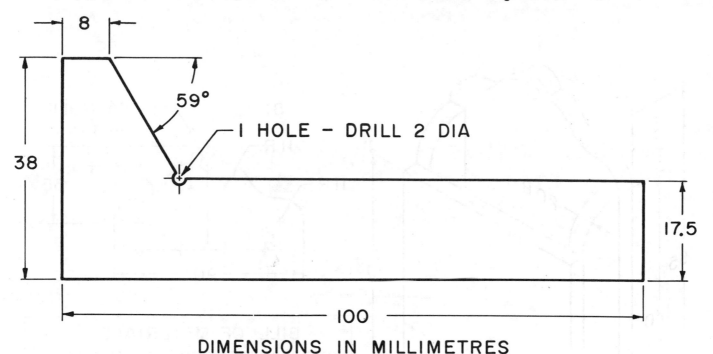

DIMENSIONS IN MILLIMETRES

Fig. 25-1a
The thickness of the stock needed to make this drill gage will be the *customary* thickness of 1/4" (6.35 mm) or the *metric* module thickness of 6 mm.

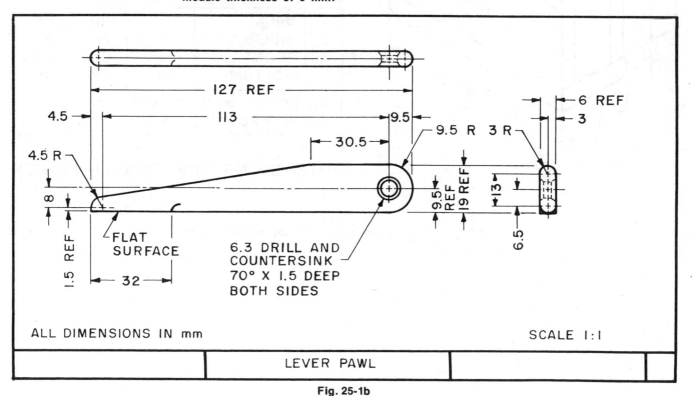

Fig. 25-1b
This lever pawl is made of 6 mm stock.

For example, if the customary square bar stock measures 1 in, then the dimension must be listed as 25.4 mm unless it is to be machined to an even metric module of 25 mm. Metric sizes of metal materials are available. If the product calls for 3/8 in walnut, the material can easily be planed to a rounded 9 mm thickness before building the product. **Fig. 25-2.**

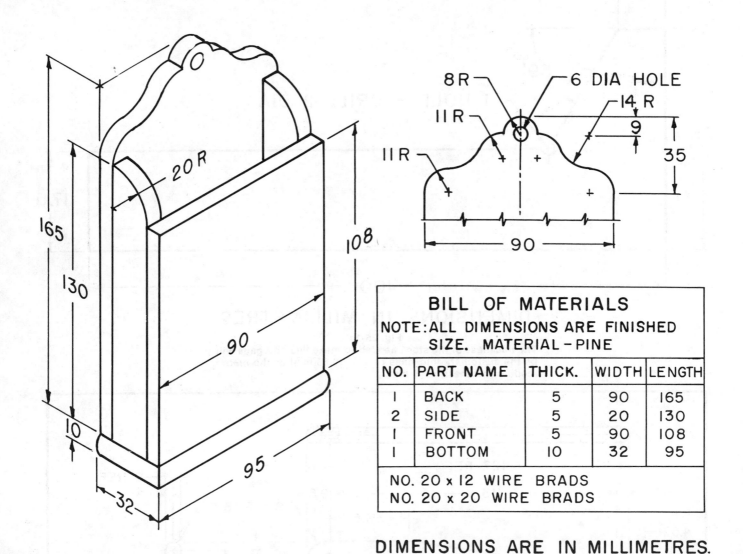

BILL OF MATERIALS

NOTE: ALL DIMENSIONS ARE FINISHED SIZE. MATERIAL – PINE

NO.	PART NAME	THICK.	WIDTH	LENGTH
1	BACK	5	90	165
2	SIDE	5	20	130
1	FRONT	5	90	108
1	BOTTOM	10	32	95

NO. 20 x 12 WIRE BRADS
NO. 20 x 20 WIRE BRADS

DIMENSIONS ARE IN MILLIMETRES.

Fig. 25-2
Most lumber is purchased in the rough and can be surfaced to rounded metric thicknesses.

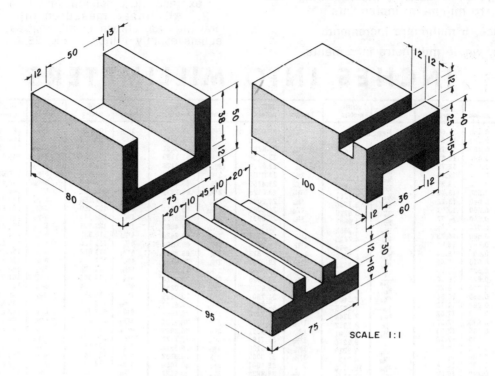

Fig. 25-3a
These parts are dimensioned following the first three preferred choices.

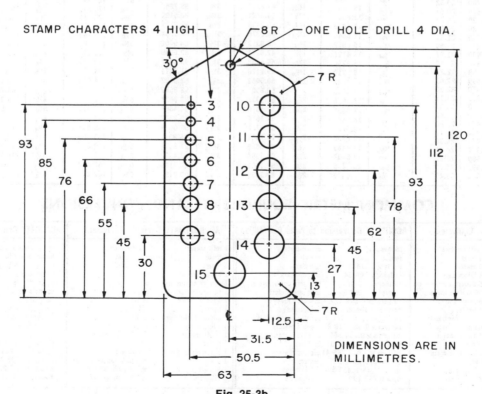

STAMP CHARACTERS 4 HIGH

8 R — ONE HOLE DRILL 4 DIA.

7 R

DIMENSIONS ARE IN MILLIMETRES.

Fig. 25-3b
All dimensions except three are in full millimetres. This is a metal product so a machinist's rule graduated in 0.5 mm (1/2 mm) is used to make the layout.

General Suggestions

1. All designs should be in metric modules. **Fig. 25-3a,b.** Wherever possible when designing in metric, select millimetre dimensions in the following order:

First choice, 10 millimetre increments

Second choice, 5 millimetre increments

Third choice, whole millimetre increments

Fourth choice, half millimetre increments (smallest division on a machinist's rule)

Fifth choice, select basic dimensions that will best express the precision shown in the drawing

2. All linear measurements on engineering drawings are shown in millimetres; 25.4 millimetres equals exactly 1 inch. **Fig. 25-4.**

INCHES INTO MILLIMETERS

Inches	Millimeters	Inches	Millimeters	Inches	Millimeters	Inches	Millimeters	Inches	Millimeters	Inches	Millimeters	Inches	Millimeters	Inches	Millimeters
Decimals				**Fractions**		53/64	21.0344	2 5/16	58.7376	3 31/32	100.806	5 21/32	143.669	8 11/16	220.663
0.001	0.0254	0.460	11.68	1/64	0.3969	27/32	21.4312	2 11/32	59.5314	4	101.600	5 11/16	144.463	8 3/4	222.250
0.002	0.0508	0.470	11.94	1/32	0.7937	55/64	21.8281	2 3/8	60.3251	4 1/32	102.394	5 23/32	145.257	8 13/16	223.838
0.003	0.0762	0.480	12.19	3/64	1.1906	7/8	22.2250	2 13/32	61.1189	4 1/16	103.188	5 3/4	146.050	8 7/8	225.425
0.004	0.1016	0.490	12.45	1/16	1.5875	57/64	22.6219	2 7/16	61.9126	4 3/32	103.981	5 25/32	146.844	8 15/16	227.013
0.005	0.1270	0.500	12.70	5/64	1.9844	29/32	23.0187	2 15/32	62.7064	4 1/8	104.775	5 13/16	147.638	9	228.600
0.006	0.1524	0.510	12.95	3/32	2.3812	59/64	23.4156	2 1/2	63.5001	4 5/32	105.569	5 27/32	148.432	9 1/16	230.188
0.007	0.1778	0.520	13.21	7/64	2.7781	15/16	23.8125	2 17/32	64.2939	4 3/16	106.363	5 7/8	149.225	9 1/8	231.775
0.008	0.2032	0.530	13.46	1/8	3.1750	61/64	24.2094	2 9/16	65.0876	4 7/32	107.156	5 29/32	150.019	9 3/16	233.363
0.009	0.2286	0.540	13.72	9/64	3.5719	31/32	24.6062	2 19/32	65.8814	4 1/4	107.950	5 15/16	150.813	9 1/4	234.950
0.010	0.254	0.550	13.97	5/32	3.9687	63/64	25.0031	2 5/8	66.6751	4 9/32	108.744	5 31/32	151.607	9 5/16	236.538
0.020	0.508	0.560	14.22	11/64	4.3656	1	25.4001	2 21/32	67.4689	4 5/16	109.538	6	152.400	9 3/8	238.125
0.030	0.762	0.570	14.48	3/16	4.7625	1 1/32	26.1938	2 11/16	68.2626	4 11/32	110.331	6 1/16	153.988	9 7/16	239.713
0.040	1.016	0.580	14.73	13/64	5.1594	1 1/16	26.9876	2 23/32	69.0564	4 3/8	111.125	6 1/8	155.575	9 1/2	241.300
0.050	1.270	0.590	14.99	7/32	5.5562	1 3/32	27.7813	2 3/4	69.8501	4 13/32	111.919	6 3/16	157.163	9 9/16	242.888
0.060	1.524	0.600	15.24	15/64	5.9531	1 1/8	28.5751	2 25/32	70.6439	4 7/16	112.713	6 1/4	158.750	9 5/8	244.475
0.070	1.778	0.610	15.49	1/4	6.3500	1 5/32	29.3688	2 13/16	71.4376	4 15/32	113.506	6 5/16	160.338	9 11/16	246.063
0.080	2.032	0.620	15.75	17/64	6.7469	1 3/16	30.1626	2 27/32	72.2314	4 1/2	114.300	6 3/8	161.925	9 3/4	247.650
0.090	2.286	0.630	16.00	9/32	7.1437	1 7/32	30.9563	2 7/8	73.0251	4 17/32	115.094	6 7/16	163.513	9 13/16	249.238
0.100	2.540	0.640	16.26	19/64	7.5406	1 1/4	31.7501	2 29/32	73.8189	4 9/16	115.888	6 1/2	165.100	9 7/8	250.825
0.110	2.794	0.650	16.51	5/16	7.9375	1 9/32	32.5438	2 15/16	74.6126	4 19/32	116.681	6 9/16	166.688	9 15/16	252.413
0.120	3.048	0.660	16.76	21/64	8.3344	1 5/16	33.3376	2 31/32	75.4064	4 5/8	117.475	6 5/8	168.275	10	254.001
0.130	3.302	0.670	17.02	11/32	8.7312	1 11/32	34.1313	3	76.2002	4 21/32	118.269	6 11/16	169.863	10 1/16	255.588
0.140	3.56	0.680	17.27	23/64	9.1281	1 3/8	34.9251	3 1/32	76.9939	4 11/16	119.063	6 3/4	171.450	10 1/8	257.176
0.150	3.81	0.690	17.53	3/8	9.5250	1 13/32	35.7188	3 1/16	77.7877	4 23/32	119.856	6 13/16	173.038	10 3/16	258.763
0.160	4.06	0.700	17.78	25/64	9.9219	1 7/16	36.5126	3 3/32	78.5814	4 3/4	120.650	6 7/8	174.625	10 1/4	260.351
0.170	4.32	0.710	18.03	13/32	10.3187	1 15/32	37.3063	3 1/8	79.3752	4 25/32	121.444	6 15/16	176.213	10 5/16	261.938
0.180	4.57	0.720	18.29	27/64	10.7156	1 1/2	38.1001	3 5/32	80.1689	4 13/16	122.238	7	177.800	10 3/8	263.526
0.190	4.83	0.730	18.54	7/16	11.1125	1 17/32	38.8938	3 3/16	80.9627	4 27/32	123.031	7 1/16	179.388	10 7/16	265.113
0.200	5.08	0.740	18.80	29/64	11.5094	1 9/16	39.6876	3 7/32	81.7564	4 7/8	123.825	7 1/8	180.975	10 1/2	266.701
0.210	5.33	0.750	19.05	15/32	11.9062	1 19/32	40.4813	3 1/4	82.5502	4 29/32	124.619	7 3/16	182.563	10 9/16	268.288
0.220	5.59	0.760	19.30	31/64	12.3031	1 5/8	41.2751	3 9/32	83.3439	4 15/16	125.413	7 1/4	184.150	10 5/8	269.876
0.230	5.84	0.770	19.56	1/2	12.7000	1 21/32	42.0688	3 5/16	84.1377	4 31/32	126.206	7 5/16	185.738	10 11/16	271.463
0.240	6.10	0.780	19.81	33/64	13.0969	1 11/16	42.8626	3 11/32	84.9314	5	127.000	7 3/8	187.325	10 3/4	273.051
0.250	6.35	0.790	20.07	17/32	13.4937	1 23/32	43.6563	3 3/8	85.7252	5 1/32	127.794	7 7/16	188.913	10 13/16	274.638
0.260	6.60	0.800	20.32	35/64	13.8906	1 3/4	44.4501	3 13/32	86.5189	5 1/16	128.588	7 1/2	190.500	10 7/8	276.226
0.270	6.86	0.810	20.57	9/16	14.2875	1 25/32	45.2438	3 7/16	87.3127	5 3/32	129.382	7 9/16	192.088	10 15/16	277.813
0.280	7.11	0.820	20.83	37/64	14.6844	1 13/16	46.0376	3 15/32	88.1064	5 1/8	130.175	7 5/8	193.675	11	279.401
0.290	7.37	0.830	21.08	19/32	15.0812	1 27/32	46.8313	3 1/2	88.9002	5 5/32	130.969	7 11/16	195.263	11 1/16	280.988
0.300	7.62	0.840	21.34	39/64	15.4781	1 7/8	47.6251	3 17/32	89.6939	5 3/16	131.763	7 3/4	196.850	11 1/8	282.576
0.310	7.87	0.850	21.59	5/8	15.8750	1 29/32	48.4188	3 9/16	90.4877	5 7/32	132.557	7 13/16	198.438	11 3/16	284.163
0.320	8.13	0.860	21.84	41/64	16.2719	1 15/16	49.2126	3 19/32	91.2814	5 1/4	133.350	7 7/8	200.025	11 1/4	285.751
0.330	8.38	0.870	22.10	21/32	16.6687	1 31/32	50.0063	3 5/8	92.0752	5 9/32	134.144	7 15/16	201.613	11 5/16	287.338
0.340	8.64	0.880	22.35	43/64	17.0656	2	50.8001	3 21/32	92.8689	5 5/16	134.938	8	203.200	11 3/8	288.926
0.350	8.89	0.890	22.61	11/16	17.4625	2 1/32	51.5939	3 11/16	93.6627	5 11/32	135.732	8 1/16	204.788	11 7/16	290.513
0.360	9.14	0.900	22.86	45/64	17.8594	2 1/16	52.3876	3 23/32	94.4564	5 3/8	136.525	8 1/8	206.375	11 1/2	292.101
0.370	9.40	0.910	23.11	23/32	18.2562	2 3/32	53.1814	3 3/4	95.2502	5 13/32	137.319	8 3/16	207.963	11 9/16	293.688
0.380	9.65	0.920	23.37	47/64	18.6531	2 1/8	53.9751	3 25/32	96.0439	5 7/16	138.113	8 1/4	209.550	11 5/8	295.276
0.390	9.91	0.930	23.62	3/4	19.0500	2 5/32	54.7688	3 13/16	96.8377	5 15/32	138.907	8 5/16	211.138	11 11/16	296.863
0.400	10.16	0.940	23.88	49/64	19.4469	2 3/16	55.5626	3 27/32	97.6314	5 1/2	139.700	8 3/8	212.725	11 3/4	298.451
0.410	10.41	0.950	24.13	25/32	19.8437	2 7/32	56.3564	3 7/8	98.4252	5 17/32	140.494	8 7/16	214.313	11 13/16	300.038
0.420	10.67	0.960	24.38	51/64	20.2406	2 1/4	57.1501	3 29/32	99.2189	5 9/16	141.288	8 1/2	215.900	11 7/8	301.626
0.430	10.92	0.970	24.64	13/16	20.6375	2 9/32	57.9439	3 15/16	100.013	5 19/32	142.082	8 9/16	217.488	11 15/16	303.213
0.440	11.18	0.980	24.89							5 5/8	142.875	8 5/8	219.075	12	304.801
0.450	11.43	0.990	25.15												
		1.000	25.40												

COMMON METRIC EQUIVALENTS AND CONVERSIONS

APPROXIMATE Common Equivalents		ACCURATE Conversion to Parts Per Million			APPROXIMATE Common Equivalents		ACCURATE Conversion to Parts Per Million		
1 inch	= 25 millimeters	inches × 25.4*	= millimeters		1 millimeter	= 0.04 inch	millimeters × 0.039 370 1	= inches	
1 foot	= 0.3 meter	feet × 0.3048*	= meters		1 meter	= 3.3 feet	meters × 3.280 84	= feet	
1 yard	= 0.9 meter	yards × 0.9144*	= meters		1 meter	= 1.1 yards	meters × 1.093 61	= yards	
1 mile	= 1.6 kilometers	miles × 1.609 34	= kilometers		1 kilometer	= 0.6 mile	kilometers × 0.621 371	= miles	
1 square inch	= 6.5 square centimeters	sq inches × 6.4516*	= square centimeters		1 square centimeter	= 0.16 square inch	sq centimeters × 0.155 000	= square inches	
1 square foot	= 0.09 square meter	sq feet × 0.092 903 0	= square meters		1 square meter	= 11 square feet	sq meters × 10.7639	= square feet	
1 square yard	= 0.8 square meter	sq yards × 0.836 127	= square meters		1 square meter	= 1.2 square yards	sq meters × 1.195 99	= square yards	
1 acre	= 0.4 hectare†	acres × 0.404 686	= hectares		1 hectare†	= 2.5 acres	hectares × 2.471 05	= acres	
1 cubic inch	= 16 cubic centimeters	cu inches × 16.3871	= cubic centimeters		1 cubic centimeter	= 0.06 cubic inch	cu centimeters × 0.061 023 7	= cubic inches	
1 cubic foot	= 0.03 cubic meter	cu feet × 0.028 316 8	= cubic meters		1 cubic meter	= 35 cubic feet	cu meters × 35.3147	= cubic feet	
1 cubic yard	= 0.8 cubic meter	cu yards × 0.764 555	= cubic meters		1 cubic meter	= 1.3 cubic yards	cu meters × 1.307 95	= cubic yards	
1 quart (lq)	= 1 liter†	quarts (lq) × 0.946 353	= liters		1 liter†	= 1 quart (lq)	liters × 1.056 69	= quarts (lq)	
1 gallon	= 0.004 cubic meter	gallons × 0.003 785 41	= cubic meters		1 cubic meter	= 250 gallons	cu meters × 264.172	= gallons	
1 ounce (avdp)	= 28 grams	oz (avdp) × 28.349 5	= grams		1 gram	= 0.035 ounces (avdp)	grams × 0.035 274 0	= ounces (avdp)	
1 pound (avdp)	= 0.45 kilogram	lbs (avdp) × 0.453 592	= kilograms		1 kilogram	= 2.2 pounds (avdp)	kilograms × 2.204 62	= pounds (avdp)	
1 horsepower	= 0.75 kilowatt	hp × 0.745 700	= kilowatts		1 kilowatt	= 1.3 hrosepower	kilowatts × 1.341 02	= horsepower	

†Common term not used in SI.   *Exact.

Fig. 25-4
Conversion Chart

Other common units used in drafting are:
kilogram for weight or mass -- 1 kg equals 2.20462 lb

litres for fluid volume -- 1 litre equals 1.05669 qt

kilopascals for pressure -- 1 kPa equals 7.182 psi

3. Decimal marker for metric values should be the same as that used for inch decimal dimensions, namely the dot period or decimal point on the line. Some countries will use the comma as the decimal marker.

4. All drawings should be in third angle projection.

It is recommended that the ISO symbol for projection be added to the drawing.

5. All drawings should be clearly marked or stamped METRIC. If dimensions are in millimetres, then the symbol for millimetre (mm) does not have to be added to every dimension providing a note is placed on the drawing which includes one of the following:

Large stamp on drawing   METRIC

All dimensions in millimetres, **Fig. 25-5a,b**

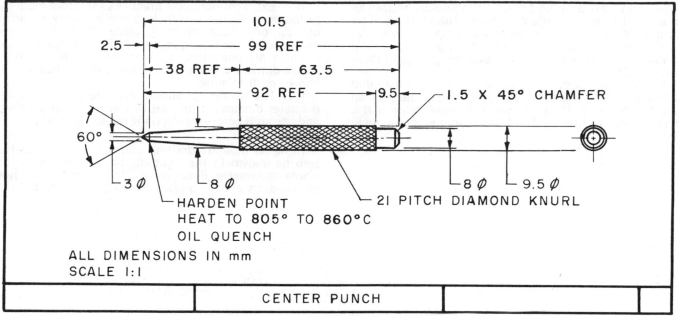

Fig. 25-5a
One of the several methods that can be used to indicate that this is a metric drawing.

Minutes and Seconds into Decimals of a Degree and Vice Versa

Minutes into Decimals of a Degree						Seconds into Decimals of a Degree					
min	deg	min	deg	min	deg	s	deg	s	deg	s	deg
1	0.0167	21	0.3500	41	0.6833	1	0.0003	21	0.0058	41	0.0114
2	0.0333	22	0.3667	42	0.7000	2	0.0006	22	0.0061	42	0.0117
3	0.0500	23	0.3833	43	0.7167	3	0.0008	23	0.0064	43	0.00119
4	0.0667	24	0.4000	44	0.7333	4	0.0011	24	0.0067	44	0.0122
5	0.0833	25	0.4167	45	0.7500	5	0.0014	25	0.0069	45	0.0125
6	0.1000	26	0.4333	46	0.7667	6	0.0017	26	0.0072	46	0.0128
7	0.1167	27	0.4500	47	0.7833	7	0.0019	27	0.0075	47	0.0131
8	0.1333	28	0.4667	48	0.8000	8	0.0022	28	0.0078	48	0.0133
9	0.1500	29	0.4833	49	0.8167	9	0.0025	29	0.0081	49	0.0136
10	0.1667	30	0.5000	50	0.8333	10	0.0028	30	0.0083	50	0.0139
11	0.1833	31	0.5167	51	0.8500	11	0.0031	31	0.0086	51	0.0142
12	0.2000	32	0.5333	52	0.8667	12	0.0033	32	0.0089	52	0.0144
13	0.2167	33	0.5500	53	0.8833	13	0.0036	33	0.0092	53	0.0147
14	0.2333	34	0.5667	54	0.9000	14	0.0039	34	0.0094	54	0.0150
15	0.2500	35	0.5833	55	0.9167	15	0.0042	35	0.0097	55	0.0153
16	0.2667	36	0.6000	56	0.9333	16	0.0044	36	0.0100	56	0.0156
17	0.2833	37	0.6167	57	0.9500	17	0.0047	37	0.0103	57	0.0158
18	0.3000	38	0.6333	58	0.9667	18	0.0050	38	0.0106	58	0.0161
19	0.3167	39	0.6500	59	0.9833	19	0.0053	39	0.0108	59	0.0164
20	0.3333	40	0.6667	60	1	20	0.0056	40	0.0011	60	0.0167

Fig. 25-5b
Conversion table.

mm/in, $\dfrac{mm}{(inch)}$, or $\dfrac{mm}{in}$
(for dual dimensioning if the design is in millimetres)

When possible, a different colored yellow paper should be used to identify metric drawings.

6. Angles will be in degrees, minutes and seconds expressed in decimal parts of a degree. An included angle of 60° 30' should be shown as 60.5° .

7. Commas are never used to show thousands. This practice is avoided because the comma is used as a decimal point in some countries. (Note: There is no space between groups of three numbers, for example, 37465 mm. This practice is for *drafting only*. Tabular material should have a space between groups of three numbers.)

8. In expressing metric dimensions make sure that a minimum of one digit is on either side of the decimal point. For example, 13.0, 6.0, 0.7, 0.09. Note that a zero to the right or left of the decimal point must always be used.

9. Always place a zero before any unit of less than one. While it has been the practice in the customary system not to use a zero before the decimal point, many industries are now changing to make the practice uniform with metric practices.

10. Always leave a space between the amount or number and symbol. For example, twenty-five millimetres should be written as 25 mm.

11. Exact rounding off practices vary from industry to industry. Metric dimensions are normally rounded off to one less decimal place than customary dimensions; or in reverse, inch dimensions are rounded off one more decimal place than shown in metric dimensions. A dimension of 0.010 inches will be shown as 0.25 mm.

12. The symbol ϕ should precede (or follow) the diameter dimension (or use DIA after the dimension) and use an R before (or after) the radius dimension. **Fig. 25-6.**

13. Most industry drafting standards require that a zero be shown to the right of the decimal point for whole millimetre dimensions. This practice is not followed on simple project drawings. **Fig. 25-6.**

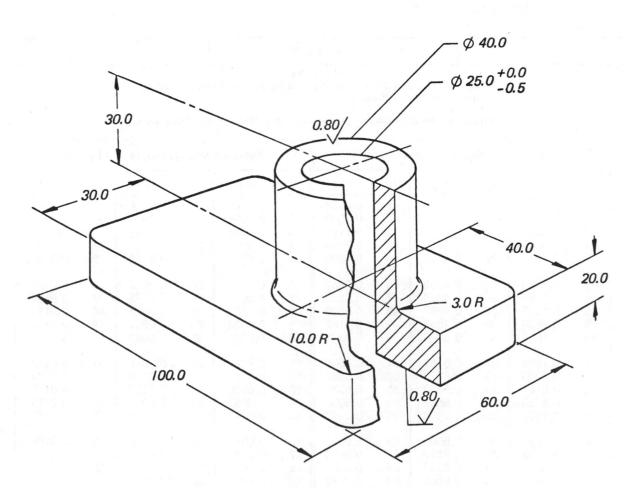

Fig. 25-6
The symbol for diameter is used on this pictorial drawing.

13. Tapers should be expressed in terms of a ratio. A taper of twenty-five hundredths per one millimetre should be shown as 0.25:1.

14. Limits and fits will be expressed in U.S. standards. There is an ISO standard for limits and fits, however, it is not generally used in the United States. When limits dimensions are used, always use the same number of decimal places for both limits. For example, 24 millimetres plus 0.02 and minus zero could be shown as $24 \, ^{+0.02}_{-0.00}$. This practice eliminates the question of whether a number was intentionally omitted or was lost in poor reproduction. Other forms of dimensioning may be used such as:

Limit	Unilateral
25.5	
25.0	$25.0 \, ^{+0.5}_{-0.0}$

Equal Bilateral	Unequal Bilateral
25.25 ± 0.25	
	$25.3 \, ^{+0.2}_{-0.3}$

15. Customary and metric threads use the same 60° thread form although they are not in-terchangeable. A metric part may be any of the following.:

　1. The ISO inch (Unified National Series) thread
　2. The ISO metric thread

The method of dimensioning threads will be expressed by the thread system used. For example, the ISO inch (Unified National Series) thread is shown as follows:

1/4 - 20 UNC

1/4 is the diameter in inches
20 is the threads per inch
UNC is the Unified National Coarse Series
The ISO metric thread is shown as follows:

M10 x 1.5

M means it is an ISO metric thread
10 is the diameter in millimetres
1.5 is the pitch in millimetres (the distance from the top of one thread to the top of the next)

Beginning Drafting Practices

1. Determine the dimensioning method to use. Preference should be given to using only metric dimensions on the part or product with a readout chart attached if necessary. Generally speaking, dual dimensioning should be avoided. **Fig. 25-7.**

2. When dual dimensioning design (metric) dimensions should appear above the line or first and other dimensions below the line or second. The inch dimension can also be in a bracket. **Fig. 25-8.**

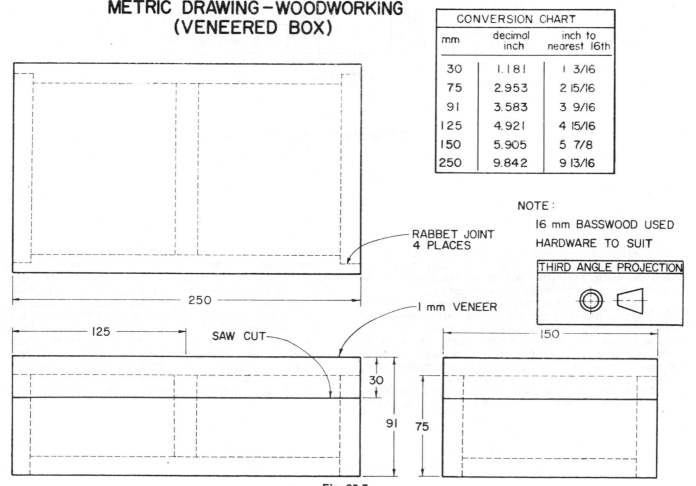

METRIC DRAWING — WOODWORKING
(VENEERED BOX)

CONVERSION CHART		
mm	decimal inch	inch to nearest 16th
30	1.181	1 3/16
75	2.953	2 15/16
91	3.583	3 9/16
125	4.921	4 15/16
150	5.905	5 7/8
250	9.842	9 13/16

RABBET JOINT
4 PLACES

NOTE:
16 mm BASSWOOD USED
HARDWARE TO SUIT

THIRD ANGLE PROJECTION

1 mm VENEER

250

125

SAW CUT

30

91 75

150

Fig. 25-7
A metric drawing with a readout chart (the chart method).

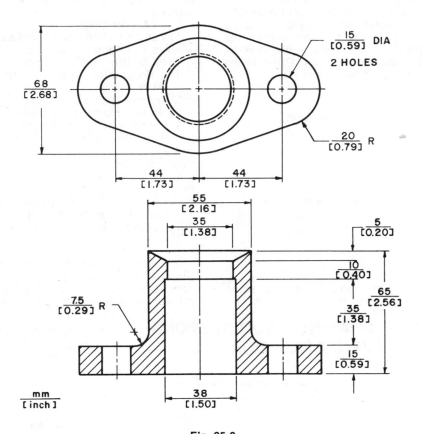

Fig. 25-8

A dual dimensioned drawing.

3. Select the appropriate scale for making the drawing. When possible, make the drawing full size using the scale 1:1. The next appropriate scale would be half size using the reduction scale of 1:2.

4. Design the part using the convenience of the full millimetre whenever possible. If the part or product is not of great precision, the rounded millimetre is all the accuracy required. For example, most simple wood, metal, leather and plastic products can have all measurements rounded to the full millimetre. Most metric rules used in actual construction of the product will have the smallest graduations in millimetres. When converting an existing drawing for a simple metal, wood or plastic product from inches to millimetres, round off the dimensions to full millimetres. For example, if the inch dimension is 1/2", round it off to 13 mm (or 12 mm if the material used tends to be slightly undersized). For example, 1/2" lumber or plastics measures about 12 mm thick. If the product calls for 1 in lumber list the size as 25 mm.

5. For more precise products such as those produced in a machine shop, round off the dimensions to the nearest 1/2 mm (0.5 mm) for layout, machining and checking. *Remember that 1/2 mm [0.5 mm] is equal to about 20 thousandths of an inch.* **Fig. 25-9**

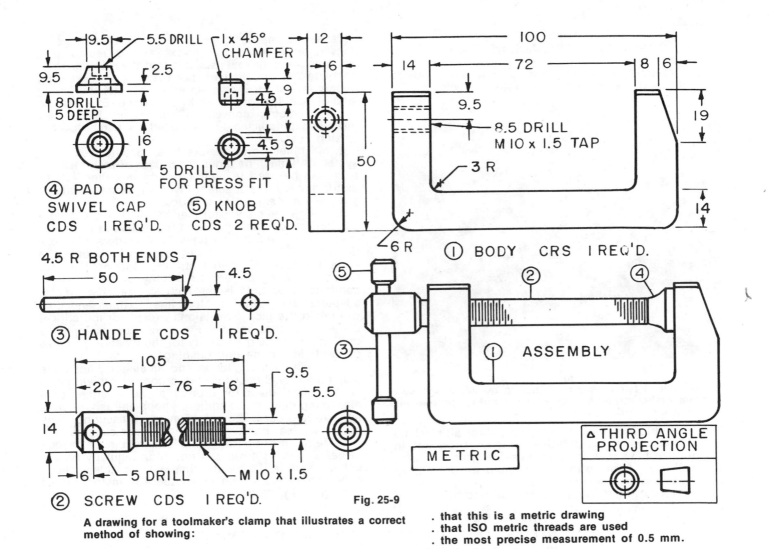

④ PAD OR
SWIVEL CAP
CDS 1 REQ'D.

⑤ KNOB
CDS 2 REQ'D.

③ HANDLE CDS 1 REQ'D.

② SCREW CDS 1 REQ'D.

Fig. 25-9

A drawing for a toolmaker's clamp that illustrates a correct method of showing:

. that this is a metric drawing
. that ISO metric threads are used
. the most precise measurement of 0.5 mm.

① BODY CRS 1 REQ'D.

ASSEMBLY

METRIC

△ THIRD ANGLE PROJECTION

6. If size A or B paper is used instead of A4 or A3, then the border lines should be made to ISO paper standards rather than of customary paper standards. For 8 1/2" x 11" size paper the dimensions on the inside of the border line should be approximately 180 x 260 mm.

7. If ISO paper sizes are used, then the margins to the border lines should be as follows: about 25 mm on the left hand side and 15 mm on the other three sides. The dimensions inside the border lines should be 180 x 260 mm.

8. The title block should be across the bottom, right side or in the bottom right hand corner of the sheet.

9. Lettering in the title block and on the drawing itself should be in proportion to the sheet size as follows:

  3 or 4 mm for A4
  5 mm for A3 and A2
  9 mm for A1 and A0

10. The dimension lines should be spaced at a *minimum* distance of 10 mm from the views and a minimum of 5 mm between parallel dimension lines. The minimum space between views should be 30 mm. The minimum space between the object line and exterior line should be 1.5 mm. **Fig. 25-10.**

Arrowheads should be about 3 mm long.
Hidden lines should have dashes about 3 mm long and spaces about 0.75 mm.
Center lines should consist of long dashes from 10 to 40 mm and short dashes and spaces about 3 mm and 1.5 mm respectively.
If the drawing is to be prepared for microfilming, only two line thicknesses should be used:
About 0.5 mm for border, outline, and hidden lines
About 0.15 to 0.30 mm for all other lines

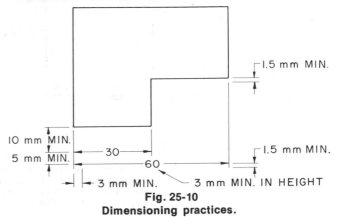

Fig. 25-10
Dimensioning practices.

UNIT 26
CONVERSION OF MACHINE TOOLS

Conversion of machine tools is usually considered the most expensive aspect of metric conversion. **Fig. 26-1**

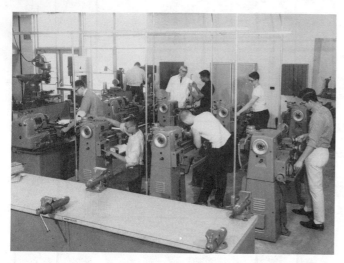

Fig. 26-1
Conversion of lathes, shapers, milling machines, grinders and many other machine tools will be one of the problems in adopting the metric system.

However, this is not necessarily true, since all machine tools have metric capabilities. Machines do not in themselves have any specific measuring capabilities. The following basic principles should be considered when converting machine tools:

1. Metal cutting machines do not have to be replaced because of metric conversion. Too often, metric conversion is used as an excuse for replacing a machine when the real reason is that the machine is (a) obsolete and should have been replaced anyway, (b) underpowered for maximum efficiency, (c) the wrong kind of machine for the work to be done. Exaggerated costs of metric conversion will result if all new machines purchased are included as a metric conversion cost.

2. Machines don't operate in a specific measuring system. All machine tools, regardless of their make or type, can be used to produce parts in either inch or metric dimensions. *Machines will cut parts to whatever size they are set up to produce.*

3. During the conversion period which will extend a number of years, many cutting tools such as drills and reamers will be a *hybrid* type. Tool holders will continue to be in the customary system with only the cutting edges ground to metric measurement. Drills, reamers, milling cutters, and many other tools will continue to be held in the inch size collets, arbors, adaptors, and spindles. Most jigs, fixtures and dies will retain the inch dimensions except for the critical dimensions that must be metric. For example, a drilling jig will be metric only for the location and size of the hole for the drill bushing.

5. In school laboratories and small job shops the major additional cost for metric conversion will be in dual reading dials (or drums) or some other dual measuring device. In addition, shops and laboratories must have a complete set of metric measuring tools such as rules, micrometers and vernier calipers.

6. Metric thread cutting on a lathe requires a change of gears. Thread cutting is not done regularly on the lathe, therefore if several lathes are available, usually only one needs to be converted for metric thread cutting. **Fig. 26-2**

THREAD CUTTING
NEED METRIC THREADING ATTACHMENT – COMPLETE
WITH GEARS, QUADRANT BRACKET, QUADRANT,
SPACERS, STUDS AND GEAR CHART.

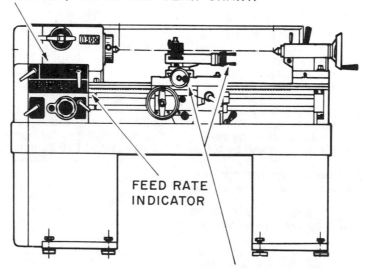

FEED RATE
INDICATOR

DUAL READING DIALS –
CUSTOMARY & METRIC

Fig. 26-2
If a number of lathes is available, only one or two need to be converted to thread cutting by adding metric threading attachments. Once this attachment is installed, the lathe will cut only metric threads.

7. The major problem in producing metric parts is for the machine operator to understand the two systems of measurement and to know how to measure in each system.

Planning for Conversion

In planning to convert a machine tool laboratory to metric, the following steps should be considered:

1. List all machine tools which have measuring capabilities.

2. Determine which measuring capabilities need conversion. Some adjustments are made so rarely, if ever, that it is unnecessary to add a metric conversion dial or unit. For example, it is very unlikely that any conversion would be done to shapers or planers. Convert only those measuring capabilities that are actually needed.

3. Replacement of machine tools can be done over a period of years, since there will be a continued demand to manufacture in the inch units for some time.

Fig. 26-3

CONVERSION OF MACHINE TOOLS

	Immediate Conversion	Intermediate Conversion	Total Conversion
Drilling Machines	Add metric depth scale using plastic tape	Replace depth scale with metric depth scale	All-metric design —not too important
Lathes	Add dual reading dials to all lathes. Add conversion kit for metric threads to **one** lathe only	Purchase new lathes with dual reading dials and quick change gear box for inch/ metric threads	Purchase new lathes of all metric design including lead screw cross feed, with only metric dials and metric thread cutting capabilities
Shapers and Planers	Consider adding dual reading dial to down feed— not too important	Phase out shaper as obsolete machine tool	No new shapers produced in metric
Horizontal Milling Machines	Add dual reading dials to horizontal and transverse adjustments. Add dual reading dial to one end of table for longitudinal feed control (Not as important as other two). Use dual dimensioned drawing or conversion tables.	Add digital read-out unit with dual capabilities to each machine. Change feed rate indicator	All-metric machines with metric spindle arbors, T slots, etc.
Vertical Milling Machines	Same as above	Same as above	Same as above
Grinders	Add dual reading dials or digital readout unit.		All-metric machine

Fig. 26-3
Plans must be made for conversion of machine tools.

4. Decide how many of the machines need to be converted to *dual* inch-metric capabilities and which ones should be *all metric.*

5. Consider adding digital readout equipment to existing machines. Digital readout units with inch-metric capabilities are little or no more expensive than those with inch measurements only.

Types of Machine Tools

From a measurement point of view, there are two basic types of machine tools used in most shops and laboratories. The first type is the kind in which the cutting adjustments are made directly on the machine using the dials or other measuring devices. For example, when the vertical milling machine is used as a jig bore, the machine's measuring system is used to position the drills, reamers or boring tools. Another example, when finished cutting is done on a lathe, the measuring dials are used to make the settings. The second type doesn't use the measuring system on the machine itself for making adjustments. For example, rarely is the scale on the drill press used to determine the depth of hole drilling. In rough turning, generally the dials on the lathe are not used for adjusting depth of cut, since the work is checked by a caliper to determine when the piece has reached the correct diameter.

Analyzing the Machine Tools

In determining needs for producing metric parts, one of the first steps is to analyze the machine tools to determine what modifications and/or replacements are necessary. The following are some suggestions:

1. *Drilling machines.* Drilling machines will require little or no change since all metric drills, reamers, etc. will fit either in a drill chuck or a Morse taper spindle. The depth gage on the drill press, if it is used for depth of drilling (which it rarely is), can either be converted by adding a metric scale of plastic tape or a metal scale.

2. *Lathes.* If a great deal of machining is to be done in both the inch and the metric systems, then at least several of the lathes should be equipped with dual reading dials on the cross feed and compound rest. Since thread cutting on a lathe is done only rarely, perhaps only one or two of the lathes need metric capabilities.

3. *Shapers and planers.* These machines will not require any conversion since dimensions are checked with measuring tools. The dials are not used for accurate settings.

4. *Vertical milling machines.* The ideal method of adding dual capabilities to the vertical milling machine is to add a digital readout unit for the x and y axis so that the measurements can be read in either thousandths of an inch or hundredths of a millimetre by merely flipping a switch.

5. *Horizontal milling machines.* Horizontal milling machines can be given dual capabilities either by adding dual reading dials or a digital readout unit.

6. *Grinders.* (a) Surface grinder. Normally, in surface grinding, the feed is adjusted without regard to the graduations on the feed handle except for the final cuts. If it is necessary to make adjustments, either dual reading dials or a digital readout unit can be added. (b) Cylindrical grinders are used primarily as production machines and the parts are checked with fixed gages. Therefore, no conversion may be necessary.

Common Conversion Scale for All Machining Operations

One of the simplest methods of adding dual capabilities to any machine is to attach a "paste on" conversion scale in some convenient location so that the operator can refer to it whenever necessary.

Fig. 26-4

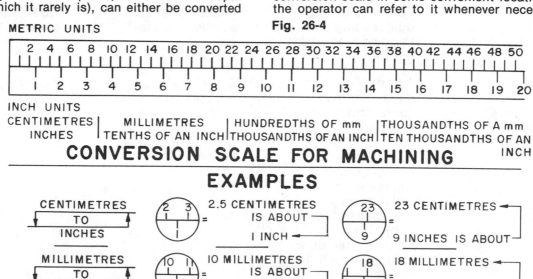

Fig. 26-4
Conversion scale for machining.

This conversion scale is a very simple length measurement with metric units above and the inch units below. Relationships between these two are 2.54 cm (25.4 mm) to the inch. The scale can be produced in any size, and will be usable for many different kinds of readings. The scales above and below the line can be multiplied or divided without changing the relationship. For example, the scale above the line could represent centimetres (cm), millimetres (mm), tenths of a millimetre (0.1 mm), hundredths of a millimetre (0.01 mm), or thousandths of a millimetre (0.001 mm). The scale below the line could represent inches (in), tenths of an inch (0.1 in), hundredths of an inch (0.01 in), thousandths of an inch (0.001 in), or ten thousandths of an inch (0.0001 in). With this scale attached to any machine, metric parts can be produced on machines that have inch-calibrated dials without any change in the machine themselves. Also, if an all-metric machine is available, the machine can be used to produce inch parts.

Reading Prints

The machinist should be acquainted with the various ways of dimensioning a drawing since he may have to read several different kinds over a very short period of time. For example, he may use a dual dimensioned drawing for one job and an all-metric dimensioned drawing for another job. Various methods of dimensioning a drawing for producing parts are described in detail in the unit, Drafting Practices and Standards. Briefly these are:

1. *Dual dimensioned drawings.* While dual dimensioning is generally discouraged, it does have several advantages that may make it the desirable way of dimensioning for certain kinds of work. With a dual dimensioned drawing, the machinist can produce the part while he thinks and works either in *metric* or *customary* units. In other words, he can produce a part that is designed to metric standards but continue to work in inch dimensions. All of the cutting and gaging can be done to the inch dimensions as shown on the drawing. This will make it possible also to produce parts that must interface with other inch dimensioned parts. In a product in which there is a gradual conversion from inch to metric measurement, dual dimensioning serves a very important purpose. Also, all types of tool drawings such as those for jigs, fixtures and dies should be made to inch dimensions except for those specific features that are related to metric dimensions. For example, if a drill jig is to be made for metric drilling, all the dimensions of the jig can be to the inch dimensions except for the location and size of the hole for the metric drill bushing.

2. *Metric dimensioning with customary readout chart.* If the drawing is made to metric measurement with customary readout chart, all the measuring instruments used and as many of the machine operations as possible should be done in metric units. The customary readout chart should be used for reference only.

3. *Dimensioning with metric dimensions only.* This type of drawing requires the machinist to "think metric."

Basic Methods of Converting Existing Equipment for Metric Capabilities

There are several basic methods of adding metric capabilities to any machine tool. These are:

1. *Dual reading dials or drums which simultaneously read both the metric and inch sizes.* These dials and drums can be used to replace existing dials on a lathe, milling machine, grinder and other machine tools. The

dial types are made with internal gears so that the inch scale attached directly to the existing lead or feed screw and the metric scale are proportioned properly to have a relationship of 1 in to 25.4 mm. **Fig. 26-5a.**

Fig. 26-5a
This dual reading dial is designed for one model of lathe and another model of milling machine.

There are two basic problems in installing this kind of unit. First, the gear arrangement must be designed for a specific lead screw. For example, if it is designed to be attached to a lathe with 5 threads per inch on the cross feed it cannot be used on a lathe that has 8 threads per inch. Therefore, normally the dual reading dials are built by the manufacturer of the machine and used only on that specific machine. The second problem is to adapt the new dial indicator to the feed or lead screw. Sometimes this requires a special bushing or a reduction in the end of the lead or feed screw to which the dial is to be attached. Some manufacturers have provided for these problems and produce several different sizes and gear ratios that will fit many different models. **Fig. 26-5b.**

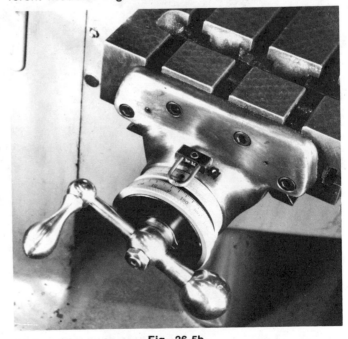

Fig. 26-5b
These dual reading dials are fitted to a milling machine. Several different sizes and models of these dual reading dials will fit a number of manufacturers' different models.

Fig. 26-5c
These dual reading dials are attached to the compound rest and cross feed dial of a lathe.

For use with leadscrew having a lead of ▸	.1	.125	.2	.25	.4	.5	Special	Inches
and having graduated markings 0 to ▸	100	125	200	250	400	500		

Fig. 26-5d
Dual reading dials must be designed for use with the lead (pitch) of the feedscrew or leadscrew. For example, if the screw has five threads per inch, then the lead (pitch) is 0.2 inches and the dial has 200 graduations each representing 0.001 inches. One complete turn of the handle would equal 0.2 inches or 5.08 millimetres. With a dual reading dial, there are two synchronized, adjacent dials, the inch dial fixed to the screw and the metric dial meshed with it at a fixed ratio. While the metric dial reads in even millimetres (in this illustration 0 to 5.0 mm in 0.02 mm graduations) the metric dial does not turn exactly one revolution for each turn of the wheel. The two dials are normally read at a common datum line. Each different leadscrew or feedscrew requires a different arrangement between the inch and metric dials.

The second type has a drum arrangement. **Fig. 26-a,b,c.**

Fig. 26-6a
These drum type dual reading dials come in two sizes and with several different belts. Check the specifications of your machine carefully before ordering the correct size of unit and belt type. There is a flip cover that reads in millimetres in one position and in decimal inches in the other position.

Fig. 26-6b
These dual reading units can be fitted to many different kinds and models of machines.

With this type a different belt can be used with different lead or feed screws so that the proper calibration is possible. Belts are available for all standard inch screw pitches such as 0 to 0.050, 0 to 0.100, 0 to 0.125, 0 to 0.150, 0 to 0.200, 0 to 0.250, 0 to 0.375, 0 to 0.400 and 0 to 0.500. The only problem with this type is that an adaptor must be machined so that the unit will fit on the lead screw or hand wheel shaft. This drum type is available in two sizes: a smaller and a larger one. The larger size is to be used on milling machines and grinders. The smaller size is better adapted to lathes. However, if this unit is attached to the compound rest, the unit may interfere so that the compound rest will not fit directly over the cross feed (with the compound rest in the zero position).

2. *Mechanical dual reading scales — either direct reading or optically magnified.* There are several types of mechanical dual reading scales that can be attached to milling machines, grinders, jig boards, and other types of tools. These scales will allow reading of the cross and longitudinal feeds either in thousandths of an inch or hundredths of a millimetre. **Fig. 26-7a,b,c.**

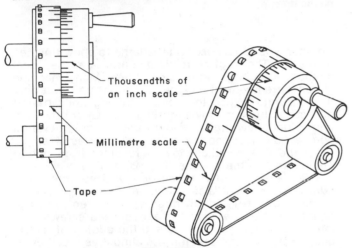

Fig. 26-6c
Note the belt arrangement on the drum type unit.

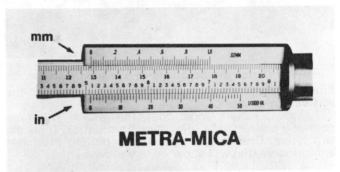

Fig. 26-7a
This mechanical dual reading unit can be fitted to many different kinds of machines.

Fig. 26-7b
The mechanical dual reading scale is shown applied to a milling machine, grinder, boring mill, and lathe.

Fig. 26-7c
Metric Optical Readout unit on a milling machine.

There is also provision for adding this unit for the vertical adjustment.

3. *Display panels which show the values.* These are normally called DROs (digital readout units). There are two types. One can be attached to milling machines and grinders that will show x and y movement.

Fig. 26-8b
A flick of the switch will change the reading from inches to millimetres.

Another type can be used on the lathe to show finished diameter. The digital readout units are the ideal method of adding metric capabilities. Many machine shops currently use this type of readout unit, but only in inch units. Since the cost of buying units having dual capabilities is only slightly more than for the inch units alone, new digital readout units should never be purchased unless they have dual capabilities. A single flip of the switch will change the readings from inch to millimetres or the reverse. **Fig. 26-8a,b.**

4. *Replacement of the lead and/or feed screw and nuts plus metric dials.* The more extensive type of conversion for machines would require the replacement of the inch lead and/or feed screws with metric lead and feed screws and the adding of metric dials. However, the cost may be almost as much as to purchase a new machine. **Fig. 26-9**

Fig. 26-8a
Digital readout units are commonly used on many machines in school and job shops.

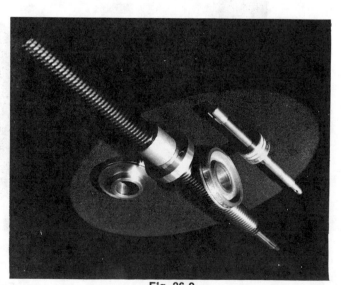

Fig. 26-9
Metric lead screws, nuts and dials for metric conversion.

5. *Purchase new machines with dual reading capabilities.* Many of the new machines are designed with dual capabilities. Namely, they have dual reading dials and, in the case of the lathe, a quick-change gear box for cutting either metric or inch threads. **Fig. 26-10a,b**

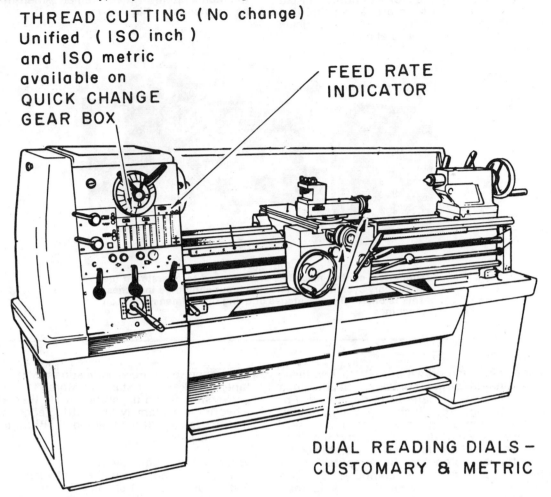

THREAD CUTTING (No change)
Unified (ISO inch)
and ISO metric
available on
QUICK CHANGE
GEAR BOX

FEED RATE
INDICATOR

DUAL READING DIALS -
CUSTOMARY & METRIC

CHANGES FOR METRIC CONVERSION
Fig. 26-10a
A lathe can be purchased with the dual reading dials and a quick change gear box for cutting both metric and customary threads.

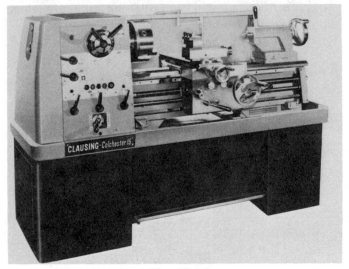

Fig. 26-10b
An all-metric lathe.

6. *All-metric machines.* Machines designed and built to metric specifications are the final answer in metric conversion. An all-metric lathe, for example, will cut only metric threads and will have a chasing dial that can be used for thread cutting. This dial will eliminate the need to keep the split nut closed at all times.

Numerical Control Machines

If the numerical control machine is designed to use the inch system of measurement, then the input must be in inches. **Fig. 26-11**

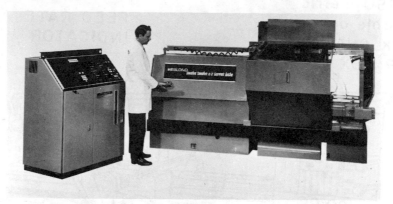

Fig. 26-11
Numerical control machines are designed to operate on the customary system; therefore, the input should be in inches. This is one of the advantages of using dual dimensioning on machines.

If the part is designed and drawn in metric, then these metric dimensions must be converted to the inch equivalent when the input material is developed. For manual programming, the inch equivalent which appears on the engineering drawing can be used. However, if the drawing does not carry the inch equivalent, these must be calculated, preferably using a mini-calculator or computer. If computer assist programming is used, then the computer must be programmed to convert metric dimensions to inch dimensions. Once the program has been prepared and checked, the operation of the NC machine is the same as when decimal inch dimensioned parts are produced.

Tool Holders

Generally chucks, collets, arbors and adaptors that hold metric tools will continue to be inch based. In other words, milling machine cutters, for example, will fit on a standard arbor even though the cutting edges are ground to metric specifications. Metric drills with a taper shank will fit standard Morse tapers. During the conversion period the cutting tools themselves will be a hybrid type. Namely, the cutting edges will be in the metric system but the holding or fitting part will be in the inch system.

Work Holding Equipment

Most work holding equipment including vises, jigs and fixtures will not change. The only equipment that may be affected will be precision holding devices such as the cross slide table.

Tapers

The common tapers used to hold cutting tools and tool holders will not change in the metric system. For example, Morse tapers will continue to be used on drills and drilling equipment. **Fig. 26-12**

ISO Morse Taper Shanks
Dimensions in Millimetres

Number of Taper	Dia. of Plug at Small End	Dia. at End of Socket	Shank		Depth of Hole	Standard Plug Depth	Tongue		Keyway		End of Socket to Keyway	Percentage Taper	Taper per Inch (Inches)
			Whole Length	Depth			Thickness	Length	Width	Length			
	D	A	B	S	H	P	t	T	W	L	K		
0	6.4	9.045	59.5	56.5	52	50	3.9	6.5	4.2	15	49	5.2	.05205
1	9.4	12.065	65.5	62	56	53.5	5.2	8.5	5.5	19	52	5	.04988
2	14.6	17.780	80	75	67	64	6.3	10	6.6	22	62	5	.04995
3	19.8	23.825	99	94	84	81	7.9	13	8.2	27	78	5	.0502
4	25.9	31.267	124	117.5	107	102.5	11.9	16	12.2	32	98	5.2	.05194
5	37.6	44.399	156	149.5	135	129.5	15.9	19	16.2	38	125	5.3	.05263
6	53.9	63.348	218	210	188	182	19	27	19.3	47	177	5.2	.05214

Fig. 26-12
Table of ISO Morse taper shank sizes.

The Brown & Sharpe and American Standard machine tapers will be used on milling and grinding machines. The change will be in the way the taper is expressed or designated. In the customary system, tapers are often given in inches per feet or inches per inch or as a relationship. If the taper is given in inches per inch, then it will be given in millimetres per 25 millimetres. If the taper is given as a ratio, this will not change. If there is a tapped hole in the end of the taper such as on the end of milling cutters, these will eventually be changed to metric threads.

Cutting Tools

ISO/R883 standardizes radii for carbide inserts. The world standard is based on inch modules and will result in no change to insert tooling.

ISO/R883 Radii

in	mm	in
1/64 0.015625	0.4	0.01575
1/32 0.03125	0.8	0.03150
3/64 0.046875	1.2	0.04724
1/16 0.0625	1.6	0.06299

Gears — Metric standards use the "module" instead of "diametral pitch" as a design base. *Diametral pitch* is defined as the number of teeth per inch of pitch diameter. A module is the number of millimetres in the pitch diameter per tooth. Therefore, a diametral pitch of 1 is equivalent to a module of 25.4. Since the design criteria of the gear does not change and tooling is related to ideal diametral pitch numbers, no change will be made in the near future. Gears are designed for a specific application and generally are not considered as standard parts.

International Standardization of Machine Tools

There are few international standards for all aspects of machine tools including standards for the machine itself, for accessories, tool angles, testing, and for machining. Many of these standards will be developed in the years ahead. In converting to the metric system and international standards, the machine tool industry will face the following problems: (1) the need to convert existing machine tools to metric units or to replace them with metric equivalents and (2) the need to design machine tools to metric modules, using international standards for threads, gears, splines, bearings, etc. Eventually all elements of machine tools will be standardized internationally with complete interchangeability between machine tools, cutting tools, and control systems. All machine tool builders must work to internationally agreed acceptance standards.

The following general suggestions apply when machining metric parts:

(1) The basic fundamentals of machine operations are the same, regardless of the measuring system involved.

(2) Dimensions controlled by the machine do not require metric cutting tools. For example, there is no need for a change of tooling for most turning, boring, shaping, grinding, and general milling practices.

(3) Metric dimensions controlled by the tool itself require metric cutting tools. For example, to produce holes either by drilling or reaming requires metric size tools. Metric size tools are also needed to produce radii, threads, keyways, keyseats, slots, and splines.

(4) Most customary cutting tools can be used for metric machining, including: (a) Lathe tools for rough and finished turning, boring and knurling. Throw-away cemented carbide tools are available in square, round, and triangular shapes to metric specifications which are identical with sizes previously given in inches. The standard radii for throw-away carbide tooling is 0.4 mm, 0.8 mm, 1.2 mm and 1.6 mm. (b) Milling cutters, including plain, side, slitting, end, shell end, and most other standard cutters need not be replaced. Some cutters that require metric design include T slot, keyway, keyseat, concave and convex, and certain types of end mills. **Fig. 27-1a,b**

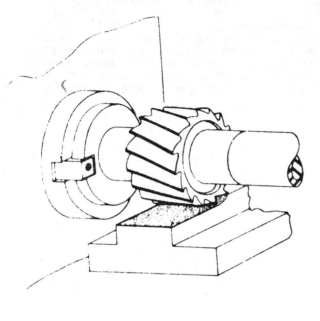

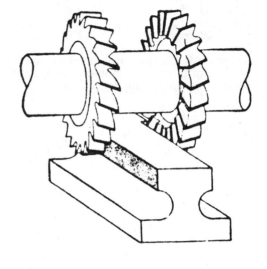

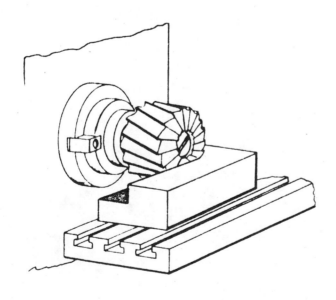

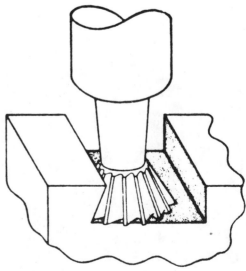

Fig. 27-1a
Typical milling machine cutters that can be used for either customary (inch) or metric machining.

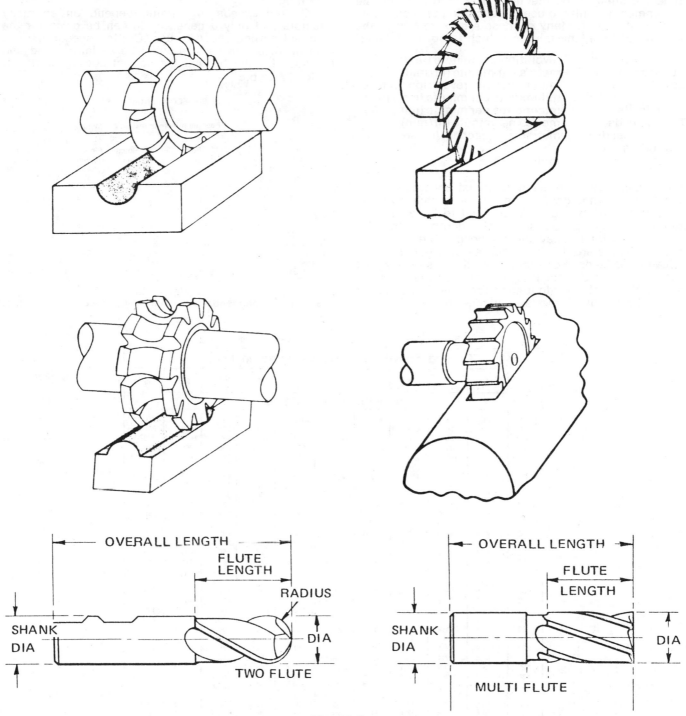

Fig. 27-1b
The cutting edges of these milling cutters must be ground to metric dimensions.

(c) Shaper and planer cutters will not require a change since these are single point cutting tools that can be ground to any shape. (d) Most grinding wheels will not require any change. Only grinding wheels with special shapes and faces must be made to metric specifications.

Speeds, Feeds, and Depth of Cut

Speeds, feeds, and depth of cut are important considerations in all machining. The cutting speed necessary to achieve the most desired result depends on such factors as the material being machined, cutting speed, depth of cut, feed, and type of tool bit. In establishing metric values for machining, the units used cannot always be pure SI. For example, the SI unit for distance per unit of time is metre per second (m/s). This might be satisfactory for expressing the surface speed of grinding, but it would not be useful to express the feed rate of a milling operation. For milling, the unit of distance is too great and the unit of time too small to be practical. The following are the recommended units to use in describing speeds, feeds and depth of cut. Many of these are expressed in the interval of time, the minute, which is *not* an SI unit.

Spindle speeds	revolution per minute (rev/min)
Cutting speeds	metres per minute (m/min)
Spindle feeds	millimetres per revolution (mm/rev)
	millimetres per minute (mm/min)
Table feeds	millimetres per minute (mm/min)
Table speeds	metres per minute (m/min)
Surface speeds of grinding wheels	metres per second (m/sec)
Depth of cut	millimetres

Individuals operating machines must become familiar with factors that govern the rate at which machine operations can be done. They need to know the optimum cutting speeds, feeds and depths of cut for many operations. They must also get the "feel" for metric speeds and feeds in contrast to the customary speeds and feeds. For example, if the customary feed for a high speed steel tool set for a certain class of steel is 150 feet per minute, then the metric equivalent would be about 45 metres per minute.

Turning

Cutting speeds for turning depend on so many factors that only a general rule can be given for the correct cutting speed to use. Cutting speeds depend on such factors as size and type of lathe, kind and shape of cutter bit and the correct cutting lubricant. **Fig. 27-2a,b,c**

SPEED RECOMMENDATIONS

Feet per minute or metres per minute

Material to be cut	Rough Cut ft/min	m/min	Rough & Finish ft/min	m/min	Light & Finish Cut ft/min	m/min
Cast Iron, Soft	70	20	80-90	24-27	120	36
Cast Iron, Medium	55	17	60-70	18-21	90	27
Cast Iron, Hard	40	12	50-60	15-18	70	20
Steel (Chrome Nickel)	30	10	40	12	50	15
Steel (Stainless)	60	18	80	24	90	27
Steel (Low Carbon)	80	25	90	27	140	45
Steel (High Carbon)	40	12	50	15	70	20
Bronze (Medium)	90	27	120	35	150	45
Bronze (Hard)	65	20	90	27	130	40
Brass (Hard)	100	30	150	45	200	60
Copper	150	45	200	60	300	90
Aluminum	600	185			1000	305

Fig. 27-2a
Specific recommendations concerning speeds for turning.

Revolutions per Minute for Various Cutting Speeds and Diameters

dia. mm	Cutting Speed, metres/per minute (m/min)									
	5	6	8	10	12	16	20	25	30	35
	revolutions/per minute									
5	318	382	509	637	764	1019	1273	1592	1910	2228
6	265	318	424	530	637	849	1061	1326	1592	1857
8	199	239	318	398	477	637	796	995	1194	1393
10	159	191	255	318	382	509	637	796	955	1114
12	133	159	212	265	318	424	531	663	796	928
16	99.5	119	159	199	239	318	398	497	597	696
20	79.6	95.5	127	159	191	255	318	398	477	557
25	63.7	76.4	102	127	153	204	255	318	382	446
30	53.1	63.7	84.9	106	127	170	212	265	318	371
35	45.5	54.6	72.8	90.9	109	145	182	227	273	318
40	39.8	47.7	63.7	79.6	95.5	127	159	199	239	279
45	35.4	42.4	56.6	70.7	84.9	113	141	177	212	248
50	31.8	38.2	51	63.7	76.4	102	127	159	191	223
55	28.9	34.7	46.3	57.9	69.4	92.6	116	145	174	203
60	26.6	31.8	42.4	53.1	63.7	84.9	106	133	159	186
65	24.5	29.4	39.2	49	58.8	78.4	98	122	147	171
70	22.7	27.3	36.4	45.5	54.6	72.8	90.9	114	136	159
75	21.2	25.5	34	42.4	51	68	84.9	106	127	149
80	19.9	23.9	31.8	39.8	47.7	63.7	79.6	99.5	119	139
90	17.7	21.2	28.3	35.4	42.4	56.6	70.7	88.4	106	124
100	15.9	19.1	25.5	31.8	38.2	51	63.7	79.6	95.5	111
110	14.5	17.4	23.1	28.9	34.7	46.2	57.9	72.3	86.8	101
120	13.3	15.9	21.2	26.5	31.8	42.4	53.1	66.3	79.6	92.8
130	12.2	14.7	19.6	24.5	29.4	39.2	49	61.2	73.4	85.7
140	11.4	13.6	18.2	22.7	27.3	36.4	45.5	56.8	68.2	79.6
150	10.6	12.7	17	21.2	25.5	34	42.4	53.1	63.7	74.3
160	9.9	11.9	15.9	19.9	23.9	31.8	39.8	49.7	59.7	69.6
170	9.4	11.2	15	18.7	22.5	30	37.4	46.8	56.2	65.5
180	8.8	10.6	14.1	17.7	21.2	28.3	35.4	44.2	53.1	61.9
190	8.3	10	13.4	16.8	20.1	26.8	33.5	41.9	50.3	58.6
200	8	9.5	12.7	15.9	19.1	25.5	31.8	39.8	47.7	55.7
220	7.2	8.7	11.6	14.5	17.4	23.1	28.9	36.2	43.4	50.6
240	6.6	8	10.6	13.3	15.9	21.2	26.5	33.2	39.8	46.4
260	6.1	7.3	9.8	12.2	14.7	19.6	24.5	30.6	36.7	42.8
280	5.7	6.8	9.1	11.4	13.6	18.2	22.7	28.4	34.1	39.8
300	5.3	6.4	8.5	10.6	12.7	17	21.2	26.5	31.8	37.1
350	4.5	5.4	7.3	9.1	10.9	14.6	18.2	22.7	27.3	31.8
400	4	4.8	6.4	8	9.5	12.7	15.9	19.9	23.9	27.9
450	3.5	4.2	5.7	7.1	8.5	11.3	14.1	17.7	21.2	24.8
500	3.2	3.8	5.1	6.4	7.6	10.2	12.7	15.9	19.1	22.3

Fig. 27-2b
Revolutions per minute (rpm) for various cutting speeds and diameters. (Range 5 to 35 m/min)

Revolutions per Minute for Various Cutting Speeds and Diameters

dia. mm	metres per minute (m/min)									
	40	45	50	55	60	65	70	75	80	85
	revolutions per minute (rpm)									
5	2546	2865	3183	3501	3820	4138	4456	4775	5093	5411
6	2122	2387	2653	2918	3183	3448	3714	3979	4244	4509
8	1592	1790	1989	2188	2387	2586	2785	2984	3183	3382
10	1273	1432	1592	1751	1910	2069	2228	2387	2546	2706
12	1061	1194	1326	1459	1592	1724	1857	1989	2122	2255
16	796	895	995	1094	1194	1293	1393	1492	1591	1691
20	637	716	796	875	955	1034	1114	1194	1273	1353
25	509	573	637	700	764	828	891	955	1019	1082
30	424	477	530	584	637	690	743	796	849	902
35	364	409	455	500	546	591	637	682	728	773
40	318	358	398	438	477	517	557	597	637	676
45	283	318	354	389	424	460	495	531	566	601
50	255	286	318	350	382	414	446	477	509	541
55	231	260	289	318	347	376	405	434	463	492
60	212	239	265	292	318	345	371	398	424	451
65	196	220	245	269	294	318	343	367	392	416
70	182	205	227	250	273	296	318	341	364	387
75	170	191	212	233	255	276	297	318	340	361
80	159	179	199	219	239	259	279	298	318	338
90	141	159	177	195	212	230	248	265	283	301
100	127	143	159	175	191	207	223	239	255	271
110	116	130	145	159	174	188	203	217	231	246
120	106	119	133	146	159	172	186	199	212	225
130	97.9	110	122	135	147	159	171	184	196	208
140	90.9	102	114	125	136	148	159	171	182	193
150	84.9	95.5	106	117	127	138	149	159	170	180
160	79.6	89.5	99.5	109	119	129	139	149	159	169
170	74.9	84.2	93.6	103	112	122	131	140	150	159
180	70.7	79.6	88.4	97.3	106	115	124	133	141	150
190	67	75.4	83.8	92.1	101	109	117	126	134	142
200	63.7	71.6	79.6	87.5	95.5	103	111	119	127	135
220	57.9	65.1	72.3	79.6	86.8	94	101	109	116	123
240	53.1	59.7	66.3	72.9	79.6	86.2	92.8	99.5	106	113
260	49	55.1	61.2	67.3	73.4	79.6	85.7	91.8	97.9	104
280	45.5	51.1	56.8	62.5	68.2	73.9	79.6	85.3	90.9	96.6
300	42.4	47.7	53.1	58.3	63.7	69	74.3	79.6	84.9	90.2
350	36.4	40.9	45.5	50	54.6	59.1	63.7	68.2	72.8	77.3
400	31.8	35.8	39.8	43.8	47.7	51.7	55.7	59.7	63.7	67.6
450	28.3	31.8	35.4	38.9	42.4	46	49.5	53.1	56.6	60.1
500	25.5	28.6	31.8	35	38.2	41.4	44.6	47.7	50.9	54.1

Fig. 27-2c
Revolutions per minute (rpm) for various cutting speeds and diameters. (Range 40 to 85 m/min)

To find the number of revolutions per minute for a given cutting speed in metres per minute, multiply the cutting speed by 1000 and divide by the circumference of the piece in millimetres. For example, to find the number of revolutions per minute to machine a shaft that is 75 mm in diameter at a cutting speed of 60 m/min,

$$rpm = \frac{60 \times 1000}{3.1416 \times 75} = \frac{60\ 000}{236} = 255$$

In SI, the hertz - HZ (one hertz equals one cycle per second) can be used to describe such things as the revolutions of engines and motors. There will be resistance to having *rpm* replaced by *hertz*. However, if it is necessary to change rpm to hertz divide by 60. For example, 600 rpm becomes 10 Hz.

If the material to be turned and the recommended cutting speeds are in different units (for example, one in customary and one in metric), the basic rule is to convert to one standard using 1 inch = 25.4 millimetres and then, as above, dividing the cutting speed by the circumference to obtain the rpm.

Feed is the distance the point of the tool moves longitudinally along the bed with each revolution of the lathe. There are no fixed rules for determining correct feed, since it varies with the depth of cut, speed, kind of material, condition of the lathe, and type of cutter bit. For example, a feed of 0.2 mm (0.008") per revolution might be used on a small, light lathe while a feed of 0.5 mm (0.020") might be desirable for a heavy rough cut on a large heavy duty lathe. Depth of cut is the distance from the bottom of the cut to the uncut surface of the workpiece. Depth of cut is one half the difference in the diameter between the cut and uncut surface.

Milling Machines

The cutting speed on a horizontal milling machine is the distance one tooth of the cutter moves in one minute as expressed in metres on its circumference. Cutting speed is expressed in surface metres per minute (sm/min). The cutting speed is also called peripheral speed or surface speed. Cutting speed is not the same as spindle speed, which is given in rpm. The spindle of a milling machine operates at a certain given revolution per minute. For example, if a 100 millimetre cutter is used on the spindle, one tooth will travel about 314 mm in one complete revolution. If a 25 mm diameter cutter is used it will travel about 80 mm per revolution. Two important factors that affect cutting speed are the kind of material being machined and the kind of material in the milling cutter. Cutting speeds and tools shown in **Fig. 27-3a,b** will provide for good removal of metal without damaging the cutter. To find the machine speed to use or the rpm at which the spindle must rotate, the following formula can be used:

$$rpm = \frac{333 \times m/min}{d\ in\ mm}\ or\ \frac{1000 \times m/min}{3.1416 \times d\ in\ mm}$$

Suppose that you want to machine a piece of mild steel with a high speed steel cutter that is 150 mm in diameter. The cutting speed range is between 25 and 35. Select a cutting speed on the low side of about 25 metres per minute. Then,

$$rpm = \frac{333 \times 25}{150} = \frac{8325}{150}\ or\ 55.5$$

Milling
Cutting speeds using H.S.S. cutters.

Material to be Milled	Cutting Speed (m/min)
Aluminum	90-180
Brass	30-45
Cast iron	15-20
Copper	50
Hard steels	12-15
Mild steels	25-35
Plastics	30-150

Fig. 27-3a
General suggestions for milling speeds.

Suggested feed per tooth for given cutters

Side and Face Cutters (mm)	Slab Cutters (mm)	Slitting Saws (mm)	End Mills (mm)
0.25	0.40	0.12	0.25
0.20	0.25	0.10	0.25
0.25	0.30	0.12	0.20
0.20	0.25	0.12	0.25
0.12	0.15	0.10	0.12
0.15	0.25	0.10	0.12
0.25	0.40	0.12	0.25

Fig. 27-3b
General suggestions for milling feeds.

Coarse Adjustment of Machines

Generally in rough machining on lathes, milling machines, shapers and other machine tools the dials are not used for setting the depth of cut, except by estimating. Often the exact measurements are made by using precision measuring tools such as micrometers and verniers. For example in turning to rough diameter the operator usually will adjust a caliper to the correct diameter using a metric rule. The turning is done to that diameter using the calipers to make frequent checks. In milling, the amount to be removed may be checked by using a vernier height gage or a metric rule.

To help the operator make approximate adjustments it may be desirable to add an information plate on each machine with general information on the relative movement of machine parts in inches and millimetres. For example, the common divisions on machine dials are as follows:

one division = 0.0002 in or 0.005 mm (used primarily on grinding machines)
one division = 0.001 in or 0.025 mm
one division = 0.002 in or 0.051 mm
A complete revolution of the dial is as follows:
one revolution = 0.050 in or 1.27 mm
one revolution = 0.100 in or 2.54 mm
one revolution = 0.125 in or 3.18 mm
one revolution = 0.200 in or 5.08 mm

Dials on Lathes

Lathes are equipped with either *direct* or *indirect* reading dials. For example, a *direct* reading dial on the cross feed that reads 0.200" revolution will reduce the *diameter* exactly 0.200" (5.08 mm). On the other hand, an *indirect* reading dial on the cross feed that equals 0.100" would reduce the radius by this amount but the diameter would be reduced 0.200" which is exactly the same as the direct reading dial of 0.200". Even though the dial readings are different, the amount of stock removed is exactly the same since both lathes have a cross feed screw with 10 threads per inch. If the cross feed screw has 8 threads per inch, then a direct reading dial would be graduated 0.250" per revolution while an indirect reading dial would be graduated 0.125" per revolution.

If the lathe is not equipped with dual reading dials, then a chart can be added to the machine to give the user the equivalent of each dial in thousandths of an inch and in millimetres.

Using the Compound Rest for Precision Setting in Millimetres

If a lathe is not equipped with dual reading dials, the compound rest can be used to make accurate settings in millimetres. Adjust the compound rest to an angle of 52 degrees to the right from the center line. **Fig. 27-4**

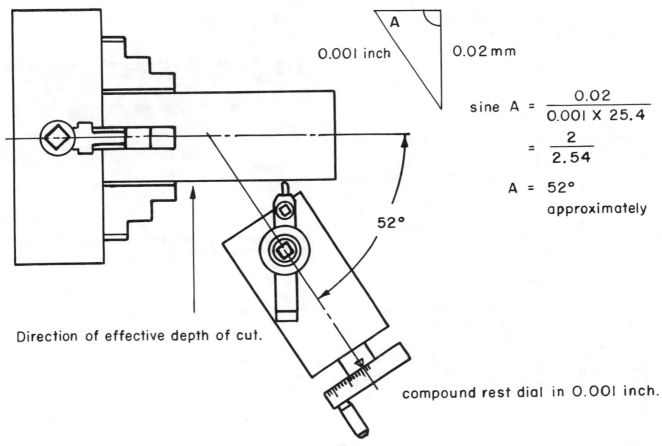

$$\text{sine } A = \frac{0.02}{0.001 \times 25.4}$$

$$= \frac{2}{2.54}$$

$$A = 52°$$

approximately

Fig. 27-4
A feed of 0.001 inches on the compound rest dial will result in a 0.02 mm depth of cut.

Then a movement of 0.001" on the compound rest dial would be equal to exactly 0.02 mm depth of cut. If the individual graduations are 0.002", then the movement would equal 0.04 mm. With this method, precise adjustments for depth of cut are made with the compound rest, not with the cross feed.

Tapers

A taper is defined as a gradual lessening in the diameter or thickness of a workpiece towards one end. Tapers can be shown in several different ways:

A. T/mm (taper per millimetre) For example, a taper of 0.001 millimetres per millimetre is expressed as TAPER 0.001:1.

B. Dimensions shown in millimetres where the taper is cut on the total length of the workpieces.

To find the taper in millimetres per millimetre for the piece shown in **Fig. 27-5**, calculate as follows:

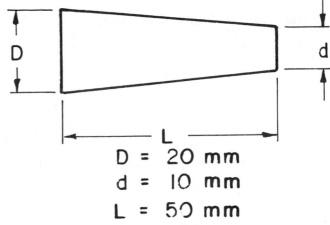

$$D = 20 \text{ mm}$$
$$d = 10 \text{ mm}$$
$$L = 50 \text{ mm}$$

Fig. 27-5
Workpiece tapered along its entire length.

$$\text{Taper} = \frac{D - d}{L} \text{ (in millimetres)}$$

$$\text{Taper} = \frac{20 - 10}{50}$$

$$= \frac{10}{50}$$

$$= 0.20 \text{ mm per 1 mm}$$

C. When the workpiece is tapered for the entire length, the setover is equal to one-half the difference between the large and the small diameter. For example:

$$\frac{D - d}{2} \text{ (in millimetres)}$$

$$= \frac{20 - 10}{2}$$

$$= \frac{10}{2} \text{ or 5 mm}$$

D. When the taper is to be cut on only part of the workpiece (a prick or center punch, for example) the setover equals the total length divided by the length to be tapered times the large diameter minus the small dimeter divided by 2.

$$\text{Setover} = \frac{L}{1} \times \frac{D - d}{2}$$

where L = the total length of the workpiece in millimetres
1 = the length to be tapered in millimetres
D = the large diameter in millimetres
d = the small diameter in millimetres

When using this formula, remember that the total length is the actual length of the workpiece as it is, not the finished length. For example, calculate the setover for turning a taper on part of the workpiece as shown in **Fig. 27-6.**
Example:

$$\frac{300}{100} \times \frac{(40 - 15)}{2} = 3 \times \frac{12}{5}$$

setover = 22.5 mm

E. Taper can also be shown as an angle.

Fig. 27-6
Workpiece tapered along only a portion of its length.

Drills and Reamsers

Metric drills and reamsers are basically the same as for customary machining. **Fig. 27-7.** The twist drills are made with either straight or tapered shanks. Most of the smaller size drills from 0.04 mm to 20 mm in size are available only with the straight shank. The intermediate to larger size drills from 14 mm to 80 mm have a Morse taper shank. Complete metric drill sets are available in the commonly used sizes. **Fig. 27-8a,b.**

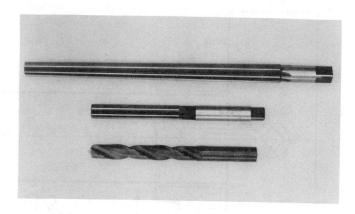

Fig. 27-7
Metric drills and reamers are identical in design to those used in the customary system.

METRIC DIMENSIONING SYSTEM

TWIST DRILL DATA					
METRIC DRILL SIZES (mm)[1]		Decimal Equivalent in Inches (Ref)	METRIC DRILL SIZES (mm)[1]		Decimal Equivalent in Inches (Ref)
Preferred	Available		Preferred	Available	
	.40	.0157	1.70		.0669
	.42	.0165		1.75	.0689
	.45	.0177	1.80		.0709
	.48	.0189		1.85	.0728
.50		.0197	1.90		.0748
	.52	.0205		1.95	.0768
.55		.0217	2.00		.0787
	.58	.0228		2.05	.0807
.60		.0236	2.10		.0827
	.62	.0244		2.15	.0846
.65		.0256	2.20		.0866
	.68	.0268		2.30	.0906
.70		.0276	2.40		.0945
	.72	.0283	2.50		.0984
.75		.0295	2.60		.1024
	.78	.0307		2.70	.1063
.80		.0315	2.80		.1102
	.82	.0323		2.90	.1142
.85		.0335	3.00		.1181
	.88	.0346		3.10	.1220
.90		.0354	3.20		.1260
	.92	.0362		3.30	.1299
.95		.0374	3.40		.1339
	.98	.0386		3.50	.1378
1.00		.0394	3.60		.1417
	1.03	.0406		3.70	.1457
1.05		.0413	3.80		.1496
	1.08	.0425		3.90	.1535
1.10		.0433	4.00		.1575
	1.15	.0453		4.10	.1614
1.20		.0472	4.20		.1654
1.25		.0492		4.40	.1732
1.30		.0512	4.50		.1772
	1.35	.0531		4.60	.1811
1.40		.0551	4.80		.1890
	1.45	.0571	5.00		.1969
1.50		.0591		5.20	.2047
	1.55	.0610	5.30		.2087
1.60		.0630		5.40	.2126
	1.65	.0650	5.60		.2205
				5.80	.2283

[1] Metric drill sizes listed in the "Preferred" column are based on the R'40 series of preferred numbers shown in the ISO Standard R497. Those listed in the "Available" column are based on the R80 series from the same document.

Fig. 27-8a
Recommended metric twist drill sizes.

METRIC DIMENSIONING SYSTEM

TWIST DRILL DATA (CONTINUED)

METRIC DRILL SIZES (mm)[1]		Decimal Equivalent in Inches (Ref)	METRIC DRILL SIZES (mm)[1]		Decimal Equivalent in Inches (Ref)
Preferred	Available		Preferred	Available	
6.00		.2362		19.50	.7677
	6.20	.2441	20.00		.7874
6.30		.2480		20.50	.8071
	6.50	.2559	21.00		.8268
6.70		.2638		21.50	.8465
	6.80[2]	.2677	22.00		.8661
	6.90	.2717		23.00	.9055
7.10		.2795	24.00		.9449
	7.30	.2874	25.00		.9843
7.50		.2953	26.00		1.0236
	7.80	.3071		27.00	1.0630
8.00		.3150	28.00		1.1024
	8.20	.3228		29.00	1.1417
8.50[2]		.3346	30.00		1.1811
	8.80	.3465		31.00	1.2205
9.00		.3543	32.00		1.2598
	9.20	.3622		33.00	1.2992
9.50		.3740	34.00		1.3386
	9.80	.3858		35.00	1.3780
10.00		.3937	36.00		1.4173
	10.30	.4055		37.00	1.4567
10.50		.4134	38.00		1.4961
	10.80	.4252		39.00	1.5354
11.00		.4331	40.00		1.5748
	11.50	.4528		41.00	1.6142
12.00		.4724	42.00		1.6535
12.50		.4921		43.50	1.7126
13.00		.5118	45.00		1.7717
	13.50	.5315		46.50	1.8307
14.00		.5512	48.00		1.8898
	14.50	.5709	50.00		1.9685
15.00		.5906		51.50	2.0276
	15.50	.6102	53.00		2.0866
16.00		.6299		54.00	2.1260
	16.50	.6496	56.00		2.2047
17.00		.6693		58.00	2.2835
	17.50	.6890	60.00		2.3622
18.00		.7087			
	18.50	.7283			
19.00		.7480			

1 Metric drill sizes listed in the "Preferred" column are based on the R'40 series of preferred numbers shown in the ISO Standard R497. Those listed in the "Available" column are based on the R80 series from the same document.

2 Recommended only for use as a tap drill size.

DUAL DIMENSIONING

CONVERSION TABLE

Drill No. or Letter	Inch	mm	Drill No. or Letter	Inch	mm	Drill No. or Letter	Inch	mm	Drill No. or Letter	Inch	mm
	.001	.0254		.051	1.2954	38 .1015	.101	2.5654	24	.152	3.8608
	.002	.0508	55	.052	1.3208		.102	2.5908		.153	3.8862
	.003	.0762		.053	1.3462		.103	2.6162	23	.154	3.9116
	.004	.1016		.054	1.3716	37	.104	2.6416		.155	3.9370
	.005	.1270	54	.055	1.3970		.105	2.6670		.156	3.9624
	.006	.1524		.056	1.4224	36 .1065	.106	2.6924	5/32	.1562	3.9687
	.007	.1778		.057	1.4478		.107	2.7178	22	.157	3.9878
	.008	.2032		.058	1.4732		.108	2.7432		.1575	4.0000
	.009	.2286		.059	1.4986		.109	2.7686		.158	4.0132
	.010	.2540	53 .0595	.060	1.5240	7/64	.1094	2.7781	21	.159	4.0386
	.011	.2794		.061	1.5494	35	.110	2.7940		.160	4.0640
	.012	.3048		.062	1.5748	34	.111	2.8194	20	.161	4.0894
80 .0135	.013	.3302	1/16	.0625	1.5875		.112	2.8448		.162	4.1148
79 .0145	.014	.3556	52 .0635	.063	1.6002	33	.113	2.8702		.163	4.1402
	.015	.3810		.064	1.6256		.114	2.8956		.164	4.1656
1/64	.0156	.3969		.065	1.6510		.115	2.9210		.165	4.1910
78	.016	.4064		.066	1.6764	32	.116	2.9464	19	.166	4.2164
	.017	.4318	51	.067	1.7018		.117	2.9718		.167	4.2418
77	.018	.4572		.068	1.7272		.118	2.9972		.168	4.2672
	.019	.4826		.069	1.7526		.1181	3.0000	18 .1695	.169	4.2926
76	.020	.5080	50	.070	1.7780		.119	3.0226		.170	4.3180
75	.021	.5334		.071	1.8034	31	.120	3.0480		.171	4.3434
74 .0225	.022	.5588		.072	1.8288		.121	3.0734	11/64	.1719	4.3656
	.023	.5842	49	.073	1.8542		.122	3.0988		.172	4.3688
73	.024	.6096		.074	1.8796		.123	3.1242	17	.173	4.3942
72	.025	.6350		.075	1.9050		.124	3.1496		.174	4.4196
71	.026	.6604	48	.076	1.9304	1/8	.125	3.1750		.175	4.4450
	.027	.6858		.077	1.9558		.126	3.2004		.176	4.4704
70	.028	.7112		.078	1.9812		.127	3.2258	16	.177	4.4958
69 .0292	.029	.7366	5/64	.0781	1.9844		.128	3.2512		.178	4.5212
	.030	.7620	47 .0785	.0787	2.0000	30 .1285	.129	3.2766		.179	4.5466
68	.031	.7874		.079	2.0066		.130	3.3020	15	.180	4.5720
1/32	.0312	.7937		.080	2.0320		.131	3.3274		.181	4.5974
67	.032	.8128	46	.081	2.0574		.132	3.3528	14	.182	4.6228
66	.033	.8382	45	.082	2.0828		.133	3.3782		.183	4.6482
	.034	.8636		.083	2.1082		.134	3.4036		.184	4.6736
65	.035	.8890		.084	2.1336		.135	3.4290	13	.185	4.6990
64	.036	.9144		.085	2.1590	29	.136	3.4544		.186	4.7244
63	.037	.9398	44	.086	2.1844		.137	3.4798		.187	4.7498
62	.038	.9552		.087	2.2098		.138	3.5052	3/16	.1875	4.7625
61	.039	.9906		.088	2.2352		.139	3.5306		.188	4.7752
	.0394	1.0000	43	.089	2.2606	28 .1405	.140	3.5560	12	.189	4.8006
60	.040	1.0160		.090	2.2860	9/64	.1406	3.5719		.190	4.8260
59	.041	1.0414		.091	2.3114		.141	3.5814	11	.191	4.8514
58	.042	1.0668		.092	2.3368		.142	3.6068		.192	4.8768
57	.043	1.0922	42 .0935	.093	2.3622		.143	3.6322	10 .1935	.193	4.9022
	.044	1.1176	3/32	.0937	2.3812	27	.144	3.6576		.194	4.9276
	.045	1.1430		.094	2.3876		.145	3.6830		.195	4.9530
56 .0465	.046	1.1684		.095	2.4130		.146	3.7084	9	.196	4.9784
3/64	.0469	1.1906	41	.096	2.4384	26	.147	3.7338		.1969	5.0000
	.047	1.1938		.097	2.4633		.148	3.7592		.197	5.0038
	.048	1.2192	40	.098	2.4892	25 .1495	.149	3.7846		.198	5.0292
	.049	1.2446		.099	2.5146		.150	3.8100		.199	5.0546
	.050	1.2700	39 .0995	.100	2.5400		.151	3.8354	8	.200	5.0800

Fig. 27-8b
Metric conversion table for drills.

CONVERSION TABLE

Drill No. or Letter	Inch	mm
7	.201	5.1054
	.202	5.1308
	.203	5.1562
13/64	.2031	5.1594
6	.204	5.1816
5 .2055	.205	5.2070
	.206	5.2324
	.207	5.2578
	.208	5.2832
4	.209	5.3086
	.210	5.3340
	.211	5.3594
	.212	5.3848
3	.213	5.4102
	.214	5.4356
	.215	5.4610
	.216	5.4864
	.217	5.5118
	.218	5.5372
7/32	.2187	5.5562
	.219	5.5626
	.220	5.5880
2	.221	5.6134
	.222	5.6388
	.223	5.6642
	.224	5.6896
	.225	5.7150
	.226	5.7404
	.227	5.7658
1	.228	5.7912
	.229	5.8166
	.230	5.8420
	.231	5.8674
	.232	5.8923
	.233	5.9182
A	.234	5.9436
15/64	.2344	5.9531
	.235	5.9690
	.236	5.9944
	.2362	6.0000
	.237	6.0198
B	.238	6.0452
	.239	6.0706
	.240	6.0960
	.241	6.1214
C	.242	6.1468
	.243	6.1722
	.244	6.1976
	.245	6.2230
D	.246	6.2484
	.247	6.2738
	.248	6.2992
	.249	6.3246
E 1/4	.250	6.3500
	.251	6.3754
	.252	6.4008
	.253	6.4262
	.254	6.4516
	.255	6.4770
	.256	6.5024
F	.257	6.5278
	.258	6.5532
	.259	6.5786
	.260	6.6040
G	.261	6.6294
	.262	6.6548
	.263	6.6802
	.264	6.7056
	.265	6.7310
17/64	.2656	6.7469
H	.266	6.7564
	.267	6.7818
	.268	6.8072
	.269	6.8326
	.270	6.8580
	.271	6.8834
I	.272	6.9088
	.273	6.9342
	.274	6.9596
	.275	6.9850
	.2756	7.0000
	.276	7.0104
J	.277	7.0358
	.278	7.0612
	.279	7.0866
	.280	7.1120
K	.281	7.1374
9/32	.2812	7.1437
	.282	7.1628
	.283	7.1882
	.284	7.2136
	.285	7.2390
	.286	7.2644
	.287	7.2898
	.288	7.3152
	.289	7.3406
L	.290	7.3660
	.291	7.3914
	.292	7.4168
	.293	7.4422
	.294	7.4676
M	.295	7.4930
	.296	7.5184
19/64	.2969	7.5406
	.297	7.5438
	.298	7.5692
	.299	7.5946
	.300	7.6200
	.301	7.6454
N	.302	7.6708
	.303	7.6962
	.304	7.7216
	.305	7.7470
	.306	7.7724
	.307	7.7978
	.308	7.8232
	.309	7.8486
	.310	7.8740
	.311	7.8994
	.312	7.9248
5/16	.3125	7.9375
	.313	7.9502
	.314	7.9756
	.3150	8.0000
	.315	8.0010
O	.316	8.0264
	.317	8.0518
	.318	8.0772
	.319	8.1026
	.320	8.1280
	.321	8.1534
	.322	8.1788
P	.323	8.2042
	.324	8.2296
	.325	8.2550
	.326	8.2804
	.327	8.3058
	.328	8.3312
21/64	.3281	8.3344
	.329	8.3566
	.330	8.3820
	.331	8.4074
Q	.332	8.4328
	.333	8.4582
	.334	8.4836
	.335	8.5090
	.336	8.5344
	.337	8.5598
	.338	8.5852
R	.339	8.6106
	.340	8.6360
	.341	8.6614
	.342	8.6868
	.343	8.7122
11/32	.3437	8.7312
	.344	8.7376
	.345	8.7630
	.346	8.7884
	.347	8.8138
S	.348	8.8392
	.349	8.8646
	.350	8.8900
	.351	8.9154
	.352	8.9408
	.353	8.9662
	.354	8.9916
	.3543	9.0000
	.355	9.0170
	.356	9.0424
	.357	9.0678
T	.358	9.0932
	.359	9.1186
23/64	.3594	9.1281
	.360	9.1440
	.361	9.1694
	.362	9.1948
	.363	9.2202
	.364	9.2456
	.365	9.2710
	.366	9.2964
	.367	9.3218
U	.368	9.3472
	.369	9.3726
	.370	9.3980
	.371	9.4234
	.372	9.4488
	.373	9.4742
	.374	9.4996
3/8	.375	9.5250
	.376	9.5504
V	.377	9.5758
	.378	9.6012
	.379	9.6266
	.380	9.6520
	.381	9.6774
	.382	9.7028
	.383	9.7282
	.384	9.7536
	.385	9.7790
W	.386	9.8044
	.387	9.8298
	.388	9.8552
	.389	9.8806
	.390	9.9060
25/64	.3906	9.9219
	.391	9.9314
	.392	9.9568
	.393	9.9822
	.3937	10.0000
	.394	10.0076
	.395	10.0330
	.396	10.0584
X	.397	10.0838
	.398	10.1092
	.399	10.1346
	.400	10.1600

Drill No. or Letter	Inch	mm	Inch	mm	Inch	mm	Inch	mm
	.401	10.1854	.451	11.4554	.501	12.7254	.551	13.9954
	.402	10.2108	.452	11.4808	.502	12.7508	.5512	14.0000
	.403	10.2362	.453	11.5062	.503	12.7762	.552	14.0208
Y	.404	10.2616	29/64 .4531	11.5094	.504	12.8016	.553	14.0462
	.405	10.2870	.454	11.5316	.505	12.8270	.554	14.0716
	.406	10.3124	.455	11.5570	.506	12.8524	.555	14.0970
13/32	.4062	10.3187	.456	11.5824	.507	12.8778	.556	14.1224
	.407	10.3378	.457	11.6078	.508	12.9032	.557	14.1478
	.408	10.3632	.458	11.6332	.509	12.9286	.558	14.1732
	.409	10.3886	.459	11.6586	.510	12.9540	.559	14.1986
	.410	10.4140	.460	11.6840	.511	12.9794	.560	14.2240
	.411	10.4394	.461	11.7094	.5118	13.0000	.561	14.2494
	.412	10.4648	.462	11.7348	.512	13.0048	.562	14.2748
Z	.413	10.4902	.463	11.7602	.513	13.0302	9/16 .5625	14.2875
	.414	10.5156	.464	11.7856	.514	13.0556	.563	14.3002
	.415	10.5410	.465	11.8110	.515	13.0810	.564	14.3256
	.416	10.5664	.466	11.8364	33/64 .5156	13.0968	.565	14.3510
	.417	10.5918	.467	11.8618	.516	13.1064	.566	14.3764
	.418	10.6172	.468	11.8872	.517	13.1318	.567	14.4018
	.419	10.6426	15/32 .4687	11.9062	.518	13.1572	.568	14.4272
	.420	10.6680	.469	11.9126	.519	13.1826	.569	14.4526
	.421	10.6934	.470	11.9380	.520	13.2080	.570	14.4780
27/64	.4219	10.7156	.471	11.9634	.521	13.2334	.571	14.5034
	.422	10.7188	.472	11.9888	.522	13.2588	.572	14.5288
	.423	10.7442	.4724	12.0000	.523	13.2842	.573	14.5542
	.424	10.7696	.473	12.0142	.524	13.3096	.574	14.5796
	.425	10.7950	.474	12.0396	.525	13.3350	.575	14.6050
	.426	10.8204	.475	12.0650	.526	13.3604	.576	14.6304
	.427	10.8458	.476	12.0904	.527	13.3858	.577	14.6558
	.428	10.8712	.477	12.1158	.528	13.4112	.578	14.6812
	.429	10.8966	.478	12.1412	.529	13.4366	37/64 .5781	14.6844
	.430	10.9220	.479	12.1666	.530	13.4620	.579	14.7066
	.431	10.9474	.480	12.1920	.531	13.4874	.580	14.7320
	.432	10.9728	.481	12.2174	17/32 .5312	13.4937	.581	14.7574
	.433	10.9982	.482	12.2428	.532	13.5128	.582	14.7828
	.4331	11.0000	.483	12.2682	.533	13.5382	.583	14.8082
	.434	11.0236	.484	12.2936	.534	13.5636	.584	14.8336
	.435	11.0490	31/64 .4844	12.3031	.535	13.5890	.585	14.8590
	.436	11.0744	.485	12.3190	.536	13.6144	.586	14.8844
	.437	11.0998	.486	12.3444	.537	13.6398	.587	14.9098
7/16	.4375	11.1125	.487	12.3698	.538	13.6652	.588	14.9352
	.438	11.1252	.488	12.3952	.539	13.6906	.589	14.9606
	.439	11.1506	.489	12.4206	.540	13.7160	.590	14.9860
	.440	11.1760	.490	12.4460	.541	13.7414	.5906	15.0000
	.441	11.2014	.491	12.4714	.542	13.7668	.591	15.0114
	.442	11.2268	.492	12.4968	.543	13.7922	.592	15.0368
	.443	11.2522	.493	12.5222	.544	13.8176	.593	15.0622
	.444	11.2776	.494	12.5476	.545	13.8430	19/32 .5937	15.0812
	.445	11.3030	.495	12.5730	.546	13.8684	.594	15.0876
	.446	11.3284	.496	12.5984	35/64 .5469	13.8906	.595	15.1130
	.447	11.3538	.497	12.6238	.547	13.8938	.596	15.1384
	.448	11.3792	.498	12.6492	.548	13.9192	.597	15.1638
	.449	11.4046	.499	12.6746	.549	13.9446	.598	15.1892
	.450	11.4300	1/2 .500	12.7000	.550	13.9700	.599	15.2146

CONVERSION TABLE

Inch	mm	Inch	mm	Inch	mm	Inch	mm
.600	15.2400	.651	16.5354	.701	17.8054	3/4 .750	19.0500
.601	15.2654	.652	16.5608	.702	17.8308	.751	19.0754
.602	15.2908	.653	16.5862	.703	17.8562	.752	19.1008
.603	15.3162	.654	16.6116	45/64 .7031	17.8594	.753	19.1262
.604	15.3416	.655	16.6370	.704	17.8816	.754	19.1516
.605	15.3670	.656	16.6624	.705	17.9070	.755	19.1770
.606	15.3924	21/32 .6562	16.6687	.706	17.9324	.756	19.2024
.607	15.4178	.657	16.6878	.707	17.9578	.757	19.2278
.608	15.4432	.658	16.7132	.708	17.9832	.758	19.2532
.609	15.4686	.659	16.7386	.7087	18.0000	.759	19.2786
39/64 .6094	15.4781	.660	16.7640	.709	18.0086	.760	19.3040
.610	15.4940	.661	16.7894	.710	18.0340	.761	19.3294
.611	15.5194	.662	16.8148	.711	18.0594	.762	19.3548
.612	15.5448	.663	16.8402	.712	18.0848	.763	19.3802
.613	15.5702	.664	16.8656	.713	18.1102	.764	19.4056
.614	15.5956	.665	16.8910	.714	18.1356	.765	19.4310
.615	15.6210	.666	16.9164	.715	18.1610	49/64 .7656	19.4469
.616	15.6464	.667	16.9418	.716	18.1864	.766	19.4564
.617	15.6718	.668	16.9672	.717	18.2118	.767	19.4818
.618	15.6972	.669	16.9926	.718	18.2372	.768	19.5072
.619	15.7226	.6693	17.0000	23/32 .7187	18.2562	.769	19.5326
.620	15.7480	.670	17.0180	.719	18.2626	.770	19.5580
.621	15.7734	.671	17.0434	.720	18.2880	.771	19.5834
.622	15.7988	43/64 .6719	17.0656	.721	18.3134	.772	19.6088
.623	15.8242	.672	17.0688	.722	18.3388	.773	19.6342
.624	15.8496	.673	17.0942	.723	18.3642	.774	19.6596
5/8 .625	15.8750	.674	17.1196	.724	18.3896	.775	19.6850
.626	15.9004	.675	17.1450	.725	18.4150	.776	19.7104
.627	15.9258	.676	17.1704	.726	18.4404	.777	19.7358
.628	15.9512	.677	17.1958	.727	18.4658	.778	19.7612
.629	15.9766	.678	17.2212	.728	18.4912	.779	19.7866
.6299	16.0000	.679	17.2466	.729	18.5166	.780	19.8120
.630	16.0020	.680	17.2720	.730	18.5420	.781	19.8374
.631	16.0274	.681	17.2974	.731	18.5674	25/32 .7812	19.8433
.632	16.0528	.682	17.3228	.732	18.5928	.782	19.8628
.633	16.0782	.683	17.3482	.733	18.6182	.783	19.8882
.634	16.1036	.684	17.3736	.734	18.6436	.784	19.9136
.635	16.1290	.685	17.3990	47/64 .7344	18.6532	.785	19.9390
.636	16.1544	.686	17.4244	.735	18.6690	.786	19.9644
.637	16.1798	.687	17.4498	.736	18.6944	.787	19.9898
.638	16.2052	11/16 .6875	17.4625	.737	18.7198	.7874	20.0000
.639	16.2306	.688	17.4752	.738	18.7452	.788	20.0152
.640	16.2560	.689	17.5006	.739	18.7706	.789	20.0406
41/64 .6406	16.2719	.690	17.5260	.740	18.7960	.790	20.0660
.641	16.2814	.691	17.5514	.741	18.8214	.791	20.0914
.642	16.3068	.692	17.5768	.742	18.8468	.792	20.1168
.643	16.3322	.693	17.6022	.743	18.8722	.793	20.1422
.644	16.3576	.694	17.6276	.744	18.8976	.794	20.1676
.645	16.3830	.695	17.6530	.745	18.9230	.795	20.1930
.646	16.4084	.696	17.6784	.746	18.9484	.796	20.2184
.647	16.4338	.697	17.7038	.747	18.9738	51/64 .7969	20.2402
.648	16.4592	.698	17.7292	.748	18.9992	.797	20.2438
.649	16.4846	.699	17.7546	.7480	19.0000	.798	20.2692
.650	16.5100	.700	17.7800	.749	19.0246	.799	20.2946

CONVERSION TABLE

Inch	mm	Inch	mm	Inch	mm	Inch	mm
.800	20.3200	.850	21.5900	.901	22.8854	.950	24.1300
.801	20.3454	.851	21.6154	.902	22.9108	.951	24.1554
.802	20.3708	.852	21.6408	.903	22.9362	.952	24.1808
.803	20.3962	.853	21.6662	.904	22.9616	.953	24.2062
.804	20.4216	.854	21.6916	.905	22.9870	61/64 .9531	24.2094
.805	20.4470	.855	21.7170	.9055	23.0000	.954	24.2316
.806	20.4724	.856	21.7424	.906	23.0124	.955	24.2570
.807	20.4978	.857	21.7678	29/32 .9062	23.0187	.956	24.2824
.808	20.5232	.858	21.7932	.907	23.0378	.957	24.3078
.809	20.5486	.859	21.8186	.908	23.0632	.958	24.3332
.810	20.5740	55/64 .8594	21.8281	.909	23.0886	.959	24.3586
.811	20.5994	.860	21.8440	.910	23.1140	.960	24.3840
.812	20.6248	.861	21.8694	.911	23.1394	.961	24.4094
13/16 .8125	20.6375	.862	21.8948	.912	23.1648	.962	24.4348
.813	20.6502	.863	21.9202	.913	23.1902	.963	24.4602
.814	20.6756	.864	21.9456	.914	23.2156	.964	24.4856
.815	20.7010	.865	21.9710	.915	23.2410	.965	24.5110
.816	20.7264	.866	21.9964	.916	23.2664	.966	24.5364
.817	20.7518	.8661	22.0000	.917	23.2918	.967	24.5618
.818	20.7772	.867	22.0218	.918	23.3172	.968	24.5872
.819	20.8026	.868	22.0472	.919	23.3426	31/32 .9687	24.6062
.820	20.8280	.869	22.0726	.920	23.3680	.969	24.6126
.821	20.8534	.870	22.0980	.921	23.3934	.970	24.6380
.822	20.8788	.871	22.1234	59/64 .9219	23.4156	.971	24.6634
.823	20.9042	.872	22.1488	.922	23.4188	.972	24.6888
.824	20.9296	.873	22.1742	.923	23.4442	.973	24.7142
.825	20.9550	.874	22.1996	.924	23.4696	.974	24.7396
.826	20.9804	7/8 .875	22.2250	.925	23.4950	.975	24.7650
.8268	21.0000	.876	22.2504	.926	23.5204	.976	24.7904
.827	21.0058	.877	22.2758	.927	23.5458	.977	24.8158
.828	21.0312	.878	22.3012	.928	23.5712	.978	24.8412
53/64 .8281	21.0344	.879	22.3266	.929	23.5966	.979	24.8666
.829	21.0566	.880	22.3520	.930	23.6220	.980	24.8920
.830	21.0820	.881	22.3774	.931	23.6474	.981	24.9174
.831	21.1074	.882	22.4028	.932	23.6728	.982	24.9428
.832	21.1328	.883	22.4282	.933	23.6982	.983	24.9682
.833	21.1582	.884	22.4536	.934	23.7236	.984	24.9936
.834	21.1836	.885	22.4790	.935	23.7490	.9843	25.0000
.835	21.2090	.886	22.5044	.936	23.7744	63/64 .9844	25.0031
.836	21.2344	.887	22.5298	.937	23.7998	.985	25.0190
.837	21.2598	.888	22.5552	15/16 .9375	23.8125	.986	25.0444
.838	21.2852	.889	22.5806	.938	23.8252	.987	25.0698
.839	21.3106	.890	22.6060	.939	23.8506	.988	25.0952
.840	21.3360	57/64 .8906	22.6219	.940	23.8760	.989	25.1206
.841	21.3614	.891	22.6314	.941	23.9014	.990	25.1460
.842	21.3868	.892	22.6568	.942	23.9268	.991	25.1714
.843	21.4122	.893	22.6822	.943	23.9522	.992	25.1968
27/32 .8437	21.4312	.894	22.7076	.944	23.9776	.993	25.2222
.844	21.4376	.895	22.7330	.9449	24.0000	.994	25.2476
.845	21.4630	.896	22.7584	.945	24.0030	.995	25.2730
.846	21.4884	.897	22.7838	.946	24.0284	.996	25.2984
.847	21.5138	.898	22.8092	.947	24.0538	.997	25.3238
.848	21.5392	.899	22.8346	.948	24.0792	.998	25.3492
.849	21.5646	.900	22.8600	.949	24.1046	.999	25.3746
						1.000	25.4000

For example, a set of 12 drills from size 1.0 mm through 6.0 mm in 0.50 mm steps would provide for most small drilling operations. A larger set consisting of sizes from 1.0 mm through 13.0 mm in 0.50 mm steps are also available. Drills can also be purchased as individual items. For production work customary drills and reamer blanks can be purchased that are very close to the metric sizes; the cutting edges are then ground to metric dimensions. Metric drills, either with the straight or taper shank, will fit directly into the chuck or spindle of a customary-designed drill press. The size of the metric drill can be checked with the metric drill gage or a metric micrometer. Measure the diameter directly across the margins.

During the early stages of conversion a complete set of metric drills is not essential. A set of metric sized drills can be assembled using customary drills.

Fig. 27-9

Metric	Customary	Metric	Customary	Metric	Customary
1.00	60	5.00	9	9.00	(T)
1.20	3/64	5.20	6 or 13/64	9.20	(23/64)
1.40	54	5.40	3	9.40	U
1.60	1/16	5.60	2 or (7/32)	9.60	V
1.80	50	5.80	1	9.80	W
2.00	47	6.00	B or (15/64)	10.00	(X) or (25/64)
2.20	44	6.20	D	10.20	Y
2.40	3/32	6.40	1/4 or E	10.50	Z
2.60	38	6.60	G	10.80	(27/64)
2.80	34 or 35	6.80	H	11.00	(7/16)
3.00	31	7.00	J	11.20	—
3.20	1/8	7.20	9/32	11.50	29/64
3.40	29	7.40	L	11.80	(15/32)
3.60	9/64	7.60	(N)	12.00	—
3.80	25	7.80	(5/16)	12.20	(31/64)
4.00	22	8.00	O	12.50	—
4.20	19	8.20	P	12.80	(1/2)
4.40	17	8.40	Q or (21/64)	13.00	(33/64)
4.60	14	8.60	R	14.00	(9/16)
4.80	12 or (3/16)	8.80	S	15.00	(19/32)

Fig. 27-9
Simplified chart of the more common metric sizes that can be obtained by substituting customary sizes.

For accurate tapping of threads it may be desirable to purchase metric drills for only the most commonly used taps. Metric drills are not necessary for ordinary machining work since drills will rarely produce a perfectly accurate hole. The diameter of the hole depends on the following factors: (a) how accurately the drill has been ground, (b) the kind of material being drilled, (c) the lubricant used, (d) the accuracy of the drill press and (e) the speed and feed of the drill in operation. A customary drill that is closest to the metric size will be accurate enough for most work including tapping a hole.

Cutting speeds on the drill press are given in surface metres per minute while drill diameters are in millimetres. **Fig. 27-10**

The following formula will be needed to find the revolution per minute.

If the cutting speed is given in surface *metres per minute,* it must be changed to millimetres per minute by multiplying by 1000. The rpm is cutting speed in millimetres per minute divided by the circumference of the drill in millimetres, or

$$rpm = \frac{m/min \times 1000}{d \text{ in } mm \times 3.1416}$$

For example, if the cutting speed is 45 m/min and the drill diameter is 12 mm the rpm =

$$\frac{45 \times 1000}{12 \times 3.1416} = \frac{45000}{37.7} = 1190 \text{ rpm}$$

Since there is a relatively wide range in recommended speeds, the suggestions given are for starting ranges. There are many variables in drilling operations such as tool construction, fixtures used, kind of machine, kind of drill, coolant, and other items.

Metric Combination Center Drills

A combination drill and countersink is used to drill center holes. These are available in several standard sizes and can be designated either in inches or in millimetres.

Reamers

Metric reamers are available in the same basic styles as those used in customary work. Straight fluted reamers are available in sizes from 1 mm to 25 mm in 0.5 mm steps in the lower sizes and in full millimetre steps in the larger sizes. Straight and taper shank reamers including chucking reamers are available also in metric modules of even millimetres or half millimetres. Straight fluted shell reamers are available in metric sizes from 18 to 80 mm in steps of 1 mm in the range from 18 to 35 and in 2 mm steps from 36 to 80.

DRILL SPEEDS

	ft/min H.S.S.	ft/min Carbide	m/min H.S.S.	m/min Carbide
Aluminum and Aluminum Alloys	150-300	230-450	45- 90	70-135
Brass and Bronze (free cutting)	150-300	230-450	45- 90	70-133
Brass and Bronze (high tensile)	70-120	120-200	20- 35	35- 90
Cast Iron (soft)	80-120	130-200	25-35	40- 90
Cast Iron (medium)	60- 90	100-150	18- 27	30- 45
Cast Iron (hard)	30- 70	50-130	10- 20	15- 40
Copper	70-100	120-170	20- 30	35- 50
Magnesium	200-400	300-600	60-120	90-180
Nickel Base Alloys	20- 50	40- 90	6- 15	12- 27
Plastic and Related Materials	100-200	150-300	30- 60	45- 90
Steel				
Alloyed—under 200 B.H.	60- 90	100-150	18- 27	30- 45
Alloyed—200-300 B.H.	40- 70	70-130	12- 20	20- 40
Alloyed—over 300 B.H.	20- 30	40- 60	6- 9	12- 18
Cast and Forged	40- 70	70-130	12- 20	20- 40
Heat Treated—35-40 R.C.	30- 40	60- 80	10- 12	18- 25
Heat Treated—40-45 R.C.	20- 30	40- 60	6- 10	12- 18
Heat Treated—over 45 R.C.	10- 20	20- 40	3- 6	6- 12
Mild—.2—.3 Carbon	70-100	120-170	20- 30	36- 50
Mild—.4—.5 Carbon	50- 80	90-150	15- 24	27- 45
Stainless—300 Series	20- 50	40- 90	6- 15	12- 27
Stainless—400 Series	30- 70	50-130	10- 20	15- 20
Tool—over 1.0 Carbon	40- 60	70-110	12- 18	20- 33
Titanium Alloys	20- 50	40- 90	6- 15	12- 27
Wood	200-300	300-450	60- 90	90-135

DRILL FEEDS

Diameter Range in	Diameter Range mm	Normal Feed in	Normal Feed mm	Heavy Feed in	Heavy Feed mm
1/16 thru 1/8	1 thru 4	0.001-0.002	0.02-0.05	.002-.004	0.05-0.10
over 1/8 thru 1/4	3 thru 5	0.002-0.004	0.05-0.10	.004-.008	0.10-0.20
over 1/4 thru 1/2	6 thru 12	0.004-0.008	0.10-0.20	.008-.016	0.20-0.40
over 1/2 thru 1	13 thru 25	0.008-0.016	0.20-0.40	.016-.024	0.40-0.60
over 1	26	0.016-0.024	0.40-0.60	.024-.032	0.60-0.80

Fig. 27-10

Recommended speeds and feeds for drilling.

UNIT 28
CUTTING METRIC THREADS

There are seven common ways of cutting a metric thread, namely, (1) cutting threads by hand with tap and die, (2) cutting threads with a single-point tool on a lathe, (3) tapping threads internally on a machine using a rotary cutter, (4) cutting external threads on a machine with a threading or die head, (5) milling threads on a milling machine, (6) grinding threads on a cylindrical grinder, (7) rolling threads. Of these methods the two most commonly used for repair and maintenance work are cutting threads with a tap and die and cutting external or internal threads with a single-point tool on a lathe.

Cutting Threads With a Tap and Die

A tap is a hard steel tool used for cutting internal threads. Taps are available in three styles, namely, taper, plug, and bottoming.
Fig. 28-1.

Fig. 28-2
A screw plate set of taps and dies.

Sets of screw plates are available from combinations with as few as five sizes up to as many as 18 sizes.
Fig. 28-3.

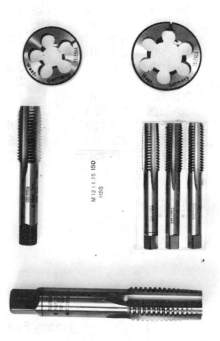

Fig. 28-1
Metric taps and dies. The three taps shown in the lower center are M12x1.75 in the three styles from top to bottom-- taper, plug, and bottoming.

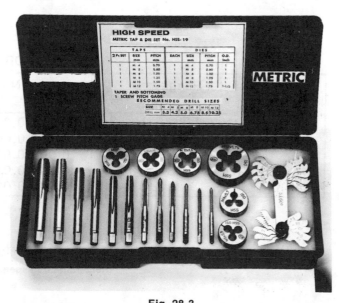

Fig. 28-3
This set consists of six sizes of dies and six taps. Each tap is available in the taper and plug style. The kit also includes a screw pitch gage.

The most common die used for cutting external threads is a *split ring* die. A complete set of taps and dies together with tap wrenches and die stock for cutting a range of common thread sizes is called a *screw plate.*
Fig. 28-2.

To cut all of the threads in the modified ISO series (OMFS) used in the United States would require 25 taps, dies and matching tap drills. **Fig. 28-4.**

NOMINAL SIZE OF FIFTEEN
COMMON ISO THREADS

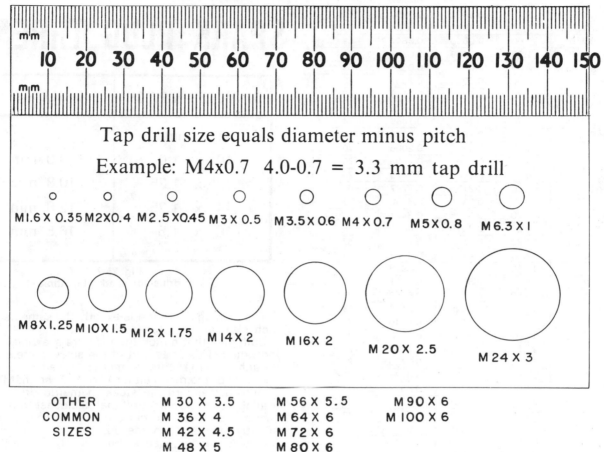

Tap drill size equals diameter minus pitch

Example: M4x0.7 4.0-0.7 = 3.3 mm tap drill

M1.6 X 0.35 M2 X 0.4 M 2.5 X 0.45 M 3 X 0.5 M 3.5 X 0.6 M 4 X 0.7 M 5 X 0.8 M 6.3 X 1

M 8 X 1.25 M 10 X 1.5 M 12 X 1.75 M 14 X 2 M 16 X 2 M 20 X 2.5 M 24 X 3

OTHER COMMON SIZES			
M 30 X 3.5	M 56 X 5.5	M 90 X 6	
M 36 X 4	M 64 X 6	M 100 X 6	
M 42 X 4.5	M 72 X 6		
M 48 X 5	M 80 X 6		

Fig. 28-4.
Common sizes of the modified ISO series for use in the United States. Check the diameter by placing the thread over the circle.

To find the correct size of tap and die needed, insert the bolt or screw in or on a metric measure gage or use a metric micrometer to check the diameter. The correct pitch is measured with the metric screw pitch gage. **Fig. 28-5.**

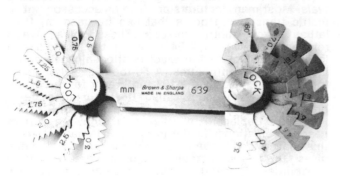

Fig. 28-5
Screw pitch gage.

The pitch of a metric thread is measured from one thread to the next. For example, an ISO M10x1.5 has a distance of 1.5 mm from the top of one thread to the top of the next. The size of the tap drill will determine the percentage of threads that result. This will also affect the fit between the external and internal thread. For average work the correct tap drill is obtained by subtracting the pitch from the outside diameter. This will produce approximately a 70 ± 3 percent thread. For example, referring to **Fig. 28-6,** if the diameter is 6 mm and the pitch is 1 mm, then the correct diameter of tap drill is 5.0 mm. Tap drills for spark plug threads are shown in **Fig. 28-7.**

METRIC TAP DRILL SIZES

METRIC TAP SIZE	RECOMMENDED METRIC DRILL			
	DRILL SIZE	Inch Equiv.	PROBABLE HOLE SIZE (Inches)	PROBABLE PERCENT OF THREAD
M1.6 × 0.35	1.25	0.0492	0.0507	69
M1.8 × 0.35	1.45	0.0571	0.0586	69
M2 × 0.4	1.60	0.0630	0.0647	69
M2.2 × 0.45	1.75	0.0689	0.0706	70
M2.5 × 0.45	2.05	0.0807	0.0826	69
M3 × 0.5	2.50	0.0984	0.1007	68
M3.5 × 0.6	2.90	0.1142	0.1168	68
M4 × 0.7	3.30	0.1299	0.1328	69
M4.5 × 0.75	3.70	0.1457	0.1489	74
M5 × 0.8	4.20	0.1654	0.1686	69
M6 × 1	5.00	0.1968	0.2006	70
M7 × 1	6.00	0.2362	0.2400	70
M8 × 1.25	6.70	0.2638	0.2679	74
M8 × 1	7.0C	0.2756	0.2797	69
M10 × 1.5	8.50	0.3346	0.3390	71
M10 × 1.25	8.70	0.3425	C.3471	73
M12 × 1.75	10.20	0.4016	0.4063	74
M12 × 1.25	10.80	0.4252	0.4299	67
M14 × 2	12.00	0.4724	0.4772	72
M14 × 1.5	12.50	0.4921	0.4969	71
M16 × 2	14.00	0.5512	0.5561	72
M16 × 1.5	14.50	0.5709	0.5758	71
M18 × 2.5	15.50	0.6102	0.6152	73
M18 × 1.5	16.50	0.6496	0.6546	70
M20 × 2.5	17.50	0.6890	0.6942	73
M20 × 1.5	18.50	0.7283	0.7335	70
M22 × 2.5	19.50	0.7677	0.7729	73
M22 × 1.5	20.50	0.8071	0.8123	70
M24 × 3	21.00	0.8268	0.8327	73
M24 × 2	22.00	0.8661	0.8720	71
M27 × 3	24.00	0.9449	0.9511	73
M27 × 2	25.00	0.9843	0.9913	70
M30 × 3.5	26.50	1.0433		
M30 × 2	28.00	1.1024		
M33 × 3.5	29.50	1.1614		
M33 × 2	31.00	1.2205		
M36 × 4	32.00	1.2598		
M36 × 3	33.00	1.2992		
M39 × 4	35.00	1.3780		
M39 × 3	36.00	1.4173		

Fig. 28-6
Tap drill sizes for the common ISO metric threads used throughout the world. If a set of metric drills is not available, use an inch equivalent that is closest to that size. The only ISO thread size used in the automobile industry in North America that is different from the original ISO series is the M6.3x1. Most other countries use either the M6x1 or the M7x1 instead of this size. Be careful when working in these diameters not to mis-match the M6x1 with the M6.3x1. They are so close in size that they will interchange.

TAP DRILLS for SPARK PLUG THREADS

DIAMETER & PITCH		DRILL SIZE
mm	mm	
10	x 1.0	9.0 mm
12	x 1.25	10.8 mm
14	x 1.25	12.8 mm
18	x 1.5	16.5 mm

Fig. 28-7
Tap drills for spark plug threads.

The tapping operation is exactly the same as with an inch size tap.

Split dies that match the taps are available in either individual sizes or as part of the screw plate set. Even though the die cuts a metric thread, the outside diameter of the die is either 1" or 1/2" so that they will fit into a standard die stock. If metric drills are not available, a customary drill that is closest to the metric size can be used. To cut a deeper thread, use a drill slightly smaller than the size shown. If a shallower thread is needed, use a drill slightly larger than the metric size.

Cutting Threads on the Engine Lathe

Cutting external and internal threads on an engine lathe with a single-point cutting tool is done primarily for repair and maintenance work. Therefore, thread cutting is a relatively infrequent lathe operation. If a machine shop is equipped with several metal cutting lathes, usually only about one in six will need to be set up for thread cutting.

The four ways of providing metric thread cutting capabilities are as follows:

(1) *Use metric transposing gears and dual reading dials.* Most manufacturers produce an accessory kit of metric transposing gears that can be used on their lathes to cut metric threads. These gears give a relationship of 1 to 2.54 between the spindle and leadscrew, which is the exact relationship between 1 inch and 2.54 centimetres. A 50-tooth gear is needed for the driving gear and a 127-tooth gear for the driven gear. These two gears called the translating gears provides the 1 to 2.54 relationship needed. This kit includes a replacement index chart showing correct gear combinations for cutting metric threads. Use of this conversion kit combined with the dual reading dial gives the lathe complete metric thread cutting capabilities. Since it is time consuming to replace gears, it is better to keep one lathe equipped for metric thread cutting only. Even with the conversion kit there are two gears that must be replaced for certain threading operations, but these are relatively easy to

install. This conversion kit limits the thread cutting capabilities to metric only. *When thread cutting, once the split or half nut on the lathe is closed, it must not be reopened until the thread is completely cut.* In other words, the motor must be reversed after each cut to return the carriage to the starting position. This procedure is necessary because the metric threads have no definite relationship to the thread chasing dial.

(2) *Use a lathe that is equipped with a quick-change gear box that will cut both metric threads and inch threads.* The lathe should also be equipped with dual reading dials on the cross feed and compound rest. In addition, the tail stock spindle is graduated both in inches and in millimetres. This type of lathe will have complete capabilities for cutting metric and inch threads. However, like the previous type, the motor must be reversed after each cut to return the carriage to the starting position.
Fig. 28-8.

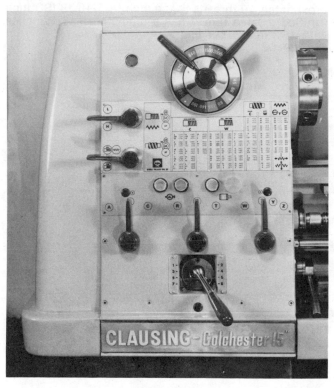

Fig. 28-8
This quick-change gear box can be adjusted to cut either customary or metric threads.

The spilt or half nut on the carriage is engaged for the first cut, but must not be released before the thread has been completed. In other words, the thread chasing dial cannot be used.

(3) *Use a lathe that has all-metric capabilities.* This machine will be completely equipped for metric machining with a lead screw and cross feed of metric design and the gearing for the quick-change gear box in metric components. The cross feed and compound rest dial are graduated in metric only. On this type of lathe there is also a thread chasing dial to use when cutting metric screw threads.
Fig. 28-9.

Fig. 28-9
This chasing dial is designed for cutting metric threads. A chasing dial allows the split or half nut to be released at the end of each cut.

The design of this thread chasing dial varies with the lathe manufacturer, but normally there are two or more gears on the vertical shaft. The vertical position of the thread chasing dial is changed as required so that the correct gear for the pitch of the thread will mesh with the lead screw. Each graduation on the dial is marked so that the operator can tell when the half nut can be engaged for the specific metric threads. *On this type of lathe the split nut can be opened at the end of each cut.*

(4) *Make a complete modification of an existing lathe.* A complete modification of an existing lathe includes a complete change of gears in the quick-change gear box, a metric lead screw, cross feed, and compound rest feed screw, and metric dials. Unless the lathe is a very current design, it is undesirable to make such a complete modification, since the cost involved will approach that of the new, all metric lathe.

Cutting Metric Threads on the Lathe
Once the gear box has been set up for cutting threads and the correct gear arrangement has been set, the procedure for cutting the threads is identical to that for the inch threads. The operator, however, must realize that in metric threads the pitch is always given as the distance from the top of one thread to the top of the next. For example, if the pitch is 1 millimetre, then there are approximately 25 threads to the inch. In the Unified thread system the pitch is given in terms of the number of threads per inch. Since the thread form is the same in both metric and inch systems, tool shape is identical in both systems.

UNIT 29
THREADED FASTENERS

The most common method of assembling metal products is with a wide variety of metal fasteners. Common metal fasteners include bolts, screws, nuts, washers, pins and rivets. Each is made in many sizes and in many kinds of metals to serve specific purposes. Generally the most common materials used are: (a) carbon steels for bolts, machine screws, carriage bolts, and other similar products that do not require great strength; (b) heat-treatable alloy steel for high strength; (c) aluminum, which weighs about one third as much as steel and can equal or even exceed the tensile strength of mild steel; (d) brass, a composition of copper and zinc, which has high resistance to corrosion; (e) stainless steel fasteners which are used for problems involving corrosion, temperature and strength. In addition to these, many other kinds of materials are used such as copper, nickel, titanium, berrilium, most of which are for special purposes. For most usages, metal fasteners made of carbon steel, alloy steel, and brass are most common.

Screw Thread Systems

A brief review of screw thread systems is useful before discussing their application to threaded fasteners. See unit on *Thread Standards*. The 60-degree V thread is the basic ISO profile. The first technical committee of ISO-TCL agreed to adopt this basic profile in 1949 from the Unified thread commonly used in North America as a basic profile for all ISO screw threads for fastener purposes. The basic thread profile is used in five accepted series, namely, *ISO metric coarse pitch, ISO metric fine pitch, ISO constant pitch, ISO inch Unified coarse pitch, and ISO inch Unified fine pitch.*

Note that even though many of the ISO metric coarse pitch threads are very close to the ISO inch Unified coarse pitch threads, *these are not interchangeable.* This is an important factor to consider in carefully identifying threaded fasteners and in keeping the two series separate. For example, an ISO M8 coarse thread has a diameter of exactly 0.315 inches and has approximately 20 threads to the inch. A 5/16 18 ISO inch (Unified) coarse thread has a diameter of .312 inches with 18 threads per inch.

Fig. 29-1a

INCH SERIES			METRIC			
Size	Dia. in.	TPI	Size	Dia. in.	Pitch (mm)	TPI (Approx.)
			M1.4	.055	0.3	85
#0	.060	80				
			M1.6	.063	0.35 (a)	74
#1	.073	64 72				
			M2	.079	0.4 (a)	64
#2	.086	56* 64				
			M2.5	.098	0.45 (a)	56
#3	.099	48 56				
#4	.112	40 48				
			M3	.118	0.5 (a)	51
#5	.125	40 44				
#6	.138	32 40	M3.5	.138	0.6 (a)	42
			M4	.157	0.7 (a)	36
#8	.164	32 36				
#10	.190	24 32				
			M5	.196	0.8 (a)	32
			M6	.236	1.0	25
1/4	.250	20 28	M6.3	.248	1.0 (a)	25
5/16	.312	18 24	M7	.275	1.0	25
			M8	.315	1.25 (a)* 1.0	20 25
3/8	.375	16 24				

INCH SERIES			METRIC			
			M10	.393	1.5 (a) 1.25	17 20
7/16	.437	14 20				
			M12	.472	1.75 (a) 1.25	14.5 20
1/2	.500	13 20				
9/16	.562	12 18	M14	.551	2 (a) 1.5	12.5 17
5/8	.625	11 18	M16	.630	2 (a) 1.5	12.5 17
			M18	.709	2.5 1.5	10 17
3/4	.750	10 16				
			M20	.787	2.5 (a) 1.5	10 17
			M22	.866	2.5 1.5	10 17
7/8	.875	9 14				
			M24	.945	3 (a) 2	8.5 12.5
1"	1.000	8 14				
			M27	1.063	3 2	8.5 12.5

* coarse series   (a) Preferred series for use in U.S.

Fig. 29-1a
There are about 2 million types of threaded fasteners produced in the United States. These threaded fasteners vary as to style of head, kind of material, thread form, length, and many other factors. Imagine a stockroom with 2 million drawers, each with a different label describing the threaded fastener stored in that drawer. The adoption of the modified or preferred ISO series that has only 25 diameters in a single pitch will greatly reduce the current impossible variety of threaded fasteners.

These two are so close in size that a nut of one will start on the bolt of the other, even though the nut will tend to strip the threads and will not hold. The ISO metric coarse pitch screw thread is the only one generally used for threaded fasteners. In England, approximately 90 percent of the threaded fasteners used are in the 12 sizes including 2, 2.5, 3, 4, 5, 6, 8, 10, 12, 16, 20 and 24 millimetres. In the United States only 25 ISO sizes are recommended. The ISO inch coarse and fine pitch series are currently used by the aerospace industry to the near exclusion of all other thread series. The ISO inch fine series is also widely used in engine manufacture, particularly in sizes of 1/2 inch and smaller. The ISO metric fine series is used only in precision instruments and, therefore, is available only on special order. The ISO metric constant pitch series is used primarily on threads cut on machine parts such as spark plugs rather than on fasteners.

Kinds of Metal Fasteners
Threaded fasteners are manufactured in a wide variety of head types.
Fig. 29-1b

HEAD STYLES

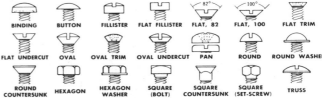

Fig. 29-1b

The most common type of threaded fastener is the bolt. A bolt is a fastening device with a head on one end and threads on the other. It joins pieces together by passing through holes in the parts and being secured with a nut. (a) A *machine bolt* is a device with a head on one end of the shank and a thread on the other. A bolt used without a nut is called a screw. Bolts are usually available with either a square or hex head, although countersunk and several other types of heads are also available. In measuring length, always measure from under the head to the end of the bolt, except for a flat head, which is indicated by the overall length. (b) *Studs* are headless threaded fasteners. (c)

Cap screws are made to an accurate finish. They are available in hexagon, round, flat, or filister heads. The heads may be slotted or recessed for a socket. The head of the socket type can be either hexagonal or fluted, both of which require special keys for turning the screws. A cap screw is a more finished product than a bolt. A cap screw is tightened by turning the head. This is in contrast to a bolt and nut which is tightened by turning the nut. (d) *Machine screws* are made with round, flat, oval, filister, binding, pan, truss, and hexagonal heads. These screws are commonly made from either brass or steel. Machine screws are used to hold parts together when one part has a tap hole and the other part has a clearance or body size hole. Square or hexagonal nuts are often available for use with these screws. (e) *Setscrews* are made with or without heads. They may have a cup, cone, or other shape point, which is designed to prevent or restrict the movement of two parts assembled. They are commonly used on a pulley to hold it firmly to a shaft. (f) Nuts of various types are used for bolts, machine screws, and studs. The most common are the hexagon and square nuts. These are made in regular and heavy. Self-locking nuts provide positive locking action under shock or vibration. The nut is fitted with a special locking pin which travels between the bolt threads. The pin acts as a ratchet, sliding along the thread as the nut is tightened but holding the nut tight and preventing any tendency to back off under vibration. A cap or acorn nut is generally used for work that requires a decorative touch or neat appearance. A wing nut is used on many types of threaded fasteners where frequent adjustment or removal is needed. (g) Washers are three basic types: the plain, the spring lock, and the mult-tooth lock. All three types are available in standard sizes to fit standard bolts and nuts. (h) Taper pins are widely used on many machine parts to hold two parts in alignment. These pins are easy to remove when necessary. The parts can be realigned to the original position when the taper pin is replaced. (i) Dowel pins are used to align two units of assembly so that they can be taken apart and put together.

Identifying Metric Threaded Fasteners

There is always a problem for the user to tell a metric nut or bolt from an inch fastener. Many are so similar in size and number of threads that it is impossible to tell by a casual glance. Several methods have been tried to help in identification. At first, fasteners were color coded to show that they were metric fasteners but this was not successful. The dying process added to the cost and changed the performance properties. In England, the hexagon bolt head has a raised imprint ISOM which indicates ISO metric dimension and threads. The strength grade is also imprinted, such as 8.8. However, this method is not practical for size M6 and smaller. On the nut, the dot represents a 12 o'clock reference point on an imaginery clock face, and the dash at 8 o'clock position means it is a grade 8 nut. **Fig. 29-4.**

Fig. 29-2
Metric bolts--on the left is a 12-spline head and on the right is a hex head.

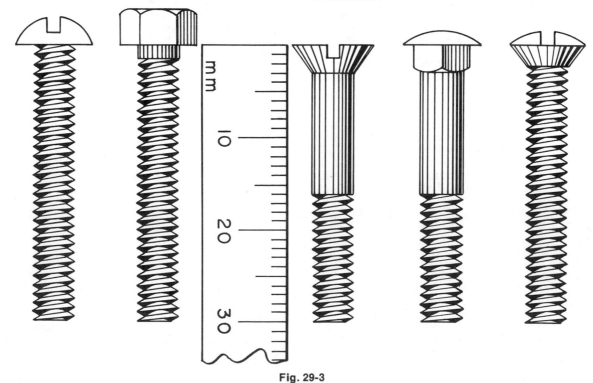

Fig. 29-3
In measuring the length of a metric bolt, note that the length is measured from under the head for all head styles except the flat head.

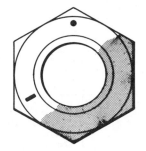

HEAD MARKING

NUT MARKING

Fig. 29-4
The head and nut markings used for metric fasteners in England.

Another British manufacturer uses a different method for identifying inch and metric cap screws. Inch cap screws have grooves running around the knurled head while metric cap screws do not.

As part of the modified or preferred ISO thread system used in the United States, two head designs are recommended. One is the typical hex head; the other is a 12-element spline head, that is an entirely different design. **Fig. 29-5.**

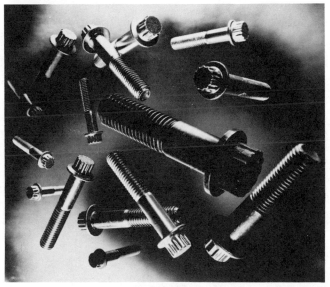

Fig. 29-5
Twelve spline flange fasteners. Only eight sizes will be produced, including 5, 6.3, 8, 10, 13, 14, 16 and 20 mm.

The 12-element spline head is of such a distinct design and shape that even a blind person could tell it is a metric fastener. The advantage of this design is, of course, its uniqueness, good performance and maximum amount of material in the head. This design

is particularly suitable where there might be confusion between the ISO metric hex head and the ISO inch hex head. For repair work a conventional 12 point or socket or box wrench can be used on this fastener head. However, for mass production assembly, more closely fitted wrenches are needed.

For flat, oval and pan head screws in addition to the slotted, two types of cross recesses are standard, namely Phillips recess and Pozidriv. **Fig. 29-6.**

DRIVING RECESSES

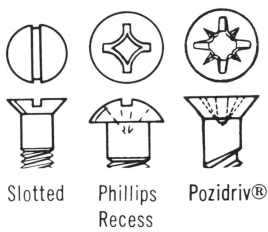

Slotted   Phillips Recess   Pozidriv®

Fig. 29-6
If the Phillips recess is retained for inch fasteners and the Pozidriv is used only for metric fasteners, there would be no chance for a mismatch.

The Phillips type recess has been commonly used in the United States for inch series fasteners. Most European countries used the Pozidriv type almost exclusively. As the U.S. "goes metric" the use of the Pozidriv recess on metric fasteners would be an excellent way of visually identifying them. Also the Pozidriv has many advantages over the Phillips particularly for mass production.

Strength Grade or Property Class
ISO has developed a system of identifying strength grades of the materials used in metal fasteners. The symbols consist of two digits such as 9.8. The first figure represents approximately 1/100 of the minimum tensile strength value in newton per square millimetre (N/mm^2). The second figure is approximately 1/10 of the ratio expressed as a percentage between minimum yield stress and the minimum tensile strength. In England the ISO grade 8.8 is commonly used. It is very close to the SAE grade 5 fastener which is the basic product of the fastener industry in the inch system. Broad definitions of steels used in metal fasteners by North American industries are shown in **Fig. 29-7.**

Bolt & Screw Property Class	Material Description	General Application
4.6	Low or medium carbon steels, hot rolled rod or bar	Long lengths (over 150 mm)— all products
4.8	Low carbon steels, partially or fully annealed	Recessed hex, hex flange, internal recesses
5.8	Low or medium carbon steels, cold worked by drawing or rolling	Hex screws up to 24 mm x 150 mm
9.8	Medium carbon steel, quenched and tempered	All product where max strength for expenditure is desired
10.9	Medium carbon alloy steel, quenched and tempered	All product where space-weight is important
12.8	Low carbon martensitic steel, quenched and tempered, usually containing .0005% boron	All products to 24 mm x 150 mm
12.9	Alloy steels, quenched and tempered	Socket screws; product requiring very high strength to space ratio

Fig. 29-7
Definitions of steel in use in North American industry.

Sizes and Lengths

For general assembly purposes, only ISO metric coarse threads are available. Distributors will not stock ISO metric fine series. A wide range of diameters and lengths of each kind of metric fastener will not be available. However, there are preferred metric sizes and lengths for each type of fastener.

Fig. 29-8 shows an example of the recommended sizes of metric fasteners in a common steel grade.

```
        Hexagon Head BOLTS

Nominal Length   Nominal Diameter
    mm        M5   M6   M8   M10  M12  M16  M20  M24
    25         1
    30         1    1
    35         1    1    1
    40         1    1    1    1
    45              1    1    1
    50              1    1    1    1
    55              1    1    1    1
    60              1    1    1    1    1
    65                   2    2    2    2    2
    70         2    1    1    1    1    1
    80         2    2    1    1    1    1    1
    90         2    2    2    1    2    1    1
   100                   2    1    1    1    1
```

Fig. 29-8
These are the common lengths of hexagon head bolts in the most popular metal: 1 indicates first choice; 2 second choice. Most metric fasteners in the United States will be available in increments of 5 mm up to 100 mm and in 10 mm increments above 100 mm.

Tapping Screws

Tapping screws of American design and manufacture are so common throughout the world that they may be considered international standards even though not recognized by ISO. There are four basic types of tapping screws, namely, *thread forming, thread cutting, thread rolling* and *self drilling*. **Fig. 29-9.**

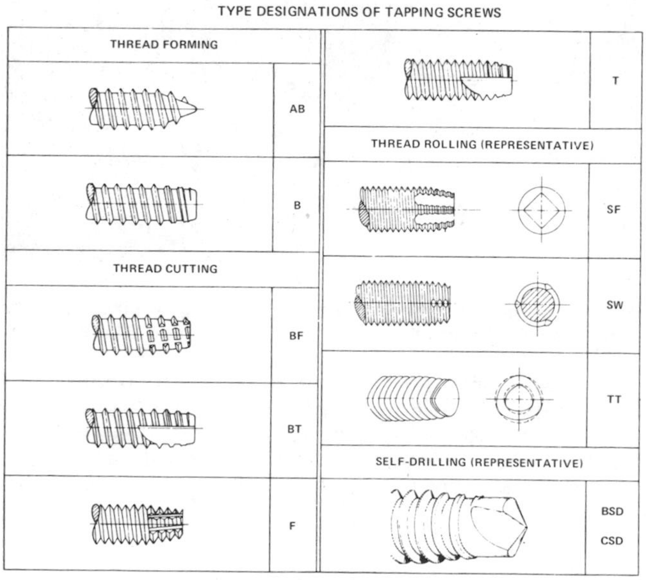

TYPE DESIGNATIONS OF TAPPING SCREWS

Fig. 29-9
Basic types of tapping screws.

The *thread forming screws,* when installed or driven in pre-formed holes, form a mating internal thread through displacement of material adjacent to the hole. *Thread cutting screws* have a cutting edge and will chip cavities at their points so that when installed in pre-formed holes the screws cut a mating internal thread. *Thread rolling screws* have performance capabilities exceeding those of other types of self-tapping screws. *Self drilling screws* have a special point design which permits the screws to drill their own holes through materials to be joined. Because there have been so many sizes and styles of tapping screws, an effort has been made to reduce the number in the diameter and thread pitch series. Because these are soft conversions from the inch to metric system, the metric sizes are not even modules. For example, a diameter of 6.3 mm is actually 1/4 inch.

Metric Fasteners

For complete information on metric fasteners, the Industrial Fasteners Institute, 1515 East Ohio Bldg., Cleveland, Ohio, has available a book METRIC FASTENER STANDARDS.

UNIT 30
WRENCHES

All types of fixed wrenches are available in metric modules to fit metric fasteners.
Fig. 30-1.

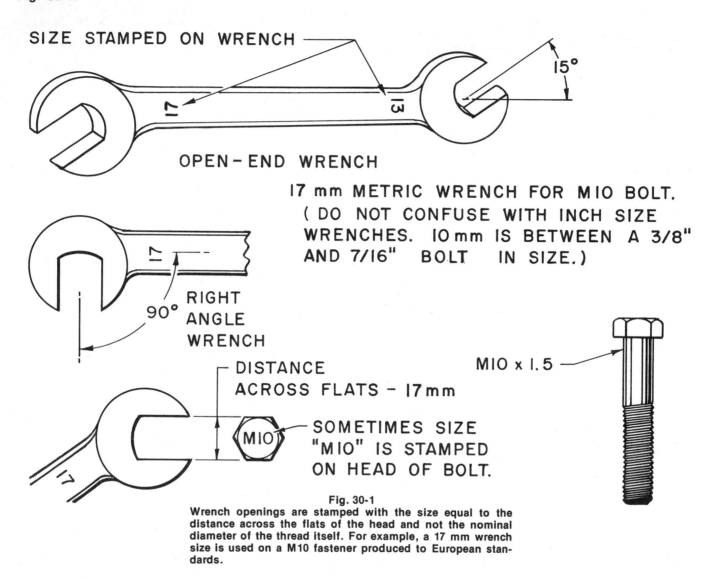

SIZE STAMPED ON WRENCH

15°

OPEN-END WRENCH

17 mm METRIC WRENCH FOR M10 BOLT. (DO NOT CONFUSE WITH INCH SIZE WRENCHES. 10 mm IS BETWEEN A 3/8" AND 7/16" BOLT IN SIZE.)

90° RIGHT ANGLE WRENCH

DISTANCE ACROSS FLATS - 17 mm

M10

SOMETIMES SIZE "M10" IS STAMPED ON HEAD OF BOLT.

M10 x 1.5

Fig. 30-1
Wrench openings are stamped with the size equal to the distance across the flats of the head and not the nominal diameter of the thread itself. For example, a 17 mm wrench size is used on a M10 fastener produced to European standards.

Inch size wrenches should not be used on most metric fasteners. The reason for this is that the distance across the flats of the heads is significantly different *even though the diameter of the thread itself may be almost identical.* For example, the shank diameter of an M6 is 0.236" while the shank diameter of a 1/4" bolt is 0.250" for a difference of 0.014" (14 thousandths). However, the maximum distance across the flats of the hexagon head of an M6 is 10 millimetres equivalent to 0.394" while the same distance for a 1/4" bolt is 0.446" for a difference of 0.052" (52 thousandths) or almost four times as great as the difference in shank diameters. Generally speaking, there is little or no interchangeability in wrenches in sizes M14 (about equivalent to the 9/16") and smaller.
Fig. 30-2a,b.
However, in hexagon metric sizes from M16 and larger, the distance across the flats is close enough to comparable size inch fasteners to allow for an in-

terchange of wrenches. Also in the larger sizes, the allowance between the bolt or screw head and the jaws of the wrench is larger. However, the best practice is to have two complete and separate sets of wrenches, one for metric and another for inch fasteners. *These should be kept in separate compartments and color coded.*

The preferred or modified ISO fasteners used in the U.S. (formerly OMFS) are available in two head styles, namely the hex head and the 12 spline head.
Fig. 30-3.
The head sizes of some of the U.S. hex and 12 spline fasteners are a different size than the head of the European ISO metric fasteners. Therefore, three different wrench sizes are needed for the same diameter fasteners: one size for the European ISO metric hex head, another size for the U.S. ISO metric hex head, and still another size for the 12 spline flange head.
Fig. 30-4.

Diameter mm	ISO METRIC		Dia in	ISO INCH (UNIFIED)	
	Max mm	Min mm		Max in	Min in
M6 (0.2362)*	10.0 (0.3937)	9.78 (0.3850)	1/4 (0.250)	0.446	0.440
M8 (0.3149)	13.0 (0.5118)	12.73 (0.5010)	5/16 (0.3125)	0.510	0.504
M10 (0.3937)	17.0 (0.6692)	16.73 (0.6580)	3/8 (0.375)	0.573	0.566
M12 (0.4724)	19.0 (0.7480)	18.67 (0.7350)	7/16 (0.4375) 1/2 (0.500)	0.636 0.763	0.629 0.755
M14 (0.5512)	22.0 (0.8861)	21.67 (0.8530)	9/16 (0.5625)	0.828	0.818
M16 (0.6299)	24.0 (0.9448)	23.67 (0.9310)	5/8 (0.625)	0.953	0.944
M20 (0.7874)	30.0 (1.1811)	29.67 (1.1680)	3/4 (0.75)	1.142	1.132
M22 (0.8661)	32.0 (1.2598)	31.61 (1.2440)	7/8 (0.875)	1.331	1.320
M24 (0.9448)	36.0 (1.4173)	35.38 (1.3930)	1 (1.000)	1.520	1.508

*Inch equivalents in decimals

Fig. 30-2a

A comparison of head size based on European standards. While most hex head sizes are the same in both Europe and the United States, there is a difference in three sizes, namely, M10, M12, and M14. See Fig. 30-2b. European standards groups are considering reducing the width across the flats of M10 to 16 mm, of M12 to 18 mm and of M14 to 21 mm. The United States will continue to manufacture the heads in the smaller dimensions because of the great savings in materials. The head sizes in no way interfere with the interchangeability of the fasteners. Regardless of head size any M10 fastener can be used with an M10 tapped hole or bolt.

NOMINAL SIZE mm	WIDTH ACROSS FLATS mm	HEIGHT OF HEAD mm	NOMINAL SIZE mm	WIDTH ACROSS FLATS mm	HEIGHT OF HEAD mm
2.5	5.0	1.7	24	36	15.0
3	5.5	2.0	30	46	18.7
3.5	6.3	2.4	36	55	22.5
4	7.0	2.8	42	65	26.0
5	8.0	3.5	48	75	30.0
6.3	10.0	4.3	56	85	35.0
8	13.0	5.3	64	95	40.0
10	15.0	6.4	72	105	45.0
12	13.0	7.5	80	115	50.0
14	21.0	8.8	90	130	56.0
16	24.0	10.0	100	145	62.0
20	30.0	12.5			

Fig. 30-2b
Basic head dimensions for hex heads on the ISO series used in the United States.

Dia and Wrench size	Maximum Head size	Wrench Opening
5	5.86	6.00
6.3	7.38	8.00
8	9.37	10.00
10	11.70	12.00
12	14.04	15.00
14	16.29	17.00
16	18.71	19.00
20	23.40	24.00

Fig. 30-3
Common sizes of 12-spline fasteners including the wrench opening.

WRENCH SIZES
for 10 millimetre nominal size bolt

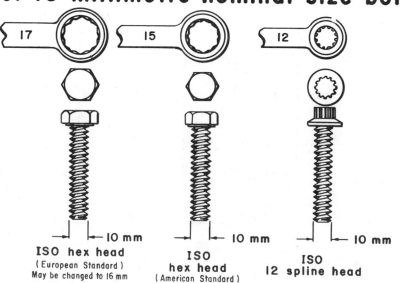

17

15

12

ISO hex head
(European Standard)
May be changed to 16 mm

10 mm

ISO hex head
(American Standard)

10 mm

ISO 12 spline head

10 mm

Fig. 30-4
Three different sizes of wrenches are needed for the same M10 fastener.

Kinds of Metric Wrenches

1. *Open end wrenches* are made to fit standard square and hex head bolts and nuts. A single head open end wrench has an opening on one end only. A double open end wrench has an opening on each end for two different distances across the openings. The head opening is usually made at an angle of 15°, 22-1/2° or 90° to the body so that the nut and bolt can be tightened where the space is limited.

2. *Box wrenches.* Box wrenches have completely enclosed ends with 12 points so that the wrench will fit over the bolt head or nut in almost any position. With box wrenches there is less danger of slippage, and they can be used in places difficult to see and reach with other wrenches. The modern box wrench has 12 points or notches around the circle which fits over the bolt head or nut.

3. *Box and open end wrenches.* This is a combination type. One end is an open end wrench at an angle of 15° and the other is a 12 point box wrench.

4. *Socket wrenches and socket sets.* Metric sockets are made with 12 points or notches around the circle which fit over the bolt head or nut. These come in millimetre openings from 6 to 36. Even though the socket opening is made to metric modules, the drives are specified in inches. The most common are 1/4, 3/8, 1/2, 3/4 and 1 inch. Several types of wrench handles fit the metric sockets. The simplest types are the T and L sockets. There are also several kinds of ratchet handles and extensions. The same handles used on the inch based socket wrench can be used on the metric sockets. The complete set of sockets and wrenches comes ranging from as few as 13 sockets to as many as 30 or more.

5. *Hex key wrenches.* L shaped hex key wrenches are used when assembling with socket head cap screws, socket set screws or socket head countersunk screws that have a socket head. The hex keys are identified by the distance across the flat, and come in common sizes from 1.27 through 19 mm. For most sizes of metric set screws, the wrench to use will have a distance across the flat of one half the diameter of the set screw. For example, if the set screw is an M8, then the hex key should be a 4 mm. However, for socket head cap screws or socket head countersunk screws, a larger size hex wrench is needed. For example, for an M8 fastener a 6 mm hex key is needed. **Fig. 30-5.**

ISO Metric Size	Socket Set Screw	Socket Head Cap Set Screw	Socket Head Countersunk Screw
M3	1.5	2.5	2.0
M4	2.0	3.0	2.5
M5	2.5	4.0	3.0
M6	3.0	5.0	4.0
M8	4.0	6.0	5.0
M10	5.0	8.0	6.0
M12	6.0	10.0	8.0
M14	6.0	12.0	10.0
M16	8.0	14.0	10.0
M18	10.0	14.0	---
M20	10.0	17.0	---
M22	12.0	17.0	---
M24	12.0	19.0	---

Fig. 30-5
The correct size of hex key wrenches to use with various kinds of socket fasteners.

Metric Torque Limiting Wrench Handles

Torque is the product of the force applied times the length of the lever arm. **Fig. 30-6.**

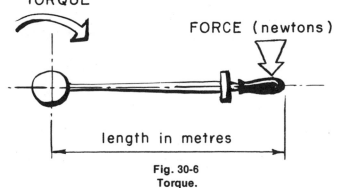

Fig. 30-6
Torque.

In other words, when a force is applied in such a way as to cause a rotational tendency about a point, torque is produced. Because force is measured in newtons (N) and length in metres (m), torque is expressed in newton-metres (N·m). A most common application of torque can be illustrated when a wrench is used to tighten a bolt or nut on a piece of machinery. For example, the torque for tightening a spark plug should be about 40 newton-metres.

In the customary system, torque limiting wrench handles are usually expressed in foot pound values. In the older metric system, torque wrench values were listed in *mass* units of either *centimetre kilograms* or *metre kilograms.* However, in the SI system, torque or moment of force is given in *force* units of newton metres (N·m). Customary torque limiting wrenches can be recalibrated by multiplying the foot pound measurement shown on the wrenches by 1.359 to obtain the N·m equivalent. For example, if the customary torque limiting wrench has a range of from 5 to 100 foot pounds, the range in metric will be 7 to 136 N·m. To convert metre kilogram values to newton metre values multiply by 9.8.
Fig. 30-7.

FROM ft lb TO N·m

ft lb	0 N·m	1 N·m	2 N·m	3 N·m	4 N·m	5 N·m	6 N·m	7 N·m	8 N·m	9 N·m
0	0	1.356	2.712	4.068	5.424	6.780	8.136	9.492	10.848	12.204
10	13.56	14.916	16.272	17.628	18.984	20.340	21.696	23.052	24.408	25.764
20	27.12	28.476	29.832	31.188	32.544	33.900	35.256	36.612	37.968	39.324
30	40.68	42.036	43.392	44.748	46.104	47.460	48.816	50.172	51.528	52.884
40	54.24	55.596	56.952	58.308	59.664	61.020	62.376	63.732	65.088	66.444
50	67.80	69.156	70.512	71.868	73.224	74.580	75.936	77.292	78.648	80.004
60	81.36	82.716	84.072	85.428	86.784	88.140	89.496	90.852	92.208	93.564
70	94.92	96.276	97.632	98.988	100.34	101.70	103.06	104.41	105.77	107.12
80	108.48	109.84	111.19	112.55	113.90	115.26	116.62	117.97	119.33	120.68
90	122.04	123.40	124.75	126.11	127.46	128.82	130.18	131.53	132.89	134.24
100	135.60	136.96	138.31	139.67	141.02	142.38	143.74	145.09	146.45	147.80

ft lb x 1.356 = N·m

FROM m kg TO N·m

m kg	0 N·m	1 N·m	2 N·m	3 N·m	4 N·m	5 N·m	6 N·m	7 N·m	8 N·m	9 N·m
0	0	9.807	19.614	29.421	39.228	49.035	58.842	68.649	78.456	88.263
10	98.07	107.88	117.68	127.49	137.30	147.11	156.91	166.72	176.53	186.33
20	196.14	205.95	215.75	225.56	235.37	245.18	254.98	264.79	274.60	284.40
30	294.21	304.02	313.82	323.63	333.44	343.25	353.05	362.86	372.67	382.47
40	392.28	402.09	411.89	421.70	431.51	441.32	451.12	460.93	470.74	480.54
50	490.35	500.16	509.96	519.77	529.58	539.39	549.19	559.00	568.81	578.61
60	588.42	598.23	608.03	617.84	627.65	637.46	647.26	657.07	666.88	676.68
70	686.49	696.30	706.10	715.91	725.72	735.53	745.33	755.14	764.95	774.75
80	784.56	794.37	804.17	813.98	823.79	833.60	843.40	853.21	863.02	872.82
90	882.63	892.44	902.24	912.05	921.86	931.67	941.47	951.28	961.09	970.89
100	980.7	990.51	1000.3	1010.1	1019.9	1029.7	1039.5	1049.3	1059.2	1069.0

m kg x 9.807 = N·m

Fig. 30-7
Conversion chart for metric torque limiting wrench handles.

UNIT 31
OTHER METALWORKING AREAS

Any metalworking area involving measurements and/or standards will be affected by conversion to the metric system. **Fig. 31-1a,b.**

The majority of changes will be in the machine shop area, but other areas will also be affected.

Metric Units

In all metalworking areas the following metric units will be in common use: (1) millimetre for thickness and width and millimetre or metre for length measurements; (2) kilogram for basic weight (mass) -- the metric ton (tonne) may be used for the sale of bulk products; (3) heat will be given in degrees Celsius (°C); (4) stress will be given in multiples of the pascal, principally in megapascals (MPa) and gigapascals (GPa).

Metric Metal Size Standards

Metal stock items such as sheets, strips, bars, wire and all other standard items are available in a wide variety of sizes in the customary system. Standards of sizes of metals in the customary system vary with the kind of material as well as the metal in it. For example, there is a different standard for aluminum than for steel.

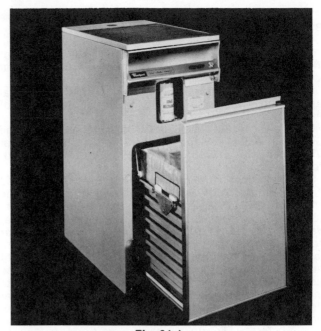

Fig. 31-1a
All types of metal products will eventually be manufactured with materials made to metric standards.

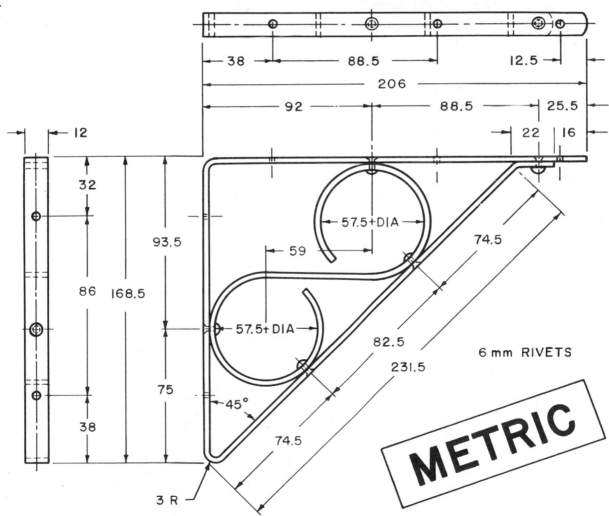

Fig. 31-1b
A typical bench metal product made of metal that measures 3 x 12 mm.

31-1

When the American National Standards Committee (B32) for materials developed the metric standard, they followed several basic ideas.

1. The terms flat and round were used instead of such previously used terms as sheet, strip, plate and bar.

2. The standards are suitable for all kinds of metal rather than a separate one for each different kind of material.

3. The preferred sizes selected were based on the ISO R388, Basic Thicknesses of Sheet and Diameter of Wire and ISO R1035, Dimensions of Hot Rolled, Round, Square and Flat Sheet Stock.

The result was the development of two approved standards, both of which are available from the American National Standards Institute. These are B32.3-1974, *Metric Thicknesses and Widths for Flat Metal Products* and B32.4-1974, *Metric Sizes for Round, Square, and Hexagon Metal Products.* Standard B32.3 includes standards for two classes of metals, namely flat and rectangle. The flats are those furnished in large widths and lengths such as sheets and plates, which are normally cut up into smaller pieces for fabrication. The rectangles are those products furnished in rectangular cross section. These products are normally cut to length for mill runs to make parts. The same thicknesses were adapted for the large flat products as for the rectangles. For the rectangles a separate set of preferred widths were developed. Standards for flat metal products include a list of preferred thicknesses and second preferred thicknesses and widths as shown in **Fig. 31-2l**. In the

FLAT METAL PRODUCTS PREFERRED THICKNESSES (MILLIMETRES)

0.050	0.50	4.0	25
0.060	0.60	4.5	30
0.080	0.80	5.0	35
0.10	1.0	6.0	40
0.12	1.2	7.0	50
0.16	1.6	8.0	60
0.20	2.0	10	80
0.25	2.5	12	100
0.30	3.0	16	120
0.40	3.5	20	140

FLAT METAL PRODUCTS SECOND-PREFERENCE THICKNESSES (MILLIMETRES)

0.14	0.90	4.8	38
0.18	1.1	5.5	45
0.22	1.4	9.0	55
0.28	1.8	11	70
0.35	2.2	14	90
0.45	2.8	18	110
0.55	3.2	22	130
0.65	3.8	28	150
0.70	4.2	32	

WIDTHS FOR FLAT METAL PRODUCTS (MILLIMETRES)

Preferred Width	2nd Preference	Preferred Width	2nd Preference
10			90
12		100	
16			110
20		120	
25		140	
30			150
35		160	
40		180	
	45	200	
50			250
60			300
80			

Fig. 31-2a
These typical metric sizes for flat metal products.

Thickness		Width	
inch	mm*	inch	mm*
1/16	1.6	3/8	10
1/8	3	1/2	12
3/16	5	5/8	16
1/4	6	3/4	20
5/16	8	1	25
3/8	10	1-1/4	30
7/16	11	1-1/2	40
1/2	12	1-3/4	45
9/16	14	2	50
5/8	16		
11/16	18		
3/4	20		
7/8	22		
1	25		
1-1/8	28		
1-1/4	30		
1-5/16	32		
1-3/8	35		
1-1/2	40		
1-3/4	45		
2	50		

*Replacement sizes based upon ANSI B32.3-1974

Fig. 31-2b
Comparison of the old customary sizes with the preferred metric sizes.

customary system there are about thirty different kinds of gages used in checking the thickness of sheet stock. For example, a number 20 gage in the *Manufacturer's Standard* Gage (which is recommended for use for carbon steel and alloy sheet steel) has a decimal thickness of 0.0359. The same number 20 in *U.S. Standard* gage established by Congress in 1893 for measuring a sheet and plate of iron and steel has a decimal thickness of 0.348. The same number 20 gage in *American Standard Wire*, or *Brown and Sharpe* gage used for measuring thickness of nonferrous sheet stock has a decimal thickness of 0.0320. **Fig. 31-3.**

Gage Number	Manufacturer's Standard Gage for Sheet Metal	U.S. STandard Gage for Iron and Steel Sheet	American Standard Wire Gage or Brown & Sharpe Gage	ISO/R388		Suggested Rounded Modules
	in	in	in	in	mm	
10	.1345	.1350	.1019	.0984	2.500	2.5
11	.1196	.1205	.0907	.0882	2.240	2.2
12	.1046	.1055	.0808	.0787	2.000	2.0
13	.0897	.0915	.0720	.0709	1.800	1.8
14	.0747	.0800	.0641	.0630	1.600	1.6
15	.0673	.0720	.0571	.0552	1.400	1.4
16	.0598	.0625	.0508	.0492	1.250	1.2
17	.0538	.0540	.0453	.0441	1.120	1.1
18	.0478	.0475	.0403	.0394	1.000	1.0
19	.0418	.0410	.0359	.0354	0.900	0.90
20	.0359	.0348	.0320	.0315	0.800	0.80
21	.0329	.0317	.0285	.0280	0.710	0.70
22	.0299	.0286	.0253	.0248	0.630	0.60
23	.0269	.0258	.0226	.0221	0.560	0.55
24	.0239	.0230	.0201	.0197	0.500	0.50
25	.0209	.0204	.0179	.0177	0.450	0.45
26	.0179	.0181	.0159	.0158	0.400	0.40

Fig. 31-3

A comparison of three common gage thicknesses with the recommendations of ISO R/388 in inches and millimetres.

This wide range of gage systems caused endless confusion. Therefore, with the metric standards, all gage designations are eliminated and thicknesses or diameters are given in millimetres. **Fig. 31-4** shows how the more common gage sizes of nonferrous and ferrous metals will be given in the preferred millimetre thicknesses.

SHEET METAL THICKNESS

GAGE	NON-FERROUS		FERROUS	
	inch	mm*	inch	mm*
16	.050	1.20	.0598	1.60
18	.040[a]	1.00	.0478	1.20
20	.032[b]	0.80	.0359	0.090
22	.025[c]	0.65	.0299	0.80
24	.020[d]	0.50	.0239	0.65
26	.015	0.40	.0179	0.45
28	.012	0.30	.0149	0.40
30	.010	0.25	.0120	0.35
32	.007	0.18	.0097	0.22

[a]32-ounce [b]24-ounce [c]20-ounce [d]16-ounce
*Replacement sizes based upon ANSI B32.3-1974

Fig. 31-4

A comparison of the old customary gages with the inch and preferred millimetre thickness.

The American National Standard B32.4 gives metric standards for round products including wire, bar and rod. This standard includes the first and second choice series and diameters from 0.020 up to 320 millimetres. These standards will replace any gage sizes used in the customary system. **Fig. 31-5.**

ROUND METAL PRODUCTS PREFERRED DIAMETERS (MILLIMETRES)

0.020	0.30	5.0	40
0.025	0.40	6.0	45
0.030	0.50	8.0	50
0.040	0.60	10	60
0.050	0.80	12	80
0.060	1.0	14	100
0.080	1.2	16	120
0.10	1.6	18	140
0.12	2.0	20	160
0.16	2.5	22	180
0.20	3.0	25	200
0.25	4.0	30	250
		35	300

ROUND METAL PRODUCTS SECOND-PREFERENCE DIAMETERS (MILLIMETRES)

0.022	0.45	7.0	42
0.028	0.55	9.0	48
0.035	0.65	11	55
0.045	0.70	13	65
0.055	0.90	15	70
0.065	1.1	17	75
0.070	1.4	19	90
0.090	1.8	21	110
0.11	2.2	23	130
0.14	2.8	24	150
0.18	3.5	26	170
0.22	4.5	28	190
0.28	5.5	32	220
0.35	6.5	38	280
			320

Fig. 31-5
Diameters of round metal products.

The preferred sizes for squares and hexagons were selected from the series established for round products. There are twenty-one preferred sizes and hexagons from 3 to 300 millimetres and thirteen second preference sizes. **Fig. 31-6a-b-c.**

SQUARE & HEXAGON METAL PRODUCTS (MILLIMETRES)

Preferred Sizes	2nd Preferred Sizes	Preferred Sizes	2nd Preferred Sizes
3.0			45
4.0		50	
5.0			55
6.0		60	
8.0			70
10		80	
12			90
	14	100	
16			110
	18	120	
20			140
	22	160	
25			180
	28	200	
30			220
	35	250	
40		300	

Fig. 31-6a
Dimensions of square and hexagon metal products.

ROUND, SQUARE AND HEXAGON BARS SIZES

inch	mm*
1/8	3
1/4	6
3/8	10
1/2	12
5/8	16
3/4	20
1	25
1-1/4	30
1-1/2	40
1-3/4	45
2	50

*Replacement sizes based upon ANSI B32.4-1974

Fig. 31-6b
A comparison of customary sizes and metric bars sizes.

Steel pipe. The nominal size, outside diameter and inside diameter of steel pipe is specified in ISO R/65 (medium series). **Fig. 31-7**

STEEL STANDARD METRIC SIZES
(In selected increments)

Wire

Alloy Steel Wire	1.6 mm through 25 mm
Manufacturers Carbon Steel Coarse Wire	1.6 mm through 25 mm
Carbon Steel Special Purpose	1.6 mm through 25 mm

Plate

Carbon and High Strength Low Alloy	5 mm through 160 mm
Alloy Steel Plate	5 mm through 160 mm

Hot Rolled Steel Bars

Carbon Merchant Quality - Hexagons	40 mm through 70 mm
Carbon Merchant Quality - Rounds	13 mm through 75 mm
Carbon Merchant Quality - Squares & Round Cornered Squares	14 mm through 70 mm
Carbon Special Quality and High Strength Low Alloy Squares & Round Cornered Squares	14 mm through 140 mm
Carbon Special Quality and High Strength Low Alloy Hexagons	40 mm through 80 mm
Carbon Special Quality and High Strength Low Alloy Rounds	13 mm through 240 mm
Alloy Steel Bars - Squares & Round Cornered Squares	14 mm through 140 mm
Alloy Steel Bars - Hexagons	40 mm through 80 mm
Alloy Steel Bars - Rounds	13 mm through 240 mm

Hot Rolled Wire Rods

Carbon Steel Rods	5.5 mm through 12 mm
Alloy Steel Rods	5.5 mm through 12 mm

Steel Sheet Carbon and High Strength Low Alloy

Hot Rolled (10.0 mm through 7.0 mm not available in HSLA)	1.6 mm through 10.0 mm
Cold Rolled 3.2 mm through 2.0 mm and 0.45 mm through 0.40 mm not available in HSLA)	0.40 mm through 3.2mm
Galvanized (4.0 mm through 2.5 mm and 0.70 mm through 0.40 mm not available in HSLA)	0.40 mm through 4.0 mm
Long Terne (not available in HSLA)	0.35 mm through 1.6 mm
Aluminum Coated (not available in HSLA)	0.50 mm through 1.8 mm

Fig. 31-6c
Typical list of steel standard metric sizes produced by one company.

Nominal size		Outside diameter			Inside diameter			
USA[1]	ISO[2]	USA[1]		ISO[2]	USA[1]		ISO[2]	R10[3]
inch	mm	inch	mm	mm	inch	mm	mm	mm
1/8	6	0.405	10.2	10.2	0.269	6.8	6.2	6.5
1/4	8	.540	13.7	13.6	.364	9.2	8.9	8.0
								10.0
3/8	10	.675	17.1	17.1	.493	12.5	12.4	12.5
1/2	15	.840	21.3	21.4	.622	15.8	16.1	16.0
3/4	20	1.050	26.7	26.9	.824	20.9	21.6	20.0
1	25	1.315	33.4	33.8	1.049	26.6	27.3	25.0
1 1/4	32	1.660	42.2	42.4	1.380	35.1	35.9	31.5
1 1/2	40	1.900	48.3	48.4	1.610	40.9	41.9	40.0
2	50	2.375	60.3	60.2	2.067	52.5	52.9	50.0
2 1/2	65	2.875	73.0	76.0	2.469	62.7	68.7	63.0
3	80	3.500	88.9	88.8	3.068	77.9	80.7	80.0
3 1/2	90	4.000	101.6	101.2	3.548	90.1	93.1	
4	100	4.500	114.3	114.0	4.026	102.3	105.0	100.0
5	125	5.563	141.3	139.6	5.047	128.2	129.9	125.0
6	150	6.625	168.3	165.2	6.065	154.1	155.5	160.0
8	200	8.625	219.1	(4)	7.981	202.7		200.0
10	250	10.750	273.0	(4)	9.970	253.2		250.0
12	300	12.750	323.9	(4)	12.000	304.8		315.0

[1] ASTM A53–68, standard pipe.
[2] ISO Recommendation R65, Medium series.
[3] R10 Series of preferred number (See table 5).
[4] USA dimensions are used.

Fig. 31-7
Diameters of standard steel pipe.

While the dimensions for outside or inside diameter are not based on preferred numbers, the inside diameters approximate the R10 series of preferred number.

Rivets. Rivets are available in metric sizes even though the most commonly used sizes are in the customary system. For example, the most popular size is 1/8" which can be given a soft conversion size of 3.175 mm or rounded to 3 mm. In addition to the fractional sizes, manufacturers produce 3, 5 and 6 mm rivets. The 5/32" rivet can be used in place of a 4 mm size. Clearance holes are not a problem since available customary sizes come within a few thousandths of the metric size, and this is accurate enough for riveting.
Fig. 31-8a,b.

Rivets

Nominal length (mm)	Nominal diameter (mm)																
	3	4	5	6	8	10	12	14	16	18	20	22	24	27	30	33	36
8	X	X															
10	X	X	X	X													
12	X	X	X	X	X	X											
14	X	X	X	X	X	X											
16	X	X	X	X	X	X	X										
20	X	X	X	X	X	X	X										
25		X	X	X	X	X	X	X	X	X	X						
30		X	X	X	X	X	X	X	X	X	X						
35			X	X	X	X	X	X	X	X	X						
40		X		X	X	X	X	X	X	X	X						
45				X	X	X	X	X	X	X	X	X					
50				X	X	X	X	X	X	X	X	X					
55					X	X	X	X	X	X	X	X					
60				X	X	X	X	X	X	X	X	X					
65					X	X	X	X	X	X	X	X					
70						X	X	X	X	X	X	X	X	X			
75						X	X	X	X	X	X	X	X	X			
80						X	X	X	X	X	X	X	X	X	X		
85							X	X	X	X	X	X	X	X	X		
90							X	X	X	X	X	X	X	X	X	X	
100							X	X	X	X	X	X	X	X	X	X	
110							X	X	X	X	X	X	X	X	X	X	X
120							X	X	X	X	X	X	X	X	X	X	X
130									X	X	X	X	X	X	X	X	X
140										X	X	X	X	X	X	X	X
150								X	X	X	X	X	X	X	X	X	X

Fig. 31-8a
Diameters and lengths for black iron rivets.

Table of Common
Rivet Sizes

Shank Diameters	
Customary Inch	Nearest ISO Metric Equivalent (mm)
—	1
—	1.2
1/16	1.6
6 oz. (0.081")	2
8 oz. (0.091")	—
10 oz. (0.097")	2.5
12 oz. (0.107")	—
14 oz. (0.111")	—
1/8	3
5/32	4
3/16	5
1/4	6
5/16	8
3/8	10

Fig. 31-8b
Comparison of diameters of sheet metal rivets in customary and metric sizes.

Sheet metal equipment. All sheet metal equipment (such as the bar folder, squaring shears, notcher, cornice brake, and box and pan brake) that are equipped with a gage or scale for indicating length will require a metric gage to supplement or replace the customary gage. **Fig. 31-9.**

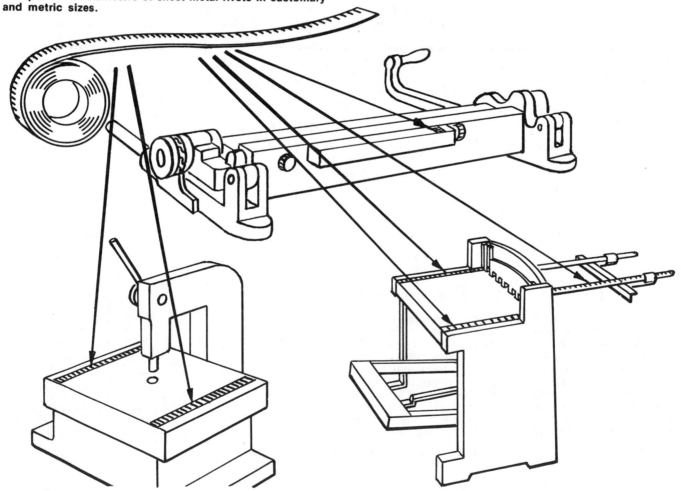

Fig. 31-9
Only rulers (scales) need to be replaced on sheet metal equipment.

As a temporary measure, plastic metric tape can be attached next to or over the customary gage. Metal gages are available to replace customary gages. All sheet metal products will give dimensions in full or rounded millimetres. **Fig. 31-10.**

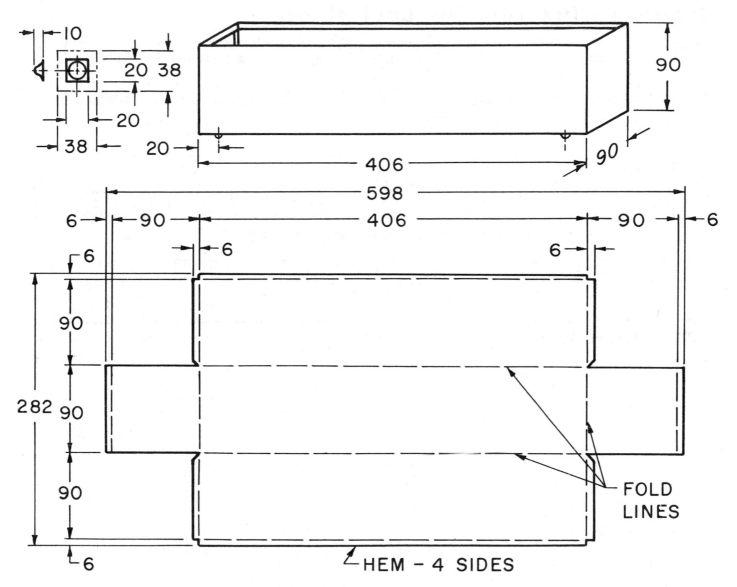

Fig. 31-10
Typical sheet metal product designed in rounded metric dimensions.

Foundry. Major changes in foundry will include the following: (1) Weight (mass) of materials will be given in kilograms. (2) Foundry heats will be given in degrees Celsius. (3) Metric shrink rules will be used for foundry patterns. The customary shrink rule has each inch slightly longer than the standard inch. For example, if the pattern is to be cast in aluminum, the shrink rule is 1/4" longer per foot. For brass it is 3/16" longer per foot. In the metric system, shrink rules will be based on slightly longer units on a proportionate basis. For example, the shrink rule for aluminum will be about 2 percent longer than the standard metric unit, and for brass it will be 1 1/2 percent longer. **Fig. 31-11.**

(4) Dimensions on all pattern drawings will be given in millimetres. **Fig. 31-12.**

(Equal to 6 mm over a 300 mm length.)

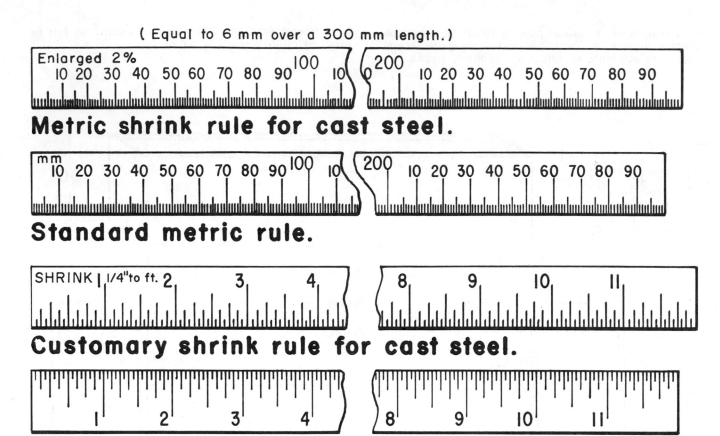

Metric shrink rule for cast steel.

Standard metric rule.

Customary shrink rule for cast steel.

Standard inch rule.

Fig. 31-11
The metric shrink rule for cast steel will be 2 percent longer
than a standard metric rule.

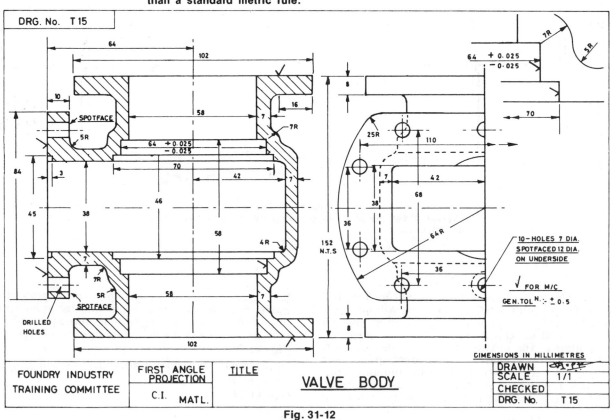

Fig. 31-12
A typical pattern drawing in metric.

Heat treating. All heat treating equipment will be graduated in degrees Celsius, and all tables will provide heat treating specifications in degrees Celsius. **Fig. 31-13a,b.**

Temperatures, Steel Colors, and Related Processes

	Colors	F	°C	Processes
Heat Colors	White	2500°	1371°	Welding
		2400°	1315°	High speed steel hardening (1177-1343°C)
	Yellow-White	2300°	1259°	
		2200°	1204°	
		2100°	1149°	
	Yellow	2000°	1093°	
		1900°	1036°	
	Orange-Red	1800°	981°	
		1700°	926°	
		1600°	871°	Alloy tool steel hardening (816-1066°C)
	Light cherry red	1500°	815°	Carbon tool steel hardening (732-843°C)
	Cherry red	1400°	760°	
		1300°	704°	
	Dark red			
		1200°	648°	
		1100°	593°	High speed steel tempering (538-593°C)
		1000°	538°	
	Very dark red	900°	482°	
		800°	426°	
	Black red in dull light or darkness	700°	371°	
Temper Colors	Pale blue (310°C)	600°	315°	Carbon tool steel tempering (149-566°C)
	Violet (285°C)			
	Purple (274°C)	500°	260°	
	Yellowish-Brown (254°C)	400°	204°	
	Dark straw (241°C)			
		300°	149°	
	Light straw (218°C)			
		200°	93°	
		100°	38°	
		0°	18°	

Fig. 31-13a
Heat treating temperatures in degrees Celsius.

MELTING TEMPERATURES OF PURE METALS

	°C	°F
Aluminum	660	1 220
Cadimum	321	610
Chromium	1 900	3 407
Cobalt	1 490	2 723
Copper	1 083	1 981
Iron	1 540	2 798
Lead	327	621
Magnesium	650	1 202
Molybdenum	2 610	4 730
Nickel	1 450	2 647
Platinum	1 770	3 218
Titanium	1 670	3 038
Tungsten	3 410	6 170
Vanadium	1 900	3 452
Zinc	419	786

Fig. 31-13b
Melting temperature of pure metal.

The kelvin temperature scale will not be used.

Material testing. Most of the current hardness testing units use the metric measurement for all aspects of the work. For example, the Brinell hardness test describes the diameter of the ball used in millimetres and the load in kilograms. For all tests of strength in which the results were previously given in psi (pounds per square inch), stress will be given in megapascals. To convert pound force per square inch (psi) to megapascals, use the table shown in **Fig. 31-14.** For example, in a tensile test of strength, if the

TYPICAL MECHANICAL PROPERTIES

METALS	YIELD STRENGTH	TENSILE STRENGTH	MODULUS OF ELASTICITY
Sheet (1008)	170 MPa	340 MPa	200 GPa
Aluminum (6061-T6)	275 MPa	310 MPa	62 GPa
Copper	310 MPa	345 MPa	125 GPa
Brass (70-30)	207 MPa	524 MPa	112 GPa

Fig. 31-15
Typical mechanical properties in metric readings.

For example, for calculations involving stress (force divided by area) the results are given megapascals. Because engineering drawings are always dimensioned in millimetres, it is convenient to use the square millimetres (mm^2) in figuring stress. Remember, however, that a pascal is a newton per square metre. Therefore, to figure stress in megapascals use this formula:

$$\text{Stress} = \frac{\text{force}}{\text{area}} = \frac{\text{newtons}}{mm^2} = \frac{\frac{\text{newtons}}{mm^2}}{10^6} =$$

$$\frac{10^6 \text{ newtons}}{m^2} = \text{megapascals}$$

QUANTITY	UNIT	SYMBOL	CONVERSIONS FROM CUSTOMARY UNITS			APPROXIMATE EQUIVALENCIES BETWEEN
			TO CONVERT FROM	TO	MULTIPLY BY	SI AND U.S. CUSTOMARY UNITS
stress	megapascal	MPa	pound-force/inch² (psi)	MPa	6.894757 E - 03	1 MPa = 145 psi
			kips/inch² (ksi)	MPa	6.894757 E + 00	7 MPa = 1000 psi 7 MPa = 1 ksi

Fig. 31-14
Use these formulas to change from customary units to metric units.

answer in customary units is 100 000 psi, the result in SI is 696 MPa.

In SI the values of mechanical properties are given in multiples of the pascal, primarily the megapascal (MPa) and the gigapascal (GPa). **Fig. 31-15.**

GENERAL WOODWORKING INCLUDING FORESTRY AND FURNITURE CONSTRUCTION

In woodworking the customary system of measurement is based on feet, inches, and fractions of an inch. The metric system is a decimal system based on units of ten and, therefore, all length measurements will be in millimetres, centimetres or metres. **Fig. 32-1**

CONVERSION TABLE FOR WOODWORK

Customary (English)	METRIC				
	Actual	Accurate Woodworkers' Language	Tool Sizes	Lumber Sizes	
				Thickness	Width
1/32 in	0.8 mm	1 mm bare			
1/16 in	1.6 mm	1.5 mm			
1/8 in	3.2 mm	3 mm full	3 mm		
3/16 in	4.8 mm	5 mm bare	5 mm		
1/4 in	6.4 mm	6.5 mm	6 mm		
5/16 in	7.9 mm	8 mm bare	8 mm		
3/8 in	9.5 mm	9.5 mm	10 mm		
7/16 in	11.1 mm	11 mm full	11 mm		
1/2 in	12.7 mm	12.5 mm full	13 mm	12 mm	
9/16 in	14.3 mm	14.5 mm bare	14 mm		
5/8 in	15.9 mm	16 mm bare	16 mm	16 mm	
11/16 in	17.5 mm	17.5 mm	17 mm		
3/4 in	19.1 mm	19 mm full	19 mm	19 mm	
13/16 in	20.6 mm	20.5 mm	21 mm		
7/8 in	22.2 mm	22 mm full	22 mm	22 mm	
15/16 in	23.8 mm	24 mm bare	24 mm		
1 in	25.4 mm	25.5 mm	25 mm	25 mm	
1 1/4 in	31.8 mm	32 mm bare	32 mm	32 mm	
1 3/8 in	34.9 mm	35 mm bare	36 mm	36 mm	
1 1/2 in	38.1 mm	38 mm full	38 mm	38 mm	
1 3/4 in	44.5 mm	44.5 mm	44 mm	44 mm	
2 in	50.8 mm	51 mm bare	50 mm	50 mm	50 mm
2 1/2 in	63.5 mm	63.5 mm	63 mm	63 mm	
3 in	76.2 mm	76 mm full		75 mm	75 mm
4 in	101.6 mm	101.5 mm		100 mm	100 mm
5 in	127.0 mm	127 mm			125 mm
6 in	152.4 mm	152.5 mm			150 mm
7 in	177.8 mm	178 mm bare			
8 in	203.2 mm	203 mm full			200 mm
9 in	228.6 mm	228.5 mm			
10 in	254.0 mm	254 mm			250 mm
11 in	279.4 mm	279.5 mm			
12 in	304.8 mm	305 mm bare			300 mm
18 in	457.2 mm	457 mm full	460 mm		
24 in	609.6 mm	609.5 mm			
36 in	914.4 mm	914.5 mm			
48 in—4'	1219.2 mm	1220 mm			
96 in—8'	2438.4 mm	2440 mm			

Panel Stock Sizes
1220 mm width
2440 mm length

Fig. 32-1
Conversion table for woodworking.

Metric Units Used

For most purposes in woodworking only three units are important, namely, length (metre), mass or weight (kilogram), and temperature (degrees Celsius). In addition, one derived unit for liquid capacity is used, the litre. A comparison of the common units used in the customary and metric systems for general woodworking is shown in **Fig. 32-2**. The units commonly used in the area of forestry are shown in **Fig. 32-3**.

Unit	Customary	Metric	Approximate Comparison
Length	feet - ft or ′	metres - m	3 feet = 1 metre
	inches - in or ″	centimetres - cm	1 in = 2.5 cm
	Fractions of an inch	millimetres - mm	⅛ in = 3 mm
Weight	pounds - lb	kilograms - kg	1 lb = 0.5 kg
	ounces - oz	grams - g	1 oz = 28 g
Volume	cubic yard - yd³	cubic metres - m³	1 yd³ = 0.76 m³
	cubic feet - ft³	cubic metres - m³	1 ft³ = 0.028 m³
	cubic inches - in³	cubic centimetres - cm³	1 in³ = 16.4 cm³
Liquid capacity	quarts - qt	litres - l	1 quart = 0.95 l
	pints - fl pt	millilitres - ml	1 liq pt = 475 ml
Temperature	Fahrenheit -°F	degree Celsius - °C	70 °F = 21 °C

Fig. 32-2
Comparison of common measuring units used in woodworking.

AREA

hectare (ha) — Areas generally greater than 1 hectare to be expressed in hectares.

square metre (m^2) — areas generally less than 1 hectare in square metres.

square kilometre (km^2) — In place of square miles.

LENGTH OR DISTANCE

kilometres (km) — Kilometres to be used for long distance on maps, for lengths of roads, etc.

metres (m) — Metres to be used for shorter distances such as in surveying, for tree heights and for log lengths.

millimetres (mm) — Where even smaller lengths are being measured millimetres may be used.

TREE MEASUREMENT
Height

metres (m) — Height measurement to be expressed in metres.

centimetres (cm)
millimetres (mm) — For seedlings and young trees centimetres or millimetres can be used.

Diameter

centimetres (cm)
millimetres (mm) — Diameter measurement to be expressed in centimetres. Where greater precision is required millimetres may be used.

Sectional Area

square metres (m^2)

Sectional area to be expressed in square metres for individual trees and for stands.

square millimetres (mm^2)

For special cases square millimetres may be used.

Volume

cubic metres (m^3)

Volume to be expressed in cubic metres. It is recognized that absolute volume is that measured over bark.

Breast Height

1.4 metres

Breast height is 1.4 metres from ground level - on the uphill side of the tree on sloping ground.

LOG MEASUREMENT

length (m)

To be expressed in metres.

girth

Girth will not be used as a log measurement.

diameter (cm)

To be expressed in centimetres. }

volume (m^3)

To be expressed in cubic metres. }

Stated as under or over bark.

Fig. 32-3
Metric measurements used in forestry.

In the metalworking industry length is described in millimetres regardless of product size. In woodworking industries, millimetres (or sometimes centimetres) may be used to describe basic materials and components. The millimetre (or centimetre) will be used to describe furniture sizes.

In changing from customary sizes to metric sizes the general practice is to round off to full millimetre sizes, rounding up for any sizes above 0.5 and rounding down for any sizes below 0.5. For example, 1/4 inch, which is actually 6.4 millimetres would become 6 millimetres; 1/2 inch, which is exactly 12.7 millimetres would become 13 millimetres. If more

precise measurements are required such as in patternmaking, customary dimensions can be rounded to the nearest 1/2 millimetre (0.5 mm).

Lumber Sizes

The actual dimensions of lumber are not the same as the nominal dimensions. For example, current standards for softwoods are determined by moisture content. A 2 x 4 actually measures 1-1/2 x 3-1/2 if it is dry (that is, with 19 percent or less moisture content), while a green or unseasoned 2 x 4 measures 1-9/16 x 3-9/16 (if the lumber has over 19 percent moisture content). **Fig. 32-4**

Thickness									
Nominal			Minimum Dressed						
			Dry			Green			
	Exact	Rounded		Exact	Rounded		Exact	Rounded	
inches	mm	mm	inches	mm	mm	inches	mm	mm	
1	25.4	25	3/4	19.1	19	25/32	19.8	20	
1 1/4	31.8	32	1	25.4	25	1 1/32	26.2	26	
1 1/2	38.1	38	1 1/4	31.8	32	1 9/32	32.51	33	
2	50.8	50	1 1/2	38.1	38	1 9/16	39.7	40	
2 1/2	63.5	63	2	50.8	50	2 1/16	52.4	52	
3	76.2	75	2 1/2	63.5	63	2 9/16	65.1	65	
3 1/2	88.9	90	3	76.2	75	3 1/16	77.8	78	
4	101.6	100	3 1/2	88.9	89	3 9/16	90.5	90	

Width								
Nominal			Minimum Dressed					
			Dry			Green		
	Exact	Rounded		Exact	Rounded		Exact	Rounded
inches	mm	mm	inches	mm	mm	inches	mm	mm
2	50.8	50	1 1/2	38.1	38	1 9/16	39.7	40
3	76.2	75	2 1/2	63.5	63	2 9/16	65.1	65
4	101.6	100	3 1/2	88.9	89	3 9/16	90.5	90
5	127.0	125	4 1/2	114.3	114	4 5/8	117.5	117
6	152.4	150	5 1/2	139.7	140	5 5/8	142.9	143
7	177.8	175	6 1/2	165.1	165	6 5/8	168.3	168
8	203.2	200	7 1/4	184.1	184	7 1/2	190.5	190

Fig. 32-4
Thicknesses and widths of softwood showing exact and rounded sizes in metric.

In the metric system a soft conversion the nominal size of a 2 x 4 would be expressed as 50 x 100 mm. The rounded dry size would be 38 x 89 millimetres, and the rounded green size would be 40 x 90 mm. However, the recommended dry size in metrics is 35 x 90 millimetres, a size reduction of about seven percent over the customary dry size. England has established metric sizes for softwoods as shown in **Fig. 32-5**. Other English-speaking countries, such as Australia, converting to the metric system have established similar standards. **Fig. 32-6**

BRITISH WOOD STANDARDS

METRIC MEASURES FOR WOOD AND BOARD

You have been used to buying timber in imperial measure ; lengths by the foot and sections in inches. Now it comes from the mills in standard metric lengths and sections and will be sold to you in metric measure. Where you used to think of lengths in feet think now in METRES (m) and where you thought of inches for sections think now of MILLIMETRES (mm).

LENGTHS

The new range of lengths supplied from the mills begin at 1.8 metres and increase in steps of 300 millimetres (300 mm) to 6.3 metres. Shorter and longer lengths can be obtained. 300 mm is close to, but shorter than, a foot.

The diagram opposite shows you the new metric lengths. Note that 300 mm is the same as 0.3 metres or 30 centimetres.

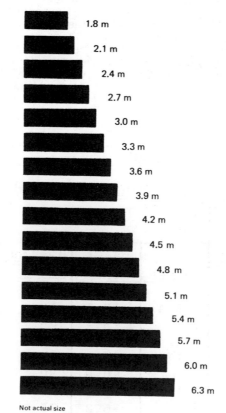

1.8 m
2.1 m
2.4 m
2.7 m
3.0 m
3.3 m
3.6 m
3.9 m
4.2 m
4.5 m
4.8 m
5.1 m
5.4 m
5.7 m
6.0 m
6.3 m

Not actual size

Fig. 32-5
British wood standards.

SECTIONS

Most of the metric sizes of sections and mouldings are very close to the customary inch sizes. They are very slightly smaller.

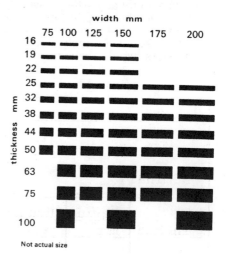

Not actual size

BOARD AND SHEET MATERIALS

These materials are also now sold in metric lengths, widths and thicknesses. For practical purposes, the dimensions are no different from those you are used to.

PREFERRED METRIC SIZES OF AUSTRALIAN HARDWOODS, AUSTRALIAN CYPRESS PINE, OREGON, AND CANADA PINE

Thickness (mm)	Width (mm) 38	50	75	100	113	125	150	175	200	250	300
15		A	A								
25	AC	AC	B	B	B		ABC				
38			ABC	ABC		A	AC	AC	AC	A	A
50		B	ABC	ABC		A	C	C	C	C	C
75			AC	ABC		AB		AC	AC	AC	AC
100				AC							

PREFERRED METRIC SIZES OF SOFTWOODS

Thickness (mm)	Width (mm) 19	35	42	70	90	120	140	170	190	240	290
8		X									
12	X				X		X				
19	X	X	X	X	X	X	X	X		X	X
30						X	X		X		
35			X	X	X	X	X		X		
45				X	X		X				
70					X						
90					X						

Fig. 32-6
Typical wood standards for Australia.

Hardwoods are normally purchased surfaced on one side (S1S) or surfaced two sides (S2S). Therefore, the nominal 1 inch board is 7/8 inches surfaced on one side (S1S) or 13/16 inches if surfaced two sides (S2S). In metric units the nominal thickness would be 25 mm, while the S1S thickness would be 22 mm, and the S2S thickness would be 21 mm. **Fig. 32-7**

Thickness (Widths vary with Grades)

Nominal (Rough)	Exact mm	Rounded mm	Surfaced 1 Side (S1S)	Exact mm	Rounded mm	Surfaced 2 Sides (S2S)	Exact mm	Rounded mm
3/8"	9.5	10	1/4"	6.4	6	3/16"	4.8	5
1/2"	12.7	13	3/8"	9.5	9	5/16"	7.9	8
5/8"	15.9	16	1/2"	12.7	13	7/16"	11.1	11
3/4"	19.1	19	5/8"	15.9	16	9/16"	14.3	14
1"	25.4	25	7/8"	22.2	22	13/16"	20.6	21
1 1/4"	31.8	32	1 1/8"	28.6	29	1 1/16"	27.0	27
1 1/2"	38.1	38	1 3/8"	34.9	35	1 5/16"	33.3	33
2"	50.8	50	1 13/16"	46.0	46	1 3/4"	44.5	44
3"	76.2	75	2 13/16"	71.4	71	2 3/4"	69.9	70
4"	101.6	100	3 13/16"	96.8	97	3 3/4"	95.3	95

Fig. 32-7
Hardwood thicknesses.

The lengths of lumber are given in metres beginning with 1.8 m up to 6.3 m, increasing in steps of 300 millimetres.

How Lumber Is Sold

The customary system has a measuring unit for lumber all its own, namely, the board foot. This is a piece of material 1 inch thick by 12 inches wide by 12 inches long, or any other combination that equals that amount. In other words, a board foot is actually 144 cubic inches. In the metric system, lumber is bought and sold in bulk by the *cubic metre.* **Fig. 32-8a**

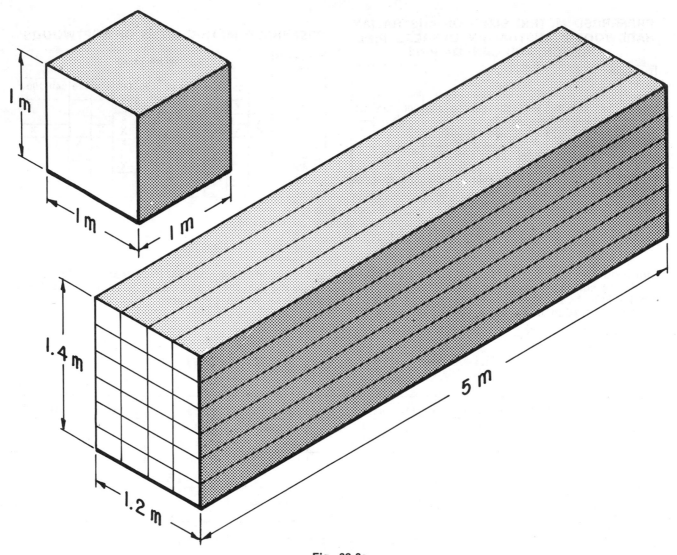

Fig. 32-8a
The cubic metre is a large unit that applies to buying and selling lumber. A closed pile of lumber measuring 1.2 x 1.4 x 5 m equals 8.4 cubic metres.

This is a relatively large unit, since it is the equivalent of 61 023 cubic inches or about 424 times as large as a board foot. **Fig. 32-8b**

Metric Unit	Number of Board Feet 1" x 12" x 12" (25.4 x 304.8 x 304.8 mm)
one cubic metre (1 m^3)	423.8
one millimetre times one square metre (1 mm·m^2)	0.4238
one deciboard one centimetre times one square decimetre (1 cm·dm^2)	0.04238

Fig. 32-8b
Possible replacement units for the board foot.

A board foot is equal to 0.002 359 7 cubic metres. For example, if the price of a good quality hardwood is listed as $1 per board foot or $1000 per 1000 board feet, it would be listed as $424 per cubic metre. For public consumption, lumber may be sold at a price per square metre in a specific thickness. For example, a piece of lumber may be listed as $11 per square metre in 25 mm thickness or $5.5 per square metre in 13 mm thickness. A square metre is approximately 11 times as large as a square foot. Remember that *a square foot 1 inch thick* is actually *a board foot.*

In the customary system, strip stock and straight millwork is sold *per linear* or running foot. In the metric system it will be sold *per metre.* The metre is approximately 3.3 feet. Veneers will be sold per square metre in thicknesses of 1.5 mm or 3 mm.

Plywood and Other Panel Stock

Plywood, particleboard, and other sheet stock used in construction is based on the 4' x 8' module. A soft

conversion to metric sizes would be 1220 x 2440 mm or 1.22 x 2.44 m. However, sizes of panel stock for metric building construction will be based on a *100 mm* building module and, therefore, the basic size of panel stock will be 1200 x 2400 mm or 1.2 x 2.4 m. See next unit.

Plywood and other panel stock is currently sold in specific thickness per square foot or per sheet. In the metric system these materials will be sold per square metre, which is 11 times as large as the square foot or per board of a particular thickness.

Fasteners

Nails, wood screws and dowels will not change in size but may be expressed in metric units. Metal bolts, nuts and screws will be in ISO metric standards or inch standards. Wood fasteners may be given only a soft conversion. For example, a 10p nail which is approximately 3 inches long would be described as a 75 mm length nail. **Fig. 32-9**

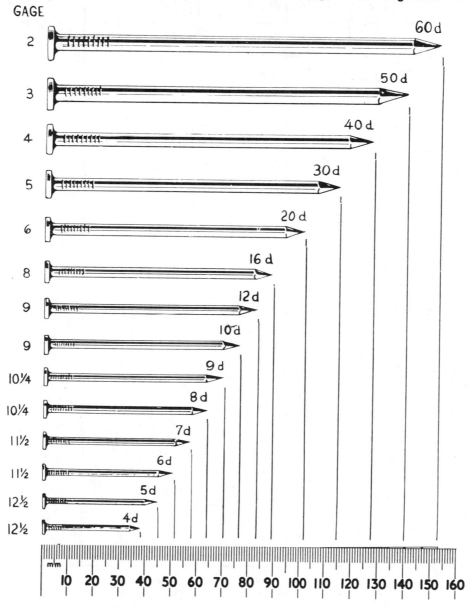

Sizes of common wire nails.

Fig. 32-9
Soft conversions used for nails.

For installing wood screws, metric or customary drills can be used. **Fig. 32-10**

BORING CHART FOR WOOD SCREWS

Customary and Metric Sizes

No. of Screw	Max. Head Dia. Inch	SHANK DIAMETER			ROOT DIAMETER			Thread per Inch	No. of Screw
		Basic Dec. Size Inch	Nearest Drill Equivalent Inch	Nearest Drill Equivalent mm	Average Dec. Size Inch	Nearest Drill Equivalent Inch	Nearest Drill Equivalent mm		
0	.119	.060	1/16	1.5	.040	3/64	1.0	32	0
1	.146	.073	5/64	2.0	.046	3/64	1.0	28	1
2	.172	.086	3/32	2.5	.054	1/16	1.5	26	2
3	.199	.099	7/64	3.0	.065	1/16	1.5	24	3
4	.225	.112	7/64	3.0	.075	5/64	2.0	22	4
5	.252	.125	1/8	3.5	.085	5/64	2.0	20	5
6	.279	.138	9/64	3.5	.094	3/32	2.5	18	6
7	.305	.151	5/32	4.0	.102	7/64	2.5	16	7
8	.332	.164	5/32	4.0	.112	7/64	2.5	15	8
9	.358	.177	11/64	4.5	.122	1/8	3.0	14	9
10	.385	.190	3/16	5.0	.130	1/8	3.0	13	10
11	.411	.203	13/64	5.5	.139	9/64	3.5	12	11
12	.438	.216	7/32	5.5	.148	9/64	3.5	11	12
14	.491	.242	1/4	6.5	.165	5/32	4.0	10	14
16	.544	.268	17/64	7.0	.184	3/16	4.5	9	16
18	.597	.294	19/64	7.5	.204	13/64	5.0	8	18
20	.650	.320	5/16	8.0	.223	7/32	5.5	8	20
24	.756	.372	3/8	9.5	.260	1/4	6.0	7	24

Fig. 32-10
Boring chart for wood screws showing both customary and metric sizes.

Items such as dowel rods will not change in diameter and, therefore, there is no need for metric drill sizes in woodworking. If metric drills are used, it is important to make sure that the drill is correct for the dowel rod. For example, a 13 mm drill would be satisfactory for a 1/2 inch dowel rod. Since wood screws will not change to metric sizes, it may be necessary only to use a different drill chart for installing wood where metric drills are available instead of customary drills.

Measuring Tools

All woodworking measuring tools will need to be replaced with metric measuring tools. **Fig. 32-11**

METRIC MEASURING TOOLS – WOODWORK

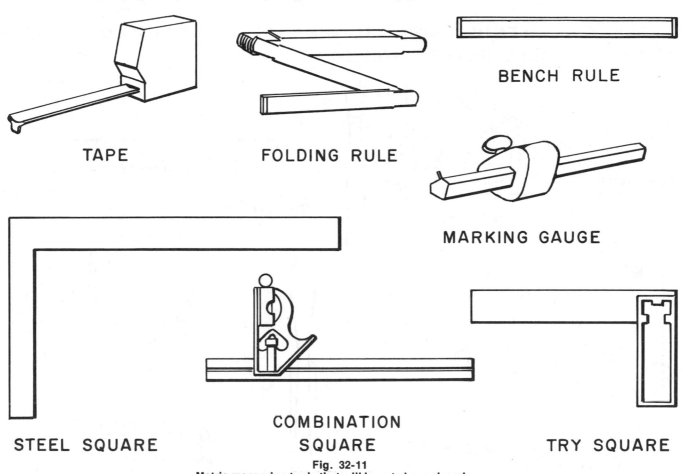

TAPE

FOLDING RULE

BENCH RULE

MARKING GAUGE

STEEL SQUARE

COMBINATION
SQUARE

TRY SQUARE

Fig. 32-11
Metric measuring tools that will have to be replaced.

However, many of the measuring tools, particularly items such as the flexible rule, are already marked with dual dimensions; one side that reads in inches and the other in centimetres and millimetres. **Fig. 32-12a,b**

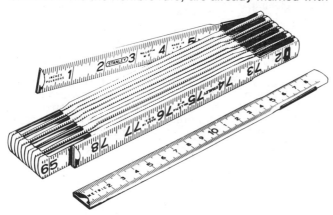

Fig. 32-12a
Note that on this folding rule the inch measurement is on one side and the metric measurement on the other.

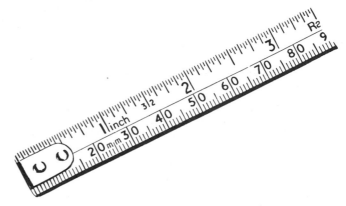

Fig. 32-12b
The top edge of the measuring tape is graduated in inches and the lower edge is graduated in millimetres.

Most other tools such as the metre stick and the bench rule are available with the customary and metric units shown side by side. Replacement metric blades are available for the combination square. A metric framing square is available, but does not have the various rafter tables on it.

Other Hand Tools

Most other woodworking tools will not change except for designating the sizes differently. A 2 inch hand plane will become a 50 millimetre plane, and a 1 inch chisel a 25 millimetre chisel. **Fig. 32-13**

TOOLS WHICH WILL NOT NEED REPLACEMENT

METRIC EQUIVALENTS SHOWN ARE THE EXPECTED REPLACEMENT SIZES TO BE AVAILABLE IN THE FUTURE.

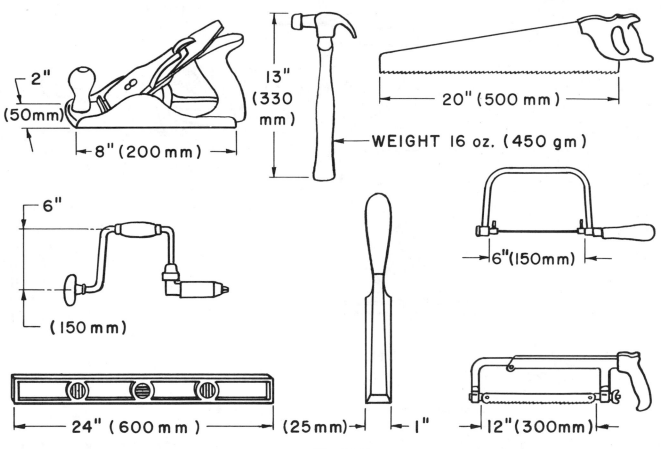

Fig. 32-13
These tools will not need replacing.

Boring tools will not need to be replaced, since these will have only a soft conversion.

Machine Conversion

Since woodworking is not a precise craft like metalworking, the problem of converting these machines is relatively easy. Most woodworking machines have adjustments for depth and width of cut with a scale in the customary units. Metric conversion can be made by adding pressure-sensitized metric tape cut to suitable lengths adjacent to the customary gage or scale. **Fig. 32-14**

MACHINE WOODWORK
GAGE AND SCALE CONVERSION

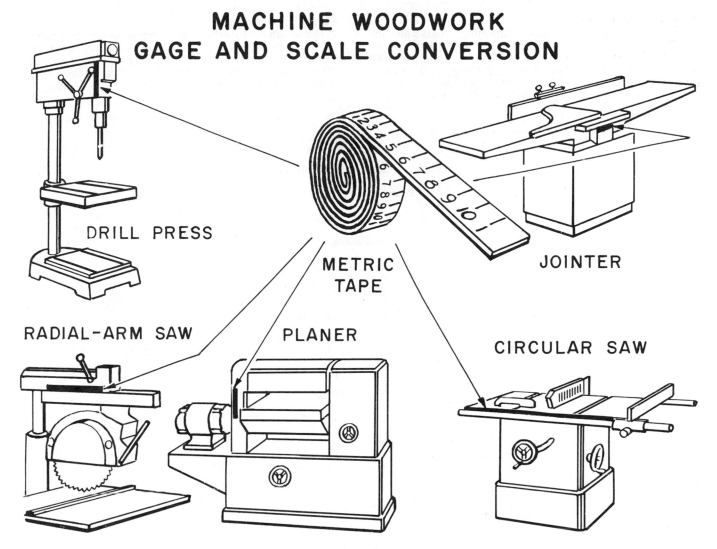

DRILL PRESS

METRIC TAPE

JOINTER

RADIAL-ARM SAW

PLANER

CIRCULAR SAW

Fig. 32-14
Machine conversion in woodworking will merely mean changing the gage or scale.

Eventually a metric metal scale can be added to the machine.

Cutting speeds in metric are given in metres per minute rather than feet per minute, as in the customary system. **Fig. 32-15** shows the approximate surface speeds for machining woods and other soft materials. Cutting speeds in metres per minute can be changed to revolutions per minute by multiplying the cutting speed times 1000 to change it to millimetres, divided by diameter times 3.1416.

Approximate surface speeds for
machining wood and similar materials

| Type of Lumber | CUTTING SPEEDS IN METRES PER MINUTE | | | | | | |
| | Drill-ing | Turn-ing | Sawing | | | Sand-ing | Plan-ing |
			Circ.	Band	Fig		
Hard	80	150	2500	650	30	850	1250
Soft	120	300	3000	1000	100	1000	1750
Very soft	160	450	4000	1250	200	1250	2000

$$CS = \frac{RPM \times \times D}{1000}$$

$$RPM = \frac{CS \times 1000}{\times D}$$

CS: Cutting Speed in metres per minute

RPM: Revs per minute

D: Diam. in millimetres

Fig. 32-15
Approximate speeds for machining woods.

Finishing Materials

Common sizes of liquid finishing materials including paint, varnish, lacquers, etc. will be in multiples and submultiples of the litre, such as 1/2 (0.5) litre (500 millilitres), 1 litre, 2 litres, and 4 litres. Since the litre is about 6 percent larger than the quart, coverage will be a little greater than for a quart.

Furniture Drawing

Drawings for furniture and other small wood projects from some metric countries use the centimetre unit. Preference, however, should be given to having all dimensions in *millimetres,* since this is the correct practice in engineering drawings.   **Fig. 32-16**

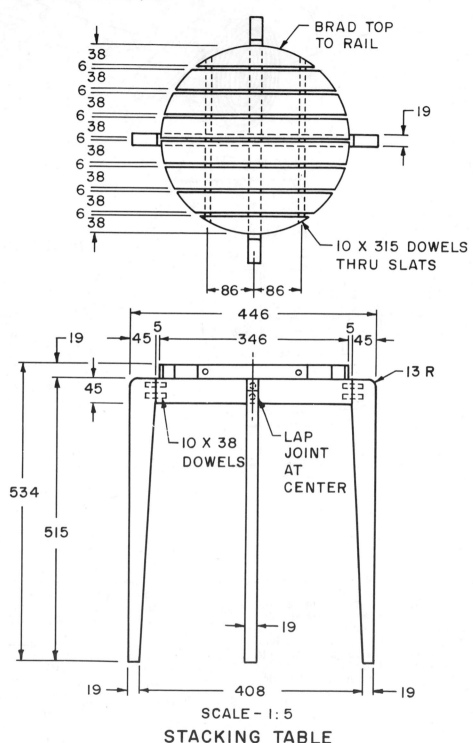

ALL DIMENSIONS IN mm

Fig. 32-16
A patio table drawing in metric.

The method for making the drawings will be the same as for metalworking.

Furniture Manufacture

Producing furniture to metric dimensions will not be any problem. Furniture manufacturers purchase lumber in the rough and usually make their own lumber core hardwood plywood. Therefore, all furniture parts can be machined to even metric modules. There will be no change in fasteners, including dowels.

To produce furniture from metric drawings, the two major problems will be to purchase metric measuring instruments and to retrain workers.

Fig. 32-17a,b,c,d

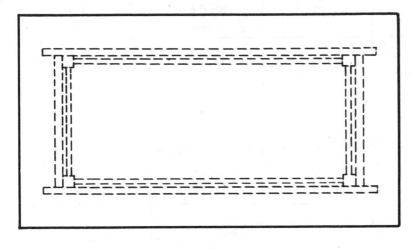

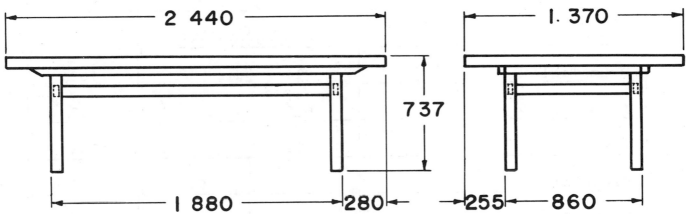

Fig. 32-17a
A large dining room table drawn to metric measurements.

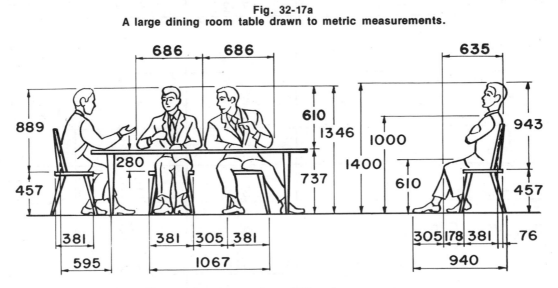

All dimensions are in millimetres — mm

Fig. 32-17b
The metric dimensions of the sitting figure can be used in designing furniture and also for determining window height in building construction.

AVERAGE FURNITURE, EQUIPMENT DIMENSIONS

Item	Length mm	Depth-Width mm	Height mm
Dining Table	1524	1067	737
Kitchen Table	1067	762	762
Card Table	914	941	762
Coffee Table	914-1524	457-610	355-457
Coffee Table round	914	dia.	355-457
End Table	610	381	610
Drum Table	914	dia.	762
Lamp Table	610	dia.	762
Desk	1219	610	762
Secretary	914	610	2134
Lowboy	762	457	762
Highboy	914	457	1524-2134
Breakfront Bookcase	1219-1524	457	1981-2134
Sofa	1829	762	914
Love Seat	1219	762	914
Occasional Chair	686	762	914
Occasional Chair armless	610	762	762
Wing Chair	762	762	914
Dining, Desk, Folding Chair	457	457	762

Item	Length mm	Depth-Width mm	Height mm
AVERAGE FURNITURE, EQUIPMENT DIMENSIONS Continued			
Twin Bed	1981	991	508-584
Double Bed	1981	1371	508-584
Dresser	1067-1524	559	813-914
Refrigerator	762-914	610-762	1371-1626
Stove	914-1067	762	914
Washing Machine	762	762	914
Dryer	762	762	914

Fig. 32-17c
Average furniture and equipment dimensions in millimetres.

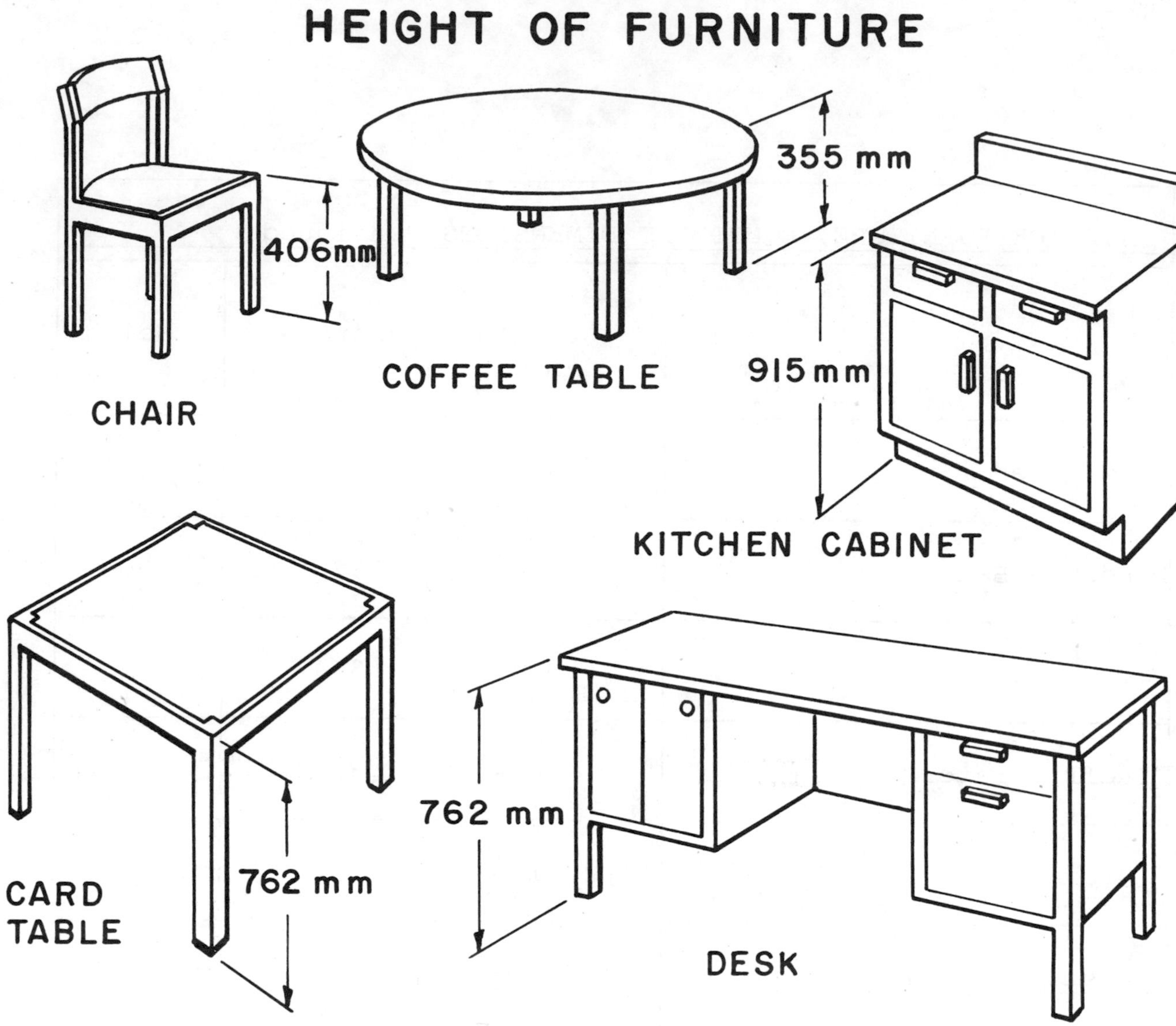

HEIGHT OF FURNITURE

CHAIR — 406mm

COFFEE TABLE — 355 mm

KITCHEN CABINET — 915 mm

CARD TABLE — 762 mm

DESK — 762 mm

Fig. 32-17d
Height of furniture in millimetres.

UNIT 33
BUILDING CONSTRUCTION

The change to the metric system of weights and measures is less urgent in construction and related fields than in manufacturing since international trade is less involved.   **Fig. 33-1**

Fig. 33-1
It will be some years before an all metric house can be built. Before this can happen all basic materials and components including lumber, panel stock, brick, cement blocks, insulation, roofing materials, windows, doors, shutters, and all others must be available in metric modules based on 100 mm.

A hard conversion in the building industry will depend on the establishment of metric standards for all materials and building components.

The construction industry in England was one of the first to "go metric". Its activities were closely interlocked with those of many manufacturing companies including steel, glass, plastics, and lumber. A wide variety of skilled and professional people including architects, civil engineers, electricians, steamfitters, experts in heating, ventilation and building maintenance were involved. The British construction industry combined a change to metric measurement with standardization of building materials into modular design. The module selected was 300 millimetres, which is very close but slightly smaller than the familiar length of one foot. While many building components are available to fit this module, some of the imported items such as plywood and other panel sheet are not. This causes serious problems since the panels must be cut to fit the module.

In building construction soft conversion from customary to metric sizes is of no value in itself and could be a waste of time. The nominal sizes of customary materials such as the familiar 2" x 4" framing material or the 4' x 8' panel are a good example. If these were converted directly to metric units, complex and unnecessary size designations would result. While there might be some educational value in showing equivalent metric sizes of customary materials, the practice could only complicate building construction.

The traditional method in architecture is to design the building to suit its function and then to select components that will fit this design. Most materials are available in customary sizes to fit basic designs. However, through the years there has been a proliferation of sizes. For example, windows are available in hundreds of different sizes. Not only has this made building construction more costly, but it has also complicated both the design and construction. As the building industry is converted to metric, one great advantage can be the reduction in the number of sizes of building components. For example, in England there has been a substantial reduction in the number of sizes of windows and doors made in metric modules.

Building Design
The concept of designing in modules is not new in architecture. A customary system of modular coordination involving all three dimensions; length, width and height is the UNICOM method of house construction. This system is based on the module of 4 inches with the entire grid divided into spaces of 4, 16, 24, and 48 inches.   **Fig. 33-2**

MODULAR COORDINATION DESIGN STANDARDS
Customary – (4" base module)

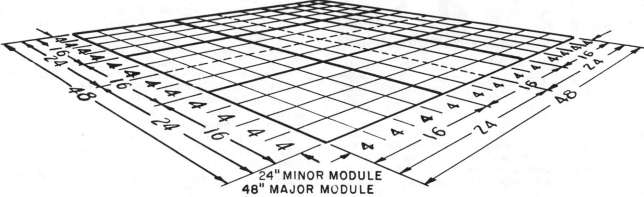

24" MINOR MODULE
48" MAJOR MODULE

Metric – (100 mm base module)

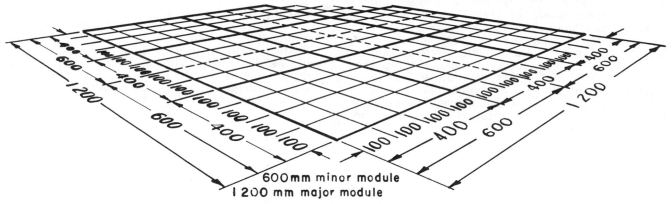

600mm minor module
1200 mm major module

Fig. 33-2
Comparison of modular coordination - design standards in
the customary system and the metric system. While these
are very similar in size, they are different enough to allow for
no interchangeability.

The total structure is designed to utilize most efficiently the customary building materials available. For example, with a standard 4' x 8' sheet of plywood or other panel stock the total width can be utilized as is without waste or it can be cut into 2 sections 24" wide. Also the 16" module provides for convenient spacing of floor joists. Maximum utilization of the UNICOM method is best achieved when the design is held exactly to the 4 inch module, and all components such as doors and windows are specified in multiples of this module.

In contrast to the UNICOM method the International Organization for Standardization (ISO) recommends that the basic module of 100 millimetres be used in building construction. **Fig. 33-3**

BASIC MODULES FOR CONSTRUCTION

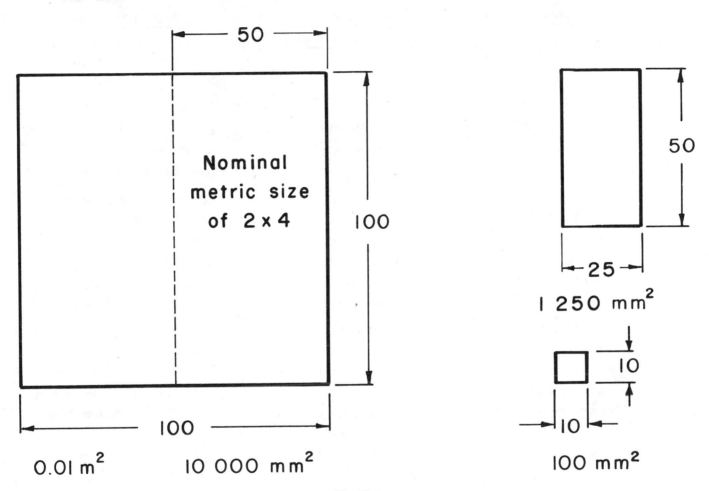

Fig. 33-3
Basic modules that may be used in building construction. The 100 mm by 100 mm square will be the basic size. The 50 x 100 mm module is the nominal size of a 2 x 4 while the 25 x 50 mm module is the nominal size of a 1 x 2.

This 100 millimetre module is approximately, but not exactly, 4". The standard also recommends that the submultiples of 25, 50 and 75 millimetres and multiples of 300, (400), 600, *(800), 900 and 1200 millimetres be utilized. Utilizing these modules, architects and manufacturers could base their design measurement on these sizes so that the total home or building will fit together without problems. This will mean that lumber, brick, cement block, plywood, panel stock, windows, doors, kitchen cabinets and everything else used in construction must rigidly adhere to this 100 millimetre module and its multiples and submultiples. Any deviation would nullify the advantages of converting to metric. The use of a modular system throughout the industry could result in a simplification of production and a reduction in the variety of sizes. In addition, it would encourage rationalization of building practices. The designer, architect and builder using dimensions based on 100 millimetre modules could specify any building material or appliance and expect it to fit within a specified area.

The major problem in using any metric module is that *all* materials must be based on the same module. Products such as panel stock that are not produced in this module will create endless problems. For example, England bases its building module on a basic 300 mm size, which is approximately but not exactly 12 inches. However, panel stock such as plywood is

*Alternate module.

currently available primarily from Canada and the United States in soft conversion of the customary size, a 4' x 8' panel with dimensions of 1220 x 2440 mm. However, to fit the 100 mm module the panel stock must be 1200 x 2400 mm such as is specified in Australia's standards.

While a 100 mm module is only about 1/16 smaller than a 4 inch module, a 1200 mm module is about 3/4 inch smaller than 48 inches, and a 2400 module is about 1-1/2 inches smaller than 96 inches. **Fig. 33-4**

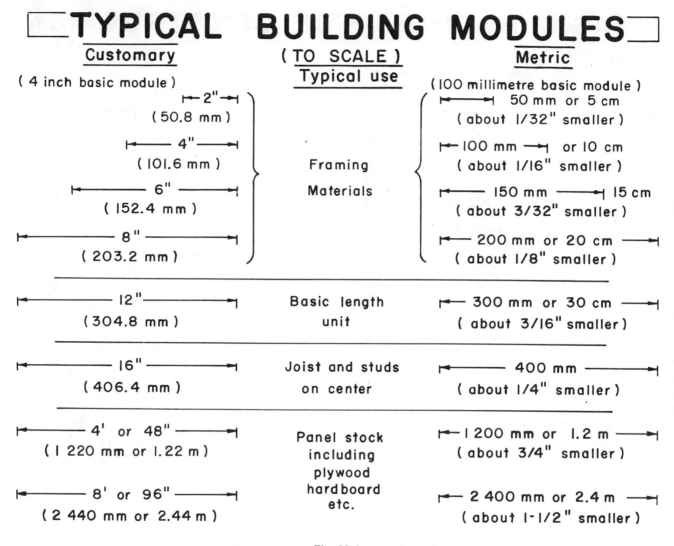

Fig. 33-4
This chart shows the difference in sizes between customary and metric modules. Notice that in the larger sizes, such as panel stock, the differences are significant.

The difference is so large in the larger modules that use of a non-modular size such as 4' x 8' panel could increase the cost of construction. If a home is designed on a 100 mm module but the panel stock is 1220 x 2440 mm, then every peice of panel must be trimmed. On the other hand, a change in panel stock size to a 1200 x 2400 mm or 1.2 x 2.4 m will create problems in all remodeling work since the panel will be too small to replace the customary size of 1220 x 2440 mm. When metric conversion is a reality in the building industry, it is entirely possible that it will be necessary to have 2 standard sizes of panel stock, namely, the 4' x 8' or 1220 x 2440 mm size for old construction and remodeling and the 1200 x 2400 mm size for all new construction based on the 100 mm module.

Dimensional Coordination
Dimensional coordination is a method whereby the design of the elements, components and systems is achieved through the use of common, basic metric dimensional units. The change to metric dimensions will mean a revision of all product sizes to make

sensible metric areas and volumes that will fit into the overall modular size. **Fig. 33-5**

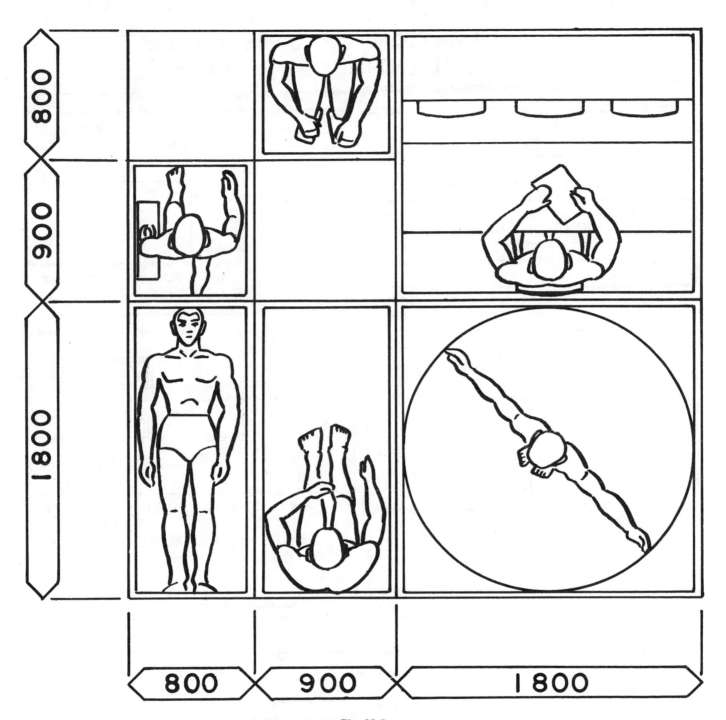

Fig. 33-5
All kinds of individual activities can fit into multiples of the 100 mm module.

This conversion presents an opportunity to coordinate the dimensions of many factory manufactured components such as windows, doors, and even larger pre-fabricated modules and to reduce the range of sizes now being produced. **Fig. 33-6**

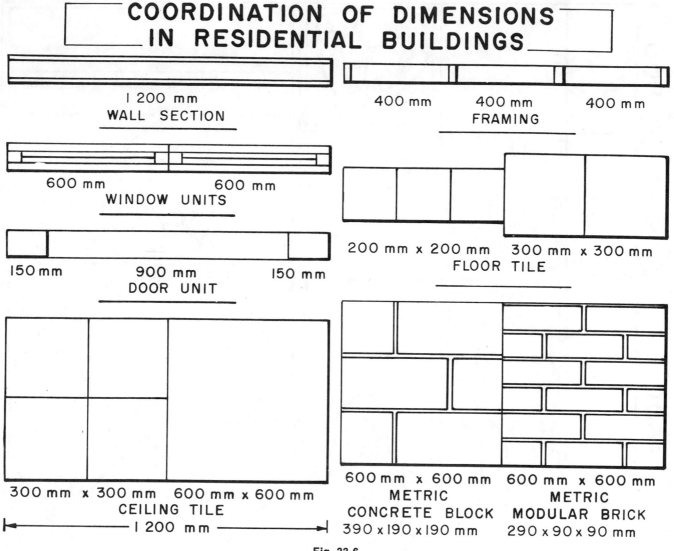

COORDINATION OF DIMENSIONS IN RESIDENTIAL BUILDINGS

1 200 mm
WALL SECTION

400 mm   400 mm   400 mm
FRAMING

600 mm   600 mm
WINDOW UNITS

200 mm x 200 mm   300 mm x 300 mm
FLOOR TILE

150 mm   900 mm   150 mm
DOOR UNIT

300 mm x 300 mm   600 mm x 600 mm
CEILING TILE
|← 1 200 mm →|

600 mm x 600 mm
METRIC
CONCRETE BLOCK
390 x 190 x 190 mm

600 mm x 600 mm
METRIC
MODULAR BRICK
290 x 90 x 90 mm

Fig. 33-6
This is the type of planning that must take place in designing building materials. All different kinds of materials must be based on the preferred multiples of 100 mm.

With modular dimensional coordination elements such as walls, floors, and functional parts of the building and the areas within the building divided into spaces, the dimensions are multiples of a base unit known as a module. Components such as wall panels, door frames, windows, masonry units and the like are made to dimensions that will enable them to fit into these spaces (with joints and tolerances) in such a way that cutting is minimized and the normal type of construction can be simplified. Dimensional coordination with rationalization in range of product sizes will be a significant benefit and saving to the construction industry. However, until all building materials are designed to metric modules, the problems of metric conversion in building construction will be tremendous.

Building Construction Materials

There are so many different kinds of materials used in building construction that it will be impossible to design and build metric structures until all building materials are available. Without rationalization of the sizes of structural and building components, the building industry will not be able to profit by metric conversion. Building material such as lumber, plywood and other panel stock, cement block, brick, insulating materials, windows, doors, roofing materials, all must be available in a series of preferred coordinated sizes in order to design and build a building efficiently in metric. **Fig. 33-7**

Metric Units in Home Construction

Item	Units	Some Suggested Sizes
Area	mm^2, m^2, ha (hectare), km^2	
Asphalt paving	t	
Bagged materials (in large quantities)	kg (t)	2.5, 5, 10, 12.5, 25, 50 kg, etc.
Bituminous concrete	t	
Blocks	mm	100 module but allow for 10 mm joint thickness
Bricks	mm	225 x 112.5 x 75 (std) 200 x 100 x 100 and 300 x 100 x 100; allow for joints
Building board (plywood particle board and hardboard)	mm, m, m^2	600, 900, 1200 width; 1800, 2400, 2700, 3000 length
Building "square"	m^2	10 m^2 (= 107.6 ft^2)
Building systems	mm	Horiz. module: 300, 400, 600, 1200, and 1800. (Grid: 600, 800, 1200) Vert. module: 100, 300, 400
Carpet	mm, m	
Ceiling panels	mm	300 (400) module. 300, 600, 900, 1200 (400, 800, 1200)
Concrete admixtures	kg	
Concrete aggregates	kg, t	(size in mm)
Concrete pavement	m^2	
Concrete portland cement	kg	40 or 50 kg sack, 200 kg barrel
Concrete precast	mm, m, m^3	
Concrete slump	mm	
Concrete, volume	m^3	
Concrete water		(one l = one kg)
Concrete "weight" (strictly mass)	t	
Conduit	mm, m	
Containers for liquids	l	5, 10, etc. up to 200
Corkboard	mm, m, m^2	100, 300, 400 module
Coverage (roads)	m^2/l (liquids) m^2/t (solids)	
Dampproofing	mm, m	
Density	kg/m^3	
Door openings—internal	mm	600, 700, 800, 900, 1000, 1200, 1500 wide x 1200 high
Door openings—external	mm	900, 1000, 1500, 1800, 2400 wide; 2100, 2400, 2700, 3000 high
Doors	mm	300 module, mainly
Drain pipes	mm, m	
Drawing scales	simple scale ratios	
Drawing scales—building and construction		1:10, 1:20, 1:30, 1:50, 1:100
Drawing scales—surveys, sites, key plans		1:100, 1:200, 1:300, 1:500, 1:1000, 1:2000, etc.
Ducting	mm, m	
Excavation	m^3	
Excavation equipment capacity	m^3	
Expansion joints	mm, m	
Flashing	mm, m	

Fig. 33-7
Proposed sizes for some metric building materials.

Metric Units in Home Construction

Item	Units	Some Suggested Sizes
Floor and wall tiles	mm, m, m²	100 module
Flooring	mm, m, m²	100, 300, 400 modules
"Foot board measure" to mm BM, or deciboard		millimetre board measure (1 mm/m² = 0.424 BM);
or m³	or cubicmetre	or deciboard (1 cm · dm²)
Formwork	mm, m, m²	
Furniture	mm	
Glass	mm, m, m²	100 module sizes. 2,3,4,5,6,8,10 mm thick
Guttering	mm	
Heating: boilers, radiator, baseboards	mm	100 module
Insulation	mm, m, kg (loose); 50 kg bags	
Iron, steel, and aluminum	mm, kg	
Lighting fixtures	mm	100 module
Lumber	mm, m	
Metal lath	m2, kg/m²	
Mortar	kg	
Nails	mm	
Paint	kg, l	
Paint coverage	m²/l	
Partitions	mm	300, 400 module
Paving	mm	300 module
Piles	mm, m	
Pipe	mm, m	
Plaster	m², m³, kg, t	40 or 50 kg bags
Plasterboard—size	mm (area m²)	600, 900, 1200 wide; 1200 to 3000 long (300, 400 module)
Roofing	mm, m, kg, l, t	50 kg (felts) etc.
Sanitary bath fixtures	mm	1700, 1800 long; 700, 800 wide; 500 high
Shingles	mm, m²	100 module
Siding	mm, m²	100 module
Sink	mm	400, 500, 600—single 800 to 1800—double
Slate	mm, m²	
Spans	mm	7200, by 1200 to 12000
Staircase	mm	
Staircase rung	mm	225
Staircase rise	mm	200
Staircase width	mm	900 or 1800
Steel—structural	mm, kg/m, kg, t	
Stone	mm, m, m², m³, kg, t	
Story height	mm	2400, 2700, 3000, 3600
Structural clay tile	mm	100 modules, but 75 thickness also
Stud spacing	mm	400
Swimming pools	mm	
Timber	mm, m	International stds. (actual sizes recommended)
Ventilation	mm	100 modules
Volumes	m³, l	
Wall finish	kg	30 kg drums
Windows	mm	100 module
Windows, height	mm	300 to 2100 (basic spaces)
Windows, width	mm	300 to 2400
Wire, dia.	mm	
length	m	

Therefore, in building construction, the first step in metric conversion will be to establish a system of coordinated preferred sizes from dimensional rationalization.   **Fig. 33-8**

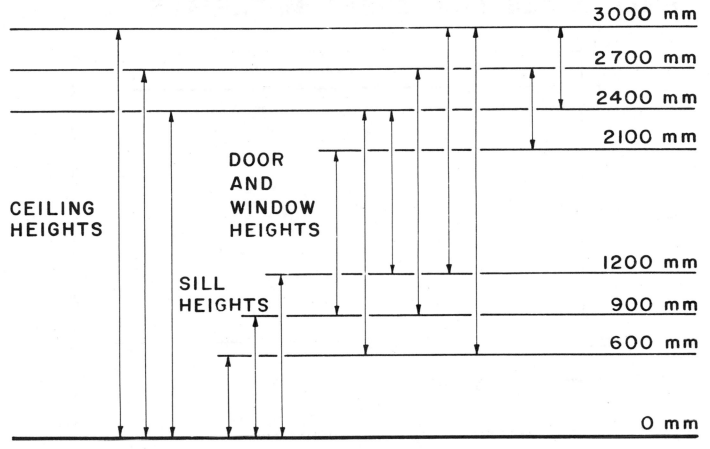

Fig. 33-8
Vertical dimensions used in metric building construction.

This will mean that trade organizations such as the American Plywood Association and the Western Wood Products Association must establish the dimensions of the components so as to reduce the variety of sizes which have to be produced, and to enable components from different sources to be used together on the site without modification. This will mean cooperation between all trade groups such as those that represent wood, metal, ceramics and other materials used in building construction. The total time that it will take to accomplish this gigantic task will depend on many factors including establishment of minimum national building codes and building material standards.

**Problems of Builders and
Home Repair Enthusiasts**
   A problem facing anyone doing construction work in the United States is that some of the large building wholesalers and lumber yards are importing building components designed and manufactured to metric standards. For example, a sink basin manufactured in metric modules may be very close to a similar customary model. However, there is just enough difference in sizes to complicate the problems for the installer. With the free flow of building components from metric to non-metric countries, the problem will increase. For example, imagine the problem of using a 1200 x 2400 mm plywood sheet imported from Australia as a substitute for a 4 x 8 sheet which measures 1220 x 2440 mm.   **Fig. 33-9**

COMPARISON OF CONVENTIONAL AND PROPOSED PANEL SIZES FOR SHEET MATERIALS

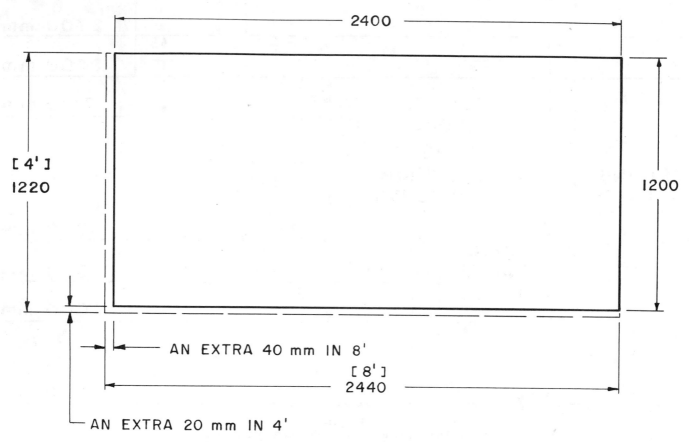

ALL DIMENSIONS IN mm AND IN FEET

Fig. 33-9
A metric size panel would be *too* small to use for a replacement of a 4' x 8' sheet.

Even though the individual in building construction may not regularly use metric measurement, he must understand the system and must own a dual reading metric tape and other measuring tools so that he can convert the metric sizes to customary sizes.

Mechanical Trades

Plumbing, heating and air conditioning are areas that will not be affected by metric conversion until new standards for materials are available. Some of these components may be imported and these will be in metric units. Factors involved in installing these units will require use of SI metric. For example, volume will be in cubic metres, area in square metres and fluid capacity in litres. Force will be expressed in kilonewtons, and pressure and stress in kilopascals or megapascals.

Architectural Drafting

The principles of graphic presentation on metric architectural designs are similar to those for designs using the customary system. One of the main decisions that must be made is to select the measuring unit to indicate size. Many countries converting to the metric system are recommending the use of the millimetre for all architectural drawings except for plot plans, which use either the millimetre or metre. This practice, however, results in very large numbers. A living room, for example, that was 15' x 20' will be 4572 x 6096 mm in size. A ten centimetre (10 cm) module with all dimensions in centimetres has been considered but will not be used.

Paper sizes. In countries utilizing the metric system the recommended size of drawing sheets is the ISO A series. These sizes are all proportional which leads to simple reduction and enlargement. The sheets can also be easily folded for filing. Any drawings larger than A4 can easily be folded to A4 size for filing or mailing. Drawings to A sizes folded to A4 will fit a C4 envelope.

Line weight. The minimum thickness of line for reproduction on a print machine should be 0.2 millimetre. For most purposes three thicknesses can be used as follows: 0.2 mm, 0.4 mm, and 0.8 mm. For lettering on a drawing, the title block should have letters from 5 to 8 mm in height with notes from 1.5 to 4 mm.

Scales. The scales used in building construction are included in ISO/R1047 as shown in **Fig. 33-10a,b**

ARCHITECTURAL

metric scale	use	customary equivalent
1:10	CONST. DETAILS	$1" = 1'\ 0"$ $(1:12)$
1:20	CONST. DETAILS	$\frac{3"}{4} = 1'\ 0"$ $(1:16)$
1:25	CONST. DETAILS	$\frac{1"}{2} = 1'\ 0"$ $(1:24)$
1:50	PLANS, ELEVATION	$\frac{1"}{4} = 1'\ 0"$ $(1:48)$
1:100	PLOT PLAN	$\frac{1"}{8} = 1'\ 0"$ $(1:96)$
1:200	PLOT PLAN	$\frac{1"}{16} = 1'\ 0"$ $(1:192)$
1:500	SITE PLANS	$\frac{1"}{32} = 1'\ 0"$ $(1:384)$

Fig. 33-10a

METRIC mm/mm	CUSTOMARY inch/inch	USE
	SCALE RATIOS	
1:1	12:12	full size
1:2	6:12	half size
1:5	3:12	quarter size**
1:10	1:12	1" = 1'-0"**
1:20	3/4:12 (1:16)	3/4" = 1'-0"**
1:25	1/2:12 (1:24)	1/2" = 1'-0"**
1:50	1/4:12 (1:48)	1/4" = 1'-0"**
1:100	1/8:12 (1:96)	1/8" = 1'-0"**
1:200	1/16:12 (1:192)	1/16" = 1'-0"**
1:500	1/32:12 (1:384)	1/32" = 1'-0"**
1:1000	1:1250 (1:768)	1/64" = 1'-0"**
1:2000	1:2500	Location or Survey

Fig. 33-10b
Use these scale ratios in developing architectural drawing.

If two or more scales are used on the same drawing they should be clearly marked.

Grid paper. With the increasing use of reference grids in architectural drawing, grid paper is very suitable for modular coordination. Use of grid paper is an extremely useful aid to architectural drafting. The grid size should be 1 x 1 mm. These millimetre squares can then be used for almost any scale. They can represent millimetres, centimetres or metres.

Building Construction

With the eventual conversion of the building industry to the metric system, the area of carpentry will drastically change. Since a hard conversion will change lumber and masonary sizes, the entire structure will have to be based on metric dimensions. All homes will be designed and built on the 100 millimetre (100 mm) module.   **Fig. 33-11**

SMALL RESIDENCE IN METRIC

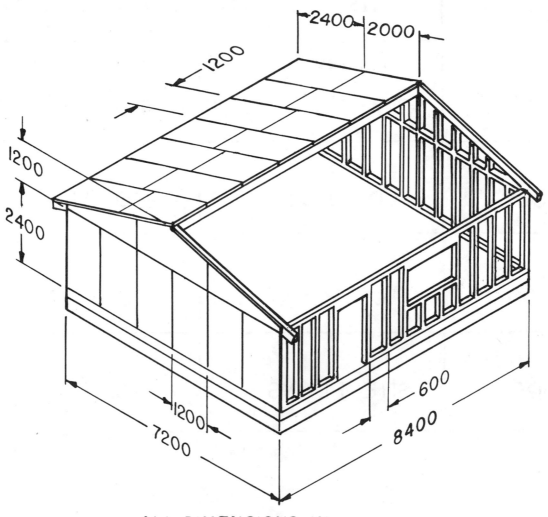

ALL DIMENSIONS IN mm

Fig. 33-11
A small residence design in the metric system.

In laying out the floor plan, floor joists will be placed on 400 millimetre centers, which is very close to the customary 16 inches on center. Most floor decking and sheathing materials will be in 1200 x 2400 mm modules to fit the 400 mm spacing of the floor joists. **Fig. 33-12**

FLOOR JOIST PLAN

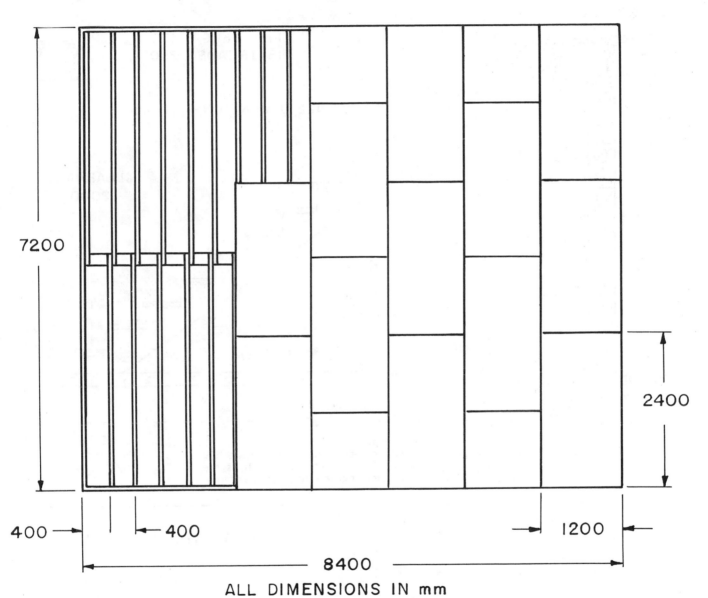

ALL DIMENSIONS IN mm

Fig. 33-12
The floor joist plan and the floor decking are designed to fit perfectly.

All structural details such as stairs will also be based on the 100 mm module even though some dimensions will not be exactly multiples of this amount. **Fig. 33-13**

STAIR DETAIL

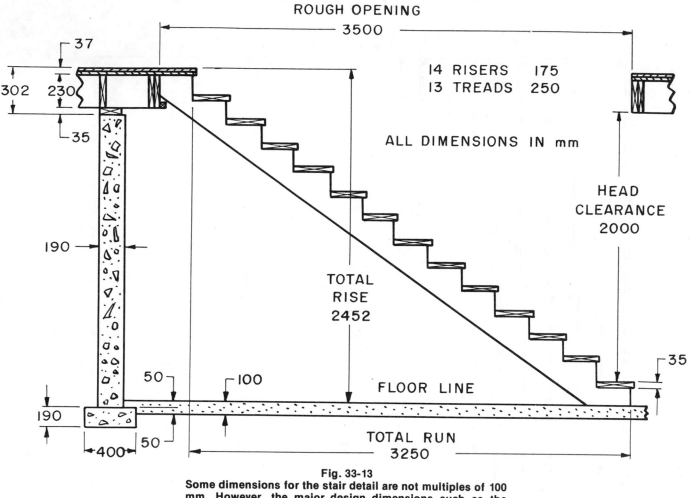

14 RISERS 175
13 TREADS 250

ALL DIMENSIONS IN mm

HEAD CLEARANCE 2000

ROUGH OPENING 3500

TOTAL RISE 2452

FLOOR LINE

TOTAL RUN 3250

Fig. 33-13
Some dimensions for the stair detail are not multiples of 100 mm. However, the major design dimensions such as the rough opening and head clearance are to these standards.

After the walls and partitions are complete, the roof must be framed. The roof may be conventionally framed with rafters and ceiling joists or framed with a truss-type of construction. **Fig. 33-14**

TYPICAL TRUSS DETAIL

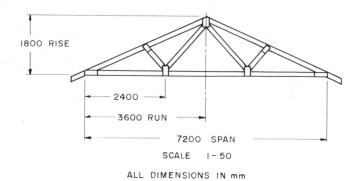

1800 RISE

2400

3600 RUN

7200 SPAN

SCALE 1 - 50

ALL DIMENSIONS IN mm

Fig. 33-14
Typical truss detail in metric.

For a conventionally framed roof, the carpenter must determine the correct lengths. In the customary system the carpenter can use rafter tables to determine the length of rafters. Since no rafter tables for the metric system exist, rafter lengths must be determined by using the Pythagorean Theorem to find the hypotenuse of a right triangle. **Fig. 33-15.** A set of plans to build a garage using the metric system is shown in **Fig 33-16**

PROPOSED METRIC RAFTER SIZING METHOD

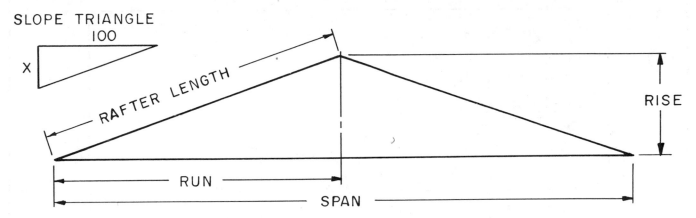

BASED ON 100 mm MODULE
100 mm = 1 DECIMETRE
SLOPE GIVEN IN mm RISE PER DECIMETRE OF RUN

PROBLEM
FIND THE RAFTER LENGTH FOR A 50:100 SLOPE WITH A 7200 mm SPAN
RUN = 3600
RISE PER DECIMETRE = 50
NUMBER OF DECIMETRES IN RUN   36
TOTAL RISE = 1800 ⟶ 50 X 36
RAFTER LENGTH = 4025 mm ⟶ $\sqrt{3600^2 + 1800^2}$

WHERE   A = 3600
                 B = 1800

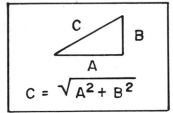

$$C = \sqrt{A^2 + B^2}$$

Fig. 33-15
Determining the length of a rafter for a metric house.

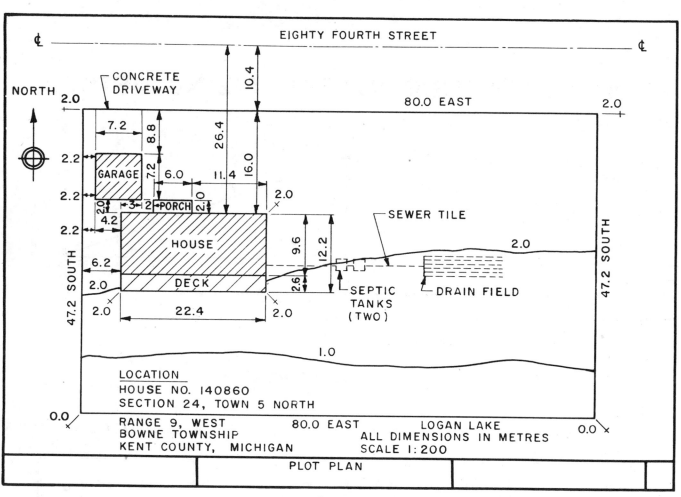

Fig. 33-16
Plans for an all-metric garage.

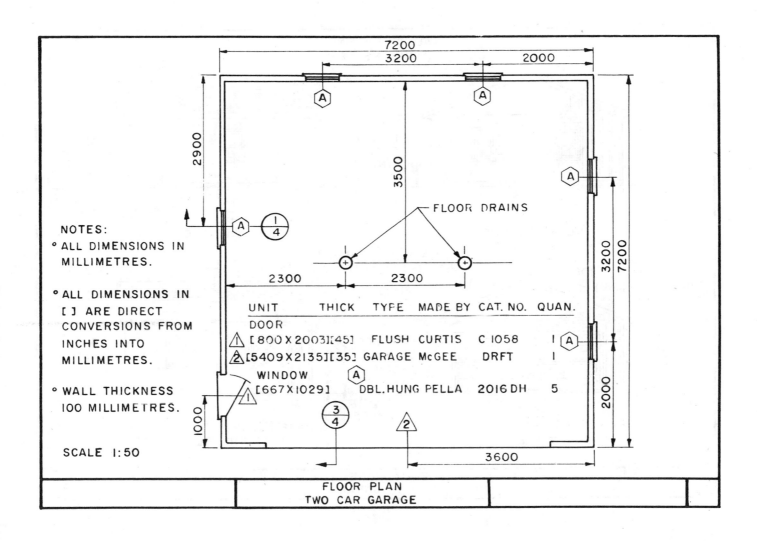

NOTES:
- ALL DIMENSIONS IN MILLIMETRES.

- ALL DIMENSIONS IN [ ] ARE DIRECT CONVERSIONS FROM INCHES INTO MILLIMETRES.

- WALL THICKNESS 100 MILLIMETRES.

SCALE 1:50

UNIT	THICK	TYPE	MADE BY	CAT. NO.	QUAN.
DOOR					
[800 X 2003][45]	FLUSH	CURTIS	C 1058		1
[5409 X 2135][35]	GARAGE	McGEE	DRFT		1
WINDOW					
[667 X 1029]	DBL. HUNG	PELLA	2016 DH		5

FLOOR DRAINS

FLOOR PLAN
TWO CAR GARAGE

33-17

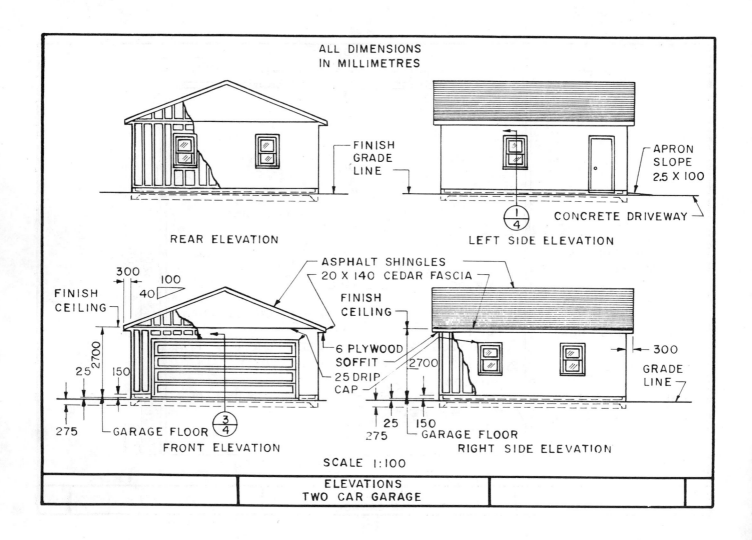

ALL DIMENSIONS
IN MILLIMETRES

REAR ELEVATION

FINISH
GRADE
LINE

LEFT SIDE ELEVATION

APRON
SLOPE
2.5 X 100

CONCRETE DRIVEWAY

300

100

40

FINISH
CEILING

2700

25   150

275

GARAGE FLOOR

FRONT ELEVATION

ASPHALT SHINGLES
20 X 140 CEDAR FASCIA

FINISH
CEILING

6 PLYWOOD
SOFFIT

25 DRIP
CAP

2700

300

GRADE
LINE

25   150

275   GARAGE FLOOR

RIGHT SIDE ELEVATION

SCALE 1:100

ELEVATIONS
TWO CAR GARAGE

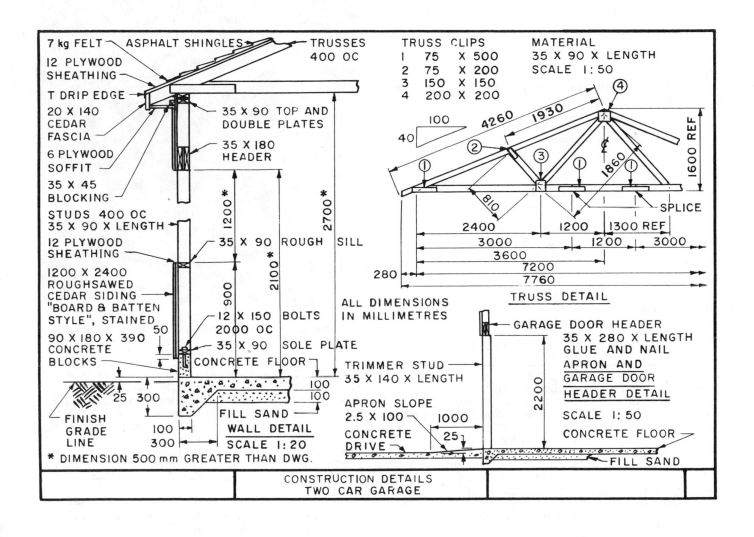

7 kg FELT — ASPHALT SHINGLES — TRUSSES 400 OC

12 PLYWOOD SHEATHING

T DRIP EDGE

20 X 140 CEDAR FASCIA

6 PLYWOOD SOFFIT

35 X 45 BLOCKING

STUDS 400 OC 35 X 90 X LENGTH

12 PLYWOOD SHEATHING

1200 X 2400 ROUGHSAWED CEDAR SIDING "BOARD & BATTEN STYLE", STAINED

90 X 180 X 390 CONCRETE BLOCKS

FINISH GRADE LINE

35 X 90 TOP AND DOUBLE PLATES

35 X 180 HEADER

35 X 90 ROUGH SILL

12 X 150 BOLTS 2000 OC

35 X 90 SOLE PLATE

CONCRETE FLOOR

FILL SAND

WALL DETAIL
SCALE 1:20

* DIMENSION 500 mm GREATER THAN DWG.

1200 2700* 2100* 900 50 25 300 100 300 100 100

TRUSS CLIPS
1   75   X 500
2   75   X 200
3   150 X 150
4   200 X 200

MATERIAL
35 X 90 X LENGTH
SCALE 1:50

100 4260 1930 1600 REF
40   810 1860
2400 1200 1300 REF
3000 1200 3000
3600
7200
280 7760

SPLICE

TRUSS DETAIL

ALL DIMENSIONS IN MILLIMETRES

TRIMMER STUD 35 X 140 X LENGTH

APRON SLOPE 2.5 X 100

CONCRETE DRIVE

1000 25

GARAGE DOOR HEADER
35 X 280 X LENGTH
GLUE AND NAIL

APRON AND GARAGE DOOR HEADER DETAIL

SCALE 1:50

CONCRETE FLOOR

FILL SAND

2200

CONSTRUCTION DETAILS
TWO CAR GARAGE

UNIT 34
GRAPHIC ARTS AND PRINTING

Conversion to the metric system will affect graphic arts both directly and indirectly. Metric conversion will necessitate certain changes in photography, paper, envelopes, microfilm, cold type layout and packaging. Because most paper has printing of some kind on it, metric conversion will require that additional information on metric weights be included. During the early stages of conversion, labels and cartons show dual measurement with both customary measurements and the metric equivalents. Eventually, most products will be available in rounded metric sizes. Hot type printing (letterpress) will not be affected by metric conversion. The reason for this is that a hard conversion of this machinery and the type sizes would be too costly.

Metric Units

In printing and allied industries, the most common units are:

Paper	Unit	Symbol
machine roll width	metre	m
	millimetre	mm
customer roll width	millimetre	mm
cut paper sizes	millimetre	mm
paper and board thickness	micrometre	μm
roll diameter	millimetre	mm
small area	square centimetre	cm^2
	square millimetre	mm^2
sheet area	square metre	m^2
mass (or weight) per unit	gram per square metre	g/m^2 (gsm)
*mass (or weight) per 1000 sheets	kilogram	kg

*expressed to the nearest one decimal point

Photography

Photography is one area in which metric has been used for many years. Metric units are used to describe many film sizes, lens sizes, focal length, and photography mixtures. This is natural, since many kinds of cameras were originally developed in traditional metric countries. For example, the 35 mm camera was designed in 1914 by Oskar Barnack, a German engineer. Movie cameras and film have traditionally been produced in 8 mm, 16 mm, and 35 mm sizes. **Fig. 34-1.**

Fig. 34-1
The photography industry has utilized metric measurement for many years.

Anyone interested in photography has a visual concept of what these sizes mean. Describing the film for a 35 mm camera as 1.3779 inches would be odd.

There is a great deal of dual measuring language used in photography. While the camera and film are described in metric, often the settings for the distance from the subject and other information such as lighting standards are given in the customary system. There is a trend to include the metric equivalent for all measurements used in photography. Many of the photographic solutions are described in metric terms but some of the terms are incorrect. Common errors are the following: (1) Using cc to describe liquids. Actually what is meant is cubic centimetres, but a more appropriate term is millilitres, since a liquid is involved. For example, to say "360 cc of warm water" is wrong. It should be "360 millilitres of warm water." (2) Weights in grams abbreviated as grms or gm, which are incorrect. The correct symbol for grams is g without a period. (3) Giving the temperature of a solution in centigrade, such as 55° centigrade. The correct term is 55 degrees Celsius, or the symbol 55 °C should be used.

ISO Paper Sizes for Printing

The ISO paper sizes described in Unit 19 are the trimmed sizes. In printing it is often necessary to start with sheets somewhat larger so that they can be trimmed to the finished sizes. For example, when illustrations are bled to the edge of the page, a somewhat larger size of paper is needed so that the sheets can be trimmed to the edge of the illustrations. There are two series available for printing: (1) The ISO sizes for normal trim, identified by the letter R. For example, RAO is 680 x 1220 mm which is about 19 mm wider and 31 mm longer than the finished size of AO. (2) Sizes for bled work or for unusually large trims are identified by the SR identification. **Fig. 34-2.**

Trimmed	Normal Trims	Bled work or extra trims
A0 841 x 1189 mm	RA0 860 x 1220 mm	SRA0 900 x 1280 mm
A1 594 x 841 mm	RA1 610 x 860 mm	SRA1 640 x 900 mm
A2 420 x 594 mm	RA2 430 x 610 mm	SRA2 450 x 640 mm

Fig. 34-2
Comparison of typical A sizes trimmed, those with prefix R which are untrimmed stock sizes, and those with the prefix SR which are suitable for bleed work or extra trim.

Some countries that are going metric are slowly phasing in some of the ISO paper sizes while retaining many of the customary sizes. A soft conversion from the customary sizes should round off the sizes to the nearest millimetre. **Fig. 34-3.**

A4 size on metric sheet size will become increasingly preferred for international correspondence.

Government Letter Size	203	x	268	mm
Industry Letter Size	215	x	280	mm
Legal Size	215	x	355	mm
A4 Size	210	x	297	mm
Metric Sheet Size	210	x	280	mm

Fig. 34-3
Comparison of the metric equivalents of common sizes used for correspondence.

Cutting Paper to Metric Sizes

It is a simple matter to convert a paper cutter for cutting paper to metric sizes. The flexible metal tape for setting the depth is available with a dual reading scale, namely, inches and fractions of an inch and millimetres.

Book Sizes

There is no standard for book sizes in the United States. As a result, books are published in every conceivable size and shape, some of which are hard to store. Many of the larger soft covered books and magazines are printed in the 8-1/2" x 11" format. For example, a change to A4 size would produce a publication that is slightly narrower and slightly longer. A change to the metric sheet size would result in a publication that is slightly narrower but the same length. Many magazines printed in England, Australia and South Africa use A4 size paper. The principal objection to using only A sizes for books and other publications is that there would be less opportunity for variety in design.

Envelopes

Envelopes designed to metric standards are described in Unit 19. The International Postal Association is attempting to force companies to adopt these standards by requiring that all first class mail fit into envelopes of approximately these size and shape relationships. With the increase of automatic handling of mail it seems essential that standard envelope sizes be adopted.

GUIDELINES FOR METRIC USE IN PAPER MARKETING

A committee of the American Paper Institute (API) has issued a set of recommendations concerning the application of the metric system in the marketing of paper.

The two basic recommendations are that:
● There should be "no changes whatsoever" in either the sizes or weights of printing and writing papers *at this time,* and
● The sizes and basis weights of the paper should be shown on packaging labels in metric measure in addition to the customary system.

It is suggested that metric measures be added to packages as follows: carton labels, junior carton lables, ream labels, skid labels or stencils, and roll labels or stencils. It was recommended that the *dimensions* of the paper, and the *weight* of the paper be shown in metric sizes. It is also suggested that metric measures not be added to invoices at this time.

The recommended procedure:

1. Paper sizes should be stated in millimeters by multiplying inches by 25.4. For example, 8-1/2 inches times 25.4 equals 215.9 mm. This should be rounded off to 216 mm.

2. In the metric system, the basis weight should be stated in grams per square meter. To convert from basis weight in pounds to grams per square meter, the basis weight should be multiplied by 1406.5 and divided by the square inches in the base sheet. For example, 20-pound paper (17 inches by 22 inches 500): 17 inches multiplied by 22 inches equals 374 square inches. Twenty pounds times 1406.5 divided by 374 equals 75.2 grams per square meter (g/m^2). This should be rounded off to 75 g/m^2.

While some buyers in Europe use "gsm" to denote grams per square meter, the proper usage is g/m^2, and the latter is recommended for use on labels. For convenience in discussion, the phrase "the basis weight is 20" could be replaced by the expression "the grammage is 20."

Placement on Packages

Each company may design labels as it deems to be most desirable. The following practices are recommended:

1. The units in metric measure should appear below the customary units. A second choice would be to have them appear to the right of the customary units. The placement of metric measurements above, or to the left of the customary units, should be avoided.

2. The printed metric units should be 1/3 or 1/4 the size of the customary units.

3. A space should be left between a number and the symbol to which it refers.

Total Weight

The total weight of paper, when stated should either be expressed in kilograms or metric tons. (To convert from pounds to kilograms, multiply by 0.4536; from pounds to metric tons, by 0.00004536; and from short tons to metric tons, by 0.9072.) The term "kilo" should be used only as a prefix to the name of a metric unit, not as a unit in itself.

Other Affects of Metric conversion on the Graphic Arts Industry

1. *Newsprint.* Newsprint suppliers will need to adopt metric units for paper widths and also paper weights.

2. *Composition.* There is no universal system of typographic measure. Eventually all measurements will be in the logical metric system.

No change is contemplated in typographic measurement for hot type. The use of points, picas and ems will continue and the Angla America type height of 0.9186 inches used in the United States will simply be converted to 23.32 mm. **Fig. 34-4a,b.**

PRINTER'S UNITS
CUSTOMARY & METRIC EQUIVALENTS

PRINTER'S		CUSTOMARY—INCHES		METRIC—millimetres
Picas	Points	Approximate Fraction	Decimal	
	1	1/64	.014	.35
	2	1/32	.028	.70
	3	3/64	.042	1.05
	4	7/128	.055	1.40
	5	1/16	.069	1.75
	6	5/64	.083	2.10
	7	3/32	.097	2.45
	8	7/64	.111	2.80
	9	1/8	.125	3.15
	10	9/64	.138	3.50
1	12	21/128	.166	4.20
	14	25/128	.194	4.90
	18	1/4	.249	6.30
2	24	21/64	.332	8.40
	30	53/128	.414	10.50
3	36	1/2	.498	12.60
	42	37/64	.581	14.70
4	48	85/128	.664	16.80
5	60	53/64	.828	21.00
6	72	1	.996	25.20

Fig. 34-4a
Printer's units with customary and metric equivalents. Note that 1 pica equals 4.2 mm.

METRIC UNITS
PRINTER'S & CUSTOMARY EQUIVALENTS

| METRIC-millimetres | PRINTER'S | | CUSTOMARY-Inches |
	Points	Approximate Picas + Points	
1	2.86		.039
2	5.71		.079
3	8.57		.118
4	11.43		.157
5	14.29	1 + 2¼	.197
6	17.14	1 + 5	.236
7	20.00	1 + 8	.276
8	22.86	1 + 10¾	.315
9	25.71	2 + 1½	.354
10	28.57	2 + 4½	.394
15	42.86	3 + 6¾	.591
20	57.14	4 + 9	.787
25	71.43	5 + 11	.984
30	85.71	7 + 1¼	1.181
35	100.00	8 + 3½	1.378
40	114.28	9 + 5¾	1.575
45	128.57	10 + 4	1.772
50	142.85	11 + 6¼	1.969
75	214.28	17 + 5¼	2.953
100	285.71	23 + 8½	3.937

Fig. 34-4b
Units showing the rounded metric units with the printer's
equivalents in points and picas plus the equivalents in
decimal inches.

Eventually, however, metric standards will be incorporated in all phototype setting equipment.

3. *Ink.* Ink manufacturers will continue to sell ink by weight so that the only change will be from the customary weights to those in kilograms for larger quantities. Mixing ink colors will be vastly more simple in metric weights than in the current customary weights. The advantage of having equivalent formulas which total 1000 parts with no fractions will make it much easier. The common sizes of ink containers most likely to be used include the following: 500 grams or 1/2 (0.5) kilogram to replace 1 pound, 1 kilogram to replace 2 pounds, 2 kilograms to replace 5 pounds, and 5 kilograms to replace 10 pounds. All the metric containers will be larger than the customary sizes, except the 2 kilogram size, which would be equivalent to 4.4 pounds instead of 5 pounds.

4. *Process of plates.* Metal plates will be defined in terms of millimetre width and length and also for thickness replacing gage measurement. The depth of each will be expressed in micrometres (1/1000 millimetre) to the nearest 5.

5. *Film.* Film currently dimensioned in customary measurements will be given equivalent metric sizes.

6. *Fluids.* Fluids will be packaged in suitable units and will be sold by the millilitre and litre.

7. *Screen ruling.* Screen ruling will be expressed in metric terms, which will follow the current practice of lines per inch. However, the lines will be described per centimetre, not per millimetre. **Fig. 34-5.**

SCREEN RULINGS

Customary Rulings	Metric Rulings
per inch	per centimetre
50	20
65	26
75	30
100	40
120	48
133	54
150	60
175	70
200	80

Fig. 34-5
Screen ruling.

8. *Description of printing presses.* Much of the printing equipment is imported from countries operating on the metric system. These machines were designed in metric units so, when specifications are given in the customary system, most dimensions show odd fractions of an inch.

Phototypesetting

While there will probably not be a hard change to the metric system for hot type processes, the metric system will eventually be used exclusively for phototypesetting. The European Common Market countries are committed to total metrication in the years ahead. The International Organization for Standardization (ISO) is considering several standards in this area. One possible system proposed by S. J. Heden of Sweden is to use the base 10 system for type sizing and spacing. This system advocates the use of a unit called the "d" which is defined as 1/10 of a millimetre (0.10 mm). With the Heden system, type specification would be given in two numbers such as: 40/60. These numbers are in "d" units. For example, the 40/60 would indicate that 40 is the height of the mainstroke and 60 shows the distance between lines or body size. This number could be read as a mainstroke of 4.0 mm and a line spacing of 6.0 mm.

Packaging

Perhaps no area of the graphic arts industry will be so totally affected by the metric change as the packaging industry.

Use of correct symbols. Many packaging companies make the mistake of using incorrect metric symbols. All symbols should be in lower case without periods. Some examples of mistakes used on food packages are shown in **Fig. 34-6.**

WEIGHT		VOLUME OR LIQUID CAPACITY	
Correct: kg	g	Correct: *l* or l, ml, kl	
Incorrect: Kg	G	Incorrect: L	cc
Kg.	g.	Litre	c.c.
Kgm.	gm.	LITRES	CC
	Gm.		C.C.
	GM		ml.
	GM.		ML
	GR.		ML.
	gms.		mls
	grs.		
	GRS.		
	GRAM		
	grams		
	GRAMS		

Fig. 34-6
The correct and incorrect methods of indicating weight and fluid volume or liquid capacity. A check of any supermarket or drug chain will show that hundreds of products are mislabeled in metric units.

Rounding down. If dual listing is used on customary packaging, it is important to round off the numerical values of the metric equivalent to a realistic value. All too often the conversion is to very exact metric equivalents such as the following: 7 fl oz = 198.87 ml, 9 oz = 255.1 g, or 2 lb = 907.2 g. The use of these unrealistic equivalents assumes that the original package size was accurate to 1 part in 1000 or 10 000. If the soft change is used, the rounded metric size should be to the next *smallest* value. For example, 6 fl oz might be rounded to 170 ml. Packaging regulations require that the package size indicate that contents is no less than the amount printed on the package. Frequently packages will be mismarked so that there are actually false package sizes in metric. For example, a package marked 1-1/2 oz (45 grams) is incorrect, since actually 1-1/2 oz is 42.5 grams; therefore, the rounded metric equivalent should probably to 40 to 42 grams.

Another example of possible false packaging practice is to label liquids by weight (mass) in grams rather than by liquid volume in millilitres. It is true that if a container is filled with water it makes no difference whether it is listed as 500 grams or 500 millilitres. However, if the solution is heavier than water (such as most oils) then 500 millilitres weigh more than 500 grams. To put it another way, if a heavy liquid is listed as 500 grams, the customer will not be getting a full 500 millilitres.

Selecting packaging sizes. In soft conversion, metric sizes are always odd. For example a 10 oz package would be 283.5 grams rounded to 280 grams, and a 14 oz package would be 396.9 grams rounded to from 390 to 395 grams. In converting to the metric system there are several desirable ways of choosing the correct sizes of packaging. **Fig. 34-7.**

Present	Possible Metric
1/2 lb, 1 lb, 2 lb	250 g, 500 g, 1 kg
2 oz, 4 oz, 8 oz	50 g, 100 g, 200 g
1 lb, 2 lb, 3 lb	500 g, 1 kg, 1.5 kg
1 pint, 1 quart	500 ml, 1 litre
3 quarts	4 litres

Fig. 34-7
Current common sizes of products and their possible metric equivalents.

Some of these are as follows:

1. Equal increase in series. This method has been used by toothpaste manufacturers in Canada who have chosen six sizes: 25, 50, 75, 100, 125, and 150 ml. These six sizes are a great reduction from the 30 or more previous sizes in the older customary system such as travel size, economy size, giant size, etc. With metric equal increase in series, it is very easy for the consumer to compare the price of a 100 ml toothpaste size in various brands.

2. 1-2-5-10 metric series. This is an ideal way of sizing all kinds of packaging, because modular sizes larger or smaller than these can be obtained by adding zeros or making smaller sizes by adding a decimal point in front of the unit. For example, the sizes may be 1 gram, 2 grams, 5 grams, 10 grams, 100 grams, 200 grams, 500 grams, and 1 kilogram. Another advantage of using this system is that most metric weighing scales are graduated in these units.

3. Preferred series. The preferred number series, or the Renard series, can be used for geometric increments. These can be particularly useful in technical work or in the packaging and sizing of technical materials.

4. Halving principle. The halving principle is commonly used in the customary series such as 1 pound (16 ounces), 1/2 pound (8 ounces), 1/4 pound (4 ounces), etc. This system can also be used to divide the kilogram into 500 grams and 250 grams.

UNIT 35
AUTOMECHANICS

All the major automobile manufacturers are committed to metric conversion and the use of metric standards in all production when feasible. **Fig. 35-1.**

Fig. 35-1
In the years ahead, the total automobile not just the engine will be manufactured to metric specifications.

Metric conversion will affect manufacturing, servicing, and customer use of automobiles in many ways.

Manufacturing

New American automobile designs will utilize materials produced to metric modules, ISO threads, and other standard metric units. During the early stages of conversion, engine development and manufacturing will be affected the most. The least change will be noted in the body, frame and drive train. Conversion to all metric measurement and standards will be a slow and gradual process extending over many years and will depend to a large extent on the availability of metric materials and components. Moving to all metric automobiles will require a large number of metric standards for such things as hose, gears, glass, splines and innumerable other items. **Fig. 35-2.**

Some Standards Important to The Automotive Industry
which require Metric Module

Bearings	Glass
Thread Fasteners	Steel and Iron
Other Fasteners	Dimensions & Shapes
Mechanical Drives	Physical Properties
Belts, Chains	Non-Ferrous Metal
Glass	Dimensions & Shapes
Hydraulic & Air	Physical Properties
Fittings	Rubber, Textile & Plastics
Equipment	Production Equipment
Electrical	Perishable Tools (Drills, Gages, Etc.)
Wire & Terminals	General Test and Performance Standards
Equipment	
Light Switches	

Fig. 35-2
Engineering standards for all materials will need to be produced to metric modules.

Only a few ISO metric standards such as those for threads, bearings, and metals are currently available. About 30 percent of all cars now in use in the United States have ISO metric threads. Wheel sizes will not change since the customary standards for these items are now used worldwide.

Metric Units Used in Automechanics and Power

In automobile manufacturing and related industries the most common units are shown in **Fig. 35-3.**

Quantity	Unit	Symbol
length	millimetre	mm
	metre	m
	kilometre	km
area	square centimetre	cm^2
	square metre	m^2
volume	cubic centimetre	cm^3
	cubic decimetre	dm^3
	cubic metre	m^3
liquid volume (capacity)	millilitte	ml
	litre	l or L
fuel consumption	litres per 100 kilometres	l /100 km
velocity (speed)	kilometre per hour	km/h
acceleration ad deceleration	metre per second squared	m/s^2
weight (mass)	gram	g
	kilogram	kg
	metric ton	t
density (mass density)	kilogram per cubic metre	kg/m^3
force	newton	N
moments of force (torque)	newton metre	N•m
pressure	kilopascal	kPa
energy	kilojoule	kJ
	megajoule	MJ
power	kilowatt	kW
stress	megapascal	MPa
temperature	degree Celsius	°C
electric current	ampere	A
electric potential	volt	V

NOTE: Engine capacity will be expressed in cubic centimetres or litre. Horsepower ratings will be replaced by power in kilowatts.

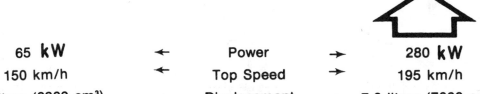

65 kW	←	Power	→	280 kW
150 km/h	←	Top Speed	→	195 km/h
2.3 litres (2300 cm³)	←	Displacement	→	7.0 litres (7000 cm³)
6 to 8 l/km	←	Fuel Consumption	→	15 to 24 l/km
900 kg	←	Weight (mass)	→	2.2 t
4200 mm	←	Length	→	6000 mm
4.7 litres	←	Oil Capacity	→	5.7 litres
14 litres	←	Cooling System	→	24 litres
40 litres	←	Gasoline Tank	→	85 litres
0.2 m³	←	Luggage Capacity	→	0.6 m³

Fig. 35-3
Specifications for a metric car.

The following will be affected by conversion to the metric system:

1. Measurements of all kinds including length, area, volume, weight, temperature, pressure, stress and all other items. **Fig. 35-4.**

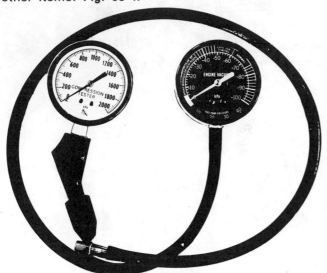

Fig. 35-4a
In the SI metric system, pressure and stress are expressed in mulitples of the pascal, primarily the kilopascal and the magapascal.

FIELD OF USE	psi	inch Hg	kPa	MPa
Gasoline engine—air cleaner intake vacuum			0.5	
			1.0	
Hydraulic pump—inlet vacuum		3	10	
		10	35	
Gasoline engine—intake manifold vacuum		5	20	
		20	70	
Power brakes—vacuum tank		15	50	
		25	80	
Internal combustion engine—exhaust back-pressure		1	3	
		4	15	
Gasoline engine—fuel pump	1.5		10	
	6		40	
Pressurized radiator—pressure relief cap	4		30	
	15		100	
Engine oil pressure	7		50	
	30		200	
Pneumatic tire	20		140	0.14
	200		1400	1.4
Internal combustion engine—cylinder compression	100		700	0.7
	200		1400	1.4
Transmission	10		70	0.07
	400		2800	2.8
Power steering	50		350	0.35
	1200		8000	8
Hydraulic brakes	200		1 400	1.4
	3000		21 000	21
Air Conditioning	0.1		0.7	
	400		2800	

Fig. 35-4b
This chart illustrates some of the uses in the area of automotive manufacturing.

2. Automotive specifications which will be expressed in metric units including such items as the capacity of the fuel tank, the amount of liquid used for cooling, engine weight, and all other items. **Fig. 35-5.**

M E T R I C   P O W E R

POWER
48 kilowatts - kW
Fig. 35-5
Horsepower will be replaced by kilowatts.

3. Physical measuring equipment including gages and tools. These will need to be recalibrated in metric or replaced (as is the case of wrenches).

4. Estimating including cost and all other forms of information will be rewritten in metric terms.

Designing and Producing an ALL Metric Engine
The first American-made, all metric engine utilizing ISO metric threads is the 2300 cm³, four cylinder overhead crankshaft engine for use in the Ford Motor Company's domestic sub-compact vehicle. The engine used in the General Motors sub-compact is also of metric design. **Fig. 35-6.**

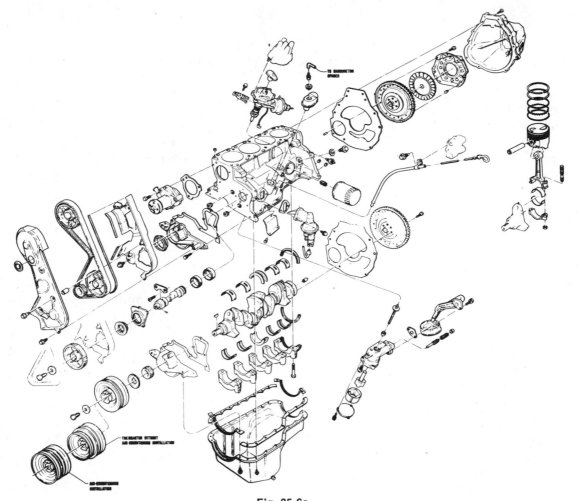

Fig. 35-6a
This four cylinder engine designed and produced to metric specification is used in sub-compact cars.

The design and production of these engines are carried out in metric measurements, using all metric fasteners. The production line Is Identical to that used for producing a customary (traditional) engine with the following exceptions: **Fig. 35-7.**

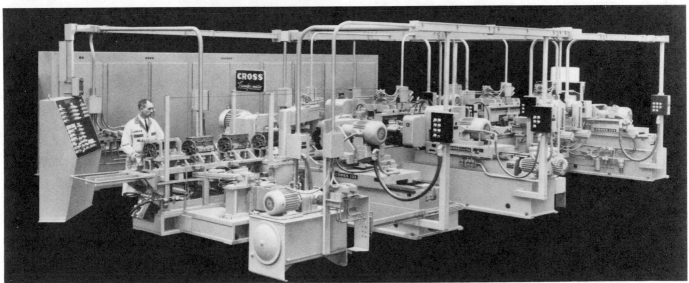

Fig. 35-7
The assembly line for the metric engine is the same as for a customary engine except for the required tooling.

GENERAL SPECIFICATIONS

	METRIC	CUSTOMARY
Engine Weight (Dry)	144.5 kg	318.6 lb
Engine Displacement	2300 cubic centi-metres	140 cubic inches
Firing Order	1-3-4-2	—
Cylinder Bore	96.037 mm	3.781 in
Piston Stroke	79.400 mm	3.126 in
Bore/Stroke Ratio	1.20	—
Cylinder Bore Spacing	105.994 mm	4.173 in
Compression Ratio	8.40:1	—
Net Horsepower at RPM		102 @ 5200
Net Torque at RPM		122 @ 3200
Carburetor: Venturi Diameter	Pri-.-26 mm Sec.-27 mm	Pri.-1.023; in Sec.-1.063 in
Throttle Bore Diameter	Pri.-32 mm Sec.-36 mm	Pri.-1.26; in Sec.-1.417 in
Crankshaft Main Bearings: Material— Copper-Lead Alloy on Steel Back		
Number of Counter Weights	4	—
Main Bearing Diameter	60.935 mm	2.399 in
Crankpin Bearing Diameter	52.00 mm	2.0472 in
Piston Pin Diameter	23.165 mm	.9120 in
Connecting Rod: Material—Forged Steel (SAE-1041-H)		
Length-Centerline to Centerline	132.199 mm	5.2047 in
Valve Lifters	Hydraulic	—
Valve Rocker Arm Ratio	1.64:1	—
Valve lift:		
Intake	10.160	.400
Exhaust	10.160	.400
Vavle Timing:		
Intake Opens, Degrees BTC	22°	—
Intake Closes, Degrees ABC	66°	—
Exhaust Opens, Degrees BBC	65°	—
Exhaust Closes, Degrees ATC	24°	—
Vavle Spring Loading:		
Valve Closed	32.2-35.8 kg	71-79 lb
Valve Open	81.2-89.8 kg	179-198 lb
Oil Capacity, including Filter	4.75 litres	5 lig. gt
Oil Pump Pressure, Capacity at RPM	345 kPa @ 2000	50 psi @ 2000
Fuel Pump Pressure Range	10 to 30 kPa	3.5-4.5 psi

Fig. 35-6b
General specifications for metric engine shown in Fig. 35-6a.

1. Hybrid tooling is used wherever metric sizes are specified. Drills and reamers have the cutting edges ground to metric specifications but the tool shanks fit into customary spindles and holders. Drill bushings are customary except for the hole size. Drills and reamers are made from customary blanks with only the cutting edges ground to metric sizes. The bushings used for reaming have interior openings ground to metric standards. However, the exterior diameters of these bushings fit the customary hole in the drilling jig.

2. ISO metric threads are used throughout, requiring the use of metric drills and taps for cutting all internal threads.

3. The keyway cutters are ground to metric standards, but the cutting tool fits the customary arbor.

4. All gages are metric.

5. Grinding wheels used for grinding the main bearings are customary size wheels that have been dressed to metric measurement.

6. The gear used on the overhead camshaft requires a metric hob.

7. In assembly, all metric wrenches are used with power driven tools.

To prevent mixup with the customary production line:

(a) The bolt heads of ISO metric fasteners may be marked with the letter "M".

(b) Metric cutting tools and gages are color coded for proper identification. The face of metric dial indicating gages is yellow in color to distinguish them from the customary gages.

(c) *Metric only* measuring tools and gages are used rather than dual reading tools and gages.

Servicing

Retraining of service personnel will be required for utilizing the metric system for service jobs and repairs. The automechanic will need a complete set of metric tools and instruments including rule, micrometer and metric wrenches. All testing equipment will need to be recalibrated. Pressure gages will be in kilopascals. Feeler gages will be in millimetre thicknesses.

Customer

1. Engine size (displacement) is specified in litres or cubic centimetres. This is the total displacement in the volume of one cylinder (area times stroke) multiplied by the number of cylinders. For example, a 2.3 litre engine is also a 2300 cubic centimetre engine (2300 cm^3) -- the old but incorrect metric term 2300 cc is frequently seen.

To determine the displacement of one cylinder, find the area of the circle formed by the head of the piston or the cylinder. The diameter or bore of the cylinder is specified in millimetres (mm). For example, if the bore is 80 millimetres, this should be changed to centimetres, namely 8 cm before finding the area. The stroke should also be changed from millimetres to centimetres since displacement is given in cubic centimetres (cm^3). For example, a 79.4 millimetre stroke is also a 7.94 centimetre stroke. To find the volume (displacement of one cylinder), multiply the area by the stroke. Then multiply this volume by the number of cylinders to find the total engine displacement. **Fig. 35-8.**

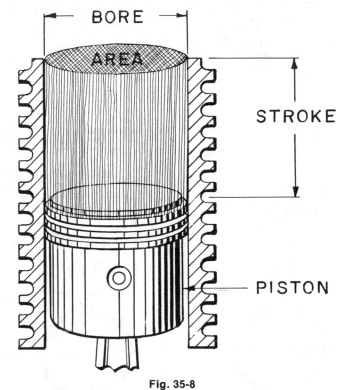

Fig. 35-8
Method for figuring engine displacement. Volume in cubic centimetres of one cylinder equals area times stroke.

For the engine shown in **Fig. 35-6** the specifications are:

   Piston bore -- 96.037 mm or 9.6 cm
   Piston stroke -- 79.40 mm or 7.94 cm
Volume equals area times length
   Area equals d^2 ÷ 4 x π or *area* equals 0.7854 d^2
   Volume of one cylinder equals 0.7854 x 9.6 x 9.6 x 7.94 = 574.7 cm^3. Total displacement equals 574.7 cm^3 x 4 = 2298 cm^3 rounded to 2300 cm^3 or 2.3 litres.

Remember, the reason all measurements are changed from millimetres to centimetres is because *volume* is shown in cubic centimetres not cubic millimetres.

2. A dual reading speedometer will show speeds in miles per hour and kilometres per hour. Automobile speedometers are in decimal units of 10 such as 10, 20, 30, etc. However, many road signs are in fractions such as 1/8 mile to exit or 1/4 mile to service area. The driver must convert one or the other to decimal or fractions. When both speedometers and highway signs are in metric, this problem will be eliminated.

3. Cars with metric engines have the users' handbook written in metric language.

4. All units involving liquid are specified in litres: the size of the gas tank, oil capacity, and coolant required.

5. Tire pressure is given in kilopascals. **Fig. 35-9.**

6. Speed limit signs will show speeds in kilometres per hour using the symbol km/h. **Fig. 35-10.**

7. Average stopping distance will be in metres at various speeds. **Fig. 35-11.**

psi lb/□"	kPa	psi lb/□"	kPa	psi lb/□"	kPa	psi lb/□"	kPa	psi lb/□"	kPa	psi lb/□"	kPa
9	60	33	230	57	395	81	560	105	725	129	890
10	70	34	235	58	400	82	565	106	730	130	895
11	75	35	240	59	405	83	570	107	740	131	905
12	85	36	250	60	415	84	580	108	745	132	910
13	90	37	255	61	420	85	585	109	750	133	915
14	95	38	260	62	430	86	595	110	760	134	925
15	105	39	270	63	435	87	600	111	765	135	930
16	110	40	275	64	440	88	605	112	770	136	940
17	115	41	285	65	450	89	615	113	780	137	945
18	125	42	290	66	455	90	620	114	785	138	950
19	130	43	295	67	460	91	625	115	795	139	960
20	140	44	305	68	470	92	635	116	800	140	965
21	145	45	310	69	475	93	640	117	805	141	970
22	150	46	315	70	485	94	650	118	815	142	980
23	160	47	325	71	490	95	655	119	820	143	985
24	165	48	330	72	495	96	660	120	825	144	995
25	170	49	340	73	505	97	670	121	835	145	1 000
26	180	50	345	74	510	98	675	122	840	146	1 005
27	185	51	350	75	515	99	685	123	850	147	1 015
28	195	52	360	76	525	100	690	124	855	148	1 020
29	200	53	365	77	530	101	695	125	860	149	1 025
30	205	54	370	78	540	102	705	126	870	150	1 035
31	215	55	380	79	545	103	710	127	875	151	1 040
32	220	56	385	80	550	104	715	128	885	152	1 050

Fig. 35-9
A comparison of the pounds per square inch with the kilopascal. If tires require a pressure of 28 psi, then the equivalent will be 195 kPa.

SPEED LIMIT SIGNS
(Customary & metric*)

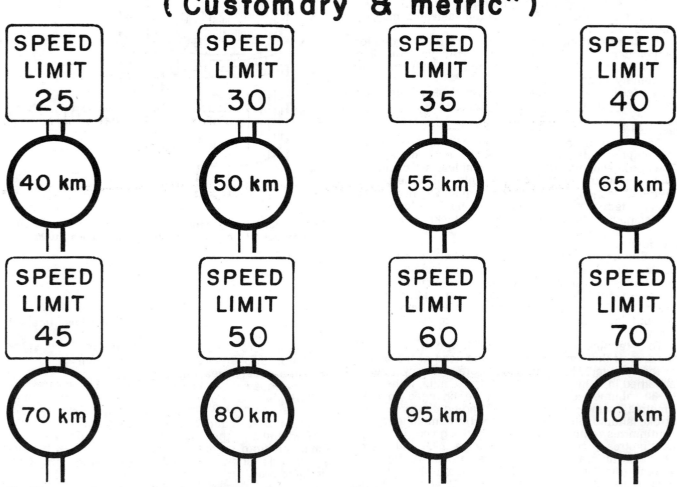

* Rounded off to the nearest 5 km

Fig. 35-10
Metric speed signs may be round in shape in contrast to present customary rectangular signs. The speed in metric may be listed as 70 km/h or just 70 km using lower case letters. Upper case letters such as 70 KM/H are incorrect. Note that metric speeds are rounded to the nearest 5 km. This difference between equivalent customary and metric speeds is not significant.

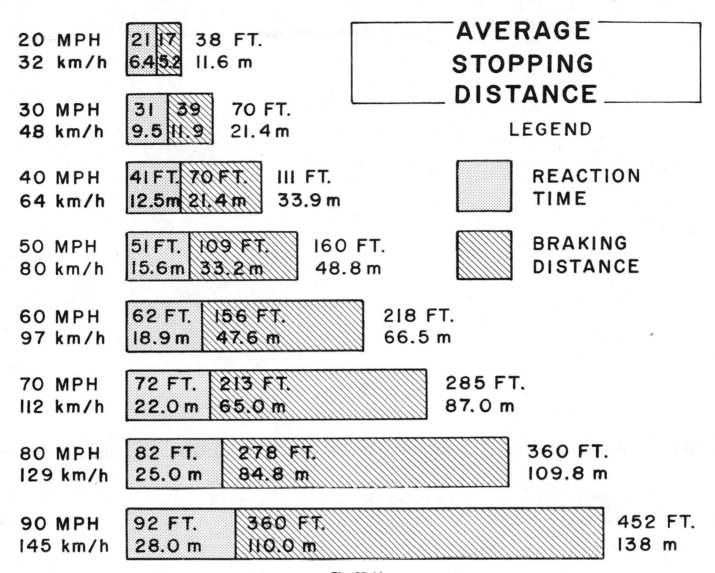

Fig. 35-11
Average stopping distance in customary and metric.

8. Gas consumption is shown in litres per hundred kilometres (ℓ/100 km). Litres per 100 kilometres shows the *quantity* of gasoline used in traveling a certain distance. It is, therefore, a unit of *fuel consumption.* In the customary system miles per gallon (MPG) shows exactly the opposite. Miles per gallon gives the distance that can be covered with a certain amount of gasoline. It is a measure of fuel *economy* since a low fuel usage always shows as a larger figure such as 38 miles per gallon. Poor fuel economy always shows as a low figure such as 10 miles per gallon.

In the metric system, however, the opposite is true. For example, 8 ℓ/100 km is obviously lower fuel usage than 15 ℓ/100 km. **Fig. 35-12.**

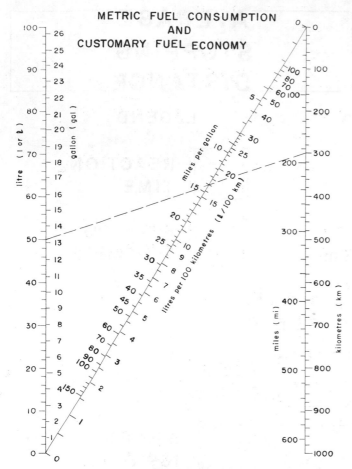

Fig. 35-12

A comparison of metric fuel consumption and customary fuel
economy. To use this chart place a straight edge across the
page from the number of litres or gallons used to the distance
traveled. For example if the car used 50 litres to drive 300
kilometres then the fuel consumption would be?

Metric Fuel Consumption = $\dfrac{50 \times 100}{300}$

$= \dfrac{5000}{300}$

$= 16.7$ ℓ / 100 km
rounded to 17 ℓ / 100 km

The same example in customary would be:
Customary Fuel Economy = $\dfrac{182}{13.2}$

$= 13.8$ mi / gal

rounded to 14 mi/gal

UNIT 36
ELECTRICITY-ELECTRONICS

Electricity-electronics is the one technical area requiring the least change in adopting the SI metric system. Electricity-electronics is closely related to the area of physics and early recognized the advantages of the metric system. **Fig. 36-1**

Fig. 36-1
Conversion to SI metric will require very few changes in electricity-electronics.

In 1881 the International Congress of Electricity established the cgs metric system which included the base units of centimetre, gram and second. This was later changed to the more convenient MKS metric system including the units metre, kilogram and second. However, in the years that followed two cgs systems were developed which caused complications in the area of electricity. One cgs system was based on electrostatic units while the other had electromagnetic units, plus a "practical" system. In the confusion that followed, in 1902 Professor Giovanni Giorgi suggested the addition of a fourth base unit, an electric unit (ampere, volt, coulomb or ohm). This became known as the MKSA, also known as the Giorgi system. This system was approved in 1935 by the International Electrotechnical Commission (IEC) and remained in common use until the adoption of the SI. With the adoption of the SI many of the units that have been in use for years in electricity-electronics were adopted for use by all areas of technology. Also, some new electrical units were introduced to replace older metric units previously used in electricity-electronics. Some examples include:

Power
   unit - *watt*
   symbol - *W*
   definition - The *watt* is the power which gives rise to the production of energy at the rate of one joule per second (J/s).

In the United States the watt has always been used for electrical power only. However, under the SI system it will be the only unit of power including all forms of mechanical power. The watt will replace more than 20 different traditional power units including the obsolete horsepower. The watt is a much more practical and realistic unit. An example of its use: if an electric motor consumes 20 kW power and has an output rating of 18 kW, its efficiency is 90 percent.

Electric Potential
  unit - *volt*
  symbol - *V*
  definition - The *volt* is the difference of electric potential between two points of a conducting wire carrying a constant current of one ampere, when the power dissipated between these points is equal to one watt (W/A).

The volt will require no change, and it is a derived SI unit. The volt can be described in terms of the metre, kilogram, second, and ampere as follows: volt = kg x m^2/s^3 x A.

Electric Conductance
  unit - *siemens*
  symbol - *S*
  definition - The *siemens* is the electric conductance of a conductor having an electric resistance of one ohm (Ω or A/W).

The siemens was first introduced in 1935 by the IEC and was finally adopted by the CGPM in October 1971. The siemens is identical with the reciprocal ohm, known as "mho" which it now replaces.

Magnetic Flux
  unit - *weber*
  symbol - *Wb*
  definition - The *weber* is the magnetic flux which, linking a circuit of one turn, produces in it an electromotive force of one volt as it is reduced to zero at a uniform rate in one second (V • s).

The weber was first introduced by the IEC in 1935, but it was not officially recognized by CGPM until 1960. The weber replaces the obsolete metric unit *maxwell*.

Magnetic Flux Density
  unit - *Tesla*
  symbol - *T*
  definition - The *Tesla* is the magnetic flux density given by a magnetic flux on one weber per square metre (Wb/m^2).

The tesla was first suggested by IEC in 1956 and was accepted by CGPM in 1960. The tesla replaces the old metric unit *gauss*.

Frequency
  unit - *hertz*
  symbol - *Hz*
  definition - The number of periods or cycles per second is called frequency. The SI unit for frequency is the *hertz*. One hertz equals one cycle per second.

Until recently frequency was referred to in terms of cycles per second (c/s). In the SI system the hertz is used to describe such things as the frequency of electrical current, the tuning numbers on radios and TV sets, the description of musical notes and the revolution of engines and motors. However, there is resistance to having the *rpm* replaced by the *hertz*. Use of the hertz for rotational frequency would make it easier to compare with the other frequencies. For example, the relationship between 4000 rpm of an electrical motor and 60 cycles per second of electrical current is not easy to see. However, if both are given in hertz, they become 66 Hz $\left(\dfrac{4000\ rpm}{60}\right)$ and 60 Hz respectively.

Other commonly used derived units in electricity-electronics include:

Electric Resistance = ohm = V/A

The ohm is the electric resistance between two points of a conductor when a constant difference of potential of one volt, applied between these two points, produces in this conductor a current of one ampere, this conductor not being the source of any electromotive force.

Electric Capacitance = farad (F) = A•s/V

The farad is the capacitance of a capacitor between the plates of which there appears a difference of potential of one volt when it is charged by a quantity of electricity equal to one coulomb.

Quantity of Electricity = coulomb (C) = A•s

The coulomb is the quantity of electricity transported in one second by a current of one ampere.

Electric Inductance = henry (H) = Wb/A

The henry is the inductance of a closed circuit in which an electromotive force of 1 volt is produced when the electric current in the circuit varies uniformly at the rate of 1 ampere per second.

IEC and Electricity-Electronics Standards

The International Electrotechnical Commission (IEC) is based in Geneva, Switzerland and is affiliated with the International Organization for Standardization (ISO). This organization has produced hundreds of standards in all areas of electricity and electronics. All standards are available from the American National Standards Institute, Inc., 1430 Broadway, New York, N.Y. 10018. A few examples will illustrate the range available.

IEC 72 (1971) Dimensions and Output Ratings for Foot-Mounted Electrical Machines with Frame Numbers 355 to 1000, Including Supplement 72-A (1970)

IEC 72-A (1970) First Supplement to Publication 72, sold separately

IEC 97 (1970) Grid System for Printed Circuits

IEC 130-0 (1970) Connectors for Frequencies below 3 MHz, Part 0: Guide to Drawing Information in Detail Specifications

IEC 136-3 (1972) Dimensions of Brushes and Brush-Holders for Electrical Machinery, Part 3: IEC Technical Questionnaire for Users of Carbon Brushes.

Materials

The major change in designating wire will be stating wire diameters in millimetres rather than gage size. Recommended diameters for conductors from diameter 0.020 mm up to and including 6.3 mm are given in a IEC Publication. This publication gives recommended diameters based on first, second and third choice. The use of millimetre sizes rather than the so called standard gage will eliminate much confusion. There are currently in use approximately 30 different types of gages for wire and sheet stock. Designating wire and other materials in standard metric diameters or thicknesses rather than gage sizes will eliminate a great deal of confusion. Generally, in electricity-electronics, sizes should be determined by the ISO recommended series of preferred numbers, commonly known as the Renard series.
Fig. 36-2.

The electronic industry also has used another series similar to the Renard series, which is recommended by the International Electrochemical Commission. This E series is recommended for use for grading components such as the value of resistors and capacitors.

House Wiring

There will be no change in the physical size of the materials used in house wiring such as outlet and switch boxes until the construction industry makes a hard change based on the 100 mm building module.

Motors and Generators

Specifications for motors and generators will not change, except that rpm may be listed as hertz (Hz), and the ratings will be in watts (W) or kilowatts (kW) instead of horsepower.

APPROXIMATE WIRE GAGE EQUIVALENTS

*Recommended metric sizes		(Brown & Sharpe or American)	
**First choice diameters mm	Second choice diameters mm	Gage	Equivalent diameter in mm
—	0.300	—	—
—	—	28	0.305
0.315	—	—	—
—	0.335	—	—
—	—	—	—
0.355	—	—	—
—	0.375	26	0.381
0.400	—	—	—
—	0.425	—	—
—	—	—	—
0.450	—	—	—
—	0.475	—	—
0.500	—	24	0.508
—	0.530	—	—
0.560	—	—	—
—	—	—	—
—	0.600	—	—
0.630	—	22	0.635
—	0.670	—	—
0.710	—	—	—
0.750	—	—	—
0.800	—	—	—
0.850	—	20	0.813
0.900	—	—	—
0.950	—	—	—
1.000	—	18	1.02
1.06	—	—	—
1.12	—	—	—
1.18	—	—	—
1.25	—	16	1.27
1.32	—	—	—
1.40	—	—	—
—	—	—	—
1.50	—	—	—
1.60	—	14	1.63
1.70	—	—	—
1.80	—	—	—
1.90	—	—	—
2.00	—	12	2.03
2.12	—	—	—
2.24	—	—	—
2.36	—	—	—
2.50	—	10	2.57
2.65	—	—	—
2.80	—	—	—
3.00	—	—	—
3.15	—	8	3.25
3.35	—	—	—

*All metric size diameters conform to the Renard series of preferred numbers (ISO 388)
**IEC Recommended sizes

**Fig. 36-2
Approximate Wire Gage Equivalents.**

Electrical Equipment

Most electrical equipment is manufactured primarily from metals with some plastics and ceramics. The timing of when a hard conversion of these products can be completed will depend largely on the availability of semi-finished materials such as metal and plastics in metric modules. All new designs should also use the ISO metric fasteners. Some of the electrical products that will be affected include:

Areas	Examples of types of products
Accessories and components.	Switches, distribution and fuse boards, conduits and conduit fittings, meters, relays, terminal blocks, batteries, transducers, plugs and sockets.
Appliances, domestic equipment, lighting equipment.	Refrigerators, washing machines, vacuum cleaners, electric stoves, fry pans, radios, television and other consumer products.
Industrial electrical and electronic equipment.	Motors, generators, motor starters, contacts and switchgear, rectifiers, inverters, transformers, machine tool control, frequency convertors, electronic controls, heating equipment, test equipment.
Power distribution equipment.	Generators, HV switchgear, transformers, voltage regulators.

In redesigning these products, the following will be affected:

Measurements of all kinds: length, area, volume, weight, temperature, etc.

Physical measuring equipment: gages and tools (may need to be recalibrated in metric or replaced); jigs may need to be adjusted or replaced.

Estimating: costing and all other forms of data may have to be rewritten in metric terms.

UNIT 37
OFFICE PRACTICE

The Correct use of SI metric units is extremely important in the office, since misuse either in spelling or in the use of the symbols can cause serious errors. **Fig. 37-1, 37-2, and 37-3.**
See unit on *Rules When Using SI Metric Units.*

LENGTH — km, m, cm, mm — **ARE COMMON UNITS**

UNIT	SYMBOL	CLOSEST CUSTOMARY EQUIVALENT	EXACT CONVERSION CUSTOMARY TO METRIC	TYPE AS BELOW								
kilometre 1 000 metres	km	5/8 mile	1 mile = 1.609 km	1	.	6	0	9		k	m	
metre	m	1 yard	1 yard = 0.914 4 m	0	.	9	1	4	4		m	
decimetre 1/10 metre	dm	4 inches	4 in = 1.016 dm	1	.	0	1	6		d	m	
centimetre 1/100 metre	cm	1/2 inch	1 in = 2.54 cm	2	.	5	4		c	m		
millimetre 1/1 000 metre	mm	1/16 inch	1 in = 25.4 mm	2	5	.	4		m	m		
micrometre 1/1 000 000 m	µm	1/25 of a thousandth	0.001 in = 25.4 µm	2	5	.	4		µ*	m		

OTHER CONVERSIONS									
1 foot = 304.8 mm	3	0	4	.	8		m	m	
1 nautical mile (6076 ft) = 1 852 m	1	8	5	2		m			

Never mix metric units.
Write 47.325 m
not 47 m 325 mm

Type u & add a tail µ by hand.

Fig. 37-1
Correct methods for typing length measurement.

AREA	ha m² (square metre) mm²			ARE COMMON UNITS						

UNIT	SYMBOL	CLOSEST CUSTOMARY EQUIVALENT	EXACT CONVERSION CUSTOMARY TO METRIC	TYPE AS BELOW						
I square kilometre = I million square metres	km²	250 acres	I square mile = 2.590 km²	2	. 5	9	0		k m	2*
I hectare = 10 000 square metres	ha	2.5 acres	I acre = 0.404 7 ha	0	. 4	0	4	7	h	a
I square metre	m²	square yard	I square yard = 0.836 I m²	0	. 8	3	6	1	m	2
I square decimetre = 1/100 square metre	dm²	16 square inches	I square foot = 9.290 dm²	9	. 2	9	0		d m	2
I square millimetre = 1/1 000 000 square metre	mm²	1/600 of a square inch	I square inch = 645.2 mm²	6	4 5	.	2		m m	2

* or type out the complete unit such as 6 square kilometres.

Fig. 37-2
Correct methods for typing area measurements.

VOLUME AND LIQUID CAPACITY	m^3 (cubic metre) dm^3 (litre) cm^3 (cubic centimetre)		ARE COMMON UNITS

UNIT	SYMBOL	CLOSEST CUSTOMARY EQUIVALENT	EXACT CONVERSION CUSTOMARY TO METRIC	TYPE AS BELOW
cubic metre	m^3	1 cubic yard	1 cubic yard = 0.764 6 m^3	0 . 7 6 4 6 m 3
cubic decimetre or litre = 1/1000 cubic metre	dm^3 litre	1 quart	1 gallon = 3.785 dm^3 1 quart = 1.057 litres	3 . 7 8 5 d m 3 or 1 . 0 5 7 L* or l
cubic centimetre or millilitre = 1/1 000 000 m^3	cm^3 or ml	1/16 cubic inch	1 fluid ounce = 29.57 cm^3 or 29.57 ml	2 9 . 5 7 or c m 3 2 9 . 5 7 m l

*The symbol L for litre has been recommended to the General Conference of Weights and Measures.

Fig. 37-3
Correct methods for typing volume and liquid capacity measurements.

Spelling

Four words that may cause a spelling problem are: (1) *metre* or *meter* - most English-speaking countries including England, South Africa, Canada and Australia use the metre spelling. *It should be the preferred method for technical publications.* However, the spelling *meter* may be used for non-technical publications. Consistency of spelling should be followed in any single piece of typed material, whether a letter, report, or papers on company policy; (2) *litre* or *liter* - the spelling *liter* may be used, but is to be avoided in international correspondence; (3) *deka* or *deca* - the prefix for ten times the base unit is spelled *deka* in the United States but *deca* in other English speaking countries. The reason for using deka is to avoid confusion with the prefix for one tenth (1/10), which is deci; (4) *gram* or *gramme* - a submultiple of kilogram, the unit of mass (weight). In some English-speaking countries the longer spellings, gramme and kilogramme, are still used although these spellings are being phased out.

Pronunciation

When using the prefix kilo- as in kilometre, the accent should be on the first syllable, such as kill-o, *not* on the middle syllable as k-lom-etre.

Rules For Typing

1. Unit names, such as metre and (meter) second, prefixes, and symbols should be typed exactly as shown in **Fig. 37-4.**

Some Units for Use With SI

Quantity	Name	Symbol	Value in SI units
Time	minute	min	1 min = 60 s
	hour	h	1 h = 3600 s
	day	d	1 d = 86 400 s
Plane Angle	degree	—°	$1° = (\pi/180)$rad
	minute	—′	$1′ = (\pi/10\ 800)$rad
	second	—″	$1″ = (\pi/648\ 000)$rad
Volume	litre	l or ℓ	$1\ell = 1\ dm^3$
Temperature	degree Celsius*	°C	An interval of 1°C = 1 K
			By definition 0°C = 273.13 K

Some Common Prefixes

Prefix	Symbol	Means Multiply by	Or by
mega	M	1 000 000	10^6
kilo	k	1 000	10^3
hecto	h	100	10^2
deca	da	10	10
deci	d	0.1	10^{-1}
centi	c	0.01	10^{-2}
milli	m	0.001	10^{-3}
micro	μ	0.000 001	10^{-6}

Fig. 37-4a

SI Base Units

Quantity	Name of Unit	Symbol
length	metre	m
mass	kilogram	kg
time	second	s
electric current	ampere	A
thermodynamic temperature	kelvin	K
amount of substance	mole	mol
luminous intensity	candela	cd

Some Derived Units

Quantity	Name	Symbol	Equivalent to
Force	newton	N	kg·m/s2
Pressure	pascal	Pa	N/m2
Work, energy, quantity of heat	joule	J	N·m
Power, heat flow rate	watt	W	J/s
Quantity of electricity	coulomb	C	A·s
Electric potential	volt	V	W/A
Electric resistance	ohm	Ω	V/A
Electric capacitance	farad	F	C/V
Magnetic flux	weber	Wb	V·s
Inductance	henry	H	Wb/A
Magnetic flux density	tesla	T	Wb/m2

Fig. 37-4a
Common units and prefixes

2. *Symbols are not followed by a period,* except at the end of the sentence. Remember that these are symbols, not abbreviations.

3. *Symbols are the same in either singular or plural.* Never add an "s" to the symbol. For example, kg is correct, but kgs is incorrect.

4. When the word is spelled out, the plural is used. For example 20 kilograms, not 20 kilogram.

5. Always leave a space between the unit number or value and the symbol. For example, 300 m, not 300m.

6. Use the decimal point as a decimal marker. In some other countries a comma is used as a decimal marker.

7. Never use a comma to divide large numbers in groups of three. Instead, always leave a space between the groups of three figures from left or right of the decimal point. For example, 472 341.253 678 is correct.

8. Numbers with only four digits on either side of the decimal point may be typed without using a space. For example, 1243 is correct.

9. If the figure is less than the value of 1, always place a zero before the decimal point. Example: 0.3 mm, not .3 mm.

10. Whenever possible, use a unit multiple or submultiple that will have a value between 0.2 and 1000. For example, 28.234 mm rather than 0.028 234 m.

11. All symbols use lower case letter only, such as m for metre (meter), g for gram and t for metric ton, *except those symbols* that are derived from the proper names of individuals. For example, N for newton, Pa for pascal, and A for ampere.

12. All units are typed in lower case without capitalization, except when they are at the beginning of a sentence. For example, two units in SI are the metre, symbol m and the newton, symbol N.

13. The *only exception* to this rule is that the *degree Celsius,* symbol °C, is always spelled with a capital letter, regardless of where it appears in a sentence.

14. The symbols for the five largest prefixes, namely, exa-, peta-, mega-, giga-, and tera- use capital letters for the symbols, such as E, P, M, G, and T.

15. If a symbol is made up of two letters, do not use a *space* or a *period* between them. For example, mm is correct; m.m. is incorrect.

Physical Quantity	Name of Unit	Symbol
length	metre	m
	millimetre	mm
	centimetre	cm
	kilometre	km
	international nautical mile (for navigation)	n mile
mass (commonly) called "weight")	kilogram	kg
	gram	g
	ton	t
time interval	second	s
	minute	min
	hour	h
	day	d
area	square metre	m2
	square millimetre	mm2
	square centimetre	cm2
	hectare	ha
volume	cubic metre	m3
	cubic millimetre	mm3
	cubic centimetre	cm3
volume (for fluids only)	litre	l or L
	millilitre	ml
	kilolitre	kl
velocity and speed	metre per second	m/s
	kilometre per hour	km/h
	knot (for navigation)	kn
force	newton	N
energy, work	joule	J
power	watt	W
density	kilogram per cubic metre	kg/m3
	gram per cubic centimetre	g/cm3
density (for fluids only)	kilogram per litre	kg/l
pressure, stress	pascal	Pa
pressure (for meteorology)	millibar	mb
electric current	ampere	A
potential difference, electromotive force	volt	V
electrical resistance	ohm	Ω
frequency	hertz	Hz
	revolution per minute	rev/min
temperature	kelvin	K
	degree Celsius	°C

Fig. 37-4b
Common metric units with their correct names and symbols.

16. If two units are to be multiplied or the product of two units is to be typed, there should be a dot between the symbols. For example, newton times metre uses the symbol N·m.

17. Unit names typed in full are always written in singular or plural, according to standard grammatical rules, but the symbols are always singular. For example, 10 metres (meters) would use the symbol 10 m or 4 kilometres would use the symbol 4 km.

18. An *oblique slash* should be used as a separator between the top and bottom of a fraction or to express per. For example, 5 metres per second should be expressed as 5 m/s.

19. Always write out the name of the unit if there is any problem that would cause confusion in the spelling. The unit litre (liter) (but not the submultiples) may be spelled out in full to avoid possible confusion. On the typewriter the lower case "ell" and figure one are often the same key. Therefore, this could cause confusion. When possible use a vertical I or a script ℓ for the symbol for the litre, or type out the unit, such as ll litres.

20. When a typewriter is not equipped with a superior 2 and 3 for such units as square metre (meter) and cubic metre (meter), these words may be spelled out completely. Never use abbreviations such as sq. m. or cu. m. The symbol m² or m³ can be typed by moving the carriage slightly.

21. When typing the symbol for micro- which means one millionth, this can be done by first typing a u and then adding a small tail by hand, such as μ. However, never use only the u as the symbol.

22. The symbol for ohm Ω, must usually be drawn in by hand or the entire word written out.

23. Never use the abbreviation kilos to mean kilograms.

Metric in Shorthand

While most dictation is transcribed from a tape, some secretaries are still required to know shorthand. Stenographers who do take shorthand notes will be required to recognize the various terms by hearing them being spoken. For example, the individual must recognize that a newton is a unit of force and not some kind of cookie, or that a pascal is a unit of pressure and not a vegetable. The person must also know the shorthand outline for each of the units and must be able to identify quickly the correct SI symbol to use. **Fig. 37-5**

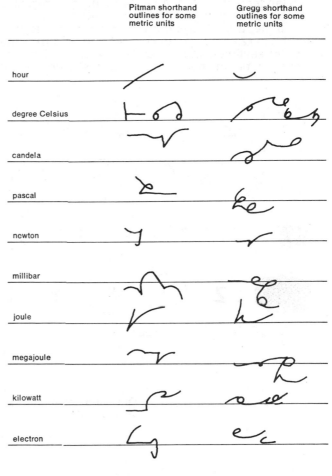

Shorthand Outlines	Pitman shorthand outlines for some metric units	Gregg shorthand out lines for some metric units
metre		
kilometre		
millimetre		
gram		
kilogram		
milligram		
litre		
kilolitre		
millilitre		
ton		
second		

	Pitman shorthand outlines for some metric units	Gregg shorthand outlines for some metric units
hour		
degree Celsius		
candela		
pascal		
newton		
millibar		
joule		
megajoule		
kilowatt		
electron		

Fig. 37-5
Shorthand strokes for common metric units.

shows some shorthand outlines for more common metric words.

Problems in Typing the Metric Rules

Typing most material that includes the metric system is no great problem except for a few changes and modifications that may have to be made.

Typing superior figures. On most ordinary typewriters the only way to obtain the superior 2 or 3 for square metre (meter) or cubic metre (meter), for example, is by moving the platen half a space before typing the figure. However, when this is done on single spaced type, the figure may run into the text on the line above. This can be avoided by using double spacing when superior figures are to be used. In printing, the superior figures are made of smaller type than the body of the text which avoids any problems. Typewriters can be modified to include a smaller size superior 2 and 3.

The letter "ell" for litre [liter]. Most typewriters make no difference at all between the lower case "ell" and the figure one. Since the single vertical I without a period is recognized as a standard symbol for litre (liter), it is usually preferable to spell the word out in full unless the typewriter has a vertical I or a special script "ell" such as ℓ. However, it is not necessary to use the script "ell" for ml (millilitre) or kl (kilolitre), since there is no possible confusion.

Special characters. For technical work it is necessary to have at least two of the Greek letters available, namely the Greek mu (µ) which is the symbol for micro meaning one millionth, and the capital omega (Ω) which is the symbol for ohm. The symbol for micro can be typed on a standard machine by using the lower case u. Then the tail can be added by hand or it can be preceeded by an inferior oblique stroke. While either method does not provide a finished appearance, it is a good substitute. However, the name for the unit can be spelled out in full. The symbol for ohm (Ω) must be drawn by hand or the word can be spelled out in full.

Modification of the Typewriter

With the introduction of the metric system, fractions will no longer be required. As a matter of fact, decimals are preferred in typing or writing SI metric symbols. For example, it is always correct to write 0.5 kilogram rather than 1/2 kilogram. Removal of fractions from the typewriter keyboard will make these keys available for the more common metric symbols. It should be em-phasized, however, that except for special scientific and engineering publications there will seldom be a need for modifying keyboards to include the superior figures and Greek letters. However, when it appears that this is necessary, the following should be useful. If the symbols for 1/2, 1/3, 3/4 and 3/8 are removed, these can be replaced by the following: (1) the superior 2 denoting squared, for example, m² or square metre (meter); (2) the superior 3 denoting cubed, for example, m³ or cubic metre (meter); (3) the degree sign (°) for temperature, for example, °C means degree Celsius; (4) the vertical l or the italics letter "ℓ" as the symbol for litre (liter); (5) the symbol for the prefix micro (µ) which means one millionth. For scientific work the symbol for ohm (Ω) may be necessary. However, for general work in the absence of this symbol the word should be spelled out completely. For ball-type typewriters a ball with all of the *correct metric symbols* is available on special order.

While several suggestions have been made for an international standard keyboard, it is not likely that one will be adopted in the near future. The main reason is that no single design will cover all the specialized requirements that might arise. **Fig. 37-6.**

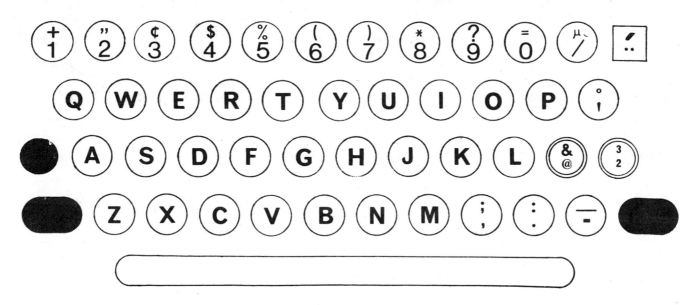

Fig. 37-6
One suggestion for a keyboard including the more common metric units.

UNIT 38
MARKETING AND DISTRIBUTION

All persons (wholesalers, retailers and consumers) concerned with the marketing and distribution of goods and services will need to:
1. Understand the metric system of weights and measures
2. Know how to convert from customary to metric measures and vice versa
3. Be acquainted with metric standards as they apply to a specific area of sales and services.

Since the metric system is a decimal system much like our money, it will be relatively easy to learn. Then too, much of the pricing of packaged goods in customary units already has changed from fractions to decimals. For example, most packaged food products list weight as 1.3 pounds instead of 1 pound 5 ounces, or 1-5/16 pounds. The three metric units involved in most distributive education will include the following:

length - metre, centimetre and millimetre
weight - kilogram and gram
liquid volume or capacity - litre **Fig. 38-1**

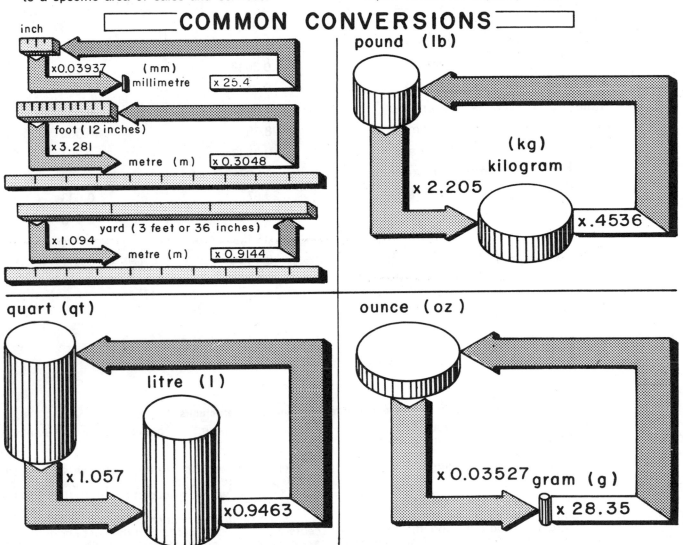

Fig. 38-1
Common conversions.

In addition to metric measurement, individuals will need to know the metric standards directly related to their own areas of business. Persons employed in printing and publishing will need to understand ISO paper sizes. Individuals employed in the sale and service of automobiles, household appliances, and hardware products must know metric threads, fasteners and wrenches. Persons dealing with wearing apparel including shoes must know and understand appropriate clothing standards.

Only a few of the international metric standards are available out of the approximately 11 000 eventually needed for all products. All international standards will use metric measurement to describe the product size,

weight and other perimeters of measurement.

Metric Measurement

Anyone dealing in the buying and selling of goods and services must know the metric system and its relationship to the customary system. A person must develop a "feel" for the metric units.
Fig. 38-2
For example, length measurements in the customary system are given in inches, feet or yards while in the metric system the length measurements are normally in millimetres, centimetres and metres (meters). The relationship between these metric units to the customary units must be appreciated. For example, a

MEASURE

Customary	Metric	To change from customary to metric multiply by	To change from metric to customary multiply by
inch	millimetre	25.4*	0.039
inch	centimetre	2.54*	0.39
foot	metre	0.3048	3.280
yard	metre	0.9144	1.093
mile	kilometre	1.609	0.621
ounce	gram	28.35	0.035
pound	kilogram	0.4536	2.204
ton	metric ton or tonne	0.907	1.102
liquid ounce	millilitre	29.57	0.033
pint	litre	0.473	2.113
quart	litre	0.946	1.057
gallon	litre	3.785	0.264

* Accurate

Fig. 38-2a
Conversion factors for common customary and metric units.

millimetre is only about 1/25 as large as an inch while a centimetre is somewhat less than 1/2 inch since there are 2.5 centimetres to the inch. A metre is slightly longer than a yard (about 10 percent longer). A metre is about 3.3 times as long as a foot.
Fig. 38-3
Weights in the customary system are normally given in ounces, pounds and tons while in the metric system they are given in grams, kilograms and metric tons (tonnes). The gram is much smaller than an ounce; only about 1/28 as large. Therefore, a 10 ounce bottle becomes a 283 gram bottle. On the other hand, a kilogram is about 2.2 times as large as a pound. Therefore, a kilogram of sugar would be about 10 percent larger than a 2 pound bag of sugar.
Fig. 38-4.
For liquid capacity the traditional system is in pints, quarts and gallons while in the metric system the units are millilitres, litres and kilolitres. A litre is slightly larger than a quart (about 6 percent) while there are about 3-3/4 litres in a gallon.
Fig. 38-5.
Conversion Guidelines
The following will help sales personnel "to think metric".
Length measurement. To change cost in *cents per foot* to *cents per metre*, multiply cost per foot by 3.3.

For example, tubing that costs $0.20 per foot would be priced at $0.66 per metre.
Fig. 38-6.
To change cost in *cents per yard* to *cents per metre*, add 10 percent to cost per yard. For example, cloth that costs $1.00 per yard is priced at about $1.10 per metre.
Fig. 38-7.
Liquid measure. To change cost in *cents per quart* to *cents per litre*, add 6 percent to the cost per quart. For example, if oil costs $0.50 per quart, the price is $0.53 per litre.
Fig. 38-8.
To change cost in *cents per gallon* to *cents per litre*, divide the cost per gallon by 4 and add 6 percent to this amount. For example, if gasoline is $0.60 per gallon, it will be 15 + 0.9 ((60 ÷ 4) + 6%) or about 16 cents per litre.
Fig. 38-9.
Weight measure. To change cost in *cents per ounce* to *cents per gram*, divide the cost per ounce by 30. For example, if a spice costs $0.60 per ounce, it is about $0.02 per gram (actually 2.12 cents per gram).
Fig. 38-10
To change cost in *cents per pound* to *cents per kilogram*, multiply the cost per pound by 2.2. For example, meat priced at $1.20 per pound costs about $2.65 per kilogram. **Fig. 38-11a,b.**

PRICE COMPARISON

MEAT	MILK	CANNED GOODS

$1.00 per pound.   35¢ per quart.   50¢ per 14 ounces.

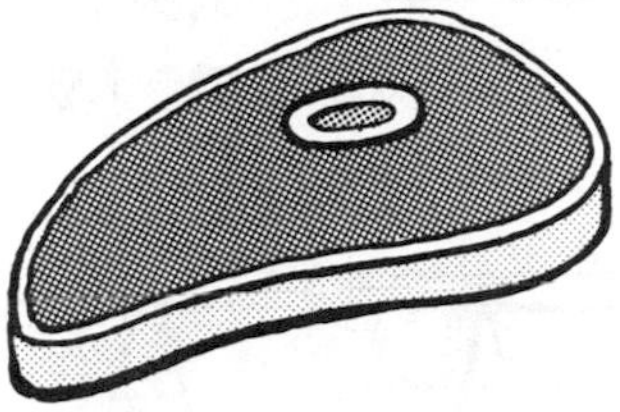

$1.10 per 0.5(1/2) kilogram.   37¢ per litre.   51¢ per 400 grams.

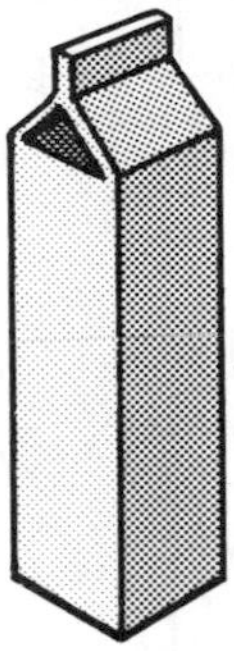

$2.20 per kilogram.

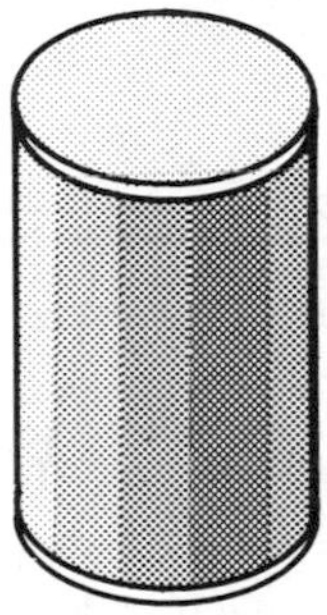

Fig. 38-2b
These price comparisons give an idea of relative costs.

LENGTH

yard - metre

1 yard

1 yard is about 9/10 of a metre.

1 metre

1 metre is about 10% longer than a yard.

foot

1 foot

300mm - 30 cm

1 foot is slightly longer than 300 millimetres or 30 centimetres.

inch

1 inch

25 millimetres

1 inch is about 2.5 centimetres or 25 millimetres.

Fig. 38-3
Common lengths.

WEIGHT

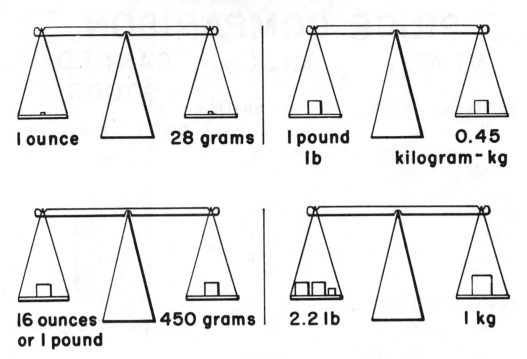

1 ounce   28 grams   1 pound lb   0.45 kilogram - kg

16 ounces or 1 pound   450 grams   2.2 lb   1 kg

Fig. 38-4
Common weights.

LIQUID VOLUME CAPACITY

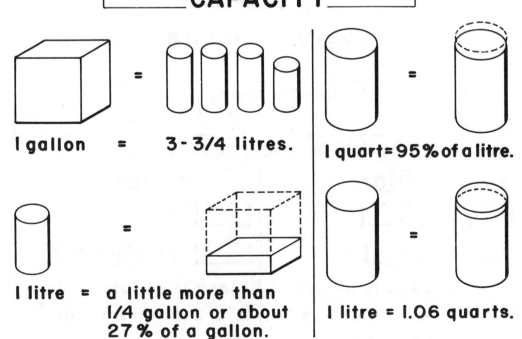

1 gallon = 3 - 3/4 litres.

1 quart = 95 % of a litre.

1 litre = a little more than 1/4 gallon or about 27 % of a gallon.

1 litre = 1.06 quarts.

Fig. 38-5a
Liquid volume or capacity.

COMMON LIQUID UNITS

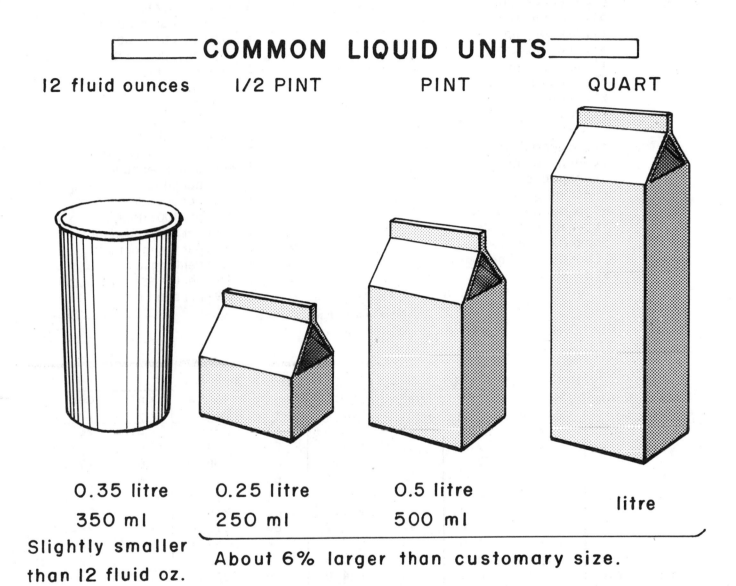

| 12 fluid ounces | 1/2 PINT | PINT | QUART |

0.35 litre
350 ml
Slightly smaller
than 12 fluid oz.

0.25 litre
250 ml

0.5 litre
500 ml

litre

About 6% larger than customary size.

Fig. 38-5b
Common liquid units.

$1 per foot	=	$ 3.28 per metre
$1 per metre	=	$ 0.30 per foot
$1 per yard	=	$ 1.09 per metre
$1 per metre	=	$ 0.91 per yard
$1 per square yard	=	$ 1.20 per square metre
$1 per square metre	=	$ 0.84 per square yard
$100 per acre	=	$247.11 per hectare
$100 per hectare	=	$ 40.47 per acre
$1 per cubic foot	=	$ 35.31 per cubic metre
$1 per cubic metre	=	$ 0.03 per cubic foot
$1 per cubic yard	=	$ 1.31 per cubic metre
$1 per cubic metre	=	$ 0.76 per cubic yard
$1 per quart	=	$ 1.06 per litre
$1 per litre	=	$ 0.94 per quart
$1 per gallon	=	$ 0.26 per litre
$1 per litre	=	$ 3.78 per gallon
1 cent per ounce	=	$ 0.035 cents per gram
1 cent per gram	=	$ 28.35 cents per ounce
$1 per pound	=	$ 2.20 per kilogram
$1 per kilogram	=	$ 0.45 per pound
$1 per hundredweight	=	$ 1.97 per 100 kilograms
$1 per 100 kilograms	=	$ 0.51 per hundredweight
$1 per long ton	=	$ 0.98 per tonne or metric ton
$1 per tonne or metric ton	=	$ 1.02 per long ton
$1 per short ton	=	$ 1.10 per tonne or metric ton
$1 per tonne or metric ton	=	$ 0.91 per short ton

Fig. 38-6a
Price conversion.

LENGTH

CONVERSION FROM PRICE PER FOOT RUN TO PRICE PER METRE RUN

Cents per ft	Cents per m	Cents per ft	Cents per m	Cents per ft	Cents per m	Cents per ft	Cents per m	Cents per ft	Cents per m
1	3.3	21	68.9	41	134.5	61	200.1	81	265.7
2	6.6	22	72.2	42	137.8	62	203.4	82	269.0
3	9.8	23	75.5	43	141.1	63	206.7	83	272.3
4	13.1	24	78.7	44	144.4	64	910.0	84	275.6
5	16.4	25	82.0	45	147.6	65	213.3	85	278.9
6	19.7	26	85.3	46	150.9	66	216.5	86	282.2
7	23.0	27	88.6	47	154.2	67	219.8	87	284.4
8	26.2	28	91.9	48	157.5	68	223.1	88	288.7
9	29.5	29	95.1	49	160.8	69	226.4	89	292.0
10	32.8	30	98.4	50	164.0	70	229.7	90	295.3
11	36.1	31	101.7	51	167.3	71	232.9	91	298.6
12	39.4	32	105.0	52	170.6	72	236.2	92	301.8
13	42.7	33	108.3	53	173.9	73	239.5	93	305.1
14	45.9	34	111.5	54	177.2	74	242.8	94	308.4
15	49.2	35	114.8	55	180.4	75	246.0	95	311.7
16	52.5	36	118.1	56	183.7	76	249.3	96	315.0
17	55.8	37	121.4	57	187.0	77	252.6	97	318.2
18	59.1	38	124.7	58	190.3	78	255.9	98	321.5
19	62.3	39	128.0	59	193.6	79	259.2	99	324.8
20	65.6	40	131.2	60	196.9	80	262.5	100	328.1

Fig. 38-6b
Price conversion for length: feet to metres.

LENGTH

CONVERSION FROM PRICE PER YARD TO PRICE PER METRE

Cents per yd	Cents per m	Cents per yd	Cents per m	Cents per yd	Cents per m	Cents per yd	Cents per m
1	1.09	26	28.43	51	55.77	76	83.11
2	2.19	27	29.53	52	56.87	77	84.21
3	3.28	28	30.62	53	57.96	78	85.30
4	4.37	29	31.71	54	59.05	79	86.40
5	5.47	30	32.81	55	60.15	80	87.49
6	6.56	31	33.90	56	61.24	81	88.58
7	7.65	32	35.00	57	62.34	82	89.68
8	8.75	33	36.09	58	63.43	83	90.77
9	9.84	34	37.18	59	64.52	84	91.86
10	10.94	35	38.28	60	65.62	85	92.96
11	12.03	36	39.37	61	66.71	86	94.05
12	13.12	37	40.46	62	67.80	87	95.14
13	14.22	38	41.56	63	68.90	88	96.24
14	15.31	39	42.65	64	69.99	89	97.33
15	16.40	40	43.74	65	71.08	90	98.42
16	17.50	41	44.84	66	72.18	91	99.52
17	18.59	42	45.93	67	73.27	92	100.61
18	19.68	43	47.02	68	74.37	93	101.71
19	20.78	44	48.12	69	75.46	94	102.80
20	21.87	45	49.21	70	76.55	95	103.89
21	22.97	46	50.31	71	77.65	96	104.99
22	24.06	47	51.40	72	78.74	97	106.08
23	25.15	48	52.49	73	79.83	98	107.17
24	26.25	49	53.59	74	80.93	99	108.27
25	27.34	50	54.68	75	82.02	100	109.36

Fig. 38-7
Price conversion for length: yards to metres.

LIQUID CAPACITY

CONVERSION FROM PRICE PER QUART TO PRICE PER LITRE

Cents per quart	Cents per litre	Cents per quart	Cents per litre	Cents per quart	Cents per litre	Cents per quart	Cents per litre
20	21.0	40	42.3	60	63.4	80	84.5
21	22.2	41	43.3	61	64.5	81	85.6
22	23.2	42	44.4	62	65.5	82	86.6
23	24.3	43	45.4	63	66.6	83	87.7
24	25.4	44	46.5	64	67.6	84	88.8
25	26.4	45	47.5	65	68.7	85	89.8
26	27.5	46	48.6	66	69.7	86	90.9
27	28.5	47	49.7	67	70.7	87	91.9
28	29.6	48	50.7	68	71.8	88	93.0
29	30.6	49	51.8	69	72.9	89	94.0
30	31.7	50	52.8	70	74.0	90	95.1
31	32.8	51	53.9	71	75.0	91	96.2
32	33.8	52	54.9	72	76.1	92	97.2
33	34.9	53	56.0	73	77.1	93	98.3
34	35.9	54	57.1	74	78.2	94	99.3
35	37.0	55	58.1	75	79.2	95	100.4
36	38.0	56	59.2	76	80.3	96	101.4
37	39.1	57	60.2	77	81.4	97	102.5
38	40.1	58	61.3	78	82.4	98	103.6
39	41.2	59	62.3	79	83.5	99	104.6
						100	105.7

Fig. 38-8
Price conversion for liquid volume: quarts to litres.

LIQUID CAPACITY

CONVERSION FROM PRICE PER GALLON TO PRICE PER LITRE

Cents per gallon	Cents per litre	Cents per gallon	Cents per litre	Cents per gallon	Cents per litre
30	7.9	54	14.3	78	20.6
31	8.1	55	14.5	79	20.9
32	8.4	56	14.8	80	21.1
33	8.7	57	15.0	81	21.4
34	9.0	58	15.3	82	21.6
35	9.2	59	15.6	83	21.9
36	9.5	60	15.8	84	22.2
37	9.8	61	16.1	85	22.4
38	10.0	62	16.3	86	22.7
39	10.3	63	16.6	87	23.0
40	10.6	64	16.9	88	23.2
41	10.8	65	17.2	89	23.5
42	11.1	66	17.4	90	23.8
43	11.4	67	17.7	91	24.0
44	11.6	68	18.0	92	24.3
45	11.9	69	18.2	93	24.6
46	12.1	70	18.5	94	24.8
47	12.4	71	18.7	95	25.1
48	12.7	72	19.0	96	25.3
49	12.9	73	19.3	97	25.6
50	13.2	74	19.5	98	25.9
51	13.5	75	19.8	99	26.1
52	13.7	76	20.0	100	26.4
53	14.0	77	20.3		

Fig. 38-9
Price conversion for liquid volume: gallons to litres.

WEIGHT

CONVERSION FROM PRICE PER OUNCE TO PRICE PER GRAM

Cents per oz	Cents per g	Cents per oz	Cents per g	Cents per oz	Cents per g	Cents per oz	Cents per g	Cents per oz	Cents per g
1	0.03	21	0.75	41	1.4	61	2.1	81	2.9
2	0.07	22	0.78	42	1.5	62	2.2	82	2.9
3	0.10	23	0.82	43	1.5	63	2.2	83	2.9
4	0.14	24	0.86	44	1.5	64	2.3	84	3.0
5	0.18	25	0.89	45	1.6	65	2.3	85	3.0
6	0.21	26	0.93	46	1.6	66	2.3	86	3.0
7	0.25	27	0.96	47	1.6	67	2.4	87	3.1
8	0.28	28	1.0	48	1.7	68	2.4	88	3.1
9	0.32	29	1.0	49	1.7	69	2.4	89	3.1
10	0.35	30	1.1	50	1.7	70	2.5	90	3.2
11	0.39	31	1.1	51	1.8	71	2.5	91	3.2
12	0.43	32	1.1	52	1.8	72	2.5	92	3.2
13	0.46	33	1.2	53	1.8	73	2.6	93	3.3
14	0.50	34	1.2	54	1.9	74	2.6	94	3.3
15	0.53	35	1.2	55	1.9	75	2.6	95	3.3
16	0.57	36	1.3	56	2.0	76	2.7	96	3.4
17	0.61	37	1.3	57	2.0	77	2.7	97	3.4
18	0.64	38	1.3	58	2.0	78	2.7	98	3.5
19	0.68	39	1.4	59	2.1	79	2.8	99	3.5
20	0.71	40	1.4	60	2.1	80	2.8	100	3.5

Fig. 38-10
Price conversion for weight: ounces to grams.

WEIGHT

CONVERSION FROM PRICE PER POUND TO KILOGRAM

Cents per lb	Cents per kg	Cents per lb	Cents per kg	Cents per lb	Cents per kg	Cents per lb	Cents per kg	Cents per lb	Cents per kg
1	2.2	21	46.3	41	90.4	61	134.5	81	178.6
2	4.4	22	48.5	42	92.6	62	136.7	82	180.8
3	6.6	23	50.7	43	94.8	63	138.9	83	183.0
4	8.8	24	52.9	44	97.0	64	141.1	84	185.2
5	11.0	25	55.1	45	99.2	65	143.3	85	187.4
6	13.2	26	57.3	46	101.4	66	145.5	86	189.6
7	15.4	27	59.5	47	103.6	67	147.7	87	191.8
8	17.6	28	61.7	48	105.8	68	149.9	88	194.0
9	19.8	29	63.9	49	108.0	69	152.1	89	196.2
10	22.0	30	66.1	50	110.2	70	154.3	90	198.4
11	24.3	31	68.3	51	112.4	71	156.5	91	200.6
12	26.5	32	70.5	52	114.6	72	158.7	92	202.8
13	28.7	33	72.8	53	116.8	73	160.9	93	205.0
14	30.9	34	75.0	54	119.1	74	163.1	94	207.2
15	33.1	35	77.2	55	121.3	75	165.3	95	209.4
16	35.3	36	79.4	56	123.5	76	167.6	96	211.6
17	37.5	37	81.6	57	125.7	77	169.8	97	213.8
18	39.7	38	83.8	58	127.9	78	172.0	98	216.1
19	41.9	39	86.0	59	130.1	79	174.2	99	218.3
20	44.1	40	88.2	60	132.3	80	176.4	100	220.5

Fig. 38-11a
Price conversion for weight: pounds to kilograms.

METRIC PRICE GUIDE

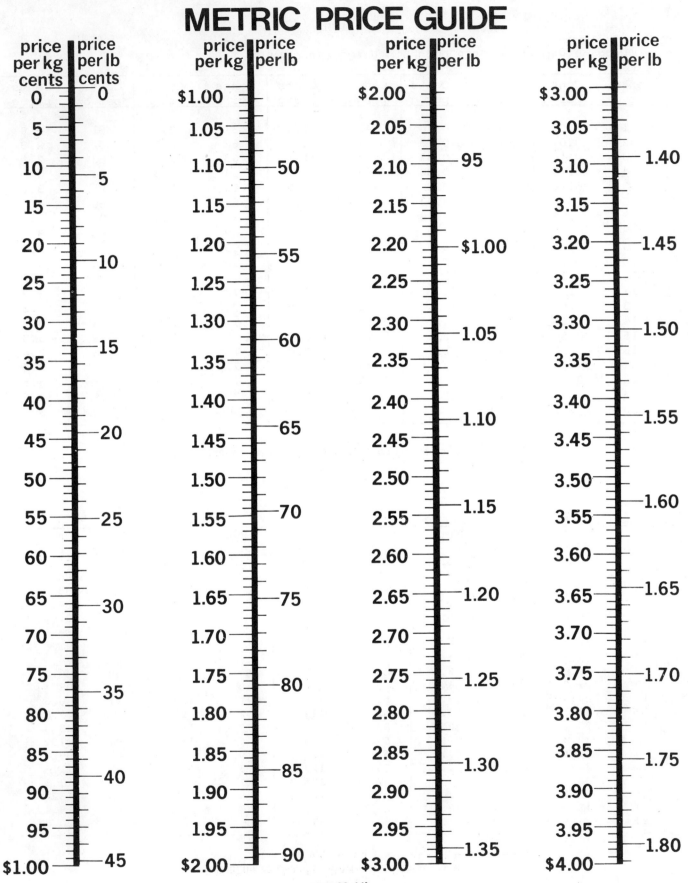

Fig. 38-11b
Metric price guide.

Area measure. To change cost in *cents [or dollars] per square foot* to *cents [or dollars] per square metre,* multiply cost per square foot by 11. For example, if plywood costs $0.80 per square foot, it should be priced at about $8.80 per square metre (meter) (actually $8.61).
Fig. 38-12.

To change cost in *cents [or dollars] per square yard* to *cents [or dollars] per square metre,* multiply cost per square yard by 1.2. For example, carpeting that costs $8.00 per square yard is about $9.60 per square metre.
Fig. 38-13.

AREA

CONVERSION FROM PRICE PER SQUARE FOOT TO PRICE PER SQUARE METRE

Cents per ft^2	Cents per m^2	Cents per ft^2	Cents per m^2	Cents per ft^2	Cents per m^2	Cents per ft^2	Cents per m^2	Cents per ft^2	Cents per m^2
1	10.8	21	226.0	41	441.3	61	656.6	81	871.8
2	21.5	22	236.8	42	452.1	62	667.4	82	882.6
3	32.3	23	247.6	43	462.8	63	678.1	83	893.4
4	43.1	24	258.3	44	473.6	64	688.9	84	904.2
5	53.8	25	269.1	45	484.4	65	699.7	85	914.9
6	64.6	26	279.9	46	495.1	66	710.4	86	925.7
7	75.3	27	290.6	47	505.9	67	721.2	87	936.5
8	86.1	28	301.4	48	516.7	68	731.9	88	947.2
9	96.9	29	312.2	49	527.4	69	742.7	89	958.0
10	107.6	30	322.9	50	538.2	70	753.5	90	968.8
11	118.4	31	333.7	51	549.0	71	764.2	91	979.5
12	129.2	32	344.4	52	559.7	72	775.0	92	990.3
13	139.9	33	355.2	53	570.5	73	785.8	93	1001.0
14	150.7	34	366.0	54	581.3	74	796.5	94	1011.8
15	161.5	35	376.7	55	592.0	75	807.3	95	1022.6
16	172.2	36	387.5	56	602.8	76	818.1	96	1033.3
17	183.0	37	398.3	57	613.5	77	828.8	97	1044.1
18	193.7	38	409.0	58	624.3	78	839.6	98	1054.9
19	204.5	39	419.8	59	635.1	79	850.3	99	1065.6
20	215.3	40	430.6	60	645.8	80	861.1	100	1076.4

Fig. 38-12
Price conversion for area: square feet to square metres.

AREA

CONVERSION FROM PRICE PER SQUARE YARD TO PRICE PER SQUARE METRE

Cents per yd^2	Cents per m^2	Cents per yd^2	Cents per m^2	Cents per yd^2	Cents per m^2	Cents per yd^2	Cents per m^2	Cents per yd^2	Cents per m^2
1	1.2	21	25.1	41	49.0	61	73.0	81	96.9
2	2.4	22	26.3	42	50.2	62	74.2	82	98.1
3	3.6	23	27.5	43	51.4	63	75.3	83	99.3
4	4.8	24	28.7	44	52.6	64	76.5	84	100.5
5	6.0	25	29.9	45	53.8	65	77.7	85	101.7
6	7.2	26	31.1	46	55.0	66	78.9	86	102.5
7	8.4	27	32.3	47	56.2	67	80.1	87	104.1
8	9.6	28	33.5	48	57.4	68	81.3	88	105.2
9	10.8	29	34.7	49	58.6	69	82.5	89	106.4
10	12.0	30	35.9	50	59.8	70	83.7	90	107.6
11	13.2	31	37.1	51	61.0	71	84.9	91	108.8
12	14.4	32	38.3	52	62.2	72	86.1	92	110.0
13	15.5	33	39.5	53	63.4	73	87.3	93	111.2
14	16.7	34	40.7	54	64.6	74	88.5	94	112.4
15	17.9	35	41.9	55	65.8	75	89.7	95	113.6
16	19.1	36	43.1	56	67.0	76	90.9	96	114.8
17	20.3	37	44.3	57	68.2	77	92.1	97	116.0
18	21.5	38	45.4	58	69.4	78	93.3	98	117.2
19	22.7	39	46.6	59	70.6	79	94.5	99	118.4
20	23.9	40	47.8	60	71.8	80	95.7	100	119.6

Fig. 38-13
Price conversion for area: square yards to square metres.

Volume measure. To change cost in *cents [or dollars] per cubic yard* to cost in *cents [or dollars] per cubic metre,* multiply the cost per cubic yard by 1.3. For example, gravel listed as $5.00 per cubic yard will cost about $6.50 per cubic metre. **Fig. 38-14.**

Conversion Problems in Retailing and Distribution
In all types of business activities individuals will be faced with several kinds of conversion problems to determine costs. Common problems include:
A. Conversion of a single size of a customary unit (for example, pounds or ounces to equivalent metric

VOLUME

CONVERSION FROM PRICE PER CUBIC YARD TO PRICE PER CUBIC METRE

Cents per yd^3	Cents per m^3	Cents per yd^3	Cents per m^3	Cents per yd^3	Cents per m^3	Cents per yd^3	Cents per m^3	Cents per yd^3	Cents per m^3
1	1.3	21	27.5	41	53.6	61	79.8	81	105.9
2	2.6	22	28.8	42	54.9	62	81.1	82	107.3
3	3.9	23	30.1	43	56.2	63	82.4	83	108.6
4	5.2	24	31.4	44	57.5	64	83.7	84	109.9
5	6.5	25	32.7	45	58.9	65	85.0	85	111.2
6	7.8	26	34.0	46	60.2	66	86.3	86	112.5
7	9.2	27	35.3	47	61.5	67	87.6	87	113.8
8	10.5	28	36.6	48	62.8	68	88.9	88	115.1
9	11.8	29	37.9	49	64.1	69	90.2	89	116.4
10	13.1	30	39.2	50	65.4	70	91.6	90	117.7
11	14.4	31	40.5	51	66.7	71	92.9	91	119.0
12	15.7	32	41.9	52	68.0	72	94.2	92	120.3
13	17.0	33	43.2	53	69.3	73	95.5	93	121.6
14	18.3	34	44.5	54	70.6	74	96.8	94	122.9
15	19.6	35	45.8	55	71.9	75	98.1	95	124.3
16	20.9	36	47.1	56	73.2	76	99.4	96	125.6
17	22.2	37	48.4	57	74.6	77	100.7	97	126.9
18	23.5	38	49.7	58	75.9	78	102.0	98	128.2
19	24.9	39	51.0	59	77.2	79	103.3	99	129.5
20	26.2	40	52.3	60	78.5	80	104.6	100	130.8

Fig. 38-14
Price conversion for volume: cubic yards to cubic metres.

units - kilograms or grams).
Example 1: You wish to change a man's weight from pounds to kilograms. Remember that *pounds* are much *smaller* than kilograms and, therefore, the metric number will be much smaller than the customary number. For example, if a man weighs 180 pounds, his weight in kilograms can be found by either dividing the 180 by 2.2 or by multiplying it by 0.454, which is about 82 kilograms.
Example 2: You wish to change the customary weight of a package from ounces to the equivalent weight in grams. Remember that *ounces* are much *larger* than *grams*. Therefore, the metric number will be much larger than the customary number. For example, if the package weighs 14 ounces, the weight in grams is obtained by multiplying by 28.35. The results will be about 454 grams.
B. Converting several different sizes of the same unit from customary to metric.
Example 1: You wish to find the total length in millimetres of three pieces of metal shown in **Fig. 38-15.** You must first change all lengths to inches, add to find the total, and then multiply this number by 25.4 to find the length in millimetres.
C. Finding the total of several different sizes of the same unit in metric.
Example 1: You have three packages in which the metric weights are not in the same size of the unit as shown in **Fig. 38-16.** You must change all weights to either kilograms, grams or milligrams before adding to find the result.

Mixed Units	Change to	Inches
1 3/4 in		1.750
2 ft 3 in		27.00
1 yd 4.5 in		40.5
		69.250 in
69.250 x 25.4 = 1758.95 mm		

Fig. 38-15
Change all customary lengths to decimal inches, then add and multiply by 25.4 to obtain the length in millimetres.

	kg	g	mg
0.3 kg	0.3000	300.0	300 000
3.5 g	0.0035	3.5	3 500
400.0 mg	0.0004	0.4	400
	0.3039 kg	303.9 g	303 900 mg

Fig. 38-16
Changing metric weights to the same unit.

Example 2: You have three lengths of material that are marked in different metric length units. You must change all lengths to metres, centimetres or millimetres before adding to find the result. **Fig. 38-17.**

LENGTH

Material	m	cm	mm
4 m	4.000	400	4000
50 cm	0.500	50	500
350 mm	0.350	35	350
	4.850	485	4850

Fig. 38-17
Changing metric length to the same unit.

D. Finding the cost of products in metric units.

Example 1: If gas costs 15 cents per litre, what is the cost of 60 litres? To find the result multiply 15 x 60 to equal $9.00.

Example 2: If meat costs $2.30 per kilogram, what is the cost of 5 kilograms? To find the result multiply $2.30 x 5 to equal $11.50.

Example 3: If carpeting costs $7.00 per square metre (6500 x 4000 mm), what is the cost of wall-to-wall carpeting in a room 6.5 m x 4 m? To find the area in square metres, multiply length times width, or 6.5 x 4 to equal 26 square metres. At $7.00 per square metre, the total cost is 26 x $7.00 which equals $182.00. **Fig. 38-18**

Fig. 38-18
You must be able to figure the cost of material in square metres.

Metrics for Retailers

Retail establishments will have many problems in conversion to the metric system. During the transition from customary to metric most products will be shown with dual measurements. However, many producers of food and drug products use incorrect *abbreviations* instead of the correct metric symbols.

1. *Foods and beverages.* All dry, packaged and canned foods including meats, vegetables and most canned goods will have weights listed in grams or kilograms. All liquids will be listed in litres or in millilitres. For example, by 1979 the required wine bottle sizes are as shown in **Fig. 38-19.**
The six distilled spirits bottle sizes will be 50 ml, 200 ml, 500 ml, 750 ml, 1 litre and 1.75 litres.

2. *Paper products.* All paper products will be labeled with metric units. The amount of toweling and other rolls of paper will be shown in square metres (meters) as well as square feet. Boxes of tissue will show the total number and the sizes both in centimetres and inches. Paper cups and other containers will show liquid capacity in millilitres.

3. *Clothing and apparel.* All measurements for clothing and other wearing apparel will be in centimetres. The relationship between metric measurements and clothing sizes is described in the unit on clothing. Shoe sizes will be specified in centimetres according to the system described in the section on clothing.

4. *Service stations.* All gasoline, oil and antifreeze will be sold by the litre. Since the litre is slightly larger than the quart, but significantly smaller than the gallon, it is important for both the retailer and consumer to understand the comparison. For example, a litre of oil will cost about 6 percent more than a quart of oil, while a litre of gas should cost a little more than 1/4 gallon. In other words, there are 3.785 litres in a U.S. gallon (there are 4.6 litres in an Imperial gallon). **Fig. 38-20**
Tire pressure will be given in kilopascals. Most service stations must have sets of metric wrenches for making adjustments and doing minor repairs on automobiles that have the ISO threads.

5. *Household furnishings and carpeting.* Since most household furnishings are sold by the individual piece or set, a change to metric language will have no effect on actual sizes or pricing. Carpeting will be sold by the square metre instead of the square yard. Therefore, the cost per square metre will be somewhat more. For example, a carpet that sells for $5.00 per square yard would cost approximately $6.00 per square metre. (about 20% more)

6. *Appliances.* There is little change in appliances except for specifying capacity and motor size. For example, the amount of water a washing machine uses will be given in litres instead of quarts or gallons and the amount of clothes that can be dried will be given in kilograms rather than pounds. The capacity of motors will be given in kilowatts rather than horsepower. Heat temperature will be given in degrees Celsius instead of Fahrenheit.

Conversion of Measuring Equipment

Four types of measuring equipment will need to be converted in most retail establishments including:

1. *Linear measurement.* In many retail establishments length of materials is determined by using a simple yardstick mounted on a cabinet. This will have to be replaced with a metre stick. In other kinds of commercial establishments some type of automatic length measuring equipment is used. For example, in

WINE BOTTLES

OLD CUSTOMARY SIZES	METRIC SIZES	
	CORRECT SI	COMMON USAGE
Gallon (128 fl oz)	3 litres	3 litres (101.47 fl oz)
Half gallon (64 fl oz)	1.5 litres	1 1/2 litres (50.74 fl oz)
Quart (32 fl oz)	1 litre	1 litre (33.825 fl oz)
4/5 quart (25.6 fl oz)	750 ml	3/4 litre (25.317 fl oz)
4/5 pint (12.8 fl oz)	375 ml	3/8 litre (12.68 fl oz)
2/5 pint (6.4 fl oz)	187 ml	3/16 litre (6.34 fl oz)
3 or 4 fl oz	100 ml	1/10 litre (3.4 fl oz)

The seven metric sizes replace all of the following sixteen customary sizes:

4.9 gallons	1 pint
3 gallons	4/5 pint
1 gallon	1/2 pint
4/5 gallon	2/5 pint
1/2 gallon	4 ounces
2/5 gallon	3 ounces
1 quart	2 ounces
4/5 quart	15/16 quart - for aperitif wines only

Fig. 38-19
Wine bottles in metric sizes.

BUY YOUR GAS, OIL AND ANTI-FREEZE
IN LITRES
LIQUID CAPACITY – GALLONS TO LITRES

GALLONS	LITRES	GALLONS	LITRES	GALLONS	LITRES	GALLONS	LITRES
1	3.8	11	42	21	80	31	117
2	7.6	12	45	22	83	32	121
3	11	13	49	23	87	33	125
4	15	14	53	24	91	34	129
5	19	15	57	25	95	35	132
6	23	16	61	26	98	36	136
7	26	17	64	27	102	37	140
8	30	18	68	28	106	38	144
9	34	19	72	29	110	39	148
10	38	20	76	30	113	40	151

Fig. 38-20
Comparison of gallons to litres. A 20 gallon tank will hold 76 litres.

fabric shops an automatic gage registers the length of the material. These must be converted to read in metres and tenths of a metre rather than in yards, feet and inches.

2. *Weight measurement.* Scales used in business and industry are available either in customary, combination metric-customary and totally metric scales. Most of the 5 million scales currently in use in retail establishments have customary unit designations. These will all need to have some conversion work done on them as follows:

(a) To convert an open-face of fan-type scale, all that is required is a new printed face which will show the readings in metric units.
Fig. 38-21

(b) Cylindrical scales. Metric charts are available for all cylinder scales to replace the customary chart. An expert serviceman will have to replace the chart for reading weights. However, the mechanism of the scale itself will not have to be changed.
Fig. 38-22

(c) Automatic dial scales used in industrial establishments are available in combination metric-customary units or in total metric units. If a customary scale is in use, the only part that will need to be replaced is the face.

(d) Small balance scales used on farms and small commercial establishments are used for general weighing purposes. To convert the small balance scale to metric, review the procedure in the section on agriculture.

Fig. 38-21
An open face weighing scale.

Fig. 38-22
A cylindrical weighing scale.

(e) Electronic scales with digital weight indications are the most modern type used in many large commercial establishments. It is a relatively easy job to change these units to read in metric rather than customary units. This is done simply by respanning the device and changing the weight identifications. If the marking label is part of the scale, this will print the unit price per kilogram, the net weight in kilograms, and the total price.
Fig. 38-23

Fig. 38-23
An electronic weighing scale.

3. *Gasoline pumps.* All gasoline pumps and other liquid dispensers will need to be readjusted to register the number of litres and tenths of a litre, price per litre and total price.
Fig. 38-4

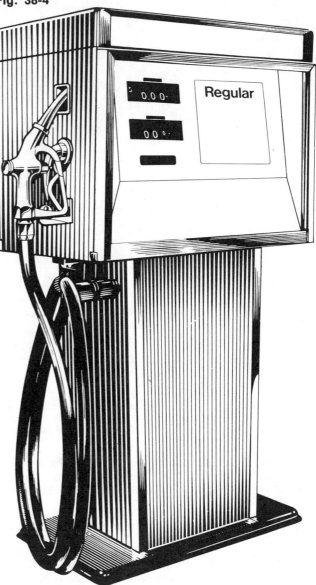

Fig. 38-24
Gas pumps must be changed to measure litres.

4. *Pressure gages.* Pressure gages for all machinery will have to be recalibrated so that pressure is shown in kilopascals instead of pounds per square inch. For example, tire pressure gages in all service stations will register tire pressure in kilopascals.

Advertising
The primary function of advertising is to sell people on new products. A secondary responsibility is to instruct the reader as to any new information that may be included in or on the product. Recognizing that Americans will be living in a predominantly metric environment in the years ahead, it is imperative that all advertising should:
1. Use correct symbols for metric units.
2. Explain, during the transition period, the equivalents of customary sizes into metric sizes. For

example, if the weight of a product is 100 kilograms, then the reader should understand that this is equivalent to 220 pounds.

3. Avoid obsolete metric terms. Many automobile engines, for example, are advertised as 2300 cc's which is incorrect and should be listed as 2300 cm^3 or 2.3 litres. The purchaser of an automibile should realize that a 2300 cubic centimetre displacement is equal to a 140 cubic inch engine.

FTC Guidelines for Metric Usage in Packaging

The Federal Trade Commission has issued a set of guidelines for the use of metric units on consumer packaging. The guidelines are an adjunct to Section 500.21 of the Fair Packaging and Labelling Act.

The guidelines apply to metric equivalents which appear in conjunction with customarily-dimensioned net quantity statements on a package's principal display panel (*exclusive* use of metric units will require an amendment to the Act). All elements which appear in the required customary net quantity statement must also appear in the metric equivalent statement, "except for a statement of count, ply, or a dual statement of quantity."

The guidelines contain the following elements:
● *Units* As a general rule, only the units metre, kilogram, and litre should be used, with appropriate multiple or submultiple prefixes representing steps of 1000, kilometre, metre, or millimetre.
● *Symbols* For the purposes of uniformity, the following symbols should be used in metric statements of net quantity:

litre — l
millilitre — ml
kilogram — kg
gram — g
metre — m
millimetre — mm
square metre — m^2
square centimetre — cm^2

Symbols are not capitalized unless the unit is derived from a proper name, i.e., °C for degree Celsius. Periods should not be used after the symbol. Symbols are always written in the singular form.

Care should be exercised so that the symbol "l" for litre will not be mistaken as a "1" in the numerical expression. Accordingly, where it is possible for the symbol to be misread, it is recommended that litre be spelled out or that the symbol "l" be a lower case letter or script ℓ.
● *Numerical Values* (The guidelines recommended a set of exact conversion factors carried out to between four and six decimal places from customary units of mass, volume, area, and length to metric equivalents for accuracy.)
● *Rounding* In all conversions, the number of significant digits retained should be such that accuracy is neither sacrificed nor exaggerated. As a general rule, converted values should be rounded down by dropping any digit beyond the first three, i.e., 196.4 g becomes 196 g, or 1.759 m becomes 1.75 m.

● *Rule of 1000* For packaged goods, it is preferred that selected multiple or submultiple prefixes for units result in numerical values between 1 and 1000, i.e., 1.96 kg, not 1960 g; or 750 mm, not 0.75 m. Use only decimal fractions—common fractions such as 1/2 or 1/4 are not permitted.
● *Location, Type Size, and Separation* A metric statement located on any principal display panel is considered a part of the required net quantity statement for the purposes of location, separation, and

type size. Since lower case letters are required for metric symbols, care must be exercised to insure that the rule in Section 500.18(d) of the Fair Packaging and Labelling Act governing letter height is followed. In lieu of the symbol, the metric unit may be used, i.e., "GRAM" or "gram" but *not* "Gram". Exponents should be one-half the type size of the symbol letter used. For purposes of uniformity and clarity, the metric statement should follow the required statement using parentheses where appropriate, or be positioned just *below* the required statement.

Metrication of Bulk Grocery Products
The following are proposed guidelines of rational package sizes for bulk-packed such products as coffee and cereals, and for reconstituted type products, i.e. cake mixes, dessert mixes, and so forth which are sold to yield a given volume or number of table servings.

In considering the conversion of bulk packed and reconstituted type grocery products to metric package sizes, it is important to recognize:
1. The need for a consistent and logical decimal system of weight subdivision; and
2. The need to convert to new package weights without undue consumer confusion or disruption of current consumer purchase patterns.

A proposed system of package weights has been developed which is consistent and logical and will provide the increments necessary to accommodate the needs of the consumer.

Bulk Packed Products
Consumers currently relate to subdivision or fractions of a pound (454 g). Since the basic metric unit of weight is the significantly greater kilogram (1000 g), a flexible system of subdivision is needed to accommodate the majority of products currently packaged in the range of 1/4 lb. (113 g) to 1-1/2 lbs. (680 g).

1. Metrics is basically a decimal system so the initial subdivision of the kilogram is by 100 g increments.

1000 g ÷ 10 = 100 g, 200 g, 300 g, 400, 500 g, 600 g, 700 g, 800 g, 900 g, 1000 g.

2. Since consumers are accustomed to subdivision by quarters, the kilogram is further subdivided in this manner.

1000 g ÷ 4 = 250 g, 500 g, 750 g, 1000 g.

3. The 1/2 kilogram (500 g) is the metric increment closest to the current pound. It is anticipated that products such as butter will be marketed in 500 gram packages containing four 125 gram sticks. To accommodate this 500 gram secondary base, it is similarly subdivided by 10 and 4.

500 g ÷ 10 = 50 g, 100 g, 150 g, 200 g, 250 g, 350 g, 400 g, 450 g, 500 g,

500 g ÷ 4 = 125 g, 250 g, 375 g, 500 g.

4. For lighter packages of 100 g and less, the system is expanded following the preceding 1/4 and 1/10 subdivision pattern as follows:

100 g ÷ 10 = 10 g, 20 g, 30 g, 40 g, 50 g, 60 g, 70 g, 80 g, 90 g, 100 g,

100 g ÷ 4 = 25 g, 50 g, 75 g, 100 g

5. To complete the proposed system, packages of 50 g or less will be subdivided as follows:

25—50 g — 5 g increments
10—25 g — 1 g increments
1—10 — 0.1 g (100 mg) increments
0—1 g — 0.01 g (10 mg) increments

6. Package weights greater than 1 kilogram will increase at 500 g increments.

Reconstituted Type Products

In addition to the package patterns for bulk packed products, there is a second category of products. These are the reconstituted products such as cake mixes, soft drink mixes, dessert mixes, etc. which are packaged to provide the consumer with a given number of table servings or volume of product. The consumer is not desirous to purchase significantly different quantities as a result of metrication. Therefore, metric conversion is minimal and can be accomplished by rounding to the following pattern:

```
   0—    1 g + to nearest  10 mg
   1—   25 g + to nearest 100 mg
  25—   50 g + to nearest   1 g
  50—  200 g + to nearest   5 g
 200— 1000 g + to nearest 100 g
1000 g +      - to nearest 100 g
```

UNIT 39
FOODS AND NUTRITION

As the United States converts to the international system of metric weights and measures, the change may be viewed with some apprehension by the millions of American homemakers. However, there is no need for concern. Many packaged and bottled foods already are dual dimensioned. **Fig. 39-1.**

Fig. 39-1
Most packaged foods are dual dimensioned even though some of the metric symbols are incorrect, such as the use of "cc" instead of ml for millilitres.

While it is inevitable that all industrial activities "go metric", cooks may continue to use their old, trusted recipes in customary (English) measurements. It's quite possible that experienced cooks may never use the metric system at all but, instead, will continue to use customary measures because ingredients remain the same, after all.

Cooking will not go metric over night but, as more and more ingredients are sold by metric measure, the time will come when it is more convenient to cook in metric. Also, all home economists and dieticians must be thoroughly familiar with metrics related to foods. Both homemakers and home economists will discover that the metric system is more accurate than the customary system, leaving less chance for failure.

There are only a few new words or descriptions that cooks will need to learn: grams or kilograms instead of ounces and pounds for measuring dry weights, millilitres or litres instead of fluid ounces, pints or quarts for measuring liquids, degrees Celsius instead of degrees Fahrenheit for temperature, and kilojoules instead of Calories for energy. Metric conversion presents the ideal opportunity to create a uniform method for indicating quantity. A suitable system for recipes is a follows:

-quantities of dry ingredients will be expressed in milligrams, grams and kilograms, and

-volumes of liquids will be expressed in millilitres and litres.

The quantities of dry ingredients are normally given in terms of the unit of weight but, until kitchen scales are in general use, the corresponding volume in millilitres or litres of dry ingredients may also be specified.

In the food industry the most common units are:

Quantity	Unit	Symbol
length	millimetre	mm
	metre	m
weight (mass)	milligram	mg
	gram	g
	kilogram	kg
	metric ton (tonne)	t
area	square centi-metre	cm^2
	square metre	m^2
	hectare	ha
volume	cubic centi-metre	cm^3
	cubic metre	m^3
volume (fluids)	millilitre	ml
	litre	l or L
force	newton	N
pressure	kilopascal	kPa
tempera-ture	degree Celsius	°C
density (mass density)	kilo grams per cubic metre	kg/m^3
energy	kilojoule	kJ
power	watt	W
	kilowatt	kW

Weight Measurement

The two units for weight needed by the average homemaker are kilogram and gram. A kilogram equals a thousand grams, and equals about 2.2 pounds. There are about 28 grams in an ounce. **Fig. 39-2a,b,c.**

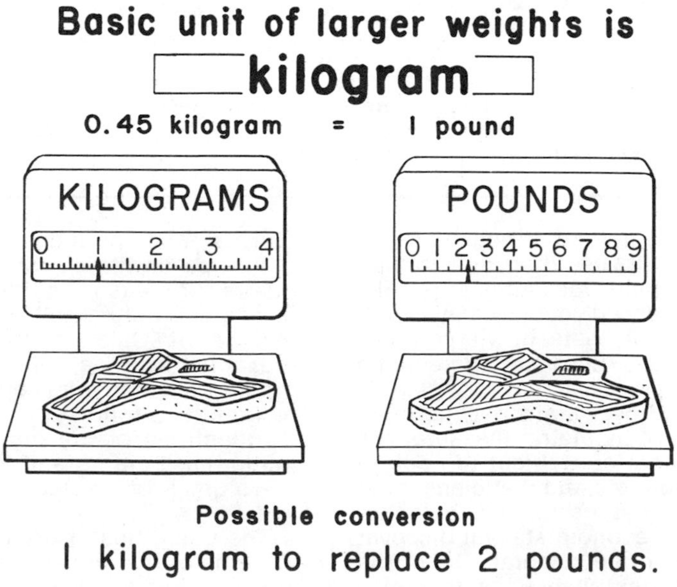

Basic unit of larger weights is
☐kilogram☐

0.45 kilogram = 1 pound

Possible conversion
1 kilogram to replace 2 pounds.

Fig. 39-2a
The kilogram is used as the base unit for larger weights such as meat, potatoes, sugar and rice. Note that a kilogram is about 10 percent more than 2 pounds.

Basic unit of small weights is the
⌐gram⌐

453.6 grams = 1 pound
28.35 grams = 1 ounce

Possible rounded conversions

28 grams	to replace	1 ounce
125 grams	to replace	1/4 pound
250 grams	to replace	1/2 pound
500 grams	to replace	1 pound

Fig. 39-2b
The gram will be used as the unit of weight for smaller items.

Customary Quantity	Metric Replacement	U.S. Equivalent of Metric Quantity
Weight:		
2 oz	50 g	1.76 oz
4 oz	125 g	4.41 oz
8 oz	250 g	8.82 oz
12 oz	375 g	13.23 oz
1 lb	500 g	17.64 oz
1 cwt (100 lb)	50 kg	110.23 lb
1 ton (2000 lb)	1 metric ton (1000 kg)	0.91 ton
Capacity:		
1/2 pint	250 ml	0.44 pint
1 pint	500 ml	0.88 pint
1 gallon	5 litres	1.10 gallons
1 fl oz	25 ml (cm³)	0.70 fl oz

Fig. 39-2c
Possible metric replacements for weights and measures in everyday use.

In commercial cookery, all metric recipes will list ingredients by weight because this is more accurate. For example, a cup of flour and a cup of sugar don't weigh the same amount (have a different mass). However, except for the dieter, chances are that the average person will not need an accurate set of scales for the kitchen. For the cook who does have a metric scale handy, it won't be long before measuring is done by weighing the ingredients rather than measuring some other way.

Liquid Volume

In the metric system, liquid volume will be measured in litres or millilitres. **Fig. 39-3a, b.**

A litre is about 6 percent more than a quart. Five hundred millilitres is slightly more than a pint and 250 millilitres is slightly more than a half pint. Five hundred ml, or about a pint, is also slightly more than two cups. The metric cup will be 250 ml. In the customary system one cup is equal is 236.6 ml which is 16 tablespoons; one tablespoon equals three teaspoons. In the metric system the cup will become 250 ml, while the metric tablespoon will be 15 ml, and the metric teaspoon 5 ml. Matching recipes with the measuring units is a matter of simple conversion.

Basic liquid measure is the
litre

500 millilitres =
1.06 pints

4 litres =
1.06 gallons

one litre = 1.06 quarts

Fig. 39-3a
The base unit of liquid measure is the litre.

POSSIBLE STANDARD MEASURES

customary	exact conversion soft conversion	rounded metric hard conversion
1 quart	946 ml	1 000 ml
1 pint	473.2 ml	500 ml
1 cup	236.6 ml	250 ml
1 Tbsp	14.8 ml	15 ml
1 tsp	4.9 ml	5 ml

Fig. 39-3b
If liquid measures are rounded to even modules, they will be
slightly larger than our present customary sizes.

Temperatures

Cooking temperatures for food preparation in the customary system are now stated in degrees Fahrenheit. **Fig. 39-4.**

In metric, temperatures will be given in degrees Celsius. Oven temperature controls are commonly calibrated in 25 or 50 degree intervals in the Fahrenheit scale. Meat thermometers are usually in 10 degree intervals, candy at 2, and deep fat thermometers in 2 or 5 intervals. Fortunately, conversion of temperatures from degrees Fahrenheit to degrees Celsius is not difficult. If the recipe currently calls for 450 °F, this can be halved for the metric temperature of 225 °C. This would be close enough even though the actual conversion would be from 450° Fahrenheit to 232 degrees Celsius. Just remember that dividing the Fahrenheit temperature by 2 will give the approximate Celsius temperature. However, this rough estimate will not be satisfactory for cooking that requires accurate temperatures such as candy making. In this case an actual conversion table should be used.

Pressures for Cookers

In the metric system pressure is expressed in kilopascals (kPa) instead of pounds per square inch (psi). **Fig. 39-5.**

One psi is equal to about 7 kPa (7.2 is more exact). Therefore, a pressure of 15 psi on a pressure cooker would be about 100 kilopascals, while a pressure of 10 psi would be about 70 kPa. If a pressure cooker called for pressure of 5 to 10 psi, a pressure of about 50 kPa can be used.

Basic measure of temperature is
degree Celsius

Fahrenheit degree Celsius

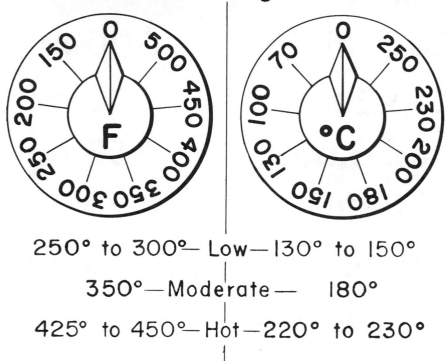

Recommended Conversion degree Celsius		Present Scale Fahrenheit
70 °C	—	150 °F
80 °C	—	175 °F
100 °C	—	200 °F
110 °C	—	225 °F
130 °C	—	250 °F
140 °C	—	275 °F
150 °C	—	300 °F
170 °C	—	325 °F
180 °C	—	350 °F
190 °C	—	375 °F
200 °C	—	400 °F
220 °C	—	425 °F
230 °C	—	450 °F
240 °C	—	475 °F
250 °C	—	500 °F
270 °C	—	525 °F
290 °C	—	550 °F

250° to 300°— Low —130° to 150°

350°—Moderate— 180°

425° to 450°—Hot—220° to 230°

Fig. 39-4
Degrees Celsius will be used for all heating temperatures.

PRESSURES

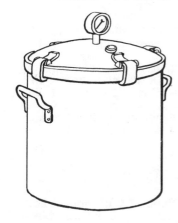

psi	ROUNDED kPa
5	35
10	70
15	100
20	140
25	175

Fig. 39-5
Pressure will be given in kilopascals, commonly referred to as "kPa". This is just as easy to say as "psi".

Equipment for Cooking
In the change from the customary to the metric system, it will be necessary to have an additional measuring device for both liquids and solids. **Fig. 39-6.**

Basic measuring tools for
food preparation

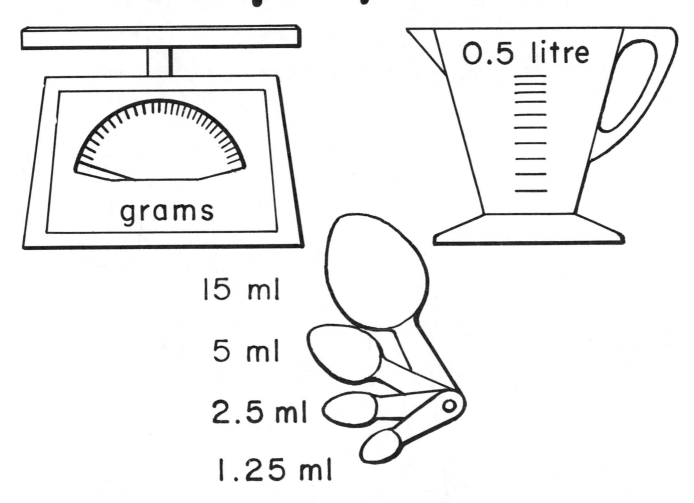

Fig. 39-6
Some basic measuring tools for food preparation. A 1/2 litre size is the equivalent of 2 metric cups and can be listed as 0.5 litre.

In commercial cookery, weight (mass) *alone* will be used in determining the quantity of materials, since it is the only accurate way of specifying amounts. However, for home cooking, the volume both of solid and liquid materials can be measured, even though there will be great variations in their weight. For example, a metric cup that measures 250 ml holds 250 g of water since 1 ml is equal to 1 cm^3 and 1 ml of water weighs 1 gram. However, the cup's contents weigh differently: butter weighs 235 g, flour 120 g, granulated sugar 210 g, and grain rice 200 g. If the liquid is thicker than water, such as syrup, 1 cup weighs more than 250 g.

Following are the common sizes of measuring instruments that will be used in cooking:

1. *Liquid measures.* A litre container that holds 1000 ml graduated in 100 ml and at every metric cup (250 ml) **Fig. 39-7.**
This container will be approximately 6 percent larger than the customary quart, which holds 946 ml.

2. *The two metric cup measure,* which holds 500 ml (1/2 litre) and is equal to a little more than 1 pint (473 ml). This container may be divided into 50 ml units such as 50, 100, 150, 200, 250, 300, 350, etc. **Fig. 39-8.**

3. *The one metric cup measuring unit,* (250 ml) is slightly larger than the customary cup (237 ml). This may be divided into 25 ml units of 25, 50, 75, 100, 125, 150, plus 200 ml. **Fig. 39-9.**

4. *The metric tablespoon which will be 15 ml, is slightly larger than the customary tablespoon* (14.8 ml). **Fig.39-10.**

5. *The metric teaspoon* will be 5 ml. This is slightly larger than the customary teaspoon (4.93 ml).

6. Two other measuring spoons that may be used are the 2.5 ml (1/2 teaspoon) and the 1.25 ml (1/4 teaspoon).

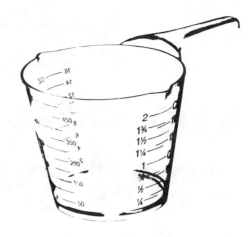

Fig. 39-8
A 2-cup metric size that is equivalent to 500 millilitres.

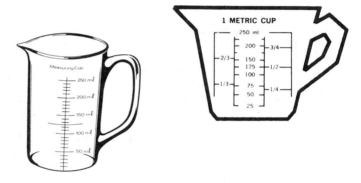

Fig. 39-9
Measuring cups may come in several different shapes and styles.

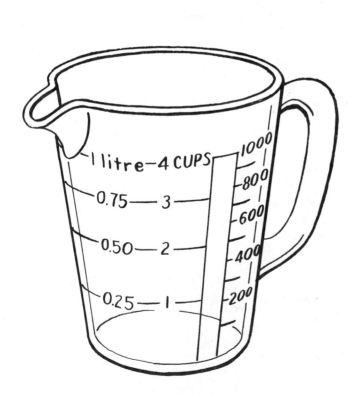

Fig. 39-7
A litre (1000 millilitres) measure graduated every 100 millilitres on one side and every metric cup (250 millilitres) on the other side.

Fig. 39-10
Measuring spoons. It is likely that the United States will use a 15 ml metric tablespoon. However, in Australia this tablespoon is 20 ml in size, and in South Africa it is 12.5 ml. There is, therefore, no equivalent standard for the tablespoon and teaspoon that is universally accepted.

Weighing Scales

Weighing scales for household use usually are one of the following types:

    a. self indicating - generally with a single scale pan
    b. balance-type with a set of weights
    c. balance-type with a sliding piece on a calibrated beam
    d. spring balance.

The spring balance is most common. **Fig. 39-11.**

Usually a scale with a capacity of 1 kilogram with 10, 20 or 25 gram divisions is most suitable.

Temperature Scales

Eventually all temperatures will be given in degrees Celsius (°C). On the Celsius scale water freezes at O °C and boils at 100 °C. In between, 22 °C is a pleasant room temperature while 37 °C is normal body temperature. If you remember these four temperatures, you will be able to orient yourself with respect to the Celsius scale. **Fig. 39-12.**

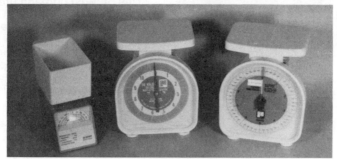

Fig. 39-11
A typical spring scale that might be used in the kitchen.

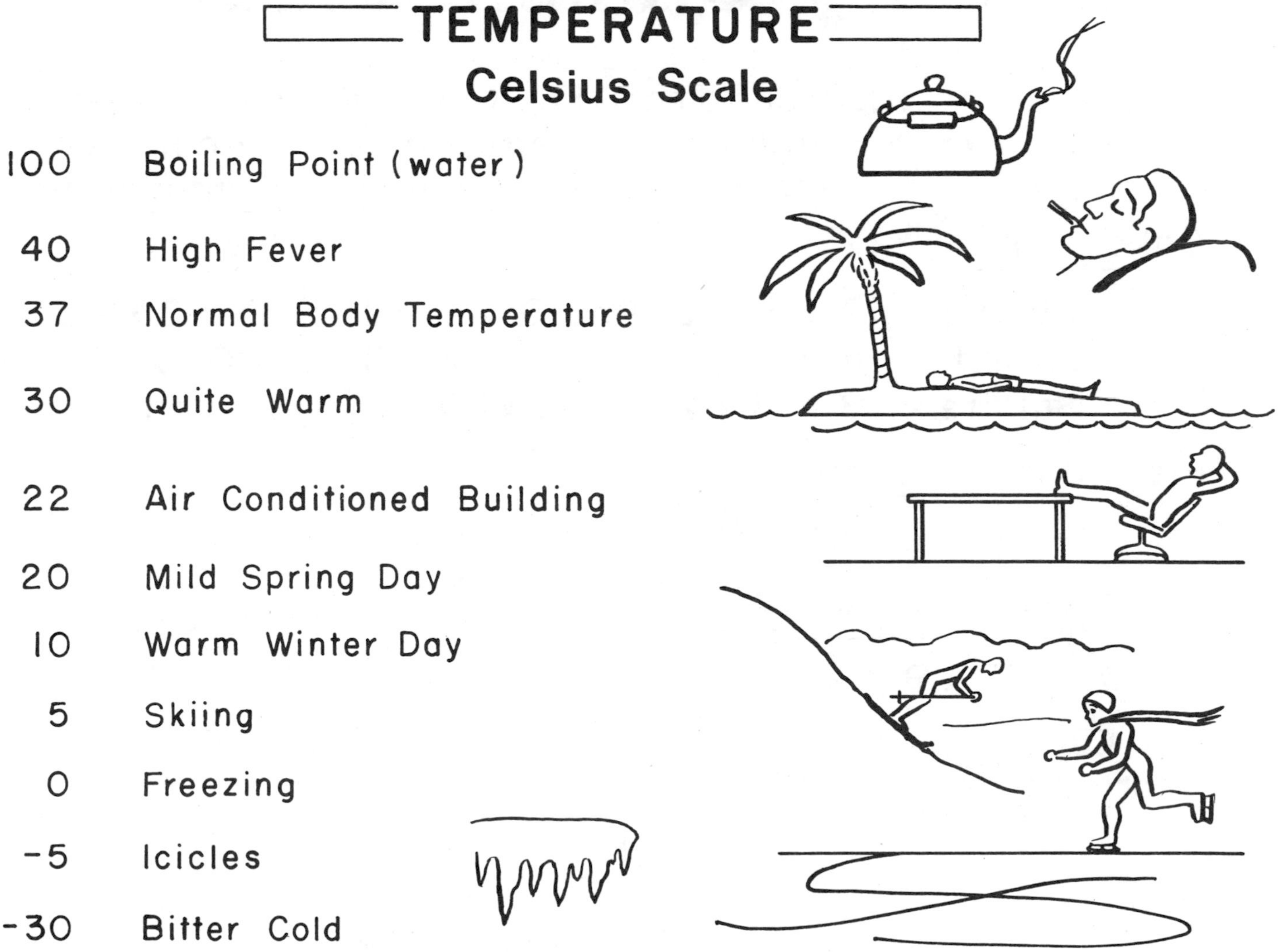

TEMPERATURE
Celsius Scale

100	Boiling Point (water)
40	High Fever
37	Normal Body Temperature
30	Quite Warm
22	Air Conditioned Building
20	Mild Spring Day
10	Warm Winter Day
5	Skiing
0	Freezing
-5	Icicles
-30	Bitter Cold

Fig. 39-12
This will give you a feel for the temperatures in degrees Celsius.

In using the Celsius scale on ovens, the temperatures may be from 100 °C to 260 °C with intervals of 20 °C and perhaps subdivisions of 10 °C. The following are the temperatures which are used to indicate the condition inside the oven.

Metric	Customary	
120 °C to 135 °C	250 °F to 275 °F	Very slow oven
150 °C to 165 °C	300 °F to 325 °F	Slow oven
175 °C to 190 °C	350 °F to 375 °F	Moderate Oven
205 °C to 220 °C	400 °F to 425 °F	Hot oven
230 °C to 245 °C	450 °F to 475 °F	Very hot oven
260 °C to 275 °C oven	500 °F to 525 °F	Extremely hot oven or broiling temperature

Oven temperatures indicated in recipes will be expressed in degrees Celsius. With customary equipment marked in the Fahrenheit scale, the simplest way to use the heat information is to double the Celsius scale. For example, if the temperature called for is 120 ° C, use 240 ° F. These temperatures are close enough except for specialized cooking.

Pot and Pans

While there will probably be no actual change in the sizes of most cooking utensils, these will be expressed in litres and millilitres. Other pans such as cake pans and casseroles will be indicated in millimetre or centimetre dimensions. **Fig. 39-13.**
Metric recipes will require a cooking utensil about 10 percent larger than the ones used for customary recipes. However, the cooking utensils already available will be suitable.

Baking Utensil Sizes

Utensil	U. S. Customary Units Inches	Equivalent in Metric Units Centimetres	Metric Units Rounded Centimetres
Cake Pans			
Oblong	13 x 9 x 2	33.0x22.9x5.1	33 x 23 x 5
Round	8 x 1-1/2	20.3 x 3.8	20 x 4
Square	8 x 8 x 2	20.3x20.3x5.1	21 x 21 x 5
Pie Pans or Plates			
	8 x 1-1/4	20.3 x 3.2	20 x 3
	9 x 1-1/4	22.9 x 3.2	23 x 3

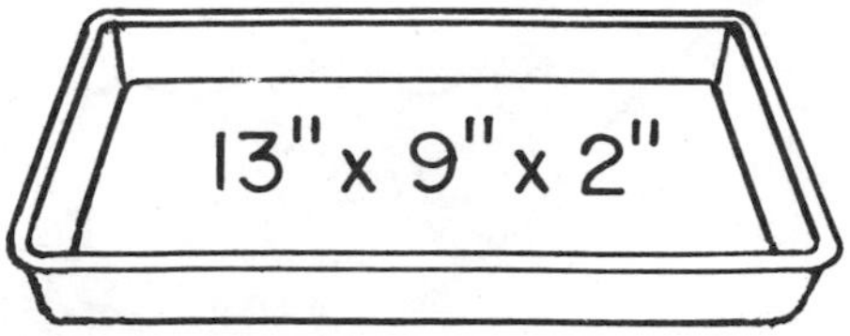

13" x 9" x 2"

Approx. 330 x 230 x 50 mm
33 x 23 x 5 cm

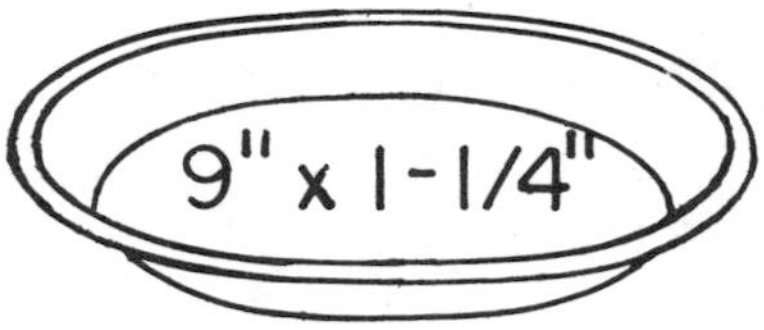

9" x 1-1/4"

Approx. 229 x 32 mm
23 x 3 cm

Fig. 39-13
Common baking utensil sizes. Actually, there is no need to change baking utensils. However, if the rounded metric cup of 250 millilitres is used, then the total ingredients will be about 10 percent more than when using the typical customary cup.

Writing Recipes
 A good metric recipe will have easy-to-measure quantities that show both weight (mass) and volume so that either a weighing scale or a cup and spoon measure may be used. **Fig. 39-14.**

APPROXIMATE WEIGHT IN GRAMS PER 250 ml OF RECIPE INGREDIENTS

Almonds (shelled)	150	Milk (liquid, whole)	260
Apricot jam	330	Milkpowder (granulated, fat free)	80
Apricots (dried)	100	Milkpowder (powder, fat free)	100
		Oil (cooking)	220
Baking Powder	200	Peaches (dried)	150
Bicarbonate of Soda	200	Peanuts (shelled)	150
Bread Crumbs (fresh)	60	Pecan Nuts (shelled)	100
Bread Crumbs (dry)	120	Prunes (dried, stoned)	150
Butter	230		
		Raisins (seeded)	150
Cheese: Grated Cheddar	100	Raisins (seedless)	150
Cottage	250	Rice	200
Cream	250		
Roquefort	120	Salt	240
Cherries (whole)	160	Spaghetti	100
Coconut	80	Spices: Mustard (ground)	80
Cocoa	120	Allspice (ground)	110
Coffee (instant)	70	Nutmeg (ground)	120
Cream of Tartar	160	Cloves (ground)	120
Crushed Wheat	200	Pepper (ground)	120
		Currypowder (ground)	130
Dates (whole)	150	Cinnamon (ground)	90
		Ginger (ground)	80
Figs (dried)	150	Sugar: Brown (granulated)	200
Flour: Cake Flour	120	Icing (granulated)	130
Bread Flour	120		
Self-raising Flour (commercial)	140	Tapioca	170
Self-raising Flour (home made)	120	Walnuts (shelled)	100
Gelatine	150	Yeast	210
Macaroni	110		
Margarine	230		
Meal: Arrowroot meal	180		
Mealie meal	120		
Mealie meal (sifted)	150		
Mealie meal (instant)	120		
Oat meal	90		
Whole-wheat meal	130		

Fig. 39-14a
Approximate weights (mass) in grams for 250 millilitres of recipe ingredients. Note that these are only approximate, and the actual measurement may vary depending on how tightly the material is packed in a cup.

COOKING MEASURES

Metric Cup	Water	Butter	Self Raising Flour	Granular Sugar	Grain Rice
1	250 ml	230 g	140 g	200 g	200 g
3/4	188 ml	170 g	105 g	150 g	150 g
2/3	167 ml	150 g	93 g	130 g	130 g
1/2	125 ml	115 g	70 g	100 g	100 g
1/3	83 ml	75 g	47 g	65 g	65 g
1/4	63 ml	60 g	35 g	50 g	50 g
1/8	31 ml	30 g	18 g	25 g	25 g

Fig. 39-14b
Note how a cupful weighs considerably different, depending on what it is.

The following should be used in writing recipes in metrics:

Dry ingredients. The weight (mass) of the ingredient is given first and the equivalent volume is stated in parentheses after the ingredient. Example: 216 g sugar (250 ml)

Liquids. The volume is given in millilitres (ml) or litres (ℓ).

Examples: 250 ml hot milk
2 ℓ water

Single items. As in the past, the quantities of eggs, olives, tomatoes, etc., are indicated by numbers.

Examples: 1 egg (large)
3 medium-size tomatoes
1 stick cinnamon

Example: **Milk Tart**

1	stick cinnamon
500 ml	hot milk
60 g	sugar (75 ml)
	pinch of salt
35 g	cake flour (75 ml)
10 g	butter (12.5 ml)
2	eggs
1	pie plate, lined with cinnamon and sugar

1. Add the cinnamon to the milk, and scald. Remove the flavoring.
2. Mix the sugar, salt and flour. Gradually add a little of the hot milk, mixing well. Pour back into a saucepan and cook, while stirring, until thick.
3. Remove from stove and stir in butter. Allow to cool, then stir in beaten egg.
   Spoon filling into a tart plate lined with puff pastry. Sprinkle with cinnamon or cinnamon and sugar. Bake 240 °C for 10 min. Reduce temperature to 180 °C and bake 10 to 15 min longer.

Another recipe is given in **Fig. 39-15.**

CHOCOLATE PUDDING

80 g (120 ml) semi-sweet chocolate
60 g (75 ml) sugar
34 g (50 ml) corn starch
700 ml milk
28 g (30 ml) margarine
1 metric teaspoon vanilla

In a heavy 2 litre saucepan, stir together chocolate pieces, sugar, and corn starch. Gradually stir in milk. Cook over medium heat, stirring constantly, until mixture comes to a boil and boils 1 minute. Remove from heat. Stir in margarine and vanilla. Pour into 6 small custard cups. To prevent film from forming on top of pudding, place a plastic wrap directly on top of pudding. Chill in refrigerator. Makes 6 servings.

NOTE: 1 metric teaspoon = 5 millilitres (ml)

Fig. 39-15
A simple metric recipe.

Energy Value of Foods

Americans have been counting calories for many years. Scientists have established that carbohydrates, fats and proteins are the chemical compounds used by the body to give heat and energy, and this has been measured in terms of calories. A small calorie (gram calorie) is the amount of heat required to raise the temperature of one gram of water one degree Celsius (1.8 degrees Fahrenheit). A great deal of confusion and disagreement has resulted in the past in the use of many different energy units. In fact, there are approximately 13 different energy units used in the old customary and older metric systems. Since small calories in simple heat calculations are very small units, home economists and dieticians sometime ago began to use the kilocalorie, (kilogram calorie) which was soon shortened to a Calorie spelled with a capital C. This is often referred to as the *large Calorie*. With the establishment of the International System of Units (SI) the joule - J is the only energy unit for all areas. The joule replaces the Calorie, the Btu and several other energy units. The joule is quite a small unit in comparison with the kilocalorie or large Calorie. Therefore, the kilojoule (kJ) is used as a practical unit in food. **Fig. 39-16** shows the relationship between kilocalories and kilojoules. Note, for example, how easy it is to see that 60 kilocalories are approximately the same as 250 kilojoules. The kilojoule - 1000 joules - is about *one quarter* (1/4) the size of the Calorie (in dietetics). Typical energy values in kilojoules (kJ) of some popular foods are:

Apple - 150 kJ

Slice of white bread - 300 kJ

Standard egg - 325 kJ

Glass of whole milk - 540 kJ

Portion of cheddar cheese - 850 kJ

Lamb Chop - 1350 kJ

Since most people refer to the kilocalorie as the Calorie, it is important always to relate this large Calorie to the kilojoule. This relationship is 1 Calorie (kilocalorie) = 4.1868 kilojoules or 1 Calorie = approximately 4.2 kilojoules. For practical purposes in foods, the ratio can be 1 Calorie = 4 kJ, since this is accurate to approximately 5 percent. Therefore, a daily diet that previously was listed as 2000 Calories would be approximately 8000 kilojoules (kJ). The exact conversion would be 8373.6 kJ.

Nutrients

Nutrients are the chemicals found in food that your body uses daily to function properly. They furnish fuel and materials for body energy and cell growth and include proteins, carbohydrates, fats, vitamins and minerals. The recommended individual dietary allowances are shown in **Fig. 39-17.**

Carbohydrates, fats and proteins produce heat and energy in the body. Using the common conversion factor of 4.2, the equivalent number of kilocalories per gram and kilojoules per gram are as follows:

pure carbohydrates	4 kcal/g = 16.8 kJ/g or approx. 17.0 kJ/g
protein	4 kcal/g = 16.8 kJ/g or approx. 17.0 kJ/g
fat	9 kcal/g = 37.8 kJ/g or approx. 38.0 kJ/g
alcohol	7 kcal/g = 29.4 kJ/g

The energy values of foods are expressed in diets as kJ for food portions and as kJ per g for nutrition. It should be remembered that it is not essential to make conversions to great accuracy in determining energy values of food. For example, energy values of food portions should be rounded off to full kilojoules per 100 grams. For larger commercial type cookery, the megajoule is recommended as a replacement for the kilocalorie. A megajoule (MJ) equals 1000 kJ which equals 1 million joules.

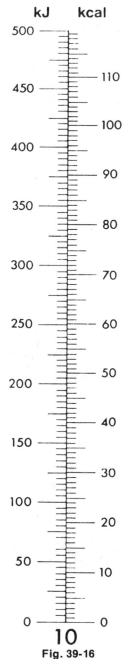

Fig. 39-16
This chart can be used to convert kilocalories to kilojoules. The kilocalorie is actually the large Calorie.

RECOMMENDED DIETARY ALLOWANCES

Sex and Age	Weight		Height		Calories*	Kilo-joules	Pro-tein	Cal-cium	Iron	Vita-min A	Thia-mine	Ribo-flavin	Niacin Equiva-lents	Ascorbic Acid
	lb	kg	in	cm			g	g	mg	I.U.	mg	mg	mg	mg
Men, 22-35 yrs	154	70	69	175	2800	11 760	65	0.8	10	5000	1.4	1.7	18	60
Women, 22-35 yrs	128	58	64	163	2000	8 400	55	0.8	18	5000	1.0	1.5	13	55
Children, 6-8 yrs	51	23	48	122	2000	8 400	35	0.9	10	3500	1.0	1.1	13	40
Boys, 10-12 yrs	77	35	55	140	2500	10 500	45	1.2	10	4500	1.3	1.3	17	40
Boys, 12-14 yrs	95	43	59	150	2700	11 340	50	1.4	18	5000	1.4	1.4	18	45
Boys, 14-18 yrs	130	59	67	170	3000	12 600	60	1.4	18	5000	1.5	1.5	20	55
Girls, 10-12 yrs	77	35	56	142	2250	9 450	50	1.2	18	4500	1.1	1.3	15	40
Girls, 12-14 yrs	97	44	61	155	2300	9 660	50	1.3	18	5000	1.2	1.4	15	45
Girls, 16-18 yrs	119	54	63	160	2300	9 660	55	1.3	18	5000	1.2	1.5	15	50

*Large Calorie or kilocalorie   Fig. 39-17

Recommended dietary allowance designed for maintenance of good nutrition of all healthy persons in the United States. These allowances are intended for persons normally active in a temperate climate.

Nutrition Labeling

Many food processors include nutrition information in their food labels. Beginning in 1975 all fortified foods, and all foods for which a nutrition claim is made must display nutrition information on their labels.

In addition to the usual information, such as name, net weight and ingredients, the label will tell what nutritional value the food contains. Information will be provided on the following:

Calories (kilojoules)

Protein

Carbohydrate

Fat

Vitamin A

Vitamin C

Thiamin

Riboflavin

Niacin

Calcium

Iron

The Labels in **Fig. 39-18** are examples of what you should look for when you shop.

Nutrition information must appear in a standard format and, unless space does not permit, always on the part of the label immediately to the right of the main panel. Having the nutrients always listed in the same order and location makes it easier to compare labels.

Reading Nutrition Labels

Nutrition information is given per serving. The label gives the size of a serving, for example, one cup (250 ml), two ounces (57 g), 1 tablespoon (15 ml) and tells how many servings are in the container.

Seven vitamins and minerals must be shown, in the same order, on all nutrition labels.

Other vitamins and minerals may also be listed.

Listing of cholesterol, fatty acid, and sodium content is optional.

Nutrition labels show amounts in grams rather than ounces, because grams are a smaller unit of measurement, and many food components are present in small amounts. Here is a guide to help you read nutrition labels:

1 pound	= 454 grams (g)
1 ounce	= 28.35 grams (g)
1 gram	= 1000 milligrams (mg)
1 milligram	= 1000 micrograms (µg)

What Does RDA Mean?

U.S. Recommended Daily Allowances (U.S. RDA) are the amounts of protein, vitamins and minerals that an adult should consume each day to keep healthy. Nutrition labels list the U.S. RDA by percentage. To make sure each individual gets enough vitamins and minerals, the percentages for each from different kinds of food should add up to about 100 per day.

NUTRITION INFORMATION
(PER SERVING)
SERVING SIZE = 1 oz (28 g)
SERVINGS PER CONTAINER = 12

CALORIES	110 (462 kJ)
PROTEIN	2 g
CARBOHYDRATE	24 g
FAT	0 g

PERCENTAGE OF U.S. RECOMMENDED DAILY ALLOWANCES (U.S. RDA)*

PROTEIN	2
THIAMIN	8
NIACIN	2

* Contains less than 2 percent of U.S. RDA for Vitamin A, Vitamin C, Riboflavin, Calcium and Iron.

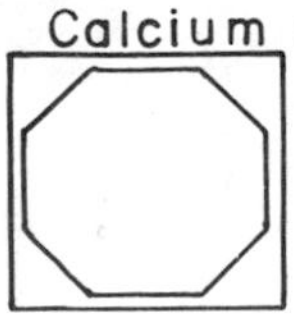

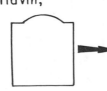

LABEL   SHAPES

NUTRITION INFORMATION
(PER SERVING)
SERVING SIZE = 8 oz (225 g)
SERVINGS PER CONTAINER = 1

CALORIES	560 - (2350 kJ)	FAT (PERCENT OF CALORIES 53%)	33 g
PROTEIN	23 g	POLYUNSAT- URATED	2 g
CARBOHYDRATE	- 43 g	SATURATED	9 g
		CHOLESTEROL (20 mg 100 g)	40 mg
		SODIUM (365 mg / 100 g)	830 mg

PERCENTAGE OF U.S. RECOMMENDED DAILY ALLOWANCES (U.S. RDA)

PROTEIN	35	RIBOFLAVIN	15
VITAMIN A	35	NIACIN	25
VITAMIN C (ASCORBIC ACID)	10	CALCIUM	2
THIAMIN (VITAMIN B₁)	15	IRON	25

Fig. 39-18
Two designs for nutrition labels that are found on most packaged and canned goods.

U.S Recommended Daily Allowances (U.S. RDA)

Protein	
Protein quality equal to or greater than casein	45 grams
Protein quality less than casein	65 grams
Vitamin A	5,000 International Units
Vitamin C (ascorbic acid)	60 milligrams
Thiamin (vitamin B1)	1.5 milligrams
Riboflavin (vitamin B2)	1.7 milligrams
Niacin	20 milligrams
Calcium	1.0 gram
Iron	18 milligrams
Vitamin D	400 International Units
Vitamin E	30 International Units
Vitamin B_6	2.0 milligrams
Folic acid (folacin)	0.4 milligram
Vitamin B_{12}	6 micrograms
Phosphorus	1.0 gram
Iodine	150 micrograms
Magnesium	400 milligrams
Zinc	15 milligrams
Copper	2 milligrams
Biotin	0.3 milligram
Pantothenic acid	10 milligrams

Weight Units to Use in Food Packaging

All weights of food will be given in units of grams (about 1/28 ounce) and kilograms (about 2.2 pounds). Actually, an ounce is equal to 28.35 grams, so that in dual dimensioning of packaging a 14 ounce package would be listed as 397 grams or rounded to 395 grams. Normally, for smaller packaged foods, the weight is given in grams rather than in kilograms. For example, the weight of a slice of bread with a thickness of approximately 10 mm (somewhat less than 1/2 inch) is about 30 grams (about 1 ounce). For larger food packages the kilogram will be used. For example, sugar that previously was packaged in 2 pound packages will probably be packaged in the kilogram size, which will be somewhat larger. Butter formerly packaged in pound packages will be in 500 gram packages, again slightly larger than a pound (a pound equals 454 grams). All liquid food measurements will be in millilitres (about 1/30 fluid ounce) and in litres (about 6 percent more than a quart).

Purchasing Food In Stores

The following are the general categories and the manner in which foods may be sold:

1. Meats, fish and poultry products will be sold by weight in grams and kilograms. For example, if ground beef weighs 1000 grams, or 1 kilogram, the price will be approximately 2.2 times as much as for a pound. Since most of these products will not be exact weight, a former one pound package may be shown as 450 grams and a 2 pound package as 1.8 kilograms.

2. Produce such as fruits, vegetables, and related produce will continue to be sold in bunches, by the dozen or by weight. If by weight, produce will be specified in grams or kilograms.

3. Dry packaged foods such as cereal and flour will be sold by weight in grams. Currently, dual dimensioning indicates the customary first and the metric in parentheses. For example, 16 ounces (454 g).

4. Canned goods will also be indicated by weight based on the contents of the specific can size. In place of the wide variety of can sizes currently used, the International Organization for Standardization (ISO) has recommended 13 can sizes that are from 52 mm to 230 mm in diameter.

5. Liquids in bottles and cartons will be marked in millilitres and litres. A typical quart will be replaced by the 1 litre size, which will be approximately 6 percent more than the quart; the 2 quart size will be replaced by the 2 litre size. Many semi-liquids such as catsup and toothpaste are not marked consistently. Catsup, for example, is marked in weight, giving the 14 ounce size as 397 grams. However, toothpaste is marked in millilitres, which is liquid capacity. Increasingly, packages will appear in metric units in rounded quantities. **Fig. 39-19.**

For example, the packages may have such values as 125 grams, 250 grams, 375 grams, and 500 grams to replace the traditional 4 ounce, 8 ounce, 12 ounce, and 1 pound packages. **Fig. 39-20.**

Each of these new sizes is about 10 percent larger than the old size. A 1 kilogram package of sugar would cost about 2.2 times as much as the old 2 pound package, because it is about 10 percent larger.

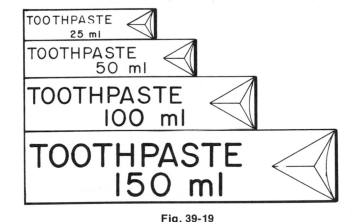

Fig. 39-19

Note the rounded size of toothpaste in millilitre modules.

Fig. 39-20

When butter is sold in rounded modules, the 500 gram size will be about 10 percent more than the pound size.

Common Errors in Marking Packages and Canned Goods

In the metric system there is a definite, specific way of using units and symbols. For example, the correct unit is the gram with the symbol g without a period, while the correct symbol for kilogram is kg without a period. The correct symbol for litre is either a vertical l or a script or italics ℓ. For millilitre it is ml, the l being either a vertical l or a script ℓ.

CLOTHING AND TEXTILES

Use of the metric system in purchasing textiles and in clothing construction is not new. Metrics has been used for measuring clothing and textiles for centuries by many countries. However, metric measurement for clothing and sewing will be a new experience for everyone in the United States.

Clothing may be divided into two categories, namely: (1) the *ready-to-wear* clothes where the customer must become familiar with the sizing system and body dimensions, and (2) *made to measure* clothing, particularly in home sewing where the individual working with patterns and textiles needs to know the metric measuring system.

The problem of changeover to the metric system is complicated by the fact that there are no universal sizing systems. For example, the much-traveled woman of trim build has to learn to ask for a size 38 dress in England, a size 14 in the United States and a size 44 in Europe. **Fig. 40-1.**

CLOTHING CONVERSION CHART

WOMEN'S SUITS AND DRESSES

British	32	34	36	38	40	42	44
American	8	10	12	14	16	18	20
Continental	38	40	42	44	46	48	50

MEN'S SUITS AND OVERCOATS

British		36	38	40	42	44	46
American		36	38	40	42	44	46
Continental		46	48	50	52	54	56

SHIRTS

British	14	14½	15	15½	16	16½	17
American	14	14½	15	15½	16	16½	17
Continental	36	37	38	39	41	42	43

MEN'S SHOES

British	7	8	9	10			
American	7½	8½	9½	10½			
Continental	41	42	43	44			

SOCKS

British	9½	10	10½	11	11½	12	12½
American		10	10½	11	11½	12	13
Continental	39	40	41	42	43	44	45

WOMEN'S SHOES

British	3	4	5	6	7		
American	4½	5½	6½	7½	8½		
Continental	35½	36½	38	39½	40½		

STOCKINGS

British	8	8½	9	9½	10	10½	11
American	--	8½	9	9½	10	10½	11
Continental	35	36	37	38	39	40	41

Fig. 40-1
A clothing conversion table that shows the confusion in clothing sizing in different countries

These sizing systems by themselves are relatively meaningless. For example, in the United States a dress marked size 14 in a moderately priced department store may be smaller than a size 12 in a higher priced department store. This confusion exists because many manufacturers use their own judgement in assigning a size to a product. Manufacturers use sizes as codes which by themselves have little or no meaning to average customers unless they know the brand name and have had previous experience with the fit of this brand. To understand the problems in clothing sizes many factors must be considered.

Body Measurement Data

A major problem in attempting to establish any kind of standardized clothing sizes is that there is limited information on the *actual body dimensions* (anthrometric data) of people in the United States and all other peoples of the world. The field of anthroprometrics can be described as that part of the anthropology having to do with the measurement of human bodies to determine differences between races, individuals, etc. **Fig. 40-2.**

A great deal of additional scientific data is needed to establish average body measurements of different people with different body types. For example, people in the United States are getting taller and heavier each year, and this will change the anthroprometric data. The average man in 1900 was 67" (170 centimetres) tall and weighed 140 pounds (64 kilograms), while by the year 2000 it is estimated that the average man will be 70" (178 cm) tall and will weigh 165 pounds (75 kg). The average woman in 1900 was 62" (157 cm) tall and weighed 127 pounds (58 kg), while in the year 2000 she will be 65" (165 cm) tall and will weigh 145 pounds (66 kg). **Fig. 40-3.**

Therefore, it has been very difficult to establish standards for height, weight, and other body measurements for various groups of people in our population. Generally, in establishing standards, people are divided into groups, namely the smallest in terms of height, weight and other measurements, the average, and the largest. Between smallest and largest, people can be grouped by body types. For example, people may be either *ectomorphic* (slender physical type), *mesomorphic* (muscular or athletic type), or *endomorphic* (large abnormal physical type).

Uniform Location of Body Measurement

Even when complete body measurement data are available for clothing manufacturers, it is essential that all manufacturers use the same body landmarks for establishing size designations. For example, if a shirt manufacturer in one country measures the length of sleeve from the shoulder to the wrist while in another country the sleeve length is measured from the center of the back of the neck to the wrist with the elbow bent, sleeve length will not have the same meaning. **Fig. 40-4.**

If one shirt manufacturer measures the neck circumference without a button overlap while another includes this overlap in the circumference, sizes are very confusing.

Sizing System

Once body measurement data is complete and there is agreement as to what body landmarks are to be used, this information could form the basis for an international sizing system. This sizing system could be meaningful if certain sizes would designate specific body measurements at certain agreed on locations. The sizing system could be code numbers or letters linked to these body dimensions. Technical committees of the ISO are working on a standardization of one or more sizing systems for clothes based on body measurement. The program of work includes clothing wear for:

Size designations for men, youths and boys
Size designations for women, junior misses and girls
Size designations for infants
Sizing systems for men, youths and boys
Sizing systems for women, junior misses and girls
Sizing systems for infants

Young Men's (Students') Data -- Regulars in Height

WAIST (cm)	| STATURE GROUPING 169-177 cm — Size 34 — CHEST (cm) |						| STATURE GROUPING 171-179 cm — Size 36 — CHEST (cm) |						| STATURE GROUPING 173-181 cm — Size 38 — CHEST (cm) |						| STATURE GROUPING 175-183 cm — Size 40 — CHEST (cm) |					
	81	82	83	84	85	86	87	88	89	90	91	92	93	94	95	96	97	98	99	100	101	102	103	104
98																					1			1
96																								1
94																								1
92																						1	2	
90																				2		1		
89																		1						
88																	1	1			2		1	
86																1		3	1	3		2		3
85															1			1	5	1		1	1	
84													1		1	1		2	1	1		1	2	2
83														1	2				2	3	2	1		
82													1	3	1	1		2						
81													1	1	3	1	7	5	7	1			2	2
80									2	3		3		1	8	2	7	3	8	2	+4	1		3
79							1	2			3	5	10	9	6	2	7	6	4	4	4	1	1	1
78									2		4	8	4	12	8	11	16	15	8	6	1	2	1	1
77								1	1	5	5		11	17	15	7	12	12	6	9		3	3	
76								4	4	8	8	6	13	11	16	22	10	10	7	7	7	1	2	1
75	1					1	1	7	6	14	17	22	25	22	19	11	9	21	8	1	3	2		
74						1	6	7	7	18	24	20	37	26	16	15	14	2	7	2	2	2		
73	1		2	1	4	5	7	19	25	28	33	22	32	21	17	13	10	7	4	2				
72			3	7	8	9	17	26	30	29	32	37	23	25	14	16	9	3	4	1	1			
71			3	6	18	17	19	21	32	33	26	38	23	18	15	6	7	3	2	1	1			
70	2	7	11	12	22	35	31	42	51	36	31	26	11	12	1	9	1		1		1			
69	7	6	10	19	26	28	38	31	27	36	17	15	16	11	4	2	1							
68	1	11	13	22	39	35	27	39	22	24	17	18	6	2										
67	6	9	13	26	36	25	20	34	13	10	14	9	5	2	1	2								
66	11	11	17	16	20	17	12	17	7	6	10	3	2											
65	6	15	8	13	10	11	7	6	7	4	1		3	2										
64	5	12	7	4	8	13	5	6	2	3	1													
63	5	4	3	5	5	2	1	1	1															
62	3	2	2	2	1	4	1	2																
61	1	4	3		2	1																		
60	1	1	2																					
Total	50	82	97	133	199	205	193	265	239	259	242	236	224	194	151	121	114	98	76	46	31	20	18	12

Size 34 total: 766 Size 36 total: 1434 Size 38 total: 902 Size 40 total: 203

Right-hand totals: 203, 902, 1434, 766 — Grand total 3305

Fig. 40-2
This chart illustrates the kind of anthrometric data that is gathered by the National Bureau of Standards to determine average body measurements for different groups of people. These body measurements in centimetres are based on a study of young men who are considered regulars in height. From this data averages are computed that are used for specifying body dimensions.

AVERAGE WOMAN

1900   2000

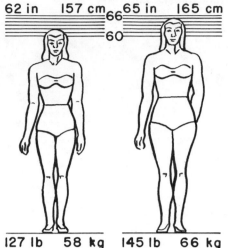

62 in   157 cm   65 in   165 cm

127 lb   58 kg   145 lb   66 kg

AVERAGE MAN

1900   2000

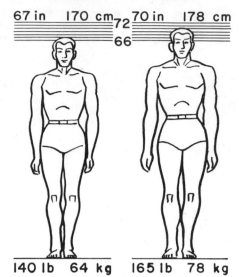

67 in   170 cm   70 in   178 cm

140 lb   64 kg   165 lb   78 kg

Fig. 40-3
The average man and woman in the United States is getting taller and heavier. This is also happening among other races where better diet and health habits are affecting the body dimensions. This is why it is so difficult to establish average body dimensions that can be used in determining clothing sizes.

☐ Metric shirt sizing ☐

Collar Size   **Sleeve Length**

38   **81**

Collar sizes

Customary Inches	Metric Centimetres
13	33
13-1/2	34-35
14	36
14-1/2	37
15	38
15-1/2	39-40
16	41
16-1/2	42
17	43
17-1/2	44-45

Fig. 40-4
A soft conversion of shirt sizes from customary to metric. Often one finds that an imported shirt is considerably smaller than the size indicated.

Status of Customary Sizing Practices

Perhaps no area of size designation is more confusing than that currently used on customary clothing. There is a bewildering variation of designations using numbers, letters and words to describe the size of an article of clothing. There is a complete lack of any kind of standardization of size measurements. The following are some examples of what the average consumer must cope with when shopping for clothing:

1. Women's ready-to-wear. There are at least seven major classifications of women's dress sizes. Many of these use numbers such as 6, 8, 10 or 38, 40, 42, etc. Most of these numbers are quite meaningless, since two dresses in the same classification marked with the same size are often different. **Fig. 40-5.**
A dress marked 16 in a moderately priced department store may be actually smaller than a dress size 14 in a higher priced department store. Even though a woman may purchase a size 16 dress, a coat might be purchased to match in size 12. **Fig. 40-6**

Shoes are often designated by a number to indicate length and a letter, such as A, B, C, etc., to indicate width.

2. Men's clothing. Men's suits are generally indicated by a size that roughly compares to the chest circumference. **Fig. 40-7.**

Fig. 40-5
The average woman must usually try on dresses of several different sizes to determine which one fits best. She cannot depend on the sizing system on the label unless she has had previous experience with that particular brand.

Fig. 40-6
Coat sizes generally run smaller for the same person than dress sizes.

3. Children's clothing. Some children's clothing manufacturers mark clothing by month sizes, such as 3, 6, 12 or 18 months, while other manufacturers mark the same clothing in 0, 1/2, 1 and 1 1/2 year garments. **Fig. 40-8.**

To add to the confusion, a size 12 month is not necessarily the same as a size 1 year. The letter x is often used to indicate an in between size. Ambiguous numbers which have no relationship to age or build also are used for indicating size. For example, shoe sizes with a range from 00 to 13 have no relationship to the age of the child being fitted. Also, some manufacturers of children's shoes use such letters as A, B, C, etc. to indicate width.

Fig. 40-7
The average man's suit is based largely on chest dimensions. However, most men must try on two or three different sizes to determine which fits best. Often the brand of suit will affect the size.

Fig. 40-8
Children's clothing sizing is most confusing of all, since manufacturers use many different methods of indicating sizes.

Theoretically, other measurements including the waist, hip and neck band have a direct relationship to the size. In addition, sizes are also marked in regulars, short and long. Special sizes are sometimes available for extra heavy or tall men. Generally, pants are indicated by the waist measurement and the inside seam length. Hat sizes are often given arbitrary numbers. Shoe sizes are normally indicated by a size number followed by a letter. Shirts and sweaters are manufactured in three kinds of sizing units. Dress shirts are marked by the neck circumference and the length of sleeves. However, shirt manufacturers in different countries do not interpret arm length the same way. Sport shirts of woven fabrics are sized by neck measurement only and are grouped in four broad classifications: small, medium, large and extra large. Knit sport shirts, on the other hand, are sized by chest measurements but, in the same group, classifications of small, medium, large and extra large.

United States Standards on Body Measurements

In cooperation with various producers, distributors, users and associations, the National Bureau of Standards has developed a series of voluntary product standards for clothing. These product standards are detailed in the following bulletins and are available from the Office of Engineering Standards Services, National Bureau of Standards, Washington, DC 20234.

PS 36-70, "Body Measurements for the Sizing of Boys' Apparel"

PS 42-70, "Body Measurements for the Sizing of Women's Patterns and Apparel" (supersedes CS 215-58)

PS 45-71, "Body Measurements for the Sizing of Apparel for Young Men (Students)"

PS 54-72, "Body Measurements for the Sizing of Girls Apparel"

CS 151-50, "Body Measurements for the Sizing of Apparel for Infants, Babies, Toddlers and Children"

The purpose of these voluntary product standards is to provide standard classifications, size designations and body measurements for consistent sizes of apparel. This information is provided for the guidance of those engaged in producing and preparing specifications for patterns and ready-to-wear garments. It is also intended to provide the consumer with a means of identifying body type and size from the wide range of body types covered.

The information contained in these standards is very complete. For example, data is given for as many as 40 to 45 principal body landmarks. **Fig. 40-9a-m.** **Fig. 40-10.**

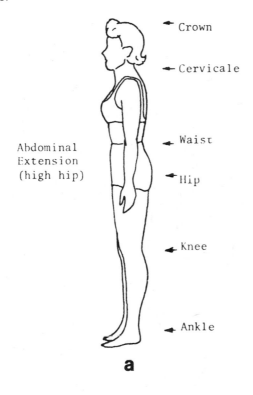

a

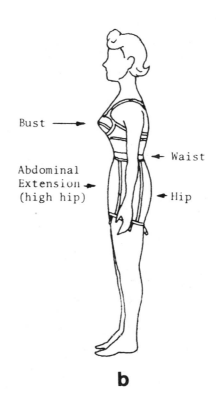

b

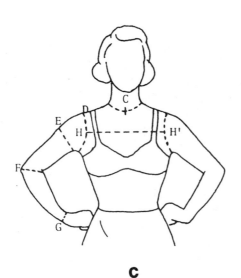

c

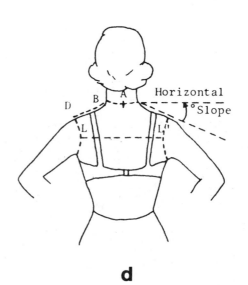

d

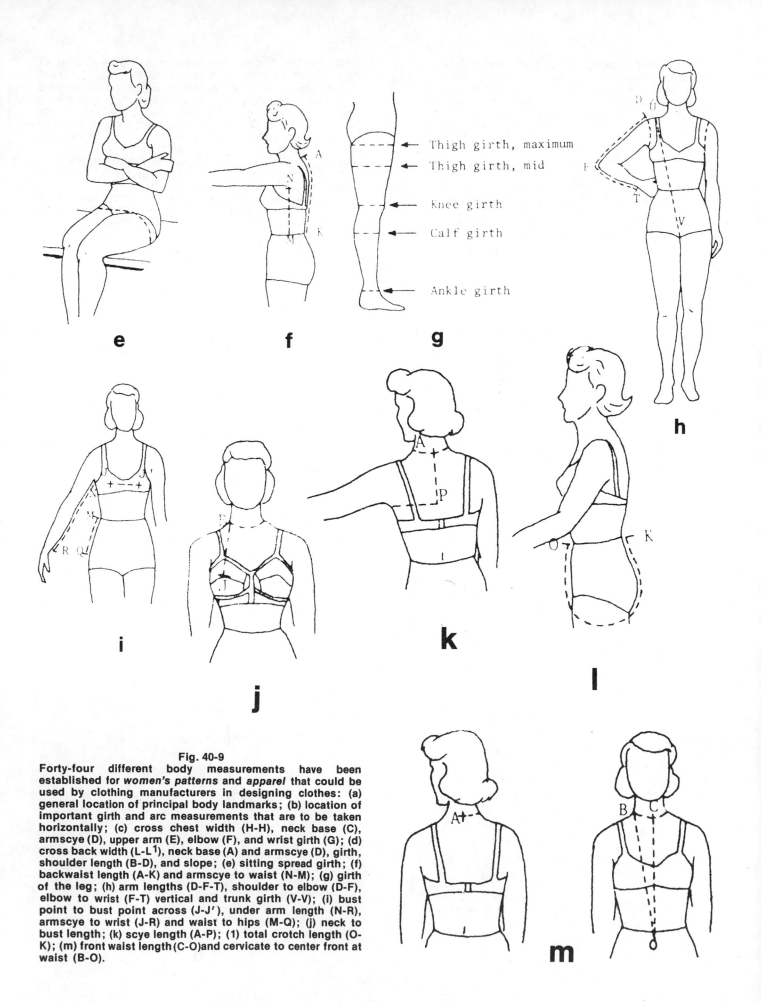

Fig. 40-9
Forty-four different body measurements have been established for *women's patterns* and *apparel* that could be used by clothing manufacturers in designing clothes: (a) general location of principal body landmarks; (b) location of important girth and arc measurements that are to be taken horizontally; (c) cross chest width (H-H), neck base (C), armscye (D), upper arm (E), elbow (F), and wrist girth (G); (d) cross back width (L-L¹), neck base (A) and armscye (D), girth, shoulder length (B-D), and slope; (e) sitting spread girth; (f) backwaist length (A-K) and armscye to waist (N-M); (g) girth of the leg; (h) arm lengths (D-F-T), shoulder to elbow (D-F), elbow to wrist (F-T) vertical and trunk girth (V-V); (i) bust point to bust point across (J-J'), under arm length (N-R), armscye to wrist (J-R) and waist to hips (M-Q); (j) neck to bust length; (k) scye length (A-P); (1) total crotch length (O-K); (m) front waist length (C-O) and cervicate to center front at waist (B-O).

Misses[1]

Size	6	8	10	12	14	16	18	20	22
GIRTH MEASUREMENTS (inches)									
Bust	31½	32½	33½	35	36½	38	40	42	44
Waist	22½	23½	24½	26	27½	29	31	33	35
Hip	33½	34½	35½	37	38½	40	42	44	46
Mid neck	13⅛	13⅜	13⅝	14	14⅜	14¾	15¼	15¾	16¼
Armscye	13⅞	14¼	14⅝	15¼	15⅞	16½	17¼	18	18¾
Abdominal extension (high hip)	29⅝	30⅝	31⅝	33⅛	34⅝	36⅛	38⅛	40⅛	42⅛
Sitting spread	33½	34½	35½	37	38½	40	42	44	46
Thigh, maximum	18¾	19½	20¼	21¼	22¼	23¼	24½	25¾	27
Thigh, mid	17	17½	18	18¾	19½	20¼	21¼	22¼	23¼
Knee	12	12⅜	12¾	13¼	13¾	14¼	14¾	15¼	15¾
Calf	11½	11⅞	12¼	12¾	13¼	13¾	14¼	14¾	15¼
Ankle	8⅛	8⅜	8⅝	8⅞	9⅛	9⅜	9⅝	9⅞	10⅛
Upper arm	9⅝	9⅞	10⅛	10½	10⅞	11¼	11⅞	12½	13⅛
Elbow	9¼	9⅜	9½	9¾	10	10¼	10⅝	11	11⅜
Wrist	5¼	5⅜	5½	5⅝	5¾	5⅞	6	6⅛	6¼
Vertical trunk	55½	57	58½	60	61½	63	64½	66	67½
ARC MEASUREMENTS (inches)									
Bust, front	17¾	18½	19¼	20¼	21¼	22¼	23⅝	25	26⅜
Waist, front	11⅞	12½	13⅛	14	14⅞	15¾	17	18¼	19½
Abdominal, front (high hip)	15⅞	16½	17⅛	18	18⅞	19¾	21	22¼	23½
Hip, back	16⅞	17¼	17⅝	18¼	18⅞	19½	20¼	21	21¾
VERTICAL MEASUREMENTS (inches)									
Stature (total height)	62½	63	63½	64	64½	65	65½	66	66½
Cervicale height	53½	54	54½	55	55½	56	56½	57	57½
Waist height	38¾	39⅛	39½	39⅞	40¼	40⅝	41	41⅜	41¾
Abdominal extension height (high hip)	35¾	36	36¼	36½	36¾	37	37¼	37½	37¾
Hip height	31½	31⅝	31¾	31⅞	32	32⅛	32¼	32⅜	32½
Crotch height	28⅜	28½	28⅝	28¾	28⅞	29	29⅛	29¼	29⅜
Knee height	16⅞	17	17⅛	17¼	17⅜	17½	17⅝	17¾	17⅞
Ankle height	2¾	2¾	2¾	2¾	2¾	2¾	2¾	2¾	2¾
WIDTH AND LENGTH MEASUREMENTS (inches)									
Cross back width	12	12¼	12½	12⅞	13¼	13⅝	14⅛	14⅝	15⅛
Cross-chest width	11⅞	12	12⅛	12⅜	12⅝	12⅞	13¼	13⅝	14
Bust point to bust point	6¾	7	7¼	7½	7¾	8	8¼	8½	8¾
Neck to bust point	8½	8¾	9	9⅜	9¾	10⅛	10⅝	11⅛	11⅝
Scye depth	7	7⅛	7¼	7⅜	7½	7⅝	7¾	7⅞	8
Armscye to waist	8	8⅛	8¼	8⅜	8½	8⅝	8¾	8⅞	9
Waist to hips	7¾	8	8¼	8½	8¾	9	9¼	9½	9¾
Shoulder length	4 3/16	4¼	4 5/16	4⅜	4 7/16	4½	4 9/16	4⅝	4 11/16
Shoulder slope (degrees)	23	23	23	23	23	23	23	23	23
Arm length, shoulder to wrist	22 11/16	22⅞	23 1/16	23¼	23 7/16	23⅝	23 13/16	24	24 3/16
Arm length, shoulder to elbow	13	13⅛	13¼	13⅜	13½	13⅝	13¾	13⅞	14
Underarm length	16 9/16	16⅝	16 11/16	16¾	16 13/16	16⅞	16 15/16	17	17 1/16
Crotch length, total	26⅜	27⅛	27⅞	28⅝	29⅜	30⅛	30⅞	31⅝	32⅜
Cervicale to center front at waist	18⅝	18⅞	19⅛	19½	19⅞	20¼	20¾	21¼	21¾
Waist length, front	12¾	13	13¼	13½	13¾	14	14¼	14½	14¾
Waist length, back	14¾	15	15¼	15½	15¾	16	16¼	16½	16¾
WEIGHTS (pounds)									
Weight, approximate	98	106	113	125	136	147	161	176	190

[1] 1 inch equals 2.54 centimeters, 1 pound equals 0.45 kilograms.

Fig. 40-10

A summary of the data for *misses* dresses. In Fig. 40-14 note that only four of these dimensions are used by the pattern industry. However, they are not exactly the same as the ones given in this table. For example, for size 6 the bust is given as 31 1/2" here and 30 1/2" for pattern measurements; the waist is given as 22 1/2" here and 23" for pattern measurements; the hip is given as 33 1/2" here 32 1/2" for pattern measurements; the back-waist length is given as 14 3/4" here and 15 1/2" for pattern measurements.

While manufacturers can use all of these measurements in designing and manufacturing the article of clothing, not more than three or four of these measurements would be shown on the clothing tag. **Fig. 40-11-12.**

Body measurements will be in ⌐centimetres⌐

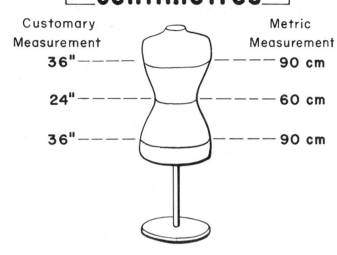

Customary Measurement		Metric Measurement
36"	---	90 cm
24"	---	60 cm
36"	---	90 cm

Fig. 40-11
These show the three primary measurements that are used in determining dress sizes, although the back-waist length is considered extremely important.

Clothing will be manufactured in ⌐Centimetres⌐

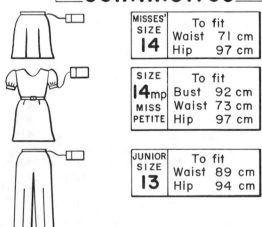

MISSES' SIZE 14	To fit	
	Waist	71 cm
	Hip	97 cm

SIZE 14mp MISS PETITE	To fit	
	Bust	92 cm
	Waist	73 cm
	Hip	97 cm

JUNIOR SIZE 13	To fit	
	Waist	89 cm
	Hip	94 cm

Fig. 40-12
This is the way clothing may be marked using metric measurements.

Interestingly enough, no voluntary product standard is available for the sizing of men's patterns and apparel due to the lack of reliable anthroprometric data. Voluntary clothing standards are being developed by other countries that are "going metric" based on metric measurement instead of inch measurement used in the United States. **Fig. 40-13.**

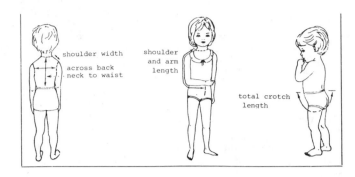
shoulder width
across back
neck to waist
shoulder and arm length
total crotch length

Fig. 40-13
Typical measurements that would be taken to determine body sizes.

The ISO system of size designation and sizing systems will probably be very similar to the voluntary standards developed by the National Bureau of Standards. The intention of the international standards is to provide a simple and direct means of indicating the body size a garment is intended to fit. Provided the size and shape of the body has been accurately determined, the proposed system will help a purchaser to select more easily the garments that fit properly. While the size designation will be based on body measurement, this is not the whole story. The choice of garment measurements is considered the prerogative of the designer and the manufacturer who are concerned with style, cut and other fashion elements. The designer must also make due allowance for garments normally worn beneath the outer garment.

Patterns and Material for Sewing
Since patterns and material for sewing are used in both customary and metric countries, a series of measurement standards has been established by the *Pattern Fashion Institute* which includes information on body measurements in both inches and centimetres. **Fig.40-14-15.**
In the customary system height is given in feet and inches, and in the metric system height is given in metres and parts of a metre. However, it is generally accepted that the centimetre would be the most desirable metric unit for indicating height. Note that for women's patterns there are seven classifications including *misses, miss petite, half size, young junior-teen, junior, junior petite* and *women.* These classifications are based on height and body types. In addition, there are two girls' sizes titled *girls* and *chubbies,* and two childrens' sizes titled *childrens* and *toddlers.* For male patterns there are two classifications, *namely men's and boys'* and *teen-boys'.*
Some interesting observations can be made concerning the relationship of body sizes to the sizing system used. First, in female clothing only four basic body dimensions are used in the sizing, namely *bust, waist, hip* and *back-waist length.* This is in contrast to some 40 to 50 body measurements for the sizing of women's patterns apparel available from the National Bureau of Standards in their voluntary product standards. Note that for all female sizing systems there appears to be little or no relationship between body measurements and the sizing system used. For example, in misses regular sizes, size 6 has a bust of 30 1/2" (78 cm), waist 23" (58 cm), hip 32 1/2" (83 cm)

Body Measurements in Inches

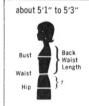
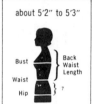

MISSES'

about 5'5" to 5'6"

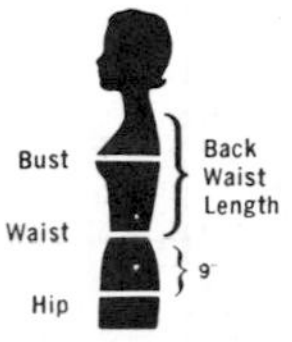

Misses' patterns are designed for a well proportioned, and developed figure; about 5'5" to 5'6" without shoes.

Size	6	8	10	12	14	16	18	20
Bust	30½	31½	32½	34	36	38	40	42
Waist	23	24	25	26½	28	30	32	34
Hip	32½	33½	34½	36	38	40	42	44
Back Waist Length	15½	15¾	16	16¼	16½	16¾	17	17¼

MISS PETITE

about 5'2" to 5'3"

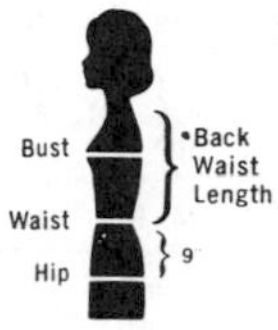

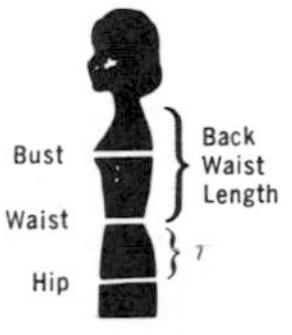

This new size range is designed for the shorter Miss figure; about 5'2" to 5'3" without shoes.

Size	6mp	8mp	10mp	12mp	14mp	16mp
Bust	30½	31½	32½	34	36	38
Waist	23½	24½	25½	27	28½	30½
Hip	32½	33½	34½	36	38	40
Back Waist Length	14½	14¾	15	15¼	15½	15¾

HALF-SIZE

about 5'2" to 5'3"

Half-size patterns are for a fully developed figure with a short backwaist length. Waist and hip are larger in proportion to bust than other figure types; about 5'2" to 5'3" without shoes.

Size	10½	12½	14½	16½	18½	20½	22½	24½
Bust	33	35	37	39	41	43	45	47
Waist	27	29	31	33	35	37½	40	42½
Hip	35	37	39	41	43	45½	48	50½
Back Waist Length	15	15¼	15½	15¾	15⅞	16	16⅛	16¼

YOUNG JUNIOR/TEEN

about 5'1" to 5'3"

This size range is designed for the developing pre-teen and teen figures; about 5'1" to 5'3" without shoes.

Size	5/6	7/8	9/10	11/12	13/14	15/16
Bust	28	29	30½	32	33½	35
Waist	22	23	24	25	26	27
Hip	31	32	33½	35	36½	38
Back Waist Length	13½	14	14½	15	15⅜	15¾

JUNIOR

about 5'4" to 5'5"

Junior patterns are designed for a well proportioned, shorter waisted figure; about 5'4" to 5'5" without shoes.

Size	5	7	9	11	13	15
Bust	30	31	32	33½	35	37
Waist	22½	23½	24½	25½	27	29
Hip	32	33	34	35½	37	39
Back Waist Length	15	15¼	15½	15¾	16	16¼

JUNIOR PETITE

about 5' to 5'1"

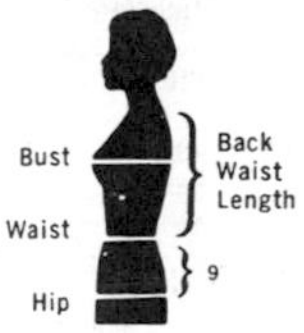

Junior Petite patterns are designed for a well proportioned, petite figure; about 5' to 5'1" without shoes.

Size	3jp	5jp	7jp	9jp	11jp	13jp
Bust	30½	31	32	33	34	35
Waist	22½	23	24	25	26	27
Hip	31½	32	33	34	35	36
Back Waist Length	14	14¼	14½	14¾	15	15¼

WOMEN'S

about 5'5" to 5'6"

Women's patterns are designed for the larger, more fully mature figure; about 5'5" to 5'6" without shoes.

Size	38	40	42	44	46	48	50
Bust	42	44	46	48	50	52	54
Waist	35	37	39	41½	44	46½	49
Hip	44	46	48	50	52	54	56
Back Waist Length	17¼	17⅜	17½	17⅝	17¾	17⅞	18

GIRLS'

Girls patterns are designed for the girl who has not yet begun to mature. See chart below for approximate heights without shoes.

Size	7	8	10	12	14
Breast	26	27	28½	30	32
Waist	23	23½	24½	25½	26½
Hip	27	28	30	32	34
Back Waist Length	11½	12	12¾	13½	14¼
Approx. Heights	50"	52"	56"	58½"	61"

CHUBBIE

Chubbie patterns are designed for the growing girl who is over the average weight for her age and height. See below for approximate height, with shoes.

Size	8½c	10½c	12½c	14½c
Breast	30	31½	33	34½
Waist	28	29	30	31
Hip	33	34½	36	37½
Back Waist Length	12½	13¼	14	14¾
Approx. Heights	52"	56"	58½"	61"

CHILDREN'S MEASUREMENTS

Measure around the breast, but not too snugly. Toddler patterns are designed for a figure between that of a baby and a child. Toddler's dresses are shorter than the similar child's dress and toddler's pants have a diaper allowance.

TODDLERS'

Size	½	1	2	3	4
Breast	19	20	21	22	23
Waist	19	19½	20	20½	21
Finished Dress Length	14"	15"	16"	17"	18"

CHILDREN'S

Size	1	2	3	4	5	6	6X
Breast	20	21	22	23	24	25	25½
Waist	19½	20	20½	21	21½	22	22½
Hip			24	25	26	26½	
Back Waist Length	8¼	8½	9	9½	10	10½	10¾
Approx. Heights	31"	34"	37"	40"	43"	46"	48"
Dress Lengths from Back Neck Base to Lower Edge							
	17"	18"	19"	20"	22"	24"	25"

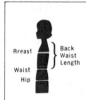
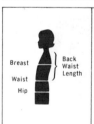

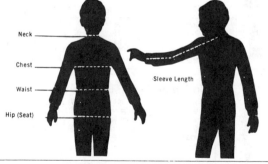

Neck
Chest
Waist
Hip (Seat)
Sleeve Length

	BOYS'				TEEN-BOYS'			
Size	7	8	10	12	14	16	18	20
Chest	26	27	28	30	32	33½	35	36½
Waist	23	24	25	26	27	28	29	30
Hip (Seat)	27	28	29½	31	32½	34	35½	37
Neckband	11¾	12	12½	13	13½	14	14½	15
Height	48	50	54	58	61	64	66	68

MEN'S (height approximately 5'10")								
Size	34	36	38	40	42	44	46	48
Chest	34	36	38	40	42	44	46	48
Waist	28	30	32	34	36	39	42	44
Hip (Seat)	35	37	39	41	43	45	47	49
Neckband	14	14½	15	15½	16	16½	17	17½
Shirt Sleeve	32	32	33	33	34	34	35	35

Fig. 40-14
Body measurements in inches.

Metric Measurement Chart

MISSES'

1,65m to 1,68m

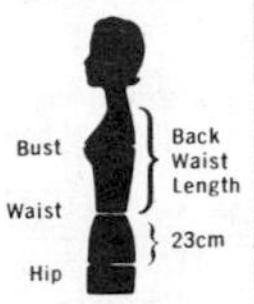

Misses' patterns are designed for a well proportioned, and developed figure; about 1,65m to 1,68m without shoes.

Size	6	8	10	12	14	16	18	20	
Bust	78	80	83	87	92	97	102	107	cm
Waist	58	61	64	67	71	76	81	87	cm
Hip	83	85	88	92	97	102	107	112	cm
Back Waist Length		39,5	40	40,5	41,5	42	42,5	43	44	cm

JUNIOR

1,63m to 1,65m

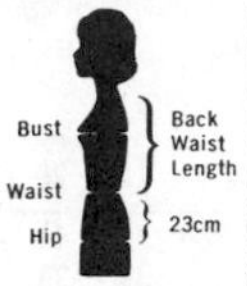

Junior patterns are designed for a well proportioned shorter waisted figure, about 1,63m to 1,65m without shoes.

Size	5	7	9	11	13	15	
Bust	76	79	81	85	89	94	cm
Waist	57	60	62	65	69	74	cm
Hip	81	84	87	90	94	99	cm
Back Waist Length	38	39	39,5	40	40,5	41,5	cm

MISS PETITE

1,57m to 1,60m

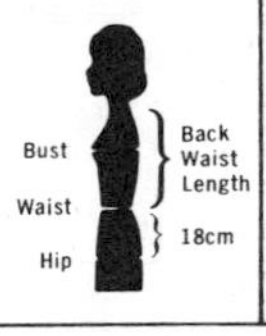

This new size range is designed for the shorter Miss figure, about 1,57m to 1,60m without shoes.

Size	6mp	8mp	10mp	12mp	14mp	16mp	
Bust	78	80	83	87	92	97	cm
Waist	60	62	65	69	73	78	cm
Hip	83	85	88	92	97	102	cm
Back Waist Length	37	37,5	38	39	39,5	40	cm

JUNIOR PETITE

1,52m to 1,55m

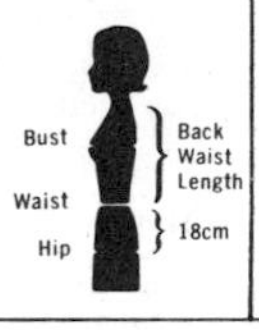

Junior Petite patterns are designed for a well proportioned petite figure, about 1,52m to 1,55m without shoes.

Size	3jp	5jp	7jp	9jp	11jp	13jp	
Bust	78	79	81	84	87	89	cm
Waist	57	58	61	64	66	69	cm
Hip	80	81	84	87	89	92	cm
Back Waist Length	35,5	36	37	37,5	38	39	cm

HALF-SIZE

1,57m to 1,60m

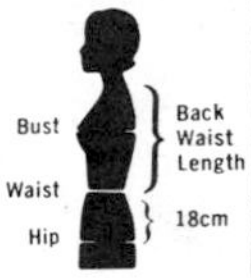

Half-size patterns are for a fully developed figure with a short backwaist length. Waist and hip are larger in proportion to bust than other figure types; about 1,57m to 1,60m without shoes.

Size	10½	12½	14½	16½	18½	20½	22½	24½	
Bust	84	89	94	99	104	109	114	119	cm
Waist	69	74	79	84	89	96	102	108	cm
Hip	89	94	99	104	109	116	122	128	cm
Back Waist Length	38	39	39,5	40	40,5	40,5	41	41,5	cm

WOMEN'S

1,65m to 1,68m

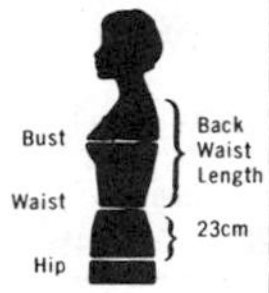

Women's patterns are designed for the larger, more fully mature figure: about 1,65m to 1,68m without shoes.

Size	38	40	42	44	46	48	50	
Bust	107	112	117	122	127	132	137	cm
Waist	89	94	99	105	112	118	124	cm
Hip	112	117	122	127	132	137	142	cm
Back Waist Length	44	44	44,5	45	45	45,5	46	cm

YOUNG JUNIOR/TEEN

1,55m to 1,60m

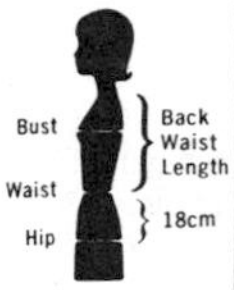

This new size range is designed for the developing pre-teen and teen figures, about 1,55m to 1,60m without shoes.

Size	5/6	7/8	9/10	11/12	13/14	15/16	
Bust	71	74	78	81	85	89	cm
Waist	56	58	61	64	66	69	cm
Hip	79	81	85	89	93	97	cm
Back Waist Length	34,5	35,5	37	38	39	40	cm

GIRLS'

Girls patterns are designed for the girl who has not yet begun to mature. See chart below for approximate heights without shoes.

Size	7	8	10	12	14	
Breast	66	69	73	76	81	cm
Waist	58	60	62	65	67	cm
Hip	69	71	76	81	87	cm
Back Waist Length	29,5	31	32,5	34,5	36	cm
Approx. Height	127	132	142	149	155	cm

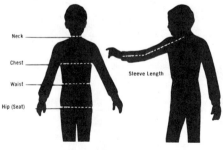

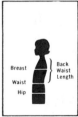

CHUBBIE

Chubbie patterns are designed for the growing girl who is over the average weight for her age and height. See below for approximate height, with shoes.

Size	8½c	10½c	12½c	14½c	
Breast	76	80	84	88	cm
Waist	71	74	76	79	cm
Hip	84	88	92	96	cm
Back Waist Length	31	32,5	34,5	36	cm
Approx. Height	132	142	149	155	cm

CHILDREN'S MEASUREMENTS

Measure around the breast, but not too snugly. Toddler patterns are designed for a figure between that of a baby and a child. Toddler's dresses are shorter than the similar child's dress and toddler's pants have a diaper allowance.

TODDLERS'

Size	1/2	1	2	3	4	
Breast or Chest	48	51	53	56	58	cm
Waist	48	50	51	52	53	cm
Finished Dress Length	35,5	38	40,5	43	46	cm

BOYS' TEEN-BOYS'

Size	7	8	10	12	14	16	18	20	
Chest	66	69	71	76	81	85	89	93	cm
Waist	58	61	64	66	69	71	74	76	cm
Hip (Seat)	69	71	75	79	83	87	90	94	cm
Neckband	30	31	32	33	34,5	35,5	37	38	cm
Height	122	127	137	147	155	163	168	173	cm

MEN'S

Size	34	36	38	40	42	44	46	48	
Chest	87	92	97	102	107	112	117	122	cm
Waist	71	76	81	87	92	99	107	112	cm
Hip (Seat)	89	94	99	104	109	114	119	124	cm
Neckband	35,5	37	38	39,5	40,5	42	43	44,5	cm
Shirt Sleeve	81	81	84	84	87	87	89	89	cm

CHILDREN'S

Size	1	2	3	4	5	6	6x	
Breast or Chest	51	53	56	58	61	64	65	cm
Waist	50	51	52	53	55	56	57	cm
Hip				61	64	66	67	cm
Back Waist Length	21	22	23	24	25,5	27	27,5	cm
Height	79	87	94	102	109	117	122	cm
Finished Dress Length	43	46	48	51	56	61	64	cm

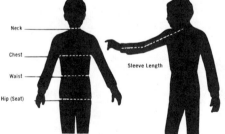

Neck
Chest
Waist
Hip (Seat)
Sleeve Length

Fig. 40-15
Metric measurement chart for body measurements. This is a soft conversion from the customary system. All the measurements shown here are the same as in Fig. -14 multiplied by 2.54 to determine the centimetre measurement.

and back-waist length 15 1/2" (39.5 cm). However, in women's sizes there is some relationship between body measurements and size, although it is a rather odd one. For example, in women's size 38 the bust is given as 42". Each size in the sizing system actually refers to body measurements 4" larger that that marked on the label or pattern for the bust. Therefore, when a woman looks for a dress or suit in women's sizes she must add 4" to the label measurement to determine the bust measurement.

In choosing the correct pattern size follow these steps:

Pattern sizes for females are based on actual body measurements. These measurements appear in **Fig. 40-16** and are standardized for all pattern companies. Body measurements also determine figure type and should be checked periodically.

(1) Choose the correct figure type by comparing body measurements with those shown on the chart. The most important measurements in determining figure type are the height and back-waist length.

(2) Choose the correct size by the *bust* measurement (not bra size) for all garments except skirts and pants. Adequate ease is provided for all patterns.

(3) Choose skirts, pants and shorts by waist measurement or if hips are much larger in proportion to waist, select size by hip measurement.

(4) Choose children's patterns by breast (chest) measurement.

(5) Choose maternity patterns by bust size before pregnancy.

Body Measurements

Taking Correct Body Measurements

For Misses , Miss Petite, Junior, Junior Petite, Young Junior/Teen, Women and Half Size:

Always measure while wearing a thin garment with the proper foundation undergarments. Draw tape close but not tight.

Take these four body measurements:

Bust—measure around the body at the fullest part of the bust, high under the arm, and straight across the back.

Waist—measure around the body at the natural waistline.

Hip—measure around the body at the fullest part. Hipline is established on pattern at:

9 inches (23cm) below the natural waistline for Misses. Women. and Junior.

7 inches (18cm) below the natural waistline for Miss Petite. Half Size. Junior Petite and Young Junior/Teen.

Back Waist Length—measure from the top of the most prominent bone at the base of neck to the natural waistline.

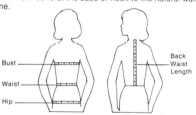

For Pants and Shorts:

Stand straight, wear correct undergarments and shoes to take these measurements:

Waist—measure the natural waistline.

Hips—measure the fullest part usually 7" to 9" (18-23cm) from waist depending on figure type.

Side Length—measure at side from waist to floor or desired length.

Sit on a hard chair:

Crotch Length—measure from side waist to chair seat and add ¾" (2cm) ease.

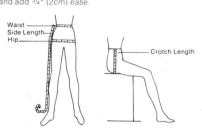

For Boys, Teen-Boys and Men:

Note: The body measurements shown on chart have been revised and are consistent with current body and fashion standards.

Please see back of pattern envelope of selected style for complete body measurements before determining size.

Neckband—measure with ease or buy shirt pattern by ready-made size.

Chest—measure around fullest part of chest.

Waist—measure at natural waist over shirt.

Hip—measure at seat or fullest part of hip.

Shirt Sleeve—measure across shoulder from back base of neck around bend of elbow to wrist.

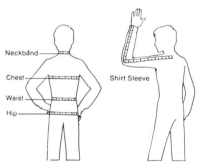

For Toddlers, Children and Girls:

The difference in dress lengths from back neck base to lower edge is important in determining sizes for Toddlers and Children .

Breast—measure around fullest part of chest, but not too tightly.

Waist—measure as shown at natural waist.

Hip—measure across hip bones or at fullest part for Girls.

Height—measure with Child standing against a wall without shoes.

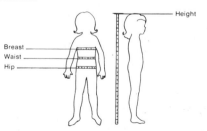

Fig. 40-16
The correct method of determining body measurements to determine correct pattern selection.

Materials, Fabrics and Textiles

Textiles will be sold in metric units. **Fig. 40-17** The width of fabrics will be given in centimetres and the length will be in metres and submultiples of the metre. Currently, fabrics are produced in a variety of widths, all expressed in inches. There may be no physical change in the width of the material available because of the heavy cost of changing the looms and other equipment that produce the fabrics. Only a soft conversion will be made to express widths in centimetres. For example, 25 inch widths will be expressed as 65 centimetres. **Fig. 40-18.**

selected, the amount of material needed for the pattern may be given both in yards and metres. If it is only given in yards the amount needed in metres can be easily found by using the chart shown in **Fig. 40-20.** For example, in chart 20a if the pattern calls for 4 1/4 yards, find the 4 yard line and move across horizontally until you are directly under the 1/4. You will see that 3.9 metres is the amount needed. If you use the chart in 20 b, 4 yards indicates that you need 3.70 metres plus 1/4 yard, which is 0.25 m; add the two together and you get 3.95 m. Note that for accurate conversion, multiply yards by 0.914. For example 4 1/4 yards equals 4.25 x 0.914, which equals 3.88 metres exactly.

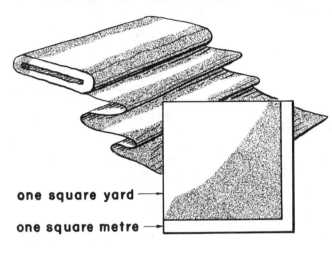

one square yard

one square metre

Fig. 40-17
Comparison of the square yard and the square metre.

⌐Available Fabric Widths⌐

Customary	Metric
Inches	Centimetres
25	65
27	70
35 – 36	90
39	100
44 – 45	115
48	122
50	127
54 – 56	140
58 – 60	150
68 – 70	175
72	180

140 cm 100 cm 65 cm

(Approximate Conversion) as approved by the Pattern Fashion Industry.

Fig. 40-18
Soft conversion of fabric widths from inches to centimetres.

Narrower fabrics such as trim materials may be expressed in millimetres or centimetres. **Fig. 40-19.** Fabrics will be sold in metre lengths. Currently the smallest amount of fabric that can be sold is 1/8 yard; 10 centimetres would be roughly equivalent to this. Charts for converting from customary length to metric length are not all the same. Once a pattern has been

NARROW FABRICS

in	mm	in	mm	in	mm
1/4	6	1 5/8	41	3 3/4	95
3/8	10	1 3/4	45	4	100
1/2	13	1 7/8	48	4 1/4	110
5/8	16	2	50	4 1/2	115
3/4	19	2 1/4	60	4 3/4	120
7/8	22	2 1/2	65	5	125
1	25	2 3/4	70	5 1/4	135
1 1/8	28	3	75	5 1/2	140
1 1/4	32	3 1/4	80	5 3/4	145
1 3/8	35	3 1/2	90	6	150
1 1/2	38				

Fig. 40-19
Very narrow fabrics and trimmings may be sold in millimetre widths.

Notions

Notions for sewing include such items as thread, zippers, buttons, and trim. **Fig. 40-21.** Thread is sold by length in yards. For example, if the spool contains 100 yards, this equals 92 metres. Eventually, thread will be sold in even metre modules in mutliples of 10. Buttons are now indicated in diameters in fractions of an inch. In the metric system they will probably be expressed in millimetre or centimetre diameters. Length of zippers will also be marked in inches and centimetres.

Metric Fabric Lengths

Yds.	1/8	1/4	3/8	1/2	5/8	3/4	7/8
metres	0.15	0.25	0.35	0.50	0.60	0.70	0.80 m
1 yard	0.95	1.05	1.15	1.30	1.40	1.50	1.60	1.75 m
2 yards	1.85	1.95	2.10	2.20	2.30	2.40	2.55	2.65 m
3 yards	2.75	2.90	3.00	3.10	3.20	3.35	3.45	3.55 m
4 yards	3.70	3.80	3.90	4.00	4.15	4.25	4.35	4.50 m
5 yards	4.60	4.70	4.80	4.95	5.05	5.15	5.30	5.40 m
6 yards	5.50	5.60	5.75	5.85	5.95	6.10	6.20	6.30 m

Fig. 40-20
You can use this chart to convert fabric amounts needed from yards to metres. For example, if a pattern calls for 2 1/2 yards, find 2 yards and move horizontally across untill you get to the vertical line marked 1/2.

Sewing Notions
(Approximate Metric Conversions)

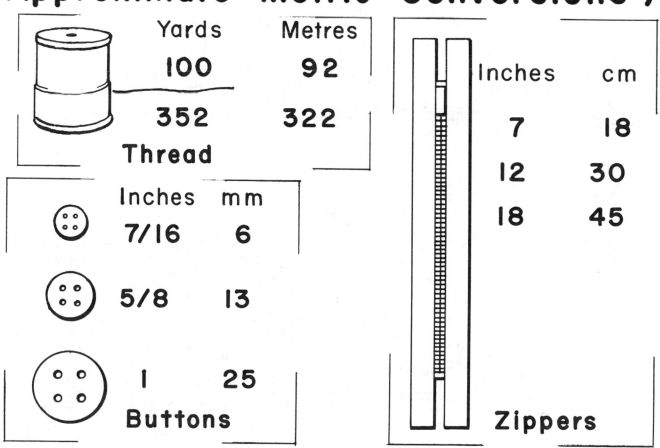

Yards	Metres
100	92
352	322

Thread

Inches	mm
7/16	6
5/8	13
1	25

Buttons

Inches	cm
7	18
12	30
18	45

Zippers

Fig. 40-21
Common sewing notions and the method by which they will be shown in metric.

Basic Measuring Tools for Sewing

Basic measuring tools for sewing will include:

A 1 metre flexible (cloth or plastic) measuring tape graduated in centimetres with millimetre divisions between the centimetre markings. **Fig. 40-22**

A seam gauge that is 15 cm long graduated in centimetres with millimetre divisions between each centimetre marking.

A hem marker which will use a 1 metre metre stick for indicating the height of the hem. Most metre sticks are graduated in centimetres and millimetres. Also, the best type is wooden with metal ends.

A 30 cm metric rule marked in centimetres will also be useful.

Sewing Machines

The majority of sewing machines available are made in Europe and Japan. This means that their stitch length and needle size is already metric. Some of these machines now have inch measurements on the throat plate, but replacement plates graduated in metric measurements will be available for some machines later. Measurements marked on the beds of some machines are frequently in centimetres as well as inches.

The sizing system for metric machine needles is based on the diameter of the needle (in hundredths of a millimetre) at the threading eye position. Customary sizes are taken at the same position, but relate to thousandths of an inch. Many needles are sold with dual markings.

Using a Pattern

Measurement information given on most patterns is in dual dimensioning (both inches and metric.) This provides for the convenience of those who use either the English (Imperial) or the metric system. Measurements under 1/2" are given in millimetres with the symbol mm. Those above 1/2" are given in centimetres with the symbol cm. These rounded figures are as follows:

1/8" = 3 mm, 1/4" = 6 mm, 3/8" = 9 mm, 1/2" = 1.2 cm, 5/8" = 1.5 cm, 3/4" = 2 cm, 1" = 2.5 cm, 1 1/4" = 3.1 cm, 2" = 5 cm. **Fig. 40-23.**

The only difference in sewing between inch and metric measurement will be that the person changing to metric will need a few different measuring tools and know how to read them properly. **Fig. 40-24.**

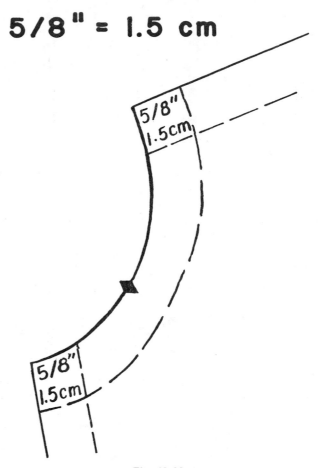

Seam allowances of
5/8" = 1.5 cm

Fig. 40-23
This shows how patterns are dual dimensioned in inches and metrics.

⌐Basic measuring tools⌐

1 inch = 2.54 cm

Hem Marker

Tape Measure

Metre Stick

Seam gauge

Fig. 40-22
Some basic measuring tools needed for sewing.

Shoe Sizes

The ISO has established an international standard for shoe sizing which is called the Mondopoint system. Under this system the shoe size is made up of two numbers that indicate the size and width index. It consists of two numbers written such as 240/95. The first number, 240, is obtained by measuring the length of the foot in millimetres while the person is standing on that foot. The width index number (95) indicates the fitting, and is obtained by measuring the girth of the foot at the base of the toe and using this measurement to obtain a percentage of the length. In this case, the measurement is 228 mm which is 95 percent of 240. Therefore, a foot which is 240 mm long with a girth of 228 mm would be marked 240/95. **Fig. 40-25 a,b.**
If the foot length is 210 mm and the girth is 185 mm, the shoe would be marked 210/88. Under the Mondopoint system, shoe sizes will be the same the world around in contrast to existing sizes, which are quite meaningless.

STITCHING GUIDE
measurements most commonly used in clothing construction

MISCELLANEOUS	metric replaces	customary	SEAMS	metric replaces	customary
Buttonholes—Size is determined by the diameter of the button, plus its thickness, e.g. 1" + 1/8"	2.5 cm + 3mm = 2.8 cm	1" + 1/8" = 1 1/8"	Flat fell (finished width)	6 mm	1/4"
			trim one seam allowance to	3 mm	1/8"
Grading—garment seams	1 cm	3/8"	trim second seam allowance to	1 cm	3/8"
Hem allowances—skirts	7.5 cm	3"	fold second seam allowance under to	6 mm	1/4"
sleeves	2.5-5 cm	1"-2"	French (finished width)	6 mm	1/4"
Pleat edge stitching	1 - 2 mm	1/16"	stitch first row away from seamline	6 mm	1/4"
Staystitching—from seamline	3 mm	1/8"	trim to	3 - 6 mm	1/8"-1/4"
Topstitching	6 mm or 1.2 cm	1/4" or 1/2"	Plain (finished width)	1.2 or 2.2 cm	1/2" or 7/8"
Trimming—enclosed seams	6 mm	1/4"			
Understitching, e.g. on collars, facings, etc.	3 mm	1/8"			

The following information gives the number of machine stitches:

14 stitches per 1" = 6 stitches per cm
12 stitches per 1" = 5 stitches per cm
10 stitches per 1" = 4 stitches per cm
8 stitches per 1" = 3 stitches per cm

Fig. 40-24
Use this stitching guide to convert from customary to metric measurements.

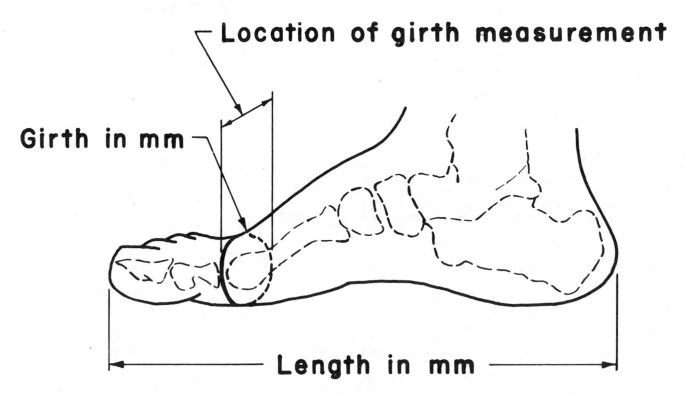

Fig. 40-25a
Location of basic measurements for the Mondopoint system.

Mondopoint System
of shoe sizing

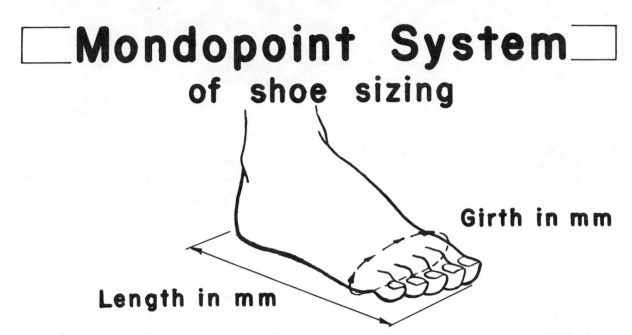

Girth in mm

Length in mm

Size is indicated by the length.

Width index indicates the fitting.

Example: Length = 240 mm
Girth = 228 mm
228 = 95 % of 240

Requires a shoe marked

240/95

Fig. 40-25b
The Mondopoint system of shoe sizing that will be universally accepted in the years ahead.

Knitting

Materials for knitting and crocheting use the metic system for designating lengths and weights. Knitting needles are already dually marked using millimetres and fractions of an inch to designate needle diameter. Balls of yarn for knitting and crocheting are frequently marked in gram modules such as 20, 25, and 50. A 25 gram ball of yarn is slightly less than an ounce (28.35 grams). Therefore, if a pattern calls for 1 ounce of yarn it will be necessary to purchase two 20 gram balls of yarn to have enough. Many of the leading yarn manufacturers market yarn in 45 gram balls, which is roughly an ounce and a half.

Clothing Care

Information about clothing care will be given in dual marking or by the use of international symbols. Washing temperatures are shown in **Fig. 40-26.** Washing and ironing symbols as shown in **Fig. 40-27** are being used on clothing labels. An "x" over the symbol indicates that it cannot or should not be used. These symbols may also be used on equipment, such as on an iron, for heat settings.

WASHING TEMPERATURE CHART

Warm	40°C	(104°F)	Pleasantly warm to the hand
Hand Hot	48°C	(118°F)	As hot as the hand can bear
Hot	60°C	(140°F)	Hotter than the hand can bear. The temperature of water coming from many domestic hot taps.
Very Hot	85°C	(185°F)	Water heated to near boiling temperature
Boil	100°C	(212°F)	Self explanatory

Fig. 40-26
Washing temperature chart.

WASHABLE

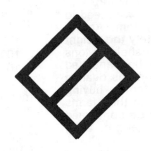

LAUNDER CAREFULLY

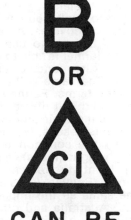

CAN BE BLEACHED

COOL   **WARM**   **HOT**   **DO NOT IRON**

         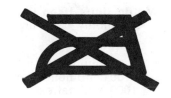

Fig. 40-27
Symbols are being used more and more as a universal
method of indicating directions for clothing care.

UNIT 41
AGRICULTURE

Careers in Agri-business and natural resources include many individual occupations such as farmers, machinery dealers, agricultural employees, foresters, managers of golf courses, and other occupations in land related activities. All of these people will need to know and be able to use the metric system. An experienced farmer is able to guess accurately the weight of livestock in pounds or crop yield in bushels or tons per acre. The same ability will need to be translated into metric terms. Farmers and other persons dealing with the land will utilize the metric system in buying goods, selling their products, and running their farms or other businesses. Generally they will be concerned with only the common units, namely, length, area, volume, weight (mass), and temperature.

One point to remember is that many of the customary (English) units used in the United States are not the same as the Imperial units used in England, Canada, Australia and other members of the British Commonwealth. For example, an Imperial gallon contains about 4 1/2 litres while there are about 3 3/4 litres in a U.S. gallon. Another difference is the hundredweight. In England the hundredweight (cwt) equals 112 pounds, and in the U.S. it is 100 pounds. The Imperial bushel is larger than the Winchester bushel used in the U.S. Different conversion factors must, therefore, be used when changing to metric.

Metric Units Used in Agriculture
Commonly used units include the following:

Length.

10 millimetres	= 1 centimetre
100 centimetres	= 1 metre
1000 millimetres	= 1 metre
1000 metres	= 1 kilometre

A metre is a little longer than a yard, or approximately 39.37 inches. A kilometre is about 5/8 mile (0.62 mile). A furlong (220 yards) is very close to 200 metres in length. An inch contains 25.4 mm. A "hand" (4 inches) is approximately 100 mm or 10 cm.

Area.

square metre (m^2)

10 000 square metres = 1 hectare (ha)

In Europe the term "are" (hectare is taken from this) has had long-standing use as the description of an area containing 100 square metres. The United States will not adopt this "are" unit, but will use instead its decimal multiple, the hectare (10 000 m^2). Areas less than a hectare will be expressed in square metres. A hectare contains almost 2 1/2 acres (2.47 acres).

Volume (dry).

1 000 000 cubic centimetres (cm^3)	= 1 cubic metre (m^3)

There will be no equivalent to the bushel in the metric system. As now used, the bushel is actually a measure of weight. In the metric system, weights may be measured in kilograms and dry volumes in cubic metres or decimal fractions thereof. Grain densities now expressed in pounds per bushel may be expressed in kilograms per hectolitre, because this is international practice.

Volume [liquid or gas].
1000 millilitres (ml) = 1 litre (ℓ) or (l)
1000 litres = 1 cubic metre (m^3)

A litre contains 0.47 pints. It is about 6 percent larger than a quart. A gallon contains approximately 3.8 litres in the U.S. and 4 1/2 litres in countries using the Imperial gallon. A 4-gallon can holds 15 litres. A 44-gallon drum holds a little more than 166 litres.

Weight.
1000 grams (g) = 1 kilogram (kg)
1000 kilograms = 1 metric ton or tonne (t)

One ton (avoirdupois) contains 2240 pounds. One metric ton (tonne) contains 2204 pounds. One pound is one-tenth (10 percent) less than half a kilogram while 28.4 grams make an ounce. One hundredweight is very close to 50 kilograms (50.8). Fifty-six pounds is very close to 25 kilograms.

Weather. To avoid confusion, an international decision has been made to measure temperatures in degrees Celsius (°C), not the old term "centigrade." Rainfall will be measured in millimetres. After a rain, the condition of sand loam soil will be as follows:

    2 mm: wet on top
    10 mm: a good shower
    25 mm: about right to start ploughing or planting
    75 mm: soaking wet

Conversion
Some examples of conversion used in agriculture are:
    -10 metres = 11 yards approximately
    -10 square metres = 12 square yards approximately
    -10 cubic metres = 13 cubic yards approximately
    -1 ton per acre = 2 1/2 metric tons per hectare
    -1 pound per acre is a little more than 1 kilogram per hectare
    -1 gallon per acre is 9 1/3 litres per hectare approximately

Metric Units Used Only in Agri-business
Most of the units shown in **Fig. 41-1** are part of the SI metric system. **Fig. 44-2.** The *hectare* is not an SI unit but is commonly used throughout the world for measuring land. A much less common unit from the older metric system is used by some government agencies in crop reporting. This unit is the quintal (or centner) which is equal to 100 kilograms, or 100 000 grams. The quintal (100 kilograms) equals 220.46 pounds. For example, a quintal (which is a weight unit) is equal to 3.67 bushels of wheat or 2.2046 cwt (hundredweight) of potatoes. The quintal is 1/10 as large as the metric ton or tonne. In other words, a *quintal* equals *100 kilograms* while a *metric ton or tonne* equals *1000 kilograms*.

Land
The hectare is the metric measure of land used for farms, fields, and other large land areas. The hectare is 10 000 square metres, or an area of 100 m x 100 m. **Fig. 41-3.**
It is about 2 1/2 times as large as an acre (exactly 2.4711 acres). If the total size of a farm is specified in the customary system to the quarter of an acre, then in the metric system it will be specified to 1/10 (0.1) hectare, which is almost the same as the quarter of an acre. To change *acres* to *hectares,* multiply by 0.4047. For example, if a farm measures 198.25 acres, it contains 80.2 hectares. If the acreage is unknown, it is best to measure the area using a 50 or 100 metre tape. Another

	Symbol	How big are they?	More accurate conversion factors
Length			
millimetre (one thousandth of a metre)	mm	about 25 to the inch	0.03937 in
centimetre (one hundredth of a metre	cm	less than half an inch	0.3937 in
metre	m	just over a yard	1.0936 yd
kilometre (one thousand metres)	km	5/8 of a mile	0.621 mile
Area			
square centimetre (one ten thousandth of a square metre)	cm^2	about 6 to the square inch	0.1550 in^2
square metre	m^2	about 1 1/4 square yards	1.1960 yd^2
hectare (ten thousand square metres)	ha	nearly 2 1/2 acres	2.4711 acres
square kilometre (one million square metres)	km^2	3/8 square miles	
Volume and Capacity			
millilitre (one thousandth of a litre)	ml	same as a cubic centimetre	0.0610 in^3
litre	l or ℓ or L	about 1 quart	1.057 qt
cubic metre	m^3	about 200 gallons or 1 1/3 cubic yards	1.3080 yd^3
Weight or Mass			
gram (one thousandth of a kilogram)	g	about 450 to the lb	0.0353 oz
kilogram	kg	nearly 2 1/4 lb	2.2046 lb
metric ton (tonne)	t	nearly a ton	2204.62 lb
Temperature			
degree Celsius "centigrade" is an obselete term	^{o}C	100 steps of 1°C between freezing and boiling	^{o}C x 9/5 + 32 = ^{o}F
Rate of Use/Yield			
quintals per hectare	quintals/ ha	1 quintal/ha is just under 90 lb/ acre	0.8922 lb/acre
kilogram per hectare	kg/ha	100 kg/ha ·is just under 90 lb/acre	0.8922 lb/acre
metric ton per hectare		1 t/ha is about 9 cwt/ acre	8.9 cwt/ acre
litres per hectare	t/ha ℓ/ha	10 ℓ/ha is about 1 gal/acre	1.069 gal/ acre
Pressure			
kilopascal	kPa	7 kPa is about 1 psi	0.145 psi

Fig. 41-1
Metric units used in agriculture.

method is to measure the distance in *long* paces of approximately *1 metre* each. Once the dimensions have been determined, the area can be calculated as follows: 1 hectare equals 10 000 m², or an area 100 metres by 100 metres. For example, an area 100 m x 250 m equals 25 000 m² or 2.5 hectares (ha).

Building

The construction industry will eventually make a metric change to standardize building components. Standard metric modules will be available for lumber, plywood, brick and all other building materials. When this happens, all farm buildings will be designed and built using these metric modules. For more information, refer to the unit on building construction.

Weight	Equivalent	Weight	Equivalent
1 ounce	= 28.3495 grams	1 gram	= .035274 ounces
1 pound	= 455.5925 grams	1 gram	= .0022046 pounds
1 pound	= .4535925 kilograms	1 kilogram	= 2.204622 pounds
1 pound	= .0045359 metric quintals	1 metric quintal	= 220.4622 pounds
1 pound	= .0005 short tons	1 short ton	= 2000 pounds
1 pound	= .0004536 metric tons	1 metric ton	= 2204.622 pounds
1 pound	= .0004464 long tons	1 long ton	= 2240 pounds
1 kilogram	= .0011023 short tons	1 short ton	= 907.1849 kilograms
1 kilogram	= .001 metric tons	1 metric ton	= 1000 kilograms
1 kilogram	= .0009842 long tons	1 long ton	= 1016.047 kilograms
1 short ton	= .907185 metric tons	1 metric ton	= 1.102311 short tons
1 long ton	= 1.016047 metric tons	1 metric ton	= .984206 long tons
1 short ton	= .892857 long tons	1 long ton	= 1.120 short tons
1 million lbs.	= 500 short tons	1 short ton	= .002 million lbs.
1 million lbs.	= 453.5925 metric tons	1 metric ton	= .0022046 million lbs.
1 million lbs.	= 446.4286 long tons	1 long ton	= .002240 million lbs.

60-lb. bushel: Wheat, white potatoes, soybeans

1 bushel	= .030 short tons	1 short ton	= 33.333 bushels
1 bushel	= .0272155 metric tons	1 metric ton	= 36.7437 bushels
1 bushel	= .0267857 long tons	1 long ton	= 37.333 bushels
1 bushel	= .272155 metric quintals	1 metric quintal	= 3.67437 bushels
1 bushel	= 27.2155 kilograms	1 kilogram	= .036744 bushels

56-lb. bushel: Corn, rye, sorghum grain, flaxseed

1 bushel	= .0280 short tons	1 short ton	= 35.714 bushels
1 bushel	= .0254 metric tons	1 metric ton	= 39.368 bushels
1 bushel	= .0250 long tons	1 long ton	= 40.0 bushels

48-lb. bushel: Barley, buckwheat, apples

1 bushel	= .0240 short tons	1 short ton	= 41.667 bushels
1 bushel	= .021772 metric tons	1 metric ton	= 45.9296 bushels
1 bushel	= .021429 long tons	1 long ton	= 46.667 bushels

32-lb. bushel: Oats

1 bushel	= .0160 short tons	1 short ton	= 62.50 bushels
1 bushel	= .014515 metric tons	1 metric ton	= 68.8944 bushels
1 bushel	= .014286 long tons	1 long ton	= 70.0 bushels

38-lb. bushel: Oats

1 bushel	= .0190 short tons	1 short ton	= 52.63 bushels
1 bushel	= .01724 metric tons	1 metric ton	= 58.016 bushels
1 bushel	= .01696 long tons	1 long ton	= 58.94 bushels

Fig. 41-2
Factors for converting customary and metric weights and measures commonly used for agricultural commodities.

Fig. 41-3
Farmland will be listed in hectares. A 400-acre farm is approximately 162 hectares.

Farm Machinery

Farm machinery manufacturers were among the first manufacturers to convert to metric measurement. This early conversion is due to the fact that much of their equipment is used world wide. Certain parts and even complete machines are now manufactured in various plants throughout the world. **Fig. 41-4.**

Fig. 41-4
Most American-made farm equipment will use inch fasteners while many machines produced in other countries will use metric fasteners.

While most farm machinery manufacturers have changed to metric measurement, some are *not using* metric threads and fasteners. Therefore, farm machinery manufactured in the United States still requires customary wrenches and thread cutting equipment, while farm machinery produced in most other countries requires metric wrenches and thread cutting equipment.

Gasoline and Diesel Oil

All gasoline, diesel fuel and oil will be sold by the litre. The tank on a tractor that holds 20 gallons has a capacity of approximately 75 litres.

Weighing Scales

All weight will be given in kilograms; therefore, it may be necessary to change the balance scale commonly used on the farm to indicate metric measurement. This can be done easily by simply adding the metric unit to the beam of the scale, which is usually calibrated from 1 to 50 pounds, with additional information as shown in **Fig. 41-5.**

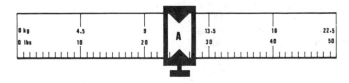

Fig. 41-5
Re-marking the beam of the scale to measure in metric units.

Also, the weight pieces on the scale should be re-marked as follows: replace 25 pounds with 11.5 kilograms, replace 50 pounds with 23 kilograms, replace 100 pounds with 45.5 kilograms, replace 200 pounds with 91 kilograms. These metric units can be either painted on the weight pieces or added by using a metal stamp or plastic tape.

Farm Supplies

All solid materials such as fertilizers and feed will be bought and sold either by the bag marked in kilogram units or in bulk by the metric ton (tonne). The probable metric packaging pattern for materials such as fertilizers will be in bags of 10, 25 or 50 kilogram size. The 100 cwt (hundredweight) equals 100 pounds in the United States and 112 pounds in England. Therefore, a 50 kilogram size would be 10 percent larger than 100 cwt U.S. bag and about 1/6 percent less than the 100 cwt English bag. The 56 pound bag of feed will be replaced by the 25 kg bag which will weigh about 1/2 kg less. Twenty (20) bags of the 50 kg size will equal one metric ton (tonne). Since the metric ton (tonne) is so similar in size to the customary ton, this change will be very slight. All liquids will be marked in millilitres and litres with the kilolitre used for larger quantities such as milk tank trucks. **Fig. 41-6.**

Fig. 41-6
The capacity of the tank on this liquid spreader will be given in either litres or kilolitres.

Planting, Fertilizing and Cultivating

Planting rates for seeds will be in terms of quintals per hectare, kilograms per hectare, or grams per square metre. A close equivalent to 1 1/4 cwt to the acre would be 140 kilograms per hectare. **Fig. 41-7a,b.**

cwt/acre	kg/ha	kg/acre
1	112	45
2	224	90
3	336	135
4	448	180
5	560	225
6	670	270
7	785	320
8	895	360
9	1000	400
10	1120	450

Fig. 41-7a
Chart for converting hundredweight per acre to kilograms per hectare and kilograms per acre.

Fertilizers will be applied in kilograms per hectare instead of pounds per acre or hundredweight per acre. Liquid spray will be given in terms of litres per hectare. The spacing between rows of plantings will be given in centimetres. For example, a spacing between rows of 24 inches will be 60 cm.

AMOUNT OF FERTILIZER

Kilograms per hectare	Pounds per acre
1	0.9
2	1.8
3	2.7
4	3.6
5	4.5
6	5.4
7	6.2
8	7.1
9	8.0
10	8.9
11	9.8
12	10.7
13	11.6
14	12.5
15	13.4
20	17.8
25	22.3
50	44.6
100	89.2
125	111.5
150	133.8
175	156.1
200	178.4
225	200.7
250	223.0
275	245.3
300	267.7
350	312.3
400	356.9
500	446.1
600	535.3
700	624.5
800	713.7
900	803.0
1000	892.2
1100	981.4

REMEMBER: THE WEIGHT OF ONE BAG OF FERTILIZER IS 50 KILOGRAMS. 20 BAGS OF FERTILIZER = ONE METRIC TON FERTILIZER.

Fig. 41-7b
This chart shows the conversion from customary to metric to use for spreading dry fertilizer.

Crop Reporting

Among the many problems with our customary system of weights and measures is the fact that there are several different sizes of bushels used as dry measure for grain, fruit, vegetables, etc. The standard U.S. bushel is the old *Winchester* bushel. This was the standard in England from Anglo Saxon times to the year 1826. This standard U.S. bushel contains 2150.42 cubic inches (an interior capacity equal to 8 inches deep and 18 1/2 inches in diameter). The Imperial bushel that was used in England until metric conversion contained 2218.192 cubic inches. **Fig. 41-8.** Since a bushel is a volume container, the weight varies with the content. For example, weights per bushel for various agricultural products are as follows:

60 pounds for wheat, white potatoes and soy beans
56 pounds for corn, rye, sorgum grain and flax seed
48 pounds for barley, buckwheat and apples
32 pounds to 38 pounds for oats

CONVERSION EQUIVALENTS

Pounds per bushel

Wheat and potatoes 60
Rye and corn 56
Barley 48
Oats 32

One kilogram	equals	2.2046 pounds
One centner or metric quintal	"	220.46 pounds
One metric ton	"	10 centners or 2204.6 pounds
One hectare	"	2.471 acres
One acre	"	0.4 hectare
One kilometer	"	0.6 mile

Metric tons to bushels

One metric ton   Bushels

Wheat and potatoes 36.743
Rye and corn 39.368
Barley 45.929
Oats 68.894

Bushels to metric tons

                                                            Metric
One bushel   tons

Wheat and potatoes 0.027 22
Rye and corn 0.025 40
Barley 0.021 77
Oats 0.014 52

To convert centners per hectare to bushels per acre, multiply by:

Wheat and potatoes 1.487
Rye and corn 1.593
Barley 1.8587
Oats 2.788

To convert bushels per acre to centners (metric quintals)
            per hectare, multiply by:

Wheat and potatoes 0.6725
Rye and corn 0.6277
Barley 0.5380
Oats 0.3587

One metric ton of ginned cotton = 4.593 bales of 480 pounds.

Fig. 41-8
Conversion equivalents for the commonly used bushels to metric units.

To convert from the Winchester bushel to the Imperial bushel, use the factors shown in **Fig. 41-9.**

	Multiply by factor
Pounds per Winchester bushel to	
Pounds per imperial bushel...................	1.032
Kilograms per hectoliter....................	1.287
Pounds per imperial bushel to	
Pounds per Winchester bushel................	.969
Kilograms per hectoliter....................	1.247
Kilograms per hectoliter to	
Pounds per Winchester bushel................	.777
Pounds per imperial bushel..................	.802

1/ Winchester bushel is the standard U.S. bushel (volume).

Fig. 41-9
Conversion factor for test weight for Winchester bushel, test weight for Imperial bushel, and kilograms per hectolitre. The Winchester bushel is the standard U.S. bushel for measuring volume. The bushel will not be used in the metric system. Where weight for a given volume is required to measure quantity, kilograms per hectolitre will be used instead of pounds per bushel.

The bushel will no longer be used in the metric system. Where weight for a given volume is required to measure quality, kilograms per hectolitre (100 litres) will be used instead of pounds per bushel.

In crop reporting by the U.S. Agriculture Department and several other countries, yields are given in *quintal per hectare* instead of bushels per acre. For example, a yield may be listed as 30.7 quintals per hectare which would be equal to 3070 kilograms per hectare. Yields for winter wheat, for example, could be expressed in any of the following four ways (all four are equal):

24   quintals per hectare
2400 kilograms per hectare
2.4   metric tons (tonnes) per hectare
36   bushels per acre (approximately)

Livestock

The weight of all livestock will be indicated in kilograms instead of pounds. Length and height will be measured in centimetres rather than inches. For example, the yearling shown in **Fig. 41-10** is 127 centimetres tall and 125 centimetres long. If the current weight is 992 pounds, this will be expressed as 450 kilograms. An 88-pound lamb weighs 40 kg, and a 198-pound pig will be listed as 90 kg. The rate of gain for beef animals will also be given in kilograms per day. For example, instead of 3.5 pounds gained per day, this will be stated as 1.6 kilograms per day. The gain for a 140-day performance test might be 4.2 pounds per day, or 1.9 kilograms per day. The average weight of livestock as they leave the farm will be approximately 40 kg for lambs, 450 kg for steers, and 90 kg for pigs. In feeding livestock, the feed requirements might be described in terms of grams of digestible protein per day. In the sale of animals, the amounts will be recorded to the nearest 0.5 kilogram with a cutoff point at 0.25 kg. That is, if the amount is less than 0.25 kg, it will be rounded off to the next lowest full kilogram. If it is 0.25 kg to 0.49 kg, it will be rounded off to the next half kilogram (0.5 kg). Cattle will be sold by the kilogram rather than the pound. For example, instead of $50 per hundredweight, the price will be $110 per 100 kilograms. To convert the number of cattle per acre to per hectare, multiply the number by 2.47, or 2.5 for a rough conversion.

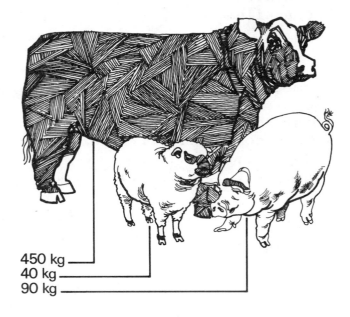

450 kg
40 kg
90 kg

Fig. 41-10.

Weights in kilograms of common farm animals.

Dairying and Milk

Farms and dairy companies will measure the amount of milk in bulk by the weight in kilograms instead of per hundredweight. Milk will be sold to the consumer by volume in quantities of a litre with its multiples and submultiples. A milk-producing dairy cow will require about 60 litres of water per day, and will yield about 20 to 28 litres per milking. If a cow tests 35 percent, this means that 35 percent of each kilogram of milk is butterfat.

*The *quintal* is an old metric unit that was legalized in the U.S. in 1866. It is no longer acceptable for use with the modernized metric system.

UNIT 42
HEALTH

In today's world, the use of several different measuring systems is not only inconvenient but could cause serious problems. This is especially true in the field of health where it is vitally important that medication standards and treatment be exact and accurate. **Fig. 42-1.**

Fig. 42-1
The SI metric system will be used in all aspects of health and medicine.

At present, five different systems of weights and measures are used to *some extent* in the field of health, including:

(1) The *apothecary* system, historically used by physicians and pharmacists, for dispensing drugs.

(2) The *avoirdupois* system, for everday activity, commonly referred to as the customary system.

(3) The *household* system, for determining dosages, which includes such familiar measures as the dropper, teaspoon, tablespoon and glass, a very loose measuring system due to differences in the sizes of these utensils.

(4) The *traditional metric* system which included the gram (g)* for weight , (mass) the centimetre (cm) and metre (m) for linear measurement, the litre (I or ℓ) and millilitre (ml) expressed in "cc's" for liquid capacity or volume and the centigrade scale for temperature.

(5) The *SI metric* system, a modernized version of the older metric system.

Variation in the Systems

The *apothecary* system, formerly used by pharmacists and physicians, is even older than the traditional metric system. It was based on weights of materials that were familiar to early civilizations. For example, a grain in the apothecary system originally meant the weight of a grain of wheat and later the weight of one drop of water. The apothecary measurements formerly used for medicines were as follows:

*Note, the *symbol* for gram is small g without a period while the *abbreviation* for grain is gr. *Do not confuse the two units.*

Volume

60 minims	= 1 fluid dram
8 fl. drams	= 1 fluid ounce
16 fl. ounces	= 1 pint

Weight

20 grains (gr)	= 1 scruple
3 scruples	= 1 dram
8 drams	= 1 ounce
12 ounces	= 1 pound

An apothecary minim is roughly equivalent to one drop. This equivalence is accurate enough to regulate intravenous feedings. However, for precise procedures or the measurement of a dose in drops, a calibrated dropper must be used. There is a great variety in the size of drops, depending on such things as the diameter of the dropper or the viscosity of the liquid.

While the apothecary system has largely disappeared from modern medicine, it is still used to some extent when referring to older drugs and for some non-prescription drugs such as aspirin.

The *avoirdupois* system of weights and measures is commonly referred to as the customary (English) system. The *avoirdupois* pound is divided into 16 ounces, or 265 grams, or 7,000 grains. Note that an *apothecary* pound is 12 ounces and not the same as an *avoirdupois* pound. It should be noted, however, that the *grain* is the same in both avoirdupois and apothecary weight systems. The avoirdupois ounce (16 ounces = 1 pound) contains 437.5 grains whereas the apothecary ounce (12 ounces = 1 pound) contains 480 grains. Both avoirdupois and apothecary liquid volumes have the gallon divided into 4 liquid quarts, or 8 liquid pints. However, in the apothecary system, the pint is further subdivided into 16 fluid ounces, or 128 fluid drams, or 7680 minims.

The *household* system of measurements is an approximate system used in the home. For example, some charts indicate the liquid volume of a teacup as 4 fluid ounces while others list it as 6 fluid ounces.

60 drops	= 1 teaspoonful (tsp.)
2 teaspoonfuls	= 1 dessertspoonful
2 dessertspoonfuls (4 teaspoonfuls)	= 1 tablespoonful
2 tablespoonfuls	= 1 fluid ounce
8 fluid ounces	= 1 glassful

To convert the units in the household system to the apothecary or metric system:

Household System	Apothecary System	Metric System
1 drop	= 1 minim (fluid dram)	
1 teaspoonful	= 1 dram (1 fluid dram)	= 5 ml
1 dessertspoonful	= 2 drams (2 fluid drams)	= 8 ml
1 tablespoonful	= 4 drams (4 fluid drams) or (2 fluid ounces)	= 15 ml
1 glassful	= 8 fluid ounces	= 240 ml

In the *SI metric* system, the base unit of weight (mass) is the kilogram. There are 1000 grams (g) in a kilogram and 1000 milligrams (mg) in a gram. The unit of liquid volume is the litre (ℓ) which contains 1000 millilitres (ml). The cubic decimetre (dm^3) is equal to a litre, and a cubic centimetre (cm^3) is equal to a millilitre. All prescription medicines and other medical products are now manufactured, controlled, labeled and administered in metric units. All drug companies specify dosages in metric units. However, some companies still package drugs in the customary system while others use the metric system.

Relationship Between the Metric System and Other Systems

Since the metric system is the preferred system of measurement in medicine, it is necessary to be able to convert from other systems. Useful equivalents of weights and liquid measures are shown in **Fig. 42-2.**

Weights

Apothecary		Apothecary		Metric
1 scruple	=	20 grains	=	1.296 grams
1 dram	=	60 grains	=	3.88 grams
1 ounce	=	480 grains (8 drams)	=	31.1 grams
1 pound	=	5760 grains (12 ounces)	=	373.24 grams

Metric		Apothecary		Metric
1 milligram	=	1/65 grain*	=	0.001 gram
1 gram	=	15.432 grains	=	0.001 kilogram
1 kilogram	=	2.2 pounds avdp.*	=	1000 grams

Avoirdupois		Apothecary		Metric
1 ounce	=	437.5 grains	=	28.35 grams
1 pound	=	7000 grains	=	453.59 grams
1 ton	=	2000 pounds avdp.	=	907.184 kilograms

*approximately

Fig. 42-2a
Comparison of weight units in the three systems: avoirdupois, apothecary and metric.

LIQUID MEASURES

1 fluid dram	=	60 minims	=	3.697 ml
1 fluid ounce	=	8 fluid drams	=	29.573 ml
1 pint	=	16 fluid ounces	=	473.167 ml
1 quart	=	32 fluid ounces	=	946.333 ml
1 gallon	=	128 fluid ounces	=	3785 ml or 3.785 litres
1 millilitre	=	0.061 cubic inch	=	1 ml
1 litre	=	61.0271 cubic inches	=	1000 ml
1 teaspoonful	=	1 fluid dram	=	5 ml
1 tablespoonful	=	1/2 fluid ounce	=	15 ml
1 teacupful	=	4 fluid ounces	=	120 ml*
1 glassful	=	8 fluid ounces	=	240 ml

*approximate

Some teacups have a capacity of 6 fluid ounces or 180 ml

Fig. 42-2b
A comparison of the liquid measures in four different systems: avoirdupois, apothecary, metric and household.

In the metric system dosages of liquid medicines should be given in millilitres (ml) and solid medicines in milligrams or grams. **Fig. 42-3.**

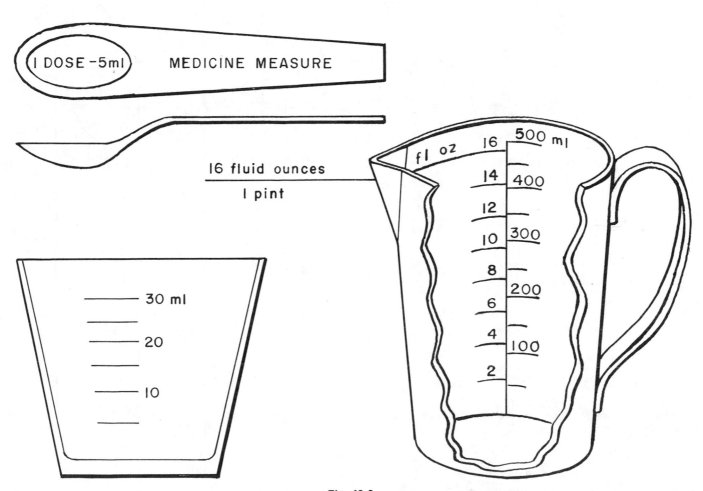

I DOSE -5ml   MEDICINE MEASURE

16 fluid ounces
1 pint

30 ml
20
10

Fig. 42-3
Liquid dosages will be given in millilitres. A 5 ml medicine
measure may be used as standard with most prescriptions.

For example, if the dosage calls for 0.648 to 1 gram, the apothecary equivalent would be 10 to 15.4 grains. **Fig. 42-4.**

Metric and Apothecary Equivalents

Metric Weights		Apothecary* Weights		Apothecary Measures
grams (g)		grains (gr)		Minims of Water at 4°C
0.0648	=	1	=	1.0517
0.130	=	2	=	2.11
0.194	=	2	=	3.15
0.259	=	4	=	4.20
0.324	=	5	=	5.26
0.389	=	6	=	6.31
0.454	=	7	=	7.37
0.5	=	7.72	=	8.12
0.518	=	8	=	8.41
0.583	=	9	=	9.46
0.648	=	10	=	10.52
0.713	=	11	=	11.57
0.778	=	12	=	12.63
0.842	=	13	=	13.67
0.907	=	14	=	14.72
0.972	=	15	=	15.78
1.000	=	15.4324	=	16.23
1.296	=	20	=	21.04
1.944	=	30	=	31.55

* approximate
Approximate equivalents may be used when prepared dosage forms, such as tablets, capsules, pills, and ampoules, are dispensed. When it is necessary to convert specific quantities of a prescription or pharmaceutical formula, exact equivalents must be used.

Metric Weights		Apothecary Weights		Metric Weights
grams (g)		grains (gr)		milligrams (mg)
0.0001	=	1/640	=	0.1
0.0002	=	1/320	=	0.2
0.0003	=	1/210	=	0.3
0.000324	=	1/200	=	0.324
0.0004	=	1/160	=	0.4
0.000432	=	1/150	=	0.432
0.0005	=	1/128	=	0.5
0.00054	=	1/120	=	0.54
0.0006	=	1/100	=	0.6
0.0008	=	1/80	=	0.8
0.001	=	1/64	=	1.0
0.0011	=	1/60	=	1.1
0.0013	=	1/50	=	1.3
0.0016	=	1/40	=	1.6
0.0018	=	1/36	=	1.8
0.0022	=	1/30	=	2.2
0.0026	=	1/25	=	2.6
0.0032	=	1/20	=	3.2
0.004	=	1/16	=	4.0
0.0065	=	1/10	=	6.5
0.0072	=	1/9	=	7.2
0.0081	=	1/8	=	8.1
0.0092	=	1/7	=	9.2
0.011	=	1/6	=	11.0
0.013	=	1/5	=	13.0
0.0162	=	1/4	=	16.2
0.0217	=	1/3	=	21.7
0.0243	=	3/8	=	24.3
0.0324	=	1/2	=	32.4
0.0432	=	2/3	=	43.2
0.0486	=	3/4	=	48.6
0.065	=	1	=	65.0

Fig. 42-4a
Conversion of weight units in the metric system to the apothecary system.

grains (gr)	grams (g)	minims	drams	cm³ or ml (cc) *	ounces	pints	quarts
				1000	32	2	1
				500	16	1	
		480		30	1		
		60		4			
		15		1			
		1		0.065			
480	30		8	30	1		
60	4	60	1				

*obsolete
Fig. 42-4c
Approximate conversions of apothecary and metric units.

grain (gr)	gram (g)	milli-gram (mg)
1/200		0.3
1/150		0.4
1/100		0.6
1/30		2
1/25		2.7
1/20		3.2
1/16		4
1/8		7.5
1/4		16
1/2		32
1	0.065	65
1 1/2	0.1	
3	0.2	
5	0.3	
10	0.6	
15	1	
30	2	

Fig. 42-4b
Approximate conversions of grains to grams or milligrams.

For dosages of liquid in household measurements, such as teaspoons or tablespoons, see the equivalents in the apothecary and metric systems given in **Fig. 42-2**.

Practices When Using the SI Metric System

With the introduction of the SI metric system, certain traditional metric practices in the health field are incorrect and should be changed. These include the following:

(1) Referring to temperature as centigrade rather than the correct unit degrees Celsius (°C).

(2) Using the abbreviation cc or c.c instead of the correct term cubic centimetre (cm^3) for solids, or millilitre (ml) for liquids. In SI metric, the letters cc stand for centi- centi-, which is meaningless. While pharmacists and others in the health field may continue to speak of so many "cc's" in conversation, it is extremely important that prescriptions be written with the correct symbols cm^3 or ml. In writing prescriptions in the metric system, it is very important to place a zero in front of the decimal point for all units less than one. For example, a dosage of five hundredths of a milligram should be written 0.05 mg. If the zero in front of the decimal point is omitted, it would read as .5 mg, which could be a serious error.

(3) Using the abbreviation "mcg" for microgram instead of the correct symbol µg.

(4) Employing the word micron instead of the correct word micrometre (µm).

(5) Using the abbreviation "grms" or "Gm." for grams instead of the correct symbol g. Never confuse the symbol g for grams with the abbreviation gr for grains.

(6) Placing a period after such symbols as kg. for kilogram instead of the correct method which calls for no period (kg) after the symbol.

(7) Using symbols and prefixes with capital letters, such as KL for kilolitre instead of lower case letters (kl).

Metric Practices in Health

The following are required changes in utilizing the metric system:

1. *Temperature.* Clinical thermometers showing degrees Celsius only should be used. When recording temperatures for the Celsius scale, the rational subdivisions on the graph should be in fifths or tenths of a degree. When a clinical thermometer in degrees Celsius is used, the normal body temperature is 37 °C. **Fig. 42-5.**

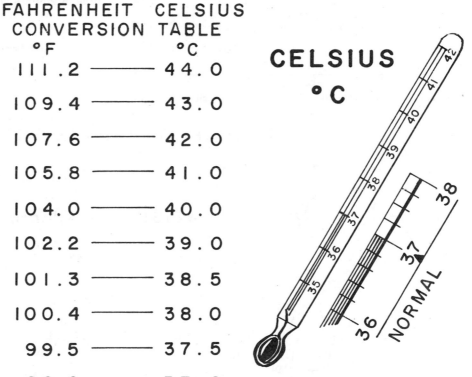

THERMOMETER SCALES

FAHRENHEIT CELSIUS CONVERSION TABLE

FAHRENHEIT °F

CELSIUS °C

°F	°C
111.2	44.0
109.4	43.0
107.6	42.0
105.8	41.0
104.0	40.0
102.2	39.0
101.3	38.5
100.4	38.0
99.5	37.5
98.6	37.0
97.7	36.5
96.8	36.0
95.0	35.0
93.2	34.0

TO CONVERT FAHRENHEIT TO DEGREES CELSIUS, SUBTRACT 32 & MULTIPLY BY 5/9.

TO CONVERT DEGREES CELSIUS TO FAHRENHEIT, MULTIPLY BY 9/5 AND ADD 32.

Fig. 42-5a
Comparison of temperatures in degrees Fahrenheit and degrees Celsius.

°C	°F	°C	°F	°C	°F
33.0	91.4	36.0	96.8	39.0	102.2
33.1	91.6	36.1	97.0	39.1	102.4
33.2	91.8	36.2	97.2	39.2	102.6
33.3	91.9	36.3	97.3	39.3	102.7
33.4	92.1	36.4	97.5	39.4	102.9
33.5	92.3	36.5	97.7	39.5	103.1
33.6	92.5	36.6	97.9	39.6	103.3
33.7	92.7	36.7	98.1	39.7	103.5
33.8	92.8	36.8	98.2	39.8	103.6
33.9	93.0	36.9	98.4	39.9	103.8
34.0	93.2	37.0	98.6	40.0	104.0
34.1	93.4	37.1	98.8	40.1	104.2
34.2	93.6	37.2	99.0	40.2	104.4
34.3	93.7	37.3	99.1	40.3	104.5
34.4	93.9	37.4	99.3	40.4	104.7
34.5	94.1	37.5	99.5	40.5	104.9
34.6	94.3	37.6	99.7	40.6	105.1
34.7	94.5	37.7	99.9	40.7	105.3
34.8	94.6	37.8	100.0	40.8	105.4
34.9	94.8	37.9	100.0	40.9	105.6
35.0	95.0	38.0	100.4	41.0	105.8
35.1	95.2	38.1	100.6	41.1	106.0
35.2	95.4	38.2	100.8	41.2	106.2
35.3	95.5	38.3	100.9	41.3	106.3
35.4	95.7	38.4	101.1	41.4	106.5
35.5	95.9	38.5	101.3	41.5	106.7
35.6	96.1	38.6	101.5	41.6	106.9
35.7	96.3	38.7	101.7	41.7	107.1
35.8	96.4	38.8	101.8	41.8	107.2
35.9	96.6	38.9	102.0	41.9	107.4
36.0	96.8	39.0	102.2	42.0	107.6

Fig. 42-5b
Clinical temperatures with the degrees Celsius given in tenths (0.1) of a degree.

The critical area in health is between the sub-normal temperature of 36 °C and the very high fever temperature of 40.7 °C. Some common references points are:

Low fever = 37.2 °C to 37.8 °C   38°C is feverish
Mild fever = 37.9 °C to 39.4 °C or 39°C is very feverish
High fever = 29.5 °C to 40.6 °C   40°C is dangerous

One degree of fever in degrees Celsius is the same as 1.8 degrees in Fahrenheit.
   2. *Human measurement.* All human measurements will be given in centimetres for heights and lengths and kilograms for weight. All tape measures for taking body measurements should be marked in centimetres with subdivisions in millimetres. Generally, all body measurements will be given in centimetres. **Fig. 42-6.**

HEIGHT AND WEIGHT

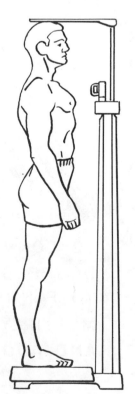

HEIGHT IN centimetres   cm

WEIGHT IN kilograms   kg

EXAMPLES

TALL HEAVY MAN
   Height   188 cm
   Weight   95 kg

MEDIUM AVERAGE MAN
   Height   175 cm
   Weight   74 kg

SMALL LIGHT MAN
   Height   164 cm
   Weight   58 kg

Fig. 42-6a
Heights of men in centimetres and weights in kilograms.

HEIGHT AND WEIGHT

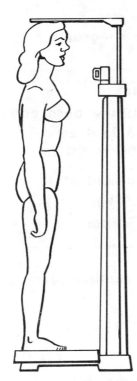

HEIGHT IN centimetres   cm

WEIGHT IN kilograms   kg

EXAMPLES

TALL HEAVY WOMAN

Height	173	cm
Weight	89	kg

MEDIUM AVERAGE WOMAN

Height	160	cm
Weight	61	kg

SMALL LIGHT WOMAN

Height	145	cm
Weight	43	kg

Fig. 42-6b
Heights of women in centimetres and weights in kilograms.

CONVERSION OF BODY HEIGHTS

CENTIMETRES : FEET AND INCHES

Metric cm	Approx ft in		Metric cm	Approx ft in		Metric cm	Approx ft in	
100	3	3	137	4	6	174	5	9
101	3	4	138	4	6	175	5	9
102	3	4	139	4	7	176	5	9
103	3	5	140	4	7	177	5	10
104	3	5	141	4	8	178	5	10
105	3	5	142	4	8	179	5	10
106	3	6	143	4	8	180	5	11
107	3	6	144	4	9	181	5	11
108	3	7	145	4	9	182	6	0
109	3	7	146	4	9	183	6	0
110	3	7	147	4	10	184	6	0
111	3	8	148	4	10	185	6	1
112	3	8	149	4	11	186	6	1
113	3	9	150	4	11	187	6	2
114	3	9	151	4	11	188	6	2
115	3	9	152	5	0	189	6	2
116	3	10	153	5	0	190	6	3
117	3	10	154	5	1	191	6	3
118	3	11	155	5	1	192	6	4
119	3	11	156	5	1	193	6	4
120	3	11	157	5	2	194	6	4
121	4	0	158	5	2	195	6	5
122	4	0	159	5	3	196	6	5
123	4	0	160	5	3	197	6	6
124	4	1	161	5	3	198	6	6
125	4	1	162	5	4	199	6	6
126	4	2	163	5	4	200	6	7
127	4	2	164	5	5	201	6	7
128	4	2	165	5	5	202	6	8
129	4	3	166	5	5	203	6	8
130	4	3	167	5	6	204	6	8
131	4	4	168	5	6	205	6	9
132	4	4	169	5	7	206	6	9
133	4	4	170	5	7	207	6	9
134	4	5	171	5	7	208	6	10
135	4	5	172	5	8	209	6	10
136	4	6	173	5	8	210	6	11

Fig. 42-6c
Conversion of body height from centimetres to feet and inches.

All scales and balances should be calibrated in kilograms with divisions in 10 or 20 grams. Typical weights will be as follows: average weight at birth, 2.50 to 3.50 kilograms; after 5 months, 5.0 to 7.0 kilograms; after 12 months, 7.5 to 10.5 kilograms; after 24 months, 10 kilograms to 35 kilograms. **Fig. 42-7.**

BABY WEIGHT AND LENGTH

Beam scale

Lay infant on measure and measure from crown of head to heel, keeping knees flat on the measure.

Weight in kilograms – kg

Example:
Typical new born baby
3 to 4 kg
50 to 55 cm

One year old child
10 kg
75 cm

Length in centimetres – cm

Fig. 42-7a
Weight and length of babies will be given in kilograms or grams and centimetres.

CONVERSION OF BODY WEIGHTS OF INFANTS GRAMS AND KILOGRAMS : POUNDS AND OUNCES

g	lb	oz	kg	lb	oz	kg	lb	oz
500	1	2	2.1	4	10	3.7	8	3
600	1	5	2.2	4	14	3.8	8	6
700	1	9	2.3	5	1	3.9	8	10
800	1	12	2.4	5	5	4.0	8	13
900	2	0	2.5	5	8	4.1	9	1
1000	2	3	2.6	5	12	4.2	9	4
1100	2	7	2.7	5	15	4.3	9	8
1200	2	10	2.8	6	3	4.4	9	11
1300	2	14	2.9	6	6	4.5	9	15
1400	3	1	3.0	6	10	4.6	10	2
1500	3	5	3.1	6	13	4.8	10	9
1600	3	8	3.2	7	1	5.0	11	0
1700	3	12	3.3	7	4	5.2	11	7
1800	3	15	3.4	7	8	5.4	11	14
1900	4	3	3.5	7	11	5.6	12	6
2000	4	7	3.6	7	15	5.8	12	13

Fig. 42-7b
Conversion of body weights of infants in grams and kilograms to pounds and ounces.

kg	lb	kg	lb	kg	lb
1	2.2	34	75.0	67	147.7
2	4.4	35	77.2	68	149.9
3	6.6	36	79.4	69	152.1
4	8.8	37	81.6	70	154.3
5	11.0	38	83.8	71	156.5
6	13.2	39	86.0	72	158.7
7	15.4	40	88.2	73	160.9
8	17.6	41	90.4	74	163.1
9	19.8	42	92.6	75	165.3
10	22.0	43	94.8	76	167.6
11	24.3	44	97.0	77	169.8
12	26.5	45	99.2	78	172.0
13	28.7	46	101.4	79	174.2
14	30.9	47	103.6	80	176.4
15	33.1	48	105.8	81	178.6
16	35.3	49	108.0	82	180.8
17	37.5	50	110.2	83	183.0
18	39.7	51	112.4	84	185.2
19	41.9	52	114.6	85	187.4
20	44.1	53	116.8	86	189.6
21	46.3	54	119.0	87	191.8
22	48.5	55	121.3	88	194.0
23	50.7	56	123.5	89	196.2
24	52.9	57	125.7	90	198.4
25	55.1	58	127.9	91	200.6
26	57.3	59	130.1	92	202.8
27	59.5	60	132.3	93	205.0
28	61.7	61	134.5	94	207.2
29	63.9	62	136.7	95	209.4
30	66.1	63	138.9	96	211.6
31	68.3	64	141.1	97	213.8
32	70.5	65	143.3	98	216.1
33	72.8	66	145.5	99	218.3
				100	220.5

Fig. 42-7c
Body weights of children and adults from kilograms to pounds.

Between the ages of 2 and 12 years, the average weight can be roughly calculated as age in years plus 2 x 2.25 kilograms. For example, average weight at 6 years would equal 6 + 3 x 2.25 kg, or 9 x 2.25 kg = 20.25 kg.

3. *Diets.* All diets should be given in kilojoules rather than in large Calories (kilocalories). See unit, "Foods and Nutrition". For example, infants 1 to 9 months old will require approximately 500 kJ per kilogram of body weight every 24 hours. An adult that previously consumed approximately 2000 Calories per day would be allowed 8000 kilojoules per day.

4. *Pressure gages.* All pressure gages should be changed to show pressure in kilopascals rather than in pounds per square inch.

5. *The 24-hour clock.* While the 24-hour time system is not SI metric, it is desirable to make this conversion at the same time as "going metric". In giving time by the 24-hour method, 1 minute after midnight would be given as 00:01, 12 o,clock noon would be given as 12:00; 8 o'clock in the evening would be listed as 20:00. In the 24-hour clock system, the hours remain unchanged from midnight to noon. After that the p.m. time is the regular time plus 12.

Conventional system	24-hour clock
7:35 am	= 07:35 or 7 35
12:00 noon	= 12:00
1:00 p.m. + 12	= 13:00
11:15 p.m. + 12	= 23:15
12:00 midnight (old day)	= 24:00
12:00 midnight (new day)	= 00:00
12:05 a.m.	= 00:05

Reasons for Going SI Metric

Changing to the SI metric system in health should be done for the following reasons:

1. All new drugs are expressed in SI metric units.

2. Use of the SI metric system will eliminate the need for several different systems of measurement currently in use.

3. The metric system allows for greater accuracy in measuring small quantities in grams, milligrams, and millilitres.

4. Calculations in SI metric are easier than those in the customary system.

UNIT 43
HOME AND FAMILY LIVING

Most areas related to home and family living have already been dealt with in other sections of this handbook. It is suggested that the reader refer to these sections for in-depth coverage of subject matter. This is a brief review of the information covered in previous sections.

Paper Sizes

The size paper which will be used for home and business stationery will be the metric sheet size -- 210 x 280 mm. This is slightly narrower but the same length as customary 8-1/2" x 11". See *Paper Standards.*

Measuring Tools

When purchasing a rule, a micrometer or vernier, buy either an all-metric type or a dual reading measuring too. See *Metric Rules, Micrometers and Verniers.*

Threaded Fasteners

Threaded fasteners will be available in the ISO threads. See *Thread Standards, Cutting Threads, Threaded Fasteners.*

Wrenches

Metric socket and/or box wrenches will be needed to work on equipment that has metric threads such as most foreign and many domestic automobile engines. See *Wrenches.*

Food and Nutrition

Many packaged goods are already dual marked in customary and metric units. Increasingly, packages will appear in rounded metric quantities such as 100 grams or 500 millilitres. For example, the purchaser will begin buying packages in values such as 125 g, 250 g, 375 g, and 500 g as replacements for the traditional 4 oz, 8 oz, 12 oz, and 1 pound (16 oz) packages. A 1 kg (2.2 lb) package of sugar will, of course, cost somewhat more than the old 2 lb package. These new sizes are approximately 10 percent larger than the old sizes. Liquids will be purchased in units such as the litre and 500 millilitres to replace the quart and pint. See *Foods and Nutrition.*

Clothing

All body measurement for clothing will be in centimetres. Fabrics will be sold in widths marked in centimetres and in lengths of metres and tenths of a metre. Patterns for sewing are marked in inches and centimetres. For footwear, a sizing system called Mondopoint is the accepted international standard. See *Clothing and Textiles.*

Medicine

All medication will be given in metric doses of grams and millilitres. Temperature will be taken in degrees Celsius. See *Health.*

Automobiles and Traveling

Driving will be affected by the following changes:

Size of an engine will be rated in cubic centimetres (cm^3) or in litres (ℓ) or (l) and the engine rating will be in kilowatts (kW).

Gasoline, oil and antifreeze will be sold by the litre.

Fuel consumption will be expressed in litres per 100 kilometres.

Tire pressure will be given in kilopascals instead of pounds per square inch (psi). If your tire now takes 26 pounds, you will ask for 180 kilopascals.

Dual reading road signs will show distances in kilometres as well as miles.

Speed limits will be posted in both kilometres per hour and miles per hour. See *Automechanics.*

Home Purchases and Maintenance

All reference to land will be in square metres for smaller areas and in hectares for larger areas.

It will be several years before you will need to know how to read architectural drawings in metric or will be able to build a home with all materials in metric modules. Eventually, homes will be built on the basis of a 100 mm module and everything in and about the home will be in metric sizes. For example, if the current living room is 12' x 14', it will be shown as 3.66 x 4.27 m or 3660 x 4270 mm. See *Building Construction.*

Home Furnishings

The measurement of most pieces of furniture is not particularly critical and, therefore, a change to metric will mean only a change in measuring language. For example, sofas are available in a wide variety of lengths. One that was previously specified as 6 feet might be shown as 183 centimetres while one that was 6'6" in length would be listed as 200 centimetres. Generally all furniture dimensions will be given in centimetres. Carpets will be measured in metres and the carpeting will be sold per square metre.

The following are some of the areas of concern to the consumer that have not previously been covered:

1. Utilities

Utilities rates will be changed to reflect metric units. Water used will be measured in cubic metres or kilolitres, gas bills will be in cubic metres, while electrical meters will continue to be read in kilowatt hours (kW/h) used.

Fig. 43-1.

Fig. 43-1
All utilities will be measured in metric units. This will mean a change of units used for water and gas bills but not for electricity.

2. Beds and Bedding

Beds are available in many sizes. A soft conversion will only mean changing the width and length from feet and inches to centimetres. Eventaully a hard conversion to metric may change the physical size of the bed slightly. Chances are that the standard length, which is now 6'3" (75 inches), will be increased to 2 metres which is approximately 79 inches. The usual width of the twin bed, which is currently 39 inches (1 metre = 39.37 inches) will not change, but a double bed may increase from 54 inches to 150 centimetres, which is equal to 59 inches. If a hard change is made in beds, corresponding corrections will of course be required simultaneously in sheets, pillowcases, blankets and spreads. The first step in metric conversion will be to dual mark all bedding equipment in feet and inches and the equivalent in centimetres.

3. Household Appliances
Household appliances are usually divided into two groups, the larger household equipment including stoves, refrigerators, washers, dryers, water heaters, vacuum cleaners, and sewing machines and the smaller appliances including coffee pots, irons, can openers, toasters, blenders, etc. In the years ahead, there will be a change in the physical size of large equipment based on the 100 mm building module. The language for describing the equipment will change from customary to metric. **Fig. 43-2.**

Appliance and measurement	Customary Units		Metric Units	
	Size	Units	Size	Units
Washer:				
Weight of clothes for maximum load	12	pounds	5.4	kilograms
Volume of water in tub	20	gallons	76	litres
Temperature of wash water	140	°F	60	°C
Power of the motor	0.5	horsepower	375	watts
Dryer:				
Weight of clothes for maximum load	12	pounds	5.4	kilograms
Rate of producing heat:				
Electric dryer	5000	watts	5000	watts
Power of the motor	1.25	horsepower	930	watts
Water heater:				
Rate of heating:				
Gas water heater	30 000	BTU/hour	8790	watts
Electric water heater	1600	watts	1600	watts
Recovery rate	30	gallons per hour	144	litres per hour
Thermostat setting	150	°F	65	°C
Heating and cooling equipment:				
Gas pressure (for gas equipment)	5	inches of water	12.5	kilopascals
Flow of air through appliance	100	cubic feet per minute	2.7	cubic metres per minute
		feet per minute	30	metres per minute
Power of the fan motor	0.25	horsepower	185	watts
Weight (window air conditioner)	100	pounds	45	kilograms
Humidity control equipment:				
Rate of evaporation or condensation	2	gallons per day	7.6	litres per day
Volume of water container	10	quarts	9.5	litres
Vacuum cleaner				
Suction	20	inches of water	50	kilopascals
Length of cord	18	feet	5.4	metres
Lighting equipment:				
Rate of using electricity	100	kW/h	100	kW/h
Efficiency of conversion:				
Electricity to light	50	lumens per watt	15	lumens per watt
Sewing machine:				
Guides	5/8	inch	1.6	centimetres
Stitch length	10	per inch	4	per centimetre
Weight	20	pounds	9.1	kilograms
Irons:				
Area of soleplate	30	square inches	195	square centimetres
Weight	4	pounds	1.8	kilograms
Length of cord	8	feet	2.4	metres
Rate of heating	1000	watts	1000	watts

Fig. 43-2.
Size and units used in describing household equipment.

4. Mailing and Postage Rates

Postage rates will be based on weights in grams and kilograms rather than ounces and pounds. The international (Universal Postal Union) agreement on metric weight steps specifies 20 grams as the equivalent of 1 ounce and 50 grams for 2 ounces. These metric weights are smaller than the equivalent customary weights. The maximum weight for international parcels is 10 kilograms, which is 22 pounds. The overall size of packages will have limits in centimetres rather than in feet and inches.

5. Maps.

Most road maps have a code that compares the distance in miles with the distance in kilometres. Airline maps have a code that compares distances in miles, kilometres and knots. Eventually all road maps will show distances in kilometres. All standard topographic maps will be based on the SI metric system.
Fig. 43-3.

Fig. 43-3
Maps including those for the moon will be in metric units.

The U.S. Geological Survey has completed mapping in metric for the state of Alaska. Each map covers an area of about 4157 square kilometres (1605 square miles). The maps are printed to a scale of 1:25 000 (1 inch equals 2083 feet or 4 centimetres equal 1 kilometre) with 5, 10 and 20 metre contour intervals. Other topographic maps are drawn to a scale of 1:250 000 (1 cm represents 2.5 km) or 1:500 000 (1 cm represents 5 km).

6. Recreation

Many sports, particularly the international sports, are already metric. These include swimming, rugby, track and field events. For example, a swimming pool used for competition must be at least 50 metres long. All track events show distances in metres such as the 100 metre dash. Such American sports as football and baseball will continue to be described in customary units. The actual size of balls used for sports will not change, since they are designed for specific sports. However, the dimensions will be given in metric instead of customary units.

7. Weather

Temperatures will be described in degrees Celsius with some guidelines as follows:
-5 °C to 5 °C (23 °F to 41 °F) will be a very cold winter day
5 °C to 15 °C (41 °F to 59 °F) is a range of temperatures experienced on a colder winter day
15 °C to 25 °C (59 °F to 77 °F) will be a mild to warm day
25 °C to 35 °C (77 °F to 95 °F) will be typical warm to hot conditions
Rainfall will be given in millimetres instead of 1/100 inch. Wind speed will be described in kilometres per hour instead of miles per hour. Barometric pressure will be in millibars or kilopascals. Such things as snow depth, river height and wave height will be given in metres rather than feet.

Fig. 43-4
The distance to center field is marked in feet (404) and a "too accurate" soft conversion of 123.13 metres. One hundredth of a metre is one centimetre which is less than 1/2". The metric distance should have been rounded to 123 metres.

A. Abbreviations

B. Metric Units and Symbols

C. Customary Units and Symbols

ABBREVIATIONS

ANMC: American National Metric Council

ANSI: American National Standards Institute

BIH: Bureau International de l'Heure

BIPM: The International Bureau of Weights and Measures

BSI: The British Standards Institution

CCTC: Consultative Committee for Thermometry and Calorimetry

CCU: Consultative Committee for Units

CGPM: The General Conference on Weights and Measures

CGS: The metric system based upon the centimetre-gram-second units

CIE: International Commission on Illumination

CR: Minutes of the Meeting of the General Conference of Weights and Measures

CSA: Canadian Standards Association

DNA: Deutscher Normenausschus (German Standards Association)

IAT: International Atomic Time

IEC: International Electrotechnical Commission

International System of Units: The modern metric system defined and adopted by the General Conference of Weights and Measures, abbreviated SI

ISO: The International Organization for Standardization

IUPAC: International Union of Pure and Applied Chemistry

IUPAP: International Union of Pure and Applied Physics

MKS: The metric system based upon the metre-kilogram-second units

MKSA: The metric system based upon the metre-kilogram-second-ampere units

MTS: The metric system based upon the metre-tonne-second units

NBS: The National Bureau of Standards (the national standardizing laboratory in the United States, located at Gaithersburg, Md.)

NPL: The National Physical Laboratory (the national standardizing laboratory in the United Kingdom, located at Teddington)

NRC: The National Research Council (the national standardizing laboratory in Canada, located at Ottawa)

PTB: The Physicalisch Technische Bundesanstalt (the national standardizing laboratory in West Germany, located at Braunschweig, West Germany)

SCC: Standards Council of Canada

SI: Universal abbreviation for Le Systeme International d'Unites (the International System of Units).

Systeme International d'Unites: The International System of Units (SI)

U.S. Customary Units: Units based upon the yard and pound formerly used in the United States of America and defined by the National Bureau of Standards. Some of these units have the same name as similar units in the United Kingdom (British, United Kingdom, or Imperial Units) but are not necessarily equal to them.

UTC: Co-ordinated universal time.

METRIC UNITS AND SYMBOLS

Unit	Symbol
absolute unit	
acceleration	
acceleration due to gravity	
activity (of a radioactive source)	
ampere	A
amount of substance	mol
ångström	Å
angular acceleration	
angular velocity	
are	a
area	
astronomical unit	AU (abbreviation in France) or AE (in German)
atmosphere, standard	atm
atomic standard of frequency	
atomic weight	
atto (10^{-18})	a
bar	bar
barn	b
base unit (SI)	
becquerel	Bq
black body	
caesium	
calorie	cal
candela	cd
capacitance	F
Celsius temperature	°C
centi (10^{-2})	c
Centigrade	
CGS units	
concentration	
coulomb	C
Co-ordinated universal time	UTC (abbreviation)
cubic decimetre (decimeter)*	dm^3
cubic metre (meter)*	m^3
curie	Ci
day	d
deci (10^{-1})	d
decimal marker	
degree	deg
degree (of arc)	°
degree (Celsius)	°C
deka (10)(deca)**	da
density	
derived units	
derived units — rules for forming products and quotients	
derived units formed from supplementary units	
dyne	dyn
electric charge	C
electric charge density	
electric current	A
electric conductance	S
electric field strength	
electric flux density	
electric inductance	H
electric potential	V
electric resistance	Ω
electrical quantities	
electromotive force	V
electronvolt	eV
energy	
energy density	
entropy	
ephemeris time	
erg	erg
exa (10^{18})	E
exponent	
factor	
farad	F
femto (10^{-15})	f
fermi	fm
force	N
frequency	Hz
gal	Gal
gamma	γ
gauss	G, Gs
giga (10^9)	G
gram	g
gram-atom (molecule)	
gray	Gy
heat flux density	
hectare	ha
hecto (10^2)	h
henry	H
hertz	Hz
hour	h
illuminance	lm
inductance	H
International Atomic Time	IAT (abbreviation)
International Practical Temperature Scale	
International System of Units	SI
irradiance	
joule	J
kelvin	K
kilo (10^3)	k
kilogram	kg
kilogram force	kgf
kilogram weight	kgf
knot (1 nautical mile per hour)	
krypton	
length	m
litre (liter)*	l or ℓ
lumen	lm
luminance	
luminous intensity	cd
luminous flux	lm
lux	lx
magnetic field strength	
magnetic flux	
magnetic flux density	T
magnetomotive force	A
mass	kg
maxwell	Mx
mega (10^6)	M
metre (meter)*	m
Metre Convention	
metric carat	
metric ton	t
Metrologia	
micro (10^{-6})	µ
milli (10^{-3})	m
minute (of arc)	′
minute (of time)	min
MKS (metre-kilogram-second)	
molar energy	
molar entropy, molar heat capacity	
mole	mol
multiples and sub-multiples	
nano (10^{-9})	n
nautical mile	
new candle	
new lumen	
newton	N
newton-metre (meter)*	N·m
numerals	
oersted	Oe
ohm	Ω
parsec	pc
pascal	Pa
permeability	
permittivity	
peta (10^{15})	P
phot	ph
photometric quantities	
photometric units	
pico (10^{-12})	p
plane angle	rad
poise	P
potential difference	V
power	W
prefixes	
pressure	Pa
product of units	
prototype	
quantity of electricity	C
quantity of heat	
rad	rad, rd
radian	rad
radiance	
radiant intensity	
röntgen	R
second (of arc)	″
second (of time)	s
siemens	S
solar day	
solid angle	sr
specific energy	
specific heat capacity	
specific volume	
speed (velocity)	
square metre (meter)*	m^2
steradian	sr
stere	st
stilb	sb
stokes	St
supplementary unit	
surface tension	
symbols	
temperature	
tera (10^{12})	T
tesla	T
thermal conductivity	

thermodynamic termperature	
time	
tonne	t
torr	
triple point of water	
tropical year	
unified atomic mass unit	u
velocity	
viscosity (kinematic)	
viscosity (dynamic)	V
volt	V
volume	
watt	W
wave number	
weber	Wb
weight	
year	a

CUSTOMARY UNITS AND SYMBOLS

Unit	Symbol
acre	acre
barrel	bbl

board foot	fbm
bushel	bu
carat	c
chain	ch
cubic foot	ft³
cubic inch	in³
cubic mile	mi³
cubic yard	yd³
dram, avoirdupois	dr avdp
fathom	fath
foot	ft
furlong	furlong
gallon	gal
grain	grain
hogshead	hhd
hundredweight	cwt
inch	in
International Nautical Mile	INM
link	link
liquid	liq
microinch	μin
mile	mi
minim	minim

ounce	oz
ounce, avoirdupois	oz avdp
ounce, liquid	liq oz
ounce, troy	oz tr
peck	peck
pennyweight	dwt
pint, liquid	liq pt
pound	lb
pound, avoirdupois	lb avdp
pound, troy	lb tr
quart, liquid	liq qt
rod	rod
square foot	ft²
square inch	in²
square mile	mi²
square yard	yd²
ton, long	long ton
ton, short	short ton
yard	yd

*Alternate spelling
**Another spelling used in other English speaking countries

APPENDIX B - RESOURCES

A. Selected Bibliography
 1. Books and Bulletins
 2. Audio-Visual Aids
 3. Metric Resources and Periodicals

B. Sources of Metric Equipment and Supplies
 1. Manufacturers
    a. Bearing, Gears, Pulleys
    b. Conversion Devices — Dual Reading Dials
    c. Cooking Equipment — Spoons, Cups, Etc.
    d. Cutting Tools — Drills, Reamers, Taps, Dies, Milling Cutters
    e. Digital Readout Equipment
    f. Drafting Supplies and Materials
    g. Fasteners
    h. Hand Tools — Rules, Wrenches, Small Tools
    i. Machine Tools
    j. Precision Tools and Gages
    k. Testing, Measuring Machines and Equipment
    m. Thermometers
    n. Weighing Scales

 2. Industrial Distributors
 3. School Distributors

SELECTED BIBLIOGRAPHY

The following is a select list of materials of interest to persons in vocational education and training in industry. For a comprehensive bibliography of metric materials, obtain the first item listed below.

Books and Bulletins

Lange, Ernst. INFORMATION ON THE METRIC SYSTEM AND RELATED FIELDS. U.S. Metric Association, Sugarloaf Star Route, Boulder, CO 80302. 1976, 274 pages.

THE ABC'S OF SI. National Fluid Power Association, P.O. Box 49, Thiensville, WI 53092. 1974, 13 pages.

AISI METRIC PRACTICE GUIDE. American Iron and Steel Institute, 1000 Sixteenth Street, N.W., Washington, D.C. 20036. 1975, 35 pages.

ANTITRUST IMPLICATIONS OF METRIC CONVERSION. American National Standards Institute, 1430 Broadway, New York, NY 10018. 1971, 9 pages.

Barbrow, Louis E. WHAT ABOUT METRIC? Superintendent of Documents, U.S. Government Printing Office, Washington, D.C. 20402. 1973, 16 pages.

Burton, William K. MEASURING SYSTEMS AND STANDARDS ORGANIZATIONS. American National Standards Institute, Inc., 1430 Broadway, New York, NY 10018. 45 pages.

Cameron, Clive A., GOING METRIC WITH THE U.S. PRINTING INDUSTRY, Graphic Arts Research Center, Rochester Institute of Technology, Rochester, NY 14623. 1972, 175 pages.

De Simone, Daniel V. A METRIC AMERICA: A DECISION WHOSE TIME HAS COME. Superintendent of Documents, U.S. Government Printing Office, Washington, D.C. 20402. 1971, 170 pages.

Donovan, Frank. LET'S GO METRIC. Weybright and Tallen, Inc. 750 Third Avenue, New York, NY 10017. 1974, 154 pages.

Donovan, Frank. PREPARE NOW FOR A METRIC FUTURE. Weybright and Talley, Inc., 750 Third Avenue, New York, NY 10017. 1970, 212 pages.

Gilbert, Thomas F., Gilbert, Marilyn B. THINKING METRIC. John Wiley & Sons, Inc., 605 Third Avenue, New York, NY 10016. 1973, 142 pages.

GOING METRIC . . . . . PAL, PROGRAMMED ASSIGNED LEARNING. Jesse D. Wallace, 1078 East 5th Avenue, Chico, CA 95926. 41 pages.

Helgren, Fred J. METRIC SUPPLEMENT TO SCIENCE AND MATHEMATICS. Ideal School Supply Company, 11000 South Lavergne Avenue, Oak Lawn, IL 60453. 1973, 28 pages.

Hopkins, Robert A. THE INTERNATIONAL (SI) METRIC SYSTEM AND HOW IT WORKS. AMJ publishing Company, P.O. Drawer L. Tarzana, CA 91356. 1973, 281 pages.

Horton, Holbrook L. and others. METRIC CONVERSION TABLES AND FACTORS. Industrial Press, Inc., 200 Madison Avenue, New York, NY 10016. 1973, 35 pages.

Johnson, Dale M., Van Osdol, Bob M. HANDBOOK FOR METRIC CONVERSION. Idaho Research Foundation, Inc., University Station Box 3367, Moscow, ID 83843. 1973, 93 pages.

THE INTERNATIONAL BUREAU OF WEIGHTS AND MEASURES, 1975. NBS Special Publication 420. U.S. Government Printing Office, Washington, D.C. 20402. 1975, 248 pages.

LEGISLATION AND REGULATORY CONTROLS — FEDERAL AND ALL STATES. J. J. Keller and Associates, Inc., 145 West Wisconsin Avenue, Neenah, WI 54956. 1974.

MACHINERY'S HANDBOOK, 20th EDITION. Industrial Press, Inc., 200 Madison Avenue, New York, NY 10016. 1975, 2482 pages.

METRIC CONVERSION IN ENGINEERING AND MANUFACTURING. American National Metric Council, 1625 Massachusetts Avenue, N.W., Washington, D.C. 20036. 1974, 136 pages.

METRIC CONVERSION OF MACHINE TOOLS. Swani Publishing Company, P.O. Box 248, Roscoe, IL 81073. 1974, 66 pages.

METRIC EDITORIAL GUIDE. American National Metric Council, 1625 Massachusetts Avenue, N.W., Washington, D.C. 20036. 1974, 10 pages.

METRIC MANUAL. J. J. Keller and Associates, Inc., 145 West Wisconsin Avenue, Neenah, Wisconsin 54956. 1974, 362 pages.

METRIC STYLE GUIDE. Council of Ministers of Education, 252 Bloor Street West, Suite S 500, Toronto, Ontario, Canada M5S1V5. 1975.

METRICATION. The Penton Publishing Company, Penton Plaza, Cleveland, OH 44114. 1974, 80 pages.

METRICATION FOR ENGINEERS. Society of Manufacturing Engineers, Publications Sales, 20501 Ford Road, Dearborn, MI 48128. 1975, 110 pages.

METRICATION — LEGAL & TRADE IMPLICATIONS. METRIC CONVERSION PAPER 1. American National Metric Council, 1625 Massachusetts Avenue, N.W., Washington, D.C. 20036. 1974, 31 pages.

METRICATION — THE CONSUMER IMPACT. METRIC CONVERSION PAPER 3. American National Metric Council, 1625 Massachusetts Avenue, N.W., Washington, D.C. 20036.

Miller, David Monroe. UNDERSTANDING THE METRIC SYSTEM. A PROGRAMMED APPROACH. Allyn and Bacon, Inc., 470 Atlantic Avenue, Boston, MA 02210, 1973, 74 pages.

Page, Chester H., Vigoureux, Paul. THE INTERNATIONAL SYSTEM OF UNITS (SI). Superintendent of Documents, U.S. Government Printing Office, Washington, D.C. 20402. 1974, 43 pages.

Porkorney, Joseph L. IMPLEMENTING METRIC MEASUREMENT UNITS IN CAREER EDUCATION. Engineering Technology, Inc., 503 East Main Street, Mahomet, IL 61853. 1975, 195 pages.

PREPARING NOW TO GO METRIC. Swani Publishing Company, P. O. Box 248, Roscoe, IL 61073. 1974, 43 pages.

Richmond, Doug. METRICS FOR MECHANICS AND OTHER PRACTICAL PEOPLE. Dos Reals Publishing, 2490 Channing Way, Berkeley, CA 94704. 1975, 172 pages.

Ryan, William T., Vest, Paul Joe. MODERN METRICS MADE EASY. Clearvue, Inc., 6666 N. Oliphant Avenue, Chicago, IL 60631, 1976, 78 pages.

SI UNITS AND RECOMMENDATIONS FOR THE USE OF THEIR MULTIPLES AND OF CERTAIN OTHER UNITS. American National Standards Institute, 1430 Broadway, New York, NY 10018. 1973, 21 pages.

Sellers, Robert C. DUN & BRADSTREET'S GUIDE TO METRIC TRANSITION FOR MANAGERS. Thomas Y. Crowell Co., 666 Fifth Avenue, New York, NY 10019. 1975, 204 pages.

Sellers, Robert C. REFERENCE HANDBOOK FOR THE PROPER USAGE OF METRIC SI IN SCIENCE AND ENGINEERING. Robert Sellers & Associates, Inc., 131 Tulip Avenue, Floral Park, NY 11002. 1974, 59 pages.

Smart, James R. METRIC MATH: THE MODERNIZED METRIC SYSTEM (SI). Brooks/Cole Publishing Company, Division of Wadsworth Publishing Company, Inc., 540 Abrego Street, Monterey, CA 93940. 1974, 85 pages.

STANDARD FOR METRIC PRACTICE, E380-1976. ASTM, 1916 Race Street, Philadelphia, PA 19103. 1976, 34 pages.

AUDIO-VISUAL AIDS

INDUSTRIAL CONVERSION TO THE METRIC SYSTEM. Uniten Systems, 246 West 34th Street, Indianapolis, IN 46208. 1974, Multi-Media Kit.

INTRODUCING THE METRIC SYSTEM. BFA Educational Media. 2211 Michigan Avenue, Santa Monica, CA 90404. 1972, Multi-Media Kit.

MEASURING THE METRIC WAY. Encyclopaedia Britannica Educational Corporation, 425 North Michigan Avenue, Chicago, IL 60611. 1974. Filmstrips.

METRICS FOR CAREER EDUCATION. Encyclopaedia Britannica Educational Corporation, 425 North Michigan Avenue, Chicago, IL 60611. 1976. Filmstrips.

METRICS ON THE JOB AND IN THE HOME. Clearvue, Inc., 666 Oliphant Avenue, Chicago, Illinois. Filmstrip.

MODERNIZED METRIC SYSTEM SERIES. Library Filmstrip Center, 3033 Aloma, Wichita KS 67211. 1974. Multi-Media Kit.

Taylor, Robert L. BASIC METRIC. LESSON A. Multi-Media Publishing, Inc., 1601 South Federal Boulevard, Denver, CO 80219. 1974, Multi-Media Kit.

Taylor, Robert L. BASIC METRIC. LESSON B. Multi-Media Publishing, Inc. 1601 South Federal Boulevard, Denver, CO 80219. 1974, Multi-Media Kit.

TRANSITION TO METRIC. United Systems, 246 West 34th Street, Indianapolis, Indiana 46208. 1976, Multi-Media Kit.

Wallach, Paul, THINK METRIC! DCA Educational Products, 424 Valley Road, Warrington, PA 18976. 1974. Transparencies.

Metric Resources and Periodicals

* AMJ Publishing Company, Drawer L. Tarzana, CA 91356. AMERICAN METRIC JOURNAL SI METRICPAC.

American Home Economics Association, 2010 Massachusetts Avenue, N.W. Washington, D.C. 20036. JOURNAL OF HOME ECONOMICS.

American Industrial Arts Association, 1201 Sixteenth Street, N.W. Washington, D.C. 20036. MAN/SOCIETY/TECHNOLOGY.

* American National Metric Council, 1625 Massachusetts Avenue, N.W., Washington, D.C. 20036. METRIC REPORTER.

American National Standards Institute, 1430 Broadway, New York, NY 10018. ISO Publications.

American Vocational Association, 1510 H Street, N.W., Washington, D.C. 20005. AMERICAN VOCATIONAL JOURNAL.

INDUSTRIAL EDUCATION. Subscription Department, Macmillan Professional Magazines, Inc. Greenwich, CT 06807.

* J. J. Keller and Associates, Inc., 145 West Wisconsin Avenue, Neenah, WI 54956. METRIC SYSTEM GUIDE BULLETIN.

* National Bureau of Standards, Metric Information Office, U.S. Department of Commerce, Washington, D.C. 20234.

SCHOOL SHOP, Box 623, 416 Longshore Drive, Ann Arbor, MI 48107.

Society of Manufacturing Engineers, Metric Information Center. 20501 Ford Road, Dearborn, MI 48128.

Superintendent of Documents, Government Printing Office, Washington, D.C. 20402.

* Key Markets Publishing Company, P.O. Box 4476 Rockford, IL 61110. METRIC NEWS.

* U.S. Metric Association, Inc., c/o Louis Sokol, Sugarloaf Star Route, Boulder, CO 80302. U.S. METRIC ASSOCIATION NEWSLETTER.

SOURCES OF METRIC EQUIPMENT AND SUPPLIES

Manufacturers

BEARINGS, GEARS, PULLEYS
Bearings Division Garlock Inc.
16 Springdale Rd.
Cherry Hill, NJ 08003

Browning Mfg. Div. Emerson Elec.
Main Street
Maysville, KY 41056

Economy Bushing Co.
1560 W. Pierce St.
Milwaukee, WI 53204

* Metric only.

Stockdrive Products Div. of Designatronics, Inc.
55 S. Denton Ave.
New Hyde Park, NY 11040

The Timken Company
1835 Dueber Ave., S.W.
Canton, OH 44706

Whittet-Higgins Company
25 Higginson Ave.
Central Falls, RI 02863

CONVERSION DEVICES — DUAL READING DIALS
The Dyer Co. Inc.
Box 449
Lancaster, PA 17604

Hamlin Leonard Associates
Box 2240
Darien, CT 06820

Metra-Tech Corporation
516 Davis Avenue
Easton, Maryland 21601

Sipco Machine Division
The Sippican Corp.
7 Barnabas Rd.
Marion, MA 02738

Staveley Machine Tool
200 Southwest Cutoff,
P.O. Box 632
Northborough, MA 01532

COOKING EQUIPMENT — SPOONS, CUPS, ETC.

Foley Manufacturing Company
3300 Fifth Street, Northeast
Minneapolis, Minnesota 55418

Union Carbide
Educational Aids Department
P.O. Box 363
Tuxedo, New York 10987

CUTTING TOOLS — DRILLS, REAMERS, TAPS, DIES, MILLING CUTTERS

The duMont Corporation
289 Wells St.
Greenfield, MA 01301

Economy Bushing Company
1560 West Pierce Street
Milwaukee, Wisconsin 53204

Greenfield Tap & Die
24 Sanderson St.
Greenfield, MA 01301

Kromhard Twist Drill Co.
1089 Sweitzer St.
Akron, OH 44301

Precision Twist Drill & Machine Co.
301 Industrial Ave.
Crystal Lake, IL 60014

Regal-Beloit Corp.
P.O. Box 38
South Beloit, IL 61080

Sossner Tap & Tool Corp.
1800 Walt Whitman Rd.
Melville, NY 11746

Tapco Tool Service
911 22nd St.
Rockford, IL 61108

Zelenda Machine & Tool Corp.
66-02 Austin Street
Forest Hills, NY 11374

DIGITAL READOUT EQUIPMENT

Anilam Electronics Corporation
25 West 21st Street
Hialeah, Florida 33010

Bendix Corporation
Automation & Measurement Division
Springfield & Thomas Streets
Dayton, Ohio 45403

Coleman Systems
18842 Teller Ave.
Irvine, CA 92664

Heidenhain Corp.
2420 E. Oakton St.
Arlington Heights, IL 60005

ITEK Measurement System
27 Christina St.
Newton, MA 02161

Moore Special Tool Company, Inc.
P.O. Box 4088
Bridgeport, Connecticut 06607

Teledyne Gurley
Fulton Plaza
Troy, New York 12180

DRAFTING SUPPLIES AND MATERIALS

Alvin & Company, Inc.
P.O. Box 188
Windsor, Connecticut 06095

Bruning
Division of Addressograph Multigraph Corp.
1834 Walden Office Square
Schaumburg, Illinois 60172

Central Instrument Co.
900 Riverside Drive
New York, NY 10032

Clearprint Paper Company
1482 67th Street
Emeryville, California 94608

Hoyle Engineering Co.
302 Orange Grove
Fillmore, CA 93015

Hunter Associates
792 Partridge Dr.
Somerville, NJ 08876

Keuffel & Esser Company
20 Whippany
Morristown, New Jersey 07960

Photo Materials Co.
500 N. Spaulding
Chicago, IL 60624

Rapidesign
Box 6039
Burbank, CA 91510

Teledyne Post
700 Northwest Highway
Des Plaines, Illinois 60016

Timely Products Co.
Box 416
Baltimore, OH 43105

FASTENERS

Avibank Mfg., Inc.
210 S. Victory Blvd.
Burbank, CA 91503

Continental Fastener Corp.
1306 Sherman Ave.
Evanston, IL 60201

Continental Screw Company
459 Mt. Pleasant St.
New Bedford, MA 02742

ESNA Division, Amerace Corp.
2330 Vauxhall Rd.
Union, NJ 07083

E-Z Lock Div. Tool Components Inc.
240 E. Rosecrans Ave.
Gardena, CA 90248

GKNI
1133 Avenue Americas
New York, NY 10036

Heli-Coil Products
Shelter Rock Lane
Danbury, CT 06810

Holo-Krome Company
Brook Street
W. Hartford, CT 06110

Long-Lok Fastener Corp.
10630 Chester Rd.
Cincinnati, OH 45215

Mac-it Company
275 E. Liberty Street
Lancaster, PA 17604

Millimeter Ind. Supply Corp.
20 Central Ave.
Farmingdale, NY 11735

Product Components Corp. (Plastic)
36 Lorraine Ave.
Mt. Vernon, NY 10553

Safety Socket Screw Corporation
6501 North Avondale Avenue
Chicago, Illinois 60631

Unbrako Div.
Standard Pressed Steel Co.
Highland Ave.
Jenkintown, PA 19046

HAND TOOLS — RULES, WRENCHES, SMALL TOOLS

Armstrong Brothers Tool Company
5200 West Armstrong Avenue
Chicago, Illinois 60646

Baum Tools Unlimited
7259 Canoga Ave.
Canoga Park, CA 91303

Winfred M. Berg, Inc.
499 Ocean Ave.
East Rockaway, NY 11518

Daido Corp. Truecraft Tool
3700 W. Morse Ave.
Lincolnwood, IL 60645

Dresser Industries, Inc.
3201 N. Wolf Road
Franklin Park, Illinois 60131

Duro Metal Products Company
2649 N. Kildare Avenue
Chicago, Illinois 60639

Eklind Tool Mfg. Co.
2627 N. Western
Chicago, IL 60647

Lufkin
The Cooper Group
P.O. Box 728
Apex, North Carolina 27502

Snap-On Tools Corporation
8049 28th Avenue
Kenosha, Wisconsin 53140

Stanley Tools
600 Myrtle
New Britain, Connecticut 06050

Thor International
Los Angeles Int'l. Airport
P.O. Box 91254
Los Angeles, CA 90009

J. H. Williams Div. of TRW Inc.
400 Vulcan St.
Buffalo, NY 14207

Xcelite Div. Cooper Inc.
Thorn Ave.
Orchard Park, NY 14127

MACHINE TOOLS

Bridgeport Machines
500 Lindley Street
Bridgeport, Connecticut

Clausing Corporation
2019 N. Pitcher Street
Kalamazoo, Michigan 49007

Do All Company
Des Plaines, Illinois 60016

Leblond, Inc.
Madison at Edwards Road
Cincinnati, Ohio 45208

K. O. Lee Company
Box 970
Aberdeen, South Dakota 57401

Powermatic
Morrison Road
McMinnville, Tennessee 37110

Rockwell International
400 North Lexington Avenue
Pittsburgh, Pennsylvania 15208

Sheldon Machine Company, Inc.
4231 N. Knox Avenue
Chicago, Illinois 60632

South Bend Lathe
400 West Sample Street
South Bend, Indiana 46621

PRECISION TOOLS AND GAGES

Brown & Sharpe Mfg. Co.
Precision Park
No. Kingstown, RI 02852

Deltronic Corporation
929 Baker St.
Costa Mesa, CA 92626

Do All Company
Des Plaines, IL 60016

Dundick Corp.
4616 W. 20th St.
Chicago, IL 60650

Dwyer Instruments, Inc.
P.O. Box 373
Michigan City, IN 46360

Flo-Tech, Inc.
403 S. Washington Blvd.
Mundelein, IL 60060

Fred W. Fowler Company
315 Auburn Street
Auburndale, Maine 02166

Minitool
15076 Dickens Ave.
San Jose, CA 95124

MTI Corporation
11 East 26th Street
New York, New York 12382

Pratt & Whitney Small Tool Div.
Charter Oak Blvd.
West Hartford, CT 06101

REB Industries
Glastonbury Gage
184 Commerce Street
Glastonbury, CT 06033

Southern Gage Company
P.O. Box 228
Erin, Tennessee 37601

The L. S. Starrett Company
1-165 Crescent St.
Athol, MA 01331

3-D Instrument Company
Santa Ana, California

The Van Keuren Co.
176 Waltham St.
Watertown, MA 02172

TESTING, MEASURING MACHINES AND EQUIPMENT

Aristo Graphics Corp.
53 S. Jefferson Rd.
Wippany, NJ 07981

W. C. Dillon & Company, Inc.
14620-F Keswich Street
Van Nuys, California 91407

Edmund Scientific Co.
380 Edscorp Bldg.
Barrington, NJ 08007

Gaertner Scientific Corporation
1201 W. Wrightwood Ave.
Chicago, IL 60614

Gem Instrument Co.
2222 W. 25th St.
Cleveland, OH 44113

Metra-Tech Industries, Inc.
516 Davis Ave., P.O. Box 699
Easton, MD 21601

Pic Design Div. Benrus Corp.
Benrus Center
Rugefield, CT 06877

Technovate
910 Southwest Avenue
Pompano Beach, Florida 33060

Tinius Olsen Testing Machine Co. Inc.
Easton Rd.
Willow Grove, PA 19090

THERMOMETERS

The Cooper Thermometer Company
Middlefield, CT 06455

H-B Instrument Company
American & Bristol Streets
Philadelphia, PA 19140

Mikron Instrument Company
P.O. Box 211-T
Ridgewood, NJ 07451

Pacific Transducer Corporation
2301 Federal Avenue
Los Angeles, CA 90064

Reotemp Instrument Corporation
13866 Saticoy Street
Van Nuys, CA 91402

Rosemount Engineering Company
P.O. Box 35129
Minneapolis, MN 55401

Taylor
Arden, NC 28704

Thermometer Corporation of America
567 E. Pleasant Street
Springfield, OH 45501

Weksler Instruments Corporation
Mill Road & Hanse Avenue
Freeport, New York 11520

WEIGHING SCALES

American Family Scale Co.
1301 W. 35th Street
Chicago, IL 60609

The Borg-Erickson Corporation
1133 North Kilbourn Avenue
Chicago, IL 60651

Colt Industries, Fairbanks Weighing Div.
700 E. St. Johnsbury Road
St. Johnsbury, CT 05819

Continental Scale Corporation
7400 West 100th Place
Bridgeview, IL 60455

Hanson Scale Company
1775 Shermer Street
Northbrook, IL 60062

Howe Scale Company
2942 Scale Ave.
Rutland, VT 05701

Mantes Scale Co.
810 E. San Carlos Ave.
San Carlos, CA 94070

Martin-Decker Company
1928 South Grand Avenue
Santa Ana, California 92705

Ohaus Scale Corporation
35 Hanover Road
Florham Park, NJ 07932

Toledo Scale, Div. of Reliance Electric
5225 Telegraph Road
Toledo, OH 43612

The Torsion Balance Company
Clifton, NJ 07012

Winslow Government Standard Scale Works, Inc.
25th & Hawthorne
P.O. Box 7523
Terre Haute, Indiana 47808

INDUSTRIAL DISTRIBUTORS

Aaron Supply
2135 South Grand Avenue
Santa Ana, CA 92705

Abrasive Specialty
6576 — Devonwood Drive
Cincinnati, OH 45224

Acme Industrial Supply
13017 South Spring Street
Los Angeles, CA 90061

Ardmore Sales
7000 Campbell Blvd.
North Tonawanda, NY 14120

Advanced Tool Sales, Inc.
120 Main St.
S. Bound Brook, NJ 08880

Alert Tool Supply
4911 West Fullerton
Chicago, IL 60639

All Metric Company
3231 — First Avenue, South
Seattle, WA 98134

All Rite Tool Company
900 Lawrence Street
Lowell, MA 01853

Ammerman Industrial Supply
617-19 Bridge Street
North Grand Rapids, MI 49504

Autometrics
14711 Tireman
Dearborn, MI 48126

Badger Mill Supply Corp.
2323 Jackson St., P.O. Box 499
Oshkosh, WI 54901

Bailey Saw & Tool
1918 SE River Road
Milwaukie, OR 97222

Bay Verte Machinery Company
127-131 North Pearl Street
Green Bay, WI 54306

Bill's Industrial Tools
207 E. California Boulevard
Ontario, CA 91761

Boyar Tool Company
248 Lincoln Boulevard
Middlesex, NJ

British Distribution Services, Ltd.
403 Kennedy Boulevard
Somerdale, New Jersey 08083

Bruckner Tool Company
2000 Plaza Road
New Hyde Park, NY 11040

Brooks Precision Supply, Incorporated
38 Montvale Avenue
Stoneham, MA 02180

Butts and Ordway Company
400 Arsenal Street
Watertown, MA 02172

C-4 Incorporated
4168-B/E Admiral Place
Post Office Box 50069
Tulsa, OK 74150

Carman Tool & Abrasive
16200 South Garfield
Paramount, CA 90723

Don Carr & Associates
7104 Forest Hills
Rockford, IL 61111

W. R. Carr Co.
934 Howard Street
San Francisco, CA 94103

Central Tool Supply
223 East Michigan
Battle Creek, MI 49016

City Hall Industrial Supply
76 Prince Street
Elizabeth, NJ 07208

Clark Auto Equipment Company
938 West College Avenue
State College, PA. 16801

Colligan Tool Sales
345 Dale Rd.
Bethel Park, PA 15102

Collins Tool Company
269 Sheffield Road
Landsdowne, PA. 19052

Commonwealth Tools & Specialties
127 Spring St.
New York, NY 10012

Couch & Heyle
2500 N. Main St.
East Peoria, IL 61611

J. B. Cox Tool Industrial Supply
5622 — East Imperial Boulevard
South Gate, CA 90280

Cramer Industrial Supply
26 Webster Street
North Tonawanda, NY 14120

D & M Associates
19 East 21st Street
Baltimore, MD 21218

Daily Industrial Tools
3197-D Airport
Costa Mesa, CA 92626

Dan Mar Tool & Supply
907 American Street
San Carlos, CA 94070

Deco Tool Supply
p808 — Bairs Ferry
Cedar Rapids, IA 52401

Deco Tool Supply Company
1440 West Third Street
Davenport, IA 52802

Deco Tool Supply
5211 — Northeast 17th
Des Moines, IA 50302

Deco Tool Supply
834 Cleveland
Waterloo, IA 50704

Dehler Brothers Company, Incorporated
1805 South Brook Street
Louisville, KY 40208

Dial Indicator Labs
7844 Lankershim
North Hollywood, CA 91605

Diamond Specialty Supply
4924 Lancaster Avenue
Philadelphia, PA 19131

DiEugenio Tool Center, Inc.
P.O. Box 563
Phoenix, AZ 85007

Dill Supply Company
242 Leo Street
Dayton, OH 45404

Dixie Mill Supply Company
901 Tchoupitoulas
New Orleans, LA 70150

Donkirk Tool
2163 East Huntington
Duarte, CA 91010

Doussan Incorporated
1100 Tchoupitoulas
New Orleans, LA 70130

Dupre Abrasive Incorporated
14535 Arminta Street
Van Nuys, CA 91402

Dura Thread Gage Company
24037 Dequindre
Hazel Park, MI 48030

Eden Industrial
2723 Hemlock Road
Eden, NY 14057

Richard E. Ela Company, Inc.
744 Williamson Street
Madison, WI 53701

Empire Cutting Tools Service
3509 Genese Street
Buffalo, NY 14225

Engis Corp.
8035 Austin Ave.
Morton Grove, IL 60053

Fayjan Tool Sales
Route #15-DD1
Montgomery, PA 17752

Flack Equipment Company
1240 McCook Avenue
Dayton, OH 45401

Ford Tool & Carbide Co., Inc.
3404 10th Ave., North
Birmingham, AL 35234

Forster Tool Supply
766 Woodward Avenue
Pontiac, MI 48053

Foster Supplies Co.
6122 Milwaukee Ave.
Chicago, IL 60646

General Motors Precision Tool
1439 Buffalo Road
Rochester, NY 14624

General Surplus Hardware
1658 Superior Avenue
Costa Mesa, CA 92627

Genesee Industrial Supply
204 Ellicott Street
Batavia, NY 14020

Gould Hardware & Machinery
4770 Ruffner Street
San Diego, CA 92111

Graff Machine Tool Company
820 West Lake Street
Chicago, IL 60607

Gransden-Hall of Flint
920 Walnut Street
Flint, MI 48503

Grenfell Supply Co.
5350 N. Broadway
Denver, CO 80216

Hammond Machinery & Supply
3033 India Street
San Diego, CA 92103

Hatt's Industrial Supply
2803 East Lincoln Highway
Thorndale, PA 19372

Holloway Bros. Tools Inc.
Basin Road Industrial Center
Basin Rd., P.O. Box 3055
Wilmington, DE 19804

Hone-A-Matic Sales Corporation
187 Westcott Drive
Rahway, NJ 07065

IKO International, Inc.
1261A Rand Rd.
Des Plaines, IL 60016

Industrial Equipment Company
7th & Myrtle Streets
Louisville, KY 40208

Industrial Suppliers of Worcester Inc.
212 Summer St., P.O. Box 601
Worcester, MA 01613

Industrial Supply Company, Incorporated
1635 South 300 West
Post Office Box 600
Salt Lake City, UT 84110

Industrial Tool Company, Incorporated
112-116 Navarre Road, Southwest
Canton, OH 44701

Industrial Tool Supply
Box 82002
Lincoln, NE 68501

Interstate Machinery & Supply Company
1006 — 10 Douglas Street
Omaha, NE 68102

Jerico Tool Supply
260 East Jerico Turnpike
Mineola,, L.I. NY 11501

Johnston Industrial Supply
2433 South Cherry Avenue
Fresno, CA 93706

Jolley Indl. Supply Co., Inc.
105-109 Agate Way, P.O. Box 671
Sharon, PA 16146

Judge Industrial Service Center
930 North 9th Street
San Jose, CA 95112

Kabaco Tools, Incorporated
111 West Eight Mile Road
Detroit, MI 48203

Kandler Machinery Corporation
618 E. Michigan Avenue
Kalamazoo, Michigan 49006

C.S. Kegerries Supply
510 South Second Street
Elkhart, IN 46514

M.J. Kelly Supply Company
New Court & East Hampton
Syracuse, NY 13206

Kendall Industrial Supply
702 North 20th Street
Battle Creek, MI 49015

Kendall Industrial Supply
1918 King Highway
Kalamazoo, MI 49001

E.F. Kilduff
37 Kensington Road
Kensington, CN 06037

Kress Tool Company
565 East Main Street
Rochester, NY 14604

Krivo Supply Company
1618 West Fullerton
Chicago, IL 60614

K-P Supply Company, Incorporated
5 North Penn
Oklahoma City, OK 73107

Laboratory Supplies Co. Inc.
29 Jefry Lane
Hicksville, NY 11801

Le Valley McLeod Incorporated
358 Water Street
Binghamton, NY 13902

Lincoln Industrial Supply
440 South 11th Street
Lincoln, NE 68501

H. E. Long Co.
3910 Anderson Rd.
Morrow, IA 45152

Lucas Supply Company
432 South 22nd Street — Heath
Newark, OH 43055

Lydys Industrial Supply Company
5407 Summit Street
Toledo, OH 43611

McCalley Tool Supply
31193 Schoolcraft
Livonia, MI 48150

MRO Supply Company
1225 Connecticut Avenue
Bridgeport, CN 06607

A.T. McAvoy Supply
2605 Baird Road
Fairport, NY 14450

C.E. McCormick
6114 Torresdale Avenue
Philadelphia, PA 19135

Machinery & Factory Equipment Company
1215-19 Douglas Avenue
Racine, WI 53402

McKilligan Industrial Supply
494 Chenango Street
Binghamton, NY 13901

McNeal Tool Company
1225 First Ave., S.E. Box 966
Cedar Rapids, IA 52406

Ike Martin Company
1316 West Douglas
Wichita, KS 67203

MediaMetric
Box 461
Media, PA 19063

Metric Fastener
2727 North Grahm Street
Charlotte, SC 28206

Metric & Multistandard
  Components Corp.
198 Saw Mill River Rd.
Elmsford, NY 10523

Metric Tool & Supply
3 Howard St.
New York, NY 10013

Metric's Inc.
6140 Wayzata Boulevard
Golden Valley, Minnesota 55427

Metrics Unlimited
4325 — 22 Mile Road
Utica, MI 48087

Mid City Industrial Supply
3110 North Kedzie Avenue
Chicago, IL 60618

Midway Tool & Supply
544 — South San Pedro Street
Los Angeles, CA 90013

Mill Supply
9 Canal Street
Rochester, NY 14608

Mill Supply & Hardware
285 North Willow Street
Trenton, NJ 08618

Millar Supply
501 Main Street
Utica, NY 13501

Millar Supply, Incorporated
19 Griswold Street
Binghamton, NY 13904

Millimeter Industrial Supply Corporation
162-T Central Avenue
Farmingdale, New York 17735

Milo Manufacturing Company
1185 Morris Avenue
Union, NJ 07083

Mize Supply Company, Incorporated
326 Ohio Street
Waynesboro, VA 22980

Monnier's Inc.
1031 East Third St.
Dayton, OH 45402

Monumental Supply
1025 South Haven Street
Baltimore, MD 21224

Morrill Tool & Machinery Co.
1509 North Broadway
St. Louis, MO 63102

Murphy Industrial Supply
3057 Northwest Yeon Avenue
Portland, OR 97210

Myers Tool Service, Incorporated
19007 St. Clair Avenue
Cleveland, OH 44117

National Camara
2000 W. Union Ave.
Englewood, CO 80110

Nebraska Industrial Supply
8813 H. Street
Omaha, NE 68127

A.N. Nelson Incorporated
30 Railroad Avenue
Hackensack, NJ 07601

Newkirk Sales Company
417 West 5th Street
Waterloo, IA 50701

North Shore Tool & Supply
2058 Lehigh Avenue
Glenview, IL 60025

Northeastern Supply Company
147 Main Street
Caribou, ME 04736

Omega Tool & Supply
12909 Haster
Orange, CA 92666

Production Association Company
Pine Street Extension
Nashua, NH 03060

Production Tool Supply
11311 E. 8 Mile
Warren, MI 48090

Quad Tool & Die
3518 Norwood Avenue
Merchantville, NJ 08109

Rank Precision Industries Inc.
411 E. Jarvis Ave.
Des Plaines, IL 60018

Reid Tool Supply
2233 Temple
Muskegon Heights, MI 49444

Reklaw Corporation
1212 North Delaware Avenue
Philadelphia, PA 19125

Roat Industrial Supply Company
725-729 Wyoming Avenue
Kingston, PA 18704

Paul Roberts Company
850 South Main
Pocatello, ID 83201

Rogers Mill Supply Company
27-29 Washington Avenue
Belleville, NJ 07109

Rutland Tool Service Incorporated
1617 East McNichols Road
Detroit, MI 48203

Sams Tool Mart
11543 — Sherman Way
North Hollywood, CA 91605

Schlesingers for Tools Ltd.
1261 Utica Ave.
Brooklyn, NY 11234

Schlitt Supply Co.
1010 East Adams, P.O. Box 487
Springfield, IL 62705

Schoeffel
24 Booker St.
Westwood, NJ 07675

Seaport Industrial Supply
920 Northwest Leary Way
Seattle, WA 98107

Sears, Roebuck and Co.
Chicago, Illinois 60684

Services and Products International,
  Incorporated
1419 — 34th Street
Lubbock, Texas 79405

Service Industrial Supply
8170 J. Ronson Road
San Diego, CA 92111

Service Supply & Co.
P.O. Box 640
Hidalgo, TX 78557

Shenango Industrial
P.O. Box 1485
New Castle, PA 16103

Sherman Brothers Mill
745 East Jefferson Street
Louisville, KY 40202

Shop Tools Incorporated
2257 — Old Middleview
Mountain View, CA 94040

E.L. Simeth Company, Incorporated
403 South Hawley Road
Milwaukee, WI 53214

Southland Metric Fasteners
804 Root Street
Daytona Beach, FL 32014

Sterling Tool Company
4202 — 6th Avenue, South
Seattle, WA 98108

Struebing-Buckheit Company
1215 Military Road
Buffalo, NY 14217

Taylor Industrial Tool
10434 Lackland
Overland, MO 63114

Threading Equipment Company
2058 South Santa Fe Avenue
Los Angeles, CA 90021

Tool Mart
6211 West Touhy
Chicago, IL 60648

Tools & Gages Incorporated
960 Terminal Way
San Carlos, CA 94070

Tyler Supply Company
3611 East Kilgore Road
Kalamazoo, MI 49002

United Tool Supply
5195 — 102nd Avenue North
Pinellas Park, FL 33565

Universal Cutting Tool Supply
44 Federal Avenue
Quincy, MA 02169

Veteran Tool & Supply
3 Howard St.
New York, NY 10013

Vodicka Supply Company
3104 North Cicero Avenue
Chicago, IL 60641

Walmer Supply Incorporated
1610 West Center Street
Warsaw, IN 46580

Wellington Supply
595 New Park Avenue
West Hartford, CT 06110

Westway Tooling
16226 South Broadway
Gardena, CA 90247

William K. Toole Company
50 Division Street
Pawtucket, RI 02862

R.B. Whitacre & Company, Incorporated
105 State Street
St. Paul, MN 55107

Whitney Industrial Products
2311 Lafayette Street
Santa Clara, CA 95050

E.M. Wick
301 East Stroop Road
Dayton, OH 45429

Zenith Tool & Supply
7735 West Belmont
Chicago, IL 60635

Zelenda Machine & Tools Corporation
66-02 Austin St.
Forest Hills, NY 11374

Zengers, Incorporated
11132 Grand Avenue
Melrose Park, IL 60164

SCHOOL DISTRIBUTORS

Brodhead-Garrett Company
45600 East 71st Street
Cleveland, Ohio 44105

Creative Publications
P.O. Box 10328
Palo Alto, California 94303

Edmund Scientific Company
Edscorp Building
Barrington, New Jersey 08007

Educational Metrics Corporation
207 Sunset Boulevard
Blacksburg, Virginia 24060

Enrich
3437 Alma Street
Palo Alto, California 94306

Graves-Humphreys, Inc.
Roanoke, Virginia 24006

McKilligan Industrial Supply Corp.
494 Chenango Street
Binghamton, New York 13901

Metric SI/USA
1906 Main Street
Cedar Falls, Iowa 50613

Midwest Shop Supplies, Inc.
2600 Bridgeport Drive
Sioux City, Iowa 51111

Modern School Supplies, Inc.
P.O. Box 958
Hartford, Connecticut 06101

Paxton/Patterson
5719 West 65th Street
Chicago, Illinois 60638

Pitsco, Inc.
P.O. Box 26
Pittsburg, Kansas 66762

Sargent-Welch Scientific Company
7300 North Linder Avenue
Skokie, Illinois 60076

The Statterlee Company
2200 East Franklin Avenue
Minneapolis, Minnesota 55404

WORLD METRIC ASSOCIATIONS

METRIC CONVERSION BOARD
18-24 Chandos Street
St. Leonards 2065, N.S.W.
AUSTRALIA

METRIC COMMISSION
320 Queen Street
Ottawa K1A 0H5
CANADA

METRICATION BOARD
22 Kingsway
London WC2B 6LE
ENGLAND

METRIC ADVISORY BOARD
P.O. Box 10-243
Wellington
NEW ZEALAND

SOUTH AFRICAN BUREAU OF STANDARDS
Metrication Department
Private Bag X191
Pretoria
SOUTH AFRICA

METRICATION BOARD OF ZAMBIA
P.O. Box 1968
Lusaka
ZAMBIA

INDEX